A MATHEMATICS TEXT UNDER THE EDITORSHIP

OF *Carl B. Allendoerfer*

JOHN T. MOORE

The University of Florida / The University of Western Ontario

Elements of

Abstract Algebra

SECOND EDITION

THE MACMILLAN COMPANY, NEW YORK

COLLIER-MACMILLAN LIMITED, LONDON

To the memory of my sister Emily

Preface to the Second Edition

There are several important respects in which the present, second edition of *Elements of Abstract Algebra* differs from the first edition: (1) it is more comprehensive, including additional material on groups and rings as well as a chapter on field extensions; (2) the number of problems in most problem sets has been more than doubled; (3) more illustrative examples have been worked out in the text, and two problems—rather than one, as in the first edition—from each problem set have been completely worked out in the Appendix. The additional material has been included to promote greater flexibility rather than an actual increase in the coverage of any one course, for I feel that a first course in abstract algebra should proceed very slowly and with more emphasis on understanding than on the amount of subject matter surveyed. However, there may be many different opinions on what topics should best be attempted within the framework of a course, and the expanded text provides a greater opportunity for making this selection. I have continued to use the asterisk * and double asterisks ** to identify certain types of problems, as described in the Preface to the first edition. It is readily admitted that many of the new problems are very simple in nature; but it is my considered opinion—well supported by experience in teaching—that the difficulties students have in mathematics can often be traced to a lack of understanding of the very basic concepts. It is the purpose of these simple problems to bring some of these difficulties to light and, hopefully, to help clarify the related concepts. While the earlier edition has been almost completely rewritten, I have tried to preserve in this revision what one user has described as its "free and easy spirit" and "without any attempt to be definitive." The reader will have to decide whether I have been successful in preserving this quality.

It is my pleasure to make a number of acknowledgments in connection with the production of the present revision. My first thanks go to Professor W. R. Scott of the University of Utah who, entirely on his own initiative, provided me with a comprehensive errata of the first edition. I am indebted to Professor W. S. Cannon of Presbyterian College, South Carolina, for his work on the lists of selected readings from *The American Mathematical Monthly*, to be found at the end of each chapter; and to Mr. A. C. Szilard of the University of Western Ontario for a helpful reading of Chapter 8. Very special thanks go to Professor Georgia del Franco of the University of Miami, and to Professor Anne Bode of the University of Western Ontario, for their careful reading—along with their useful comments—of most of the present text. Indeed, Miss Bode has also read the final pageproof, and, while it would be unrealistic to presume that no errors remain, their number has been greatly diminished because of her efforts. Professor Vincent Haag of Franklin and Marshall College was extremely helpful to me with his very pertinent comments on ways in which the first edition of the text could be improved, and I am very grateful to him for this contribution. Finally, my very pleasant association with The Macmillan Company through Mr. A. H. McLeod was continued with Mr. Arthur B. Evans. I thank them both for a very friendly business relationship.

London, Ontario   J. T. M.

From the Preface to the First Edition

There are several fine books on the subject of modern abstract algebra, and there may be some serious doubt of the need for another book on this topic. Hence a brief explanation is in order.

The present text differs from most of its predecessors in at least three important respects: level of student audience, order of material, coverage of material. While the best of the established books in the area of modern algebra are directed principally to the beginning graduate student, this book is addressed to undergraudates—usually at the junior or senior level. The order of development which we have adopted is to proceed from the most simple algebraic system, the set, to systems with one binary composition, culminating with groups, and thence to systems with two binary compositions, such as rings, fields, vector spaces, and lattices. Some books introduce integral domains first, since one of our most familiar algebraic systems—the system of ordinary integers—is of this variety. While I recognize that there is some pedagogical merit in this introduction, the order adopted here has the advantage of being logically sequential. As for coverage, it is probably true that most of the topics in this book are to be found somewhere in one or more of the fine comprehensive texts to which reference has already been made. But it is difficult to make a satisfactory selection of material for a beginning one-semester course from one of these texts—excellent as it may be. It is possible to do so, of course, but it does take extreme care not to get too much involved in one topic to the exclusion of others. Moreover, if selections are made throughout a more comprehensive book, it is difficult to avoid making assignments of problems involving material which has not been covered in class. In addition, it is my opinion that students often feel unhappy about the omission of large portions of a textbook; and, although this is

ix

admittedly a shallow reason for complaint, I feel that the psychological approach of a student to a mathematical discipline is one which should not be ignored. There is a certain sense of accomplishment in covering substantially all of a book, even though the same material might have been covered by making a proper selection of material from a larger book. For these reasons, an attempt has been made in the present text to give a survey of the principal algebraic systems of modern abstract algebra without giving too exhaustive a treatment of any one of them. For example, Chapter 2 is devoted to the real numbers, but while a whole semester could be spent on this topic, there has been included here only enough material to indicate the modern algebraic point of view on the subject. Our limited coverage of the other topics has had a similar motivation.

An earlier form of the first six chapters has been used for several semesters with junior and senior students at the University of Florida. Experience there indicates that, if too much time is not spent on working problems in class, ample time remains to cover most of this material in a three-hour course in one semester. It is hoped that each section contains the proper amount of text for presentation in one usual class period, so that any of the problems immediately following the section can be assigned without fear that the background material has not been covered.

It probably should be pointed out that this is not primarily a book on linear algebra or matrix theory. Matrices are introduced to provide us with examples of a ring, and the connection between matrices and linear transformations of a vector space is explained in Chapter 6. However, a detailed development of matrix theory is left for a separate course, which could either follow or precede this one.

The reader will observe that many routine verifications of points in the theoretical development of the text have been relegated to the problem sets —for the student to complete. In every instance these proofs are quite elementary, and in many cases some of the steps have actually been included in the descriptive material. These problems, which constitute an integral part of the theory, have been indicated by *, and their solutions will be assumed in subsequent developments. I am aware that there are very few illustrative examples actually worked out in the text proper. However, the Appendix contains the detailed solution of one somewhat representative problem from each problem set. These illustrative problems have been identified by **, and the student is invited to refer to the Appendix to help him develop some of the techniques needed for the solution of problems.

There are many people to whom I am indebted for help in the course of getting this book ready for publication. I am particularly indebted to Professor Franz E. Hohn of the University of Illinois who read an early edition of the manuscript and made many valuable comments on it. I wish to thank several of my colleagues at the University of Florida, in particular Professors

Edwin H. Hadlock, Walter P. Morse, and Henryk Minc, for assistance in reading and offering criticism on portions or all of the manuscript. In addition, I wish to acknowledge assistance from Mr. Arnold Insel, a graduate student at the University of Florida, who read the final manuscript and called attention to several points in need of revision. I would also like to recognize my colleague and friend Professor Dudley E. South who, while not directly involved in any phase of the book, has always been a source of inspiration and encouragement. Finally, to Mr. A. H. McLeod and other members of the staff of The Macmillan Company many thanks are due for their kind and friendly cooperation.

Gainesville, Florida   J. T. M.

Contents

xiii

4 Groups

5 Rings

6 Operator Systems

Elements of Abstract Algebra

1 *Introductory Concepts*

1.1. Sets

A study of modern abstract algebra consists, at least in part [see [1], pp. 54–55], of an examination of certain algebraic systems which have been subjected to an axiomatic development. If we take a careful look at these systems, we find that the notions of *sets* and *mappings* of sets are ingredients which they all have in common. Accordingly, it is proper to give a brief survey of what is usually referred to as "the theory of sets," before we begin a detailed investigation of any one particular algebraic system. Admittedly, however, we shall develop no real theory, but will simply introduce some of the symbolism commonly associated with sets which will be useful to us in the future. For a more theoretical discussion of sets, the interested reader is invited to consult [4].

A *set* (or *collection* or *class*) and its *elements* are basic undefined concepts of mathematics, but the notions are intuitively very simple. Thus, we may have a set S, the elements of which may be listed as $a, b, c, \ldots$, and indicate this symbolically by $S = \{a, b, c, \ldots\}$. The essential relationship between a set and its elements is that the latter *are members of* or *belong to* the set. In particular, with reference to the above set, b is a member of or belongs to S, an assertion which may be conveniently abbreviated by $b \in S$. It is easy to think of many examples of sets: for instance, the set of points on a line, the set of books in the Library of Congress, the set of people now living in Florida, and the set $\{1, 2, 3, \ldots\}$ of all natural numbers. We emphasize that the *nature* of the elements of a set does not concern us at this time. To illustrate further the notation introduced: if L is a line segment, considered as a set of points, we could indicate that p is a point on the line by writing $p \in L$. A stroke through this or any other symbol will indicate the denial of the symbolic assertion. Thus, if x is not a member of the set S, we may write $x \notin S$.

It is easy for confusion to arise in designating the members of a set if we fail to distinguish between the *names* of the members and the *members* themselves. For example, the set {John, Harry} could be either a set of two proper names or a set of two people named John and Harry. The set of letters of the word *CALCULUS* could be a set of eight distinct—but not all distinguishable—symbols, an interpretation which we adopt in courses in college algebra when we study the possible permutations of these letters; or we might have in mind the set whose five distinct members are the symbols A, C, L, S, and U of our alphabet. In all discussions in this book, we shall adopt the second interpretation; i.e., our sets will comprise the *objects whose names are listed.*

In the sequel, the notion of "equality" (designated $=$) will be of very frequent occurrence, and it will always be very important to know *in what sense* the objects named are equal. We have already used the equality sign in an earlier paragraph when we wrote $S = \{a, b, c, \ldots\}$, and our meaning here is intuitively clear: we are simply stating that S is a name for the set of objects listed in the braces. Of course, a given set may have more than one name, say, A and B (which may be either by design or accident), and to point out that the sets are actually *identical* we write $A = B$. To formalize the preceding remark, we are stating that two sets are *equal* $(=)$ *if and only if they contain the same elements.* A *subset* of a set B is a set all of whose elements belong to B. If A is such a subset, we say that A is *contained* in B and write $A \subset B$. If it is also known that $A \neq B$, A is said to be a *proper* subset of B. It follows immediately from the above definition of equality for sets that, if $A \subset B$ and $B \subset A$, then $A = B$. Stated verbally, this means that two sets are equal if each is contained in the other as a subset. In such a case, of course, the one set has merely had two different names, and the equality sign exposes this fact.

The *intersection* $A \cap B$ of two sets A and B is the set of all elements common to both A and B. Thus, $A \cap B$ is the set of all elements x such that $x \in A$ *and* $x \in B$, a set which it is convenient to designate as $\{x \mid x \in A \text{ and } x \in B\}$. If $A = \{1, 2, 3, 4, 5\}$ and $B = \{2, 4, 6\}$, it follows that $A \cap B = \{2, 4\}$. If S is the set of all mathematics students in your college and T is the set of all coeds, $S \cap T$ is the set of all coed mathematics students in your college. This notion of intersection may, of course, be extended to include the intersection of any finite number of sets $A_1, A_2, A_3, \ldots, A_n$, in which case we use the notation $\bigcap\limits_{i=1}^{n} A_i$ to designate the intersection.

A similar notion is that of *logical sum* or *union* of sets. Thus, $A \cup B$ is the set of all elements x such that $x \in A$ *or* $x \in B$ (or possibly both); i.e., in the notation introduced above, $A \cup B = \{x \mid x \in A \text{ or } x \in B\}$. For example, if

$A = \{a, b, c, d\}$ and $B = \{b, d, e, f\}$, it follows that $A \cup B = \{a, b, c, d, e, f\}$.
More generally, $x \in \bigcup\limits_{i=1}^{n} A_i$, if $x \in A_j$ for at least one integer j on the range from 1 to n.

The *difference* $A - B$ of two sets A and B may be described as the set whose elements consists of *those in A which are not in B*; i.e., $A - B = \{x \mid x \in A$ and $x \notin B\}$. Using the definitions of A and B given in the preceding paragraph, we see in this case, that $A - B = \{a, c\}$. It should be noted that our definition of $A - B$ does *not* require that $B \subset A$, but this possibility may, of course, occur. We complete our symbolism for an "algebra of sets" with the introduction of the *empty set* $\varnothing$; i.e., $\varnothing$ is a set with no members. For example, the set of all even prime integers greater than 2 is the set $\varnothing$. It might seem that the empty set could not possibly be of much importance, but it so happens that it plays a role in the algebra of sets similar to that played by 0 in ordinary arithmetic. For example, if A and B are sets which are *disjoint* (i.e., they have no elements in common), it follows immediately that $A \cap B = \varnothing$.

Example. If X and Y are, respectively, the sets of letters in the words *ALPHABET* and *POTATO*, let us determine the sets (a) $X \cup Y$, (b) $X \cap Y$, and (c) $X - Y$.

(a) The set $X \cup Y$ consists of those letters found in at least one of X and Y, and so $X \cup Y = \{A, B, E, H, L, O, P, T\}$.

(b) The members of $X \cap Y$ are letters common to both X and Y. Hence $X \cap Y = \{A, P, T\}$.

(c) $X - Y$ is the set of letters in X which are not in Y, so that $X - Y = \{B, E, H, L\}$.

PROBLEMS 1–1

**1. If S_1 is the set of letters of the word *ALTERNATE* and S_2 is the corresponding set for the word *ILLITERATE*, find the sets $S_1 \cup S_2$ and $S_1 \cap S_2$.

2. The *power set* of a set is the set of its subsets, including the empty set and the whole original set. Determine the membership of the power set of $\{a, b, c, d\}$.

3. Determine $S_1 - S_2$ for the sets S_1 and S_2 in Problem 1.

4. If A, B, and C are the sets of points comprising the three sides of a triangle, describe the sets $A \cap B$, $B \cup C$, $A \cap B \cap C$, $A \cup B \cup C$, $A - B$ and $B - A$.

*5. If R, S, and T are subsets of a set, prove that: (a) $(R \cup S) \cup T = R \cup (S \cup T)$; (b) $(R \cap S) \cup T = (R \cup T) \cap (S \cup T)$.

6. If S is a set of n elements, how many elements does the power set of S contain? [See Problem 2.]

7. Let A, B, and C be the sets of points inside or on three intersecting circles. Use crosshatched diagrams (known as "Venn" diagrams) to designate: (a) $A \cap B$; (b) $A \cap B \cap C$; (c) $A \cup C$; (d) $A \cup B \cup C$; (e) $A - B$; (f) $B - A$.

**8. In general, what should be the procedure used to prove that two sets are equal?

*9. If A and B are arbitrary sets, prove that $A \cup B = B \cup A$ and $A \cap B = B \cap A$.

10. If $A = \{a\}$ is a *singleton* (i.e., a set containing only one element), can you think of any possible reason for distinguishing between A and a? (Hint: for example, consider the matter of membership.)

11. For any two sets A and B, prove that $A \cap (B - A) = \varnothing$.

12. For arbitrary sets A, B, C, prove that $A \cap (B - C) = (A \cap B) - (A \cap C)$.

13. Give a different representation of the empty set from that given in the text.

14. If $X \subset Y$, for sets X and Y, $Y - X$ is called the *complement* of X with respect to Y. Regard Y as fixed, designate $Y - X$ as X', and then prove each of the following:

    (a) $Y' = \varnothing$; (b) $X \cup X' = Y$; (c) $\varnothing' = Y$; (d) $(X')' = X$.

15. For arbitrary sets A, B, X, prove the following (De Morgan) formulas:

    (a) $X - (A \cup B) = (X - A) \cap (X - B)$;

    (b) $X - (A \cap B) = (X - A) \cup (X - B)$.

*16. If we think of *intersection* and *union* as corresponding loosely to *multiplication* and *addition*, respectively, in ordinary algebra, give a statement of the distributive laws for the algebra of sets and prove them.

1.2. The Cardinality of a Set

In our everyday lives there occur many instances in which the elements of one set may be seen to *correspond* to the elements of another set. We do not define the word "correspond," but rather accept the fact that it has an intuitive meaning. For example, each telephone in operation in your city corresponds to a number in your local telephone directory; to each of the United States there corresponds a governor; to each cubic equation with real coefficients there correspond one or more real solutions; to each article in a store there corresponds a price. Another very familiar example of this intuitive notion of correspondence is that established between two sets of real numbers by means of an algebraic equation. Thus, the equation $y = x^3$ may be considered to establish a correspondence in which a real number x, of one set, corresponds to the real number y (which is equal to x^3) in the other.

If two sets S and T are so related that each element in S corresponds to a unique element in T, and each element in T is the correspondent of one and only one element in S, the two sets are said to be in *one-to-one correspondence*. For example, the set of fingers on one of your hands may be seen to be in one-to-one correspondence with the set of fingers on your other hand. Two sets whose members can be put in one-to-one correspondence are also said to be (*cardinally*) *equivalent* or to have the *same cardinal number*. For example, if a theater is completely filled and there are no people standing, the set of people and the set of chairs in the theater have the same cardinal number. A set which is cardinally equivalent to the set $\{1, 2, 3, \ldots, n\}$ of natural

numbers for some n is said to be *finite* with *cardinal number n*. This number n
is familiarly known as *the number* of elements in the set. We note in passing
that it is quite possible—as in the example of the theater above—to know
that two sets have the *same* cardinal number without our knowing the actual
cardinal number of either set. If a set is neither finite nor the empty set, it is
said to be *infinite*. The most familiar example of an infinite set is the set
$\{1, 2, 3, \ldots\}$ of all natural numbers, and any set which is cardinally equivalent
to this set is said to be *denumerable*. A set which is either finite or denumerable
may be said to be *countable*, though there is some variation in the usage of
the words "denumerable" and "countable." *We shall always use* **N, Z, Q, R**
*to designate the sets of all natural numbers, integers, rational numbers, and real
numbers, respectively.*

It is a characteristic of finite sets—and one which can be proved—that no
proper subset can have the same cardinal number as the whole set. It is easy
to see, however, that this is not true for infinite sets. For example, the set of
all even natural numbers has the same cardinal number as the set of all natural
numbers, for it is possible to set up a one-to-one correspondence between
the two sets so that each even number corresponds to the number half as large.
This correspondence can be illustrated as follows:

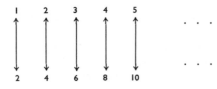

It can also be shown that both the rational numbers [Problem 13] and the
algebraic numbers [Problem 14] form denumerable sets. (It may be necessary
for the student to look up the meaning of "algebraic" as applied to numbers.
For example, see Chapter 5 of [3]). The set of real numbers is not denumerable,
however, as can be seen by a simple argument: for let us suppose that the
real numbers between 0 and 1 do form a denumerable set and that e_k is the
real number corresponding in the enumeration to the natural number k. We
shall reach a contradiction by constructing a real number r between 0 and 1,
such that $r \neq e_k$ for any $k \in$ **N**. First, we recall that every real number has
a representation as an infinite decimal, and that these representations are
unique except for those involving a repeated 9 or 0: for example, $0.2999 \ldots =$
$0.3000. \ldots$ We then construct the real number r by defining it to be $0.r_1r_2r_3 \ldots$,
where $r_n = 7$ if the nth decimal digit in the representation of e_n is 3, and
otherwise $r_n = 3$. (Of course, there is no special significance to be attached
to the digits 7 and 3, except that they are both different from 9 and 0.) This
number r cannot have two decimal representations, since it contains neither
9 nor 0; and since it differs in at least one digit from e_n for every natural
number n, it is then different from each e_n. Hence, although $0 < r < 1$, r is

not included in the assumed-denumerable arrangement of the real numbers between 0 and 1, and so these numbers are not denumerable. The cardinal number of a denumerable set is considered the first infinite cardinal, and is usually designated $\aleph_0$ ("aleph-null"), where $\aleph$ is the first letter of the Hebrew alphabet.

PROBLEMS 1–2

1. Show that the set of all positive integral multiples of 3 has the same cardinality as **N**.

**2. Show that the cardinal number of the union of two finite disjoint sets is the sum of the cardinal numbers of the individual sets.

3. Define a different real number r, which has the same characteristic property as the number r in the paragraph immediately preceding the problems.

4. If $S = A \cup B$, where A is finite and B is a denumerable set, show that S is denumerable.

5. Exhibit a proper subset which is cardinally equivalent to the set of all real numbers.

6. Show that the set $\{x \in \mathbf{R} \mid 1/2 < x < 3/4\}$ is not denumerable.

7. What can be said about the cardinality of the set $\{x \mid x = 2^a, a \in \mathbf{R}\}$?

8. If A and B are finite sets with $B \subset A$, what can be said about the cardinality of $A - B$?

**9. Try to answer the question raised in the preceding problem if both A and B are denumerable.

10. Let A be a denumerable set, and $B = \{a, x\}$ where $A \cap B = \varnothing$ and $x \neq a$. Then show that $A \cup B$ is denumerable.

*11. If A, B, C are sets such that A is equivalent to B and B is equivalent to C, show that A is equivalent to C.

12. Discuss the matter of cardinality as related to the empty set $\varnothing$. Do you think it should have cardinality 0?

13. Prove that the set of all irreducible fractions a/b, where a and b are natural numbers, is denumerably infinite. (If necessary, look this up in some other text on abstract algebra.)

14. Look up the proof in some other algebra book that the set of all algebraic numbers is denumerably infinite.

15. Prove that the union of two denumerable sets is itself denumerable. (Hint: If m_{ik} is a typical element of a set M_i, there are only a finite number of elements with this designation such that $i + k = j$, for any j.) Generalize this result to include the union of a denumerable number of denumerable sets.

1.3. Product Sets and Relations

If S and T are arbitrary sets, the (Cartesian) *product set* $S \times T$ is *defined* to be the set of all ordered pairs (s, t), with $s \in S$ and $t \in T$. These pairs are "ordered" in the sense that (s, t) is to be considered distinct from (t, s), if

$s \neq t$. We define the *equality* of two ordered pairs in the natural way by stating that $(s_1, t_1) = (s_2, t_2)$ provided $s_1 = s_2$ and $t_1 = t_2$. Inasmuch as the equality of elements in a set is being considered in the sense of "identity," this means that we are equating two ordered pairs if and only if the components of the pairs are respectively identical. If $S = \{1, 2, 3\}$ and $T = \{1, 2\}$, it follows from our definition of a Cartesian product that $S \times T = \{(1, 1), (1, 2), (2, 1), (2, 2), (3,1), (3, 2)\}$, where we note in passing that *here* we are using the same symbol for equality to designate equality or identity of *sets*. For a more complicated illustration of a product set, we may let $S = \{s_1, s_2, \ldots, s_m\}$ and $T = \{t_1, t_2, \ldots, t_n\}$, and in this case $S \times T$ is a set consisting of the *mn* elements (s_i, t_j), where $i = 1, 2 \ldots, m$ and $j = 1, 2, 3, \ldots, n$. More generally, if $S_1, S_2, \ldots, S_r$ are any r sets, then $S_1 \times S_2 \times \cdots \times S_r$ or $\prod_{i=1}^{r} S_i$ is the set of all r-tuples $(s_1, s_2, \ldots, s_r)$, where the *i*th component $s_i \in S_i$, $i = 1, 2, 3, \ldots, r$. It turns out that product sets play an important part in future developments, and we proceed immediately to one of these.

If a and b are real numbers, the meanings of the statements "a is less than b" (written $a < b$) and "a divides b" (written $a \mid b$) are quite clear from the earlier mathematical experience of the reader. If m and n are two lines in a plane, such statements as "m is parallel to n" (written $m \parallel n$) and "m is perpendicular to n" (written $m \perp n$) are of common occurrence in elementary geometry and are well understood in that context. In such cases we say that a "relation" has been defined in the associated set, and each ordered pair of elements of the set either is or is not "in the relation." It will be assumed that if a relation $\mathcal{R}$ has been defined in a set, the statement "a is in the relation $\mathcal{R}$ to b" for any two elements a and b of the set, is meaningful—and true or false according to the choice of the elements. It is customary to write $a \mathcal{R} b$ if the statement is true, and $a \mathcal{R}\!\!\!/ \, b$ if the statement is false.

At this point we are faced with a rather perplexing question. To illustrate: everyone knows what is meant by the statement "2 is less than 4," or "6 is less than 10," but what do we mean by the "less than" *relation* itself? That is, how do we actually define the *relation* "less than" in, say, the set of real numbers? There are two simple courses open to us. One is to ignore the question—as is frequently done—and argue that after all the abstract *concept* of "less than" is not of great importance, but that rather more significant is the ability to tell, for any two distinct real numbers a and b, whether $a < b$ or $b < a$. The other alternative is to give a definition which may not be completely satisfactory to all people. We choose the second of these alternatives, in spite of its noted deficiency, and seek a definition for the abstract concept within the realm of set theory. It is clear that the ordered pair (a, b) is *determined* whenever $a \mathcal{R} b$, and so it may not seem too farfetched if we actually *define* $\mathcal{R}$ to be the set of all such ordered pairs! This is formalized by the following definition for a general relation $\mathcal{R}$ in a set S.

Definition. A *relation* in a set S is a subset of ordered pairs (a, b) of the product set $S \times S$. If $\mathcal{R}$ is a relation and $(a, b) \in \mathcal{R}$, we say that "a is in the relation $\mathcal{R}$ to b" and write $a \mathcal{R} b$.

By this definition, a relation $\mathcal{R}$ in a set S is then identified with the set of ordered pairs (a, b) such that $a \mathcal{R} b$. But even more important is the observation that *any subset of $S \times S$ constitutes a relation in S.* Sometimes—as is the case with "less than"—the relation will have an obvious interpretation, but sometimes no such interpretation is apparent.

Thus, by our definition, the relation "is less than" in the set $\mathbf{R}$ is the set of all ordered pairs (a, b) of real numbers a and b such that $a < b$. The relation "is perpendicular to" in the set of all lines in a plane is the set of all ordered pairs (m, n) of lines m and n in the plane such that $m \perp n$. The relation "is the father of" in the set of all people is the set of all ordered pairs (p, q) of people p and q such that p is the father of q. In particular, our definition of a relation identifies the relation "is a divisor of" in the set $\{1, 2, 3, 4, 5, 6\}$ with the set $\{(1, 1), (1, 2), (1, 3), (1, 4), (1, 5), (1, 6), (2, 2), (2, 4), (2, 6), (3, 3), (3, 6), (4, 4), (5, 5), (6, 6)\}$. There is a simple extension of the notion of a relation *in a set S* to a relation *from a set A to a set B,* with $A \neq B$. As an illustration of this more general sort of relation, we may think of the relation "is the Governor of" with A the set of Governors of the 50 States of the U. S. and B the set of States. Abstractly, a "relation from A to B" can then be identified with the subset of $A \times B$ consisting of those ordered pairs (a, b) such that a is in the given relation to b. In this book we shall be concerned, for the most part, with relations in a single set and will confine any further discussion of the generalization to the Problems.

A relation $\mathcal{R}$ is known as an *equivalence* relation (and then the symbol $\mathcal{R}$ is replaced by $\sim$) if it satisfies the following conditions for arbitrary members a, b, c of the set in which the relation is defined:

1. $a \mathcal{R} a$ (reflexive property);
2. If $a \mathcal{R} b$, then $b \mathcal{R} a$ (symmetric property);
3. If $a \mathcal{R} b$ and $b \mathcal{R} c$, then $a \mathcal{R} c$ (transitive property).

There are many simple examples of an equivalence relation. The relation of "equality" ($=$) in the set of all real numbers is probably the most familiar and is undoubtedly the one to which the notion owes its origin. That "equality" is an equivalence relation follows immediately from the above conditions. In the set of all lines in a plane, the relation "is parallel to" may also be seen to satisfy these conditions: for if m, n, and s are arbitrary lines in a plane, it is clear that $m \parallel m$ (if we admit that a line is parallel to itself); $n \parallel m$ if $m \parallel n$; and if $m \parallel n$ and $n \parallel s$, it follows that $m \parallel s$. Hence "is parallel to" is an equivalence relation.

In order to give the next definition we need to extend our earlier concept of set union to include infinitely many sets. Thus, for any (finite or infinite) "index" set Δ, the set $\bigcup_{i \in \Delta} S_i$ is the set of all elements which belong to *at least one* of the subsets S_i. An index set is merely a useful device for labeling a collection of items. For example, if r is a rational number, S_r might be the set of real numbers x such that $x < r$. If we wished to label all of these sets, the proper index set to use would be the set of all rational numbers. As another illustration, S_a might be the set of all real numbers x such that $x - 2a < 1$, where a is an arbitrary real number. An enumeration of all such sets S_a would then require the use of $\mathbf{R}$ as the index set. We note in this case that $\Delta = \mathbf{R}$ is an uncountable set, so that there is no restriction on the cardinal number of an index set. In a similar manner it is easy to extend our earlier definition of set-theoretic intersection to include a collection of subsets which is indexed by an arbitrary set, so that $\bigcap_{i \in \Delta} S_i$ is defined for any Δ.

Definition. A *partition* of a set S is a collection of subsets S_i of S, with i in some index set Δ, such that:

1. $S = \bigcup_{i \in \Delta} S_i$;
2. $S_i \cap S_j = \varnothing$, for $i \neq j$.

That is, a partition of a set is a collection of disjoint subsets whose union is the whole set. For example, a partition of the set of all living people might be the set whose two nonempty members are the subset of males and the subset of females. A partition of the set of all lines in a plane might be the set whose members are the subsets of parallel lines in the plane. In this geometric example the partition contains infinitely many elements.

If a is an element of a set in which an equivalence relation has been defined, the subset S_a of elements which are equivalent to the element a constitutes an *equivalence class*. In view of the reflexive property, $a \in S_a$; and the symmetric and transitive properties imply that all elements of S_a are equivalent to each other. Moreover, if $b \in S_a$, the transitive property implies further that $S_a = S_b$, so that any equivalence class is merely the subset of all elements which are equivalent to *any one* of its members. *Any* member of an equivalence class is then said to be a *representative* of the class. We are now able to derive our principal result on equivalence relations.

Theorem 1.31. *If $\sim$ is an equivalence relation defined in a set S, the set of equivalence classes related to $\sim$ is a partition of S. Conversely, for any given partition of S, there exists an equivalence relation $\sim$ in S, such that the set of equivalence classes related to $\sim$ is the given partition.*

Proof. If a and b are nonequivalent elements of S, the classes S_a and S_b have only the empty set in common; for, if $c \in S_a$ and $c \in S_b$, it follows that $a \sim c$ and $c \sim b$, whence $a \sim b$, contrary to our assumption. It is clear that each element of S is in some equivalence class—namely, the class of elements equivalent to it. Hence, if Δ is a subset of S consisting of one representative from each of the equivalence classes, it follows that $S = \bigcup_{a \in \Delta} S_a$, and $S_a \cap S_b = \varnothing$, for $a \neq b$ in Δ.

Conversely, if S is partitioned into a set of disjoint classes, we can define an equivalence relation in S as follows: $a \sim b$ if and only if a belongs to the same class as b. It is evident that the conditions **1, 2,** and **3** in the definition of an equivalence relation are satisfied [Problem 1], and the proof of the theorem is completed. ∎

The set of equivalence classes of a set S, with respect to a relation $\sim$ defined in S, is called the *quotient set* or *factor set* of S relative to $\sim$. It is worthy of note that the elements of a quotient set of S are subsets and not elements of S [see Problem 17].

Illustration. Let us consider the set **R** of all real numbers, and define the equivalence relation $\sim$ in **R** so that $a \sim b$ if and only if $a - b$ is in **Z**. It is easy to see that $\sim$ is, in fact, an equivalence relation, and we leave the verification of this to the student [Problem 5]. The set of real numbers then undergoes a partitioning into subsets, each subset consisting of those real numbers having the same digits following the decimal points in their decimal expansions. For example, one subset will consist of all the integers, one will consist of all real numbers whose "decimal part" is $0.231000\ldots$, one will consist of all real numbers whose "decimal part" is the same as that of π, etc. The factor set actually has a name, in this case, for it is usually called the set of *real numbers modulo 1*. (We shall discuss the concept of "modulo" at a later time, but for the present we shall regard the italicized phrase as merely the name for the given factor set.)

PROBLEMS 1–3

    *1. Let a set S be partitioned into a set of disjoint subsets. Then, if we define $a \mathcal{R} b$, for $a, b \in S$, provided a lies in the same subset as b, prove that $\mathcal{R}$ is an equivalence relation.

    2. If $A = \{1, 2, 3\}$ and $B = \{3, 4\}$, list the members of the product set $A \times B$.

    3. If S is the set of rational numbers and T is the set of irrational numbers, list three members of $S \times T$ and three members of $T \times S$.

    4. List the members of the relation "is less than" in the set $\{1, 2, 3, 4\}$.

    5. Prove that the relation described in the Illustration is an equivalence relation.

    6. List the members of the relation "is prime to" in the set $\{2, 3, 4, 5\}$.

    7. We have noted that "is parallel to" is an equivalence relation in any set of lines in a plane. Decide whether " is perpendicular to " is also an equivalence relation in the same set.

8. If we replace c by a in condition **3** of an equivalence relation, it would " appear" that condition **1** follows from **2** and **3**. Is this true? Explain.

9. Give two additional illustrations of an equivalence relation.

10. Discover a relation which is symmetric and reflexive but not transitive.

11. Discover a relation which is reflexive and transitive but not symmetric.

12. Decide whether $\mathcal{R}$ is an equivalence relation in the set of integers where (a) $a \mathcal{R} b$ means $a < b$; (b) $a \mathcal{R} b$ means that $a + b$ is an even integer; (c) $a \mathcal{R} b$ means that $a \le b$; (d) $a \mathcal{R} b$ means that a and b have a common integral factor.

13. Prove that equivalence is an equivalence relation in the power set of any set S [see Problem 2 of § 1.1].

14. What is the maximum number of relations possible in a set consisting of (a) 3 elements; (b) 4 elements?

15. Let A be the set of students in your college and B their total collection of books. If $\mathcal{R}$ is the relation " is the owner of" from A to B, what is the meaning of $(a, b) \in \mathcal{R}$? Give a specific example of such an element of $\mathcal{R}$.

**16. Let $A = \{y \mid y = x^2,\ x \in \mathbf{Z}\}$. If " is less than " is defined as usual from $\mathbf{Z}$ to A, describe the members of this relation.

*17. Try to think of an equivalence relation in a set such that each equivalence class is a singleton [see Problem 10, § 1.1].

18. The relations discussed so far have been " binary" in the sense that only *two* arbitrary elements of the given set have been involved in the definitions. Think of an example of what might be considered to be a " ternary" relation in a set.

19. For arbitrary sets A, B, C, what would be a reasonable definition of the (Cartesian) triple product $A \times B \times C$, using the product of *two* sets as a model on which to base a generalization.

**20. Refer to Problems 18 and 19 and then give a reasonable definition of an abstract ternary relation. Extend this to an n-ary relation.

21. If $\mathcal{R}$ is a given relation in a set S, we define the *inverse* $\mathcal{R}^{-1}$ of $\mathcal{R}$ to be the set $\{(x, y) \mid (y, x) \in \mathcal{R}\}$. List the members of the inverse of the relation defined in (a) Problem 4; (b) Problem 6.

22. If $\mathcal{R}_1$ and $\mathcal{R}_2$ are relations in a set S, we define the composition $\mathcal{R}_1 \circ \mathcal{R}_2$ to be the set $\{(a, b) \mid (a, x) \in \mathcal{R}_1,\ \text{for some}\ x \in S,\ \text{and}\ (y, b) \in \mathcal{R}_2,\ \text{for some}\ y \in S\}$. Refer to Problem 21 and then prove that $(\mathcal{R}_1 \circ \mathcal{R}_2)^{-1} = \mathcal{R}_2^{-1} \circ \mathcal{R}_1^{-1}$.

1.4. Functions or Mappings

In elementary mathematics considerable attention is usually paid to the meaning of the statement that one quantity is "a function of" another quantity. This type of discussion attempts to make it clear, for instance, that a quantity *y* *is a function of* a quantity *x* whenever *y* *is associated with* or *corresponds to* *x* in some well-defined and unique way. The meaning of the word "function" itself is either ignored or defined in some nonmathematical and intuitive form as anything from a "rule" to a "meatgrinder"! While it is readily admitted that the abstract concept of a function is of secondary importance to a knowledge of the quantities which are associated by it, it seems to be nonetheless in good mathematical form to give an appropriate definition of this important concept. It is especially desirable for us to do so at this time, since we can accomplish this easily with the newly-defined concept of a *relation*. In fact, we shall define a function as a special kind of relation! We have recalled that a "function"—whatever it may be—does determine a correspondence or association between pairs of elements from certain sets. To be more precise, if $y = f(x)$, in the familiar symbolism of functions, the quantity *y* is associated with the quantity *x*, so that the ordered pair (x, y) is *determined* by the function. It is now quite consistent with what was done in the preceding section if we *define* the abstract function *f* to be precisely the set of all ordered pairs determined in this manner.

Definition. A *mapping* or *function* α of (*from* or *on*) a set *S* to (or *into*) a set *T* is a subset of $S \times T$ such that each $s \in S$ occurs *exactly once* as the first component of an element of the subset.

Each pair $(s, t) \in \alpha$ associates *s* with *t*, where *t* is known as the *value of the function at s* or the "image" of *s* under the mapping. It would be in harmony with the custom in analysis to denote this image element or function value by $\alpha(s)$, and we shall do this on many occasions—especially when we use *f* to designate a function—without further comment. However, many algebraists prefer $s\alpha$ to $\alpha(s)$ and, while we shall use both notations, our preference will be for $s\alpha$. It will sometimes be convenient to refer to α as a "left" or "right" mapping according as the notation $\alpha(s)$ or $s\alpha$ is used to designate the image of *s* under α. Our definition above describes what used to be considered a "single-valued" function or mapping, but it is customary now to restrict the use of the words "function" and "mapping" to this case. The set of all the first components *s* of the function elements comprises the *domain* of the function, while the set of function values *y* makes up its *range*. The notion of a *mapping* or *function* takes its place alongside that of a *set* to constitute two of the most important concepts in modern mathematics.

To illustrate the notation which we are using, let α be the mapping of **R** to **R** defined by $y = x^3$, with $x\alpha = y$. Then $1\alpha = 1$, $2\alpha = 8$, $3\alpha = 27$, etc. (In the "left" notation of functions, this would be written: $\alpha(1) = 1$, $\alpha(2) = 8$, $\alpha(3) = 27$, etc.) As another illustration, let $S = \{a, b, c\}$ and $T = \{1, 2, 3, 4, 5\}$. Then, if θ is the mapping of *S* to *T* defined—with obvious symbolism—by $a \to 1$, $b \to 4$, $c \to 5$, we may write $a\theta = 1$, $b\theta = 4$, $c\theta = 5$. It is sometimes convenient to designate such a mapping in inexplicit form by $\theta: S \to T$, or in general explicit form by $\theta: s \to t$, with $s \in S$ and $t \in T$. The student is urged to familiarize himself with the various notations in common usage to describe mappings or functions and, in particular, with what we have called "left" and "right" mappings. Even in this book, as we have indicated above, we shall not confine ourselves exclusively to one notation, but will use the one deemed more appropriate for the occasion.

In a geometric environment, it is customary to think of a "graph" as a pictorial representation of something, and the student is familiar with this sort of graph in analytic geometry. Here, one identifies the real numbers with the points on a straight line—known as "the real line"—and two such "real" lines, when properly placed, constitute the basis for a *Cartesian coordinate system* of a plane. Each point of the plane is then uniquely associated with a pair (x, y) of real numbers, and it is appropriate to identify the whole plane with the product set $\mathbf{R} \times \mathbf{R}$. We have defined a mapping α of a set S into a set T as the subset of $S \times T$, which consists of all pairs $(s, s\alpha)$, for $s \in S$. Hence, if both S and T are subsets of $\mathbf{R}$, in view of what we have just said, it is in order to consider the *graph* of α as the subset of points $(s, s\alpha)$ in $\mathbf{R} \times \mathbf{R}$—and this procedure is the one familiar from analytic geometry. We should caution, however, that there is some variation in the usage of the word "graph" as it is applied to functions and mappings.

Illustration. An important and not entirely obvious instance of a function occurs when we construct a *sequence* of elements from a set S. We usually think of such a "sequence" as an ordered selection of elements s_i of S, indexed by the natural numbers $i = 1, 2, 3, \ldots : s_1, s_2, s_3, \ldots$. But it is sometimes convenient to think of such a sequence as a function on $\mathbf{N}$ to S! Because each natural number i is "mapped" by the sequence onto s_i, and a complete description of the sequence is given us by this mapping.

A mapping α of a set S into a set T is said to be *injective* if distinct elements of S have distinct images in T, i.e., if $s_1\alpha = s_2\alpha$ implies that $s_1 = s_2$. If each $t \in T$ occurs as an image $s\alpha$, for some $s \in S$, the mapping is said to be *onto* T or *surjective*. A mapping which is both injective and surjective is said to be *bijective*. A bijective mapping determines and is determined by a one-to-one correspondence between the elements of the two sets, as discussed previously. While the words which we have just defined are not essential, they are sometimes convenient to use. The prefix "in" suggests "within" and that it is possible that some elements of T are not image points; the prefix "sur"—from the French word for "on"—suggests that the set of image points completely "covers" T; and "bi" has its usual interpretation of "both ways."

In a bijective mapping of S to T, each element $t \in T$ is the image of some unique element $s \in S$. If we designate such a mapping by α, it is clear that we can reverse α and map T back onto S, by using the rule that $t \in T$ maps onto $s \in S$ provided that s is mapped onto t by α. We designate this mapping which is *inverse* to α by α^{-1}. The inverse mapping α^{-1} exists if and only if α is bijective; and, if α^{-1} exists, it too is bijective.

Inasmuch as we have defined mappings as sets, it is clear that two mappings are *equal* if they comprise the same set of elements. However, it is convenient to give an alternate but equivalent definition for the *equality* of mappings. Thus, if α and β are two mappings of S to T, we may make the *definition* $\alpha = \beta$ if $s\alpha = s\beta$ for each $s \in S$ [see Problem 12]. Now, let S, T, U be three sets, with α a mapping of S to T and β a mapping of T to U. Then the mapping that sends $s \in S$ onto the element $(s\alpha)\beta$ in U is called the *product* or *composite* of α and β. This composite is designated $\alpha\beta$, so that by definition $s(\alpha\beta) = (s\alpha)\beta$, for each $s \in S$. It probably should be pointed out that if the alternate notation of "left" mappings is used, the composite mapping $\alpha\beta$ would be written as $\beta\alpha$ [Problem 15].

A mapping of a set S into itself is known as a *transformation* of the set. Included among these mappings is the transformation that leaves each element of the set unchanged. We symbolize this transformation by 1 (or 1_S), so that $s1 = s$ for each $s \in S$. It is clear that $\alpha 1 = \alpha = 1\alpha$, for any transformation α [Problem 1]. Furthermore, if α is a bijective mapping of S to T, $\alpha \alpha^{-1} = 1_S$ and also $\alpha^{-1}\alpha = 1_T$ [Problem 2]. It may be appropriate to remark here that 0 and 1 will be used in many different senses in the sequel, but the context should make the meaning clear. The positive integral powers α^2, α^3, ... of a transformation α are, of course, special cases of products of mappings, as defined in the preceding paragraph. Moreover, if we agree to identify α^{-n} with $(\alpha^{-1})^n$, for any integer $n > 0$, it is clear that *every* integral power of α has been defined.

Everyone is familiar with the "operations" of addition and multiplication in the set of real numbers. That is, everyone knows how to find the *sum* and *product* of any two such numbers. But what about the abstract concepts of "addition" and "multiplication" and of "operations" in general? Since both addition and multiplication determine a mapping of pairs of real numbers onto real numbers, the following more general definition should be easy in view of what has preceded.

Definition. A (binary) *operation* or *composition* in a set S is a mapping of $S \times S$ into S.

For example, addition is the binary operation in the set of real numbers whose "rule of composition" is such that each pair (a, b) maps onto the real number $a + b$. Multiplication is a similar operation under which the pair (a, b) maps onto ab. For either of these operations it is clear that the image of (a, b) is the same as the image of (b, a). This is not true for binary operations in general, however.

PROBLEMS 1–4

*1. Prove that if α is an arbitrary mapping of a set S, and 1 is an appropriate identity mapping, then $1\alpha = \alpha = \alpha 1$.

*2. If α is a bijective mapping from S to T, prove that $\alpha\alpha^{-1} = 1_S$ and $\alpha^{-1}\alpha = 1_T$.

3. If $f = \{(1, 2), (2, -1), (3, 1), (4, -2), (5, 0)\}$, find the members of f^{-1} and also the elements of its domain and range.

4. Describe f^{-1} if f is the function defined on $\mathbf{R}$ by $f(x) = 2x - 3$.

5. If f is the function defined on $\mathbf{R}$ by $f(x) = x^2$, explain why f^{-1} does not exist.

6. If x is an arbitrary real number, decide which of the following mappings of $\mathbf{R}$ are surjective:
   (a) $x \to 1 - x$; (b) $x \to x^3$; (c) $x \to -x^2$; (d) $x \to |x| - x$; (e) $x \to 2x^2 + x$.

7. If A is a subset of S, the *characteristic function* f_A of A is defined on S so that $f_A(x) = 1$, if $x \in A$; and $f_A(x) = 0$, if $x \notin A$. Decide on the circumstances which must prevail if f_A is to be (a) a surjection on S; (b) a bijection on S.

*8. What is a necessary and sufficient condition for the existence of the composite of two functions?

*9. Prove that $\alpha(\beta\gamma) = (\alpha\beta)\gamma$, for arbitrary mappings α, β, γ for which the products are defined [see Problem 8].

*10. If f and g are the functions defined on $\mathbf{R}$ by $f : x \to 2x - 1$ and $g : x \to x^2$, respectively, describe the composite fg. Does the composite gf exist, according to our definition?

*11. Let the mappings α and β of $\mathbf{N}$ to $\mathbf{N}$ be defined, respectively, by $n\alpha = n^2$ and $n\beta = 3n - 2$, for every $n \in \mathbf{N}$. Describe the mappings α^2, $\alpha\beta$, $\alpha(\beta\alpha)$, and $(\alpha\beta)\alpha$.

12. Prove that the two definitions, given in the text for the equality of two mappings, are equivalent.

**13. Let α be a mapping of S to T and β a mapping of T to S, for sets S and T, such that $\alpha\beta = 1_S$ and $\beta\alpha = 1_T$. Then prove that (a) α and β are injective; (b) α and β are surjective and so also bijective; (c) $\beta = \alpha^{-1}$.

14. If $\alpha : x \to y$ is the mapping on $\mathbf{R}$ defined by $y = 2x^2 + 3$, determine each of the following "image" elements under α; (a) 2α; (b) $(-3)\alpha$; (c) $(1/2)\alpha$; (d) $(1/4)\alpha$.

*15. Explain why it is appropriate to replace the symbol $\alpha\beta$ of a composite mapping by $\beta\alpha$, if we change our mapping symbols from "left" to "right."

16. Describe the inverse of the function f where (a) $f(x) = x - 2$, $x \geq 0$; (b) $f(x) = 1/x$, $1 \leq x \leq 2$; (c) $f(x) = \sin x$, $0 \leq x \leq \pi/2$; (d) $f(x) = x^2$, $1 \leq x \leq 2$.

*17. Let the mappings $\alpha : S \to T$ and $\beta : T \to U$, for sets S, T, U be bijections, and prove each of the following assertions: (a) $\alpha\beta$ is a bijection from S to U; (b) $(\alpha^{-1})^{-1} = \alpha$; (c) $(\alpha\beta)^{-1} = \beta^{-1}\alpha^{-1}$.

**18. Prove that two sets are equivalent [see § 1.2] if and only if there exists a bijective mapping from one to the other.

19. Refer to Problem 13 of § 1.2, and discover a function which is a bijection from N to the set Q of all rational numbers [see Problem 18].

20. Use a suitable definition to describe the sequence, whose terms in order are $1, 1/2, 1/3, \ldots$, as a mapping of N to R.

21. Let S be a denumerable set, with α a bijection from S to N. If $(s, 7) \in \alpha$, use Problem 18 to show that $S - \{s\}$ is also denumerable.

22. If $A \subset B$, for sets A and B, show that the mapping $f_i : A \to B$, where $f_i(a) = a$, for each $a \in A$, is injective. Compare this function with the "characteristic" function f_A in Problem 7. Describe f_i if $A = B$.

23. If A is a subset of the domain of a function f, it is sometimes convenient to use $f(A)$ to designate the range of f *with domain restricted to A*. Then prove, for arbitrary subsets A and B in the domain of f, that (a) $f(A \cup B) = f(A) \cup f(B)$; (b) $f(A \cap B) \subset f(A) \cap f(B)$.

24. In line with the symbolism of Problem 23, it is convenient to define $f^{-1}(B)$, for any subset B in the range of f, to be $\{x \in D \mid f(x) \in B\}$, where D is the domain of F. The set $f^{-1}(B)$ is called the *inverse image* of B. Then prove that, if A and B are arbitrary subsets of the range of f, (a) $f^{-1}(A \cup B) = f^{-1}(A) \cup f^{-1}(B)$; (b) $f^{-1}(A \cap B) = f^{-1}(A) \cap f^{-1}(B)$.

25. Use the symbolism of Problem 24 to prove that $f^{-1}(A - B) = f^{-1}(A) - f^{-1}(B)$.

26. If A and B are arbitrary subsets of the domain of a function f, decide whether it is true that $f(A - B) = f(A) - f(B)$; compare this result with that of Problem 25.

References

[1] ALBERT, A.: *Studies in Modern Algebra* (MAA Studies in Mathematics, Vol. 2, 1963).

[2] HALMOS, P.: *Naive Set Theory* (Princeton, N. J., Van Nostrand, 1960).

[3] JACOBSON, N.: *Lectures in Abstract Algebra*, Vol. 1 (Princeton, N. J., Van Nostrand, 1951).

[4] KAMKE, E.: *Theory of Sets* (New York, Dover, 1950).

[5] NORTHROP, E. P. and staff: *Fundamental Mathematics*, Vol. 1 (Chicago, University of Chicago Press, 1948).

[6] SELBY, S. and SWEET, L.: *Sets, Relations, Functions* (New York, McGraw-Hill, 1963).

Selected Readings from The American Mathematical Monthly

BORWEIN, D.: *A Non-Enumerable Exceptional Set,* **73** (1966), 288.

FREILICH, G.: *A Denumerability Formula for the Rationals,* **72** (1965), 1013–1014.

GILMORE, P. C.: *An Alternative to Set Theory,* **67** (1960), 621–632.

HARRINGTON, W. J.: *A Note on The Denumerability of Rational Numbers,* **58** (1951), 693–696.

ISBELL, E. S.: *A Definition of Ordinal Numbers,* **67** (1960), 51–52.

WOLK, E. S.: *A Theorem on Power Sets,* **72** (1965), 397–398.

2 *An Axiomatic Approach to Our Number Systems*

2.1. The Natural Numbers

The so-called system of real numbers is the system that underlies the whole of elementary mathematical analysis. Although it is generally treated in an intuitive fashion at the elementary level, this system has in fact a very complex structure, as is evidenced by the numerous books devoted to the subject. The real number system contains the subsystems of rational numbers, integers, and natural numbers. The subject of discussion in this and the section immediately following is the natural numbers, but reference will be made to the other number systems at the appropriate time.

There are many reasons why the set N of natural numbers is an important one in any study of abstract algebra. It is, of course, a very familiar set and, as we shall see, is one which is frequently used in the construction of examples of other algebraic systems. We have already used these numbers in many illustrations of the basic concepts in Chapter 1, and *in that chapter we assumed complete familiarity with them.* The natural numbers are also useful as an index source in labeling the members of an ordered set. Thus, we often have occasion to refer to an ordered set or sequence such as $(a_1, a_2, a_3, \ldots)$, the natural number subscripts playing the role of an indexing device. In addition, if an associative multiplication is defined in an algebraic system, the natural number powers a^n of any element a of the system occur, and so the mapping $n \to a^n$ of N into the system is defined.

It is well known from the study of Euclidean geometry in high school that the theorems and results of this discipline can be derived from a few simple axioms and postulates. Unfortunately, however, it is not so generally recognized that algebra has a similar axiomatic development. In order to illustrate our meaning, in these first two sections we shall give a partial development of the natural numbers from this point of view. Our purpose is *not* to establish any properties of natural numbers which are not already well known, but rather to show that it is *possible* to use a simple set of axioms to derive some of these familiar properties. In other words we wish to show that all these properties *need* not be merely accepted as intuitive, but are logical consequences of a very few basic assumptions. If this objective is not clearly understood, it is probably inevitable that most of the material of this chapter will appear quite inconsequential to the student.

The axiomatic development of the system of natural numbers is quite recent and dates back to G. Peano in 1899, with the so-called *Peano postulates*. All the properties of N that will concern us can be seen to be consequences of these postulates, which we now give in a form slightly different from what is found in Peano's work. In this discussion we should think of N as an abstract set, whose elements may be called "natural numbers," but which possesses only those properties which are postulated or which follow from these postulates.

THE PEANO POSTULATES

1. **N** is not empty.
2. There is an injective mapping $a \to a^+$ of N into itself, a^+ being known as the "successor" of a.
3. The collection of successors is a *proper subset of* N.
4. Any subset of N which contains a nonsuccessor, and which contains the successor of each element of the subset, is the whole set N. This is known as the *Axiom of Induction*.

The student should be prepared to find statements of the Peano postulates which differ, not only from those given originally by Peano, but also from each other. We have chosen what we consider to be one of the simplest statements of these postulates, although we make no claim that even these are independent of each other [see Problem 5]. We now illustrate the use of the postulates with a proof of a very familiar result.

Theorem 2.11. *There is a unique nonsuccessor in* N.

Proof. Let e be a nonsuccessor in N [see Problem 1]. The subset consisting of e and all successors in N then satisfies the conditions of Postulate **4**, so that this subset comprises the whole set N. Hence, e is the only non-successor in N. ∎

This unique nonsuccessor is designated 1. Furthermore, the successor 1^+ is written 2, the successor 2^+ is written 3, etc. It is Postulate **4** (the Axiom of Induction) which is the basis of proofs by the First Principle of Induction.

THE FIRST PRINCIPLE OF INDUCTION

Let us suppose that E_n is a statement involving a natural number n. Then, if E_1 is true, and E_{k^+} is true whenever E_k is true, the statement E_n is true for every natural number n.

It can be seen quite readily that this principle is a direct consequence of the Axiom of Induction. Thus, let S be the subset of natural numbers s for which E_s is true. Then, $1 \in S$, and $k^+ \in S$ whenever $k \in S$. By the Axiom of Induction, $S = N$, and so E_n is true for every $n \in N$.

While it is possible—and perhaps more natural—to describe the basic operations and relations in the set of natural numbers by means of sets, it is in harmony with our present axiomatic approach to introduce them by means of *recursive* definitions. By the word "recursive" we mean that the notion has been defined for the number n^+ whenever it has been defined for n. We illustrate with the following definition.

Definition of Addition. With every pair of natural numbers m and n there is associated a unique natural number $m + n$, such that:
1. $m + 1 = m^+$;
2. $m + n^+ = (m + n)^+$.

At this point, a rather subtle question can be raised: How do we know that there really *exists* a binary operation in N with the properties stated in the definition above? The answer is that we do not! It is clear that we could define $m + 1$ to be m^+, for any $m \in N$, but there are logical difficulties in our assumption that a binary operation exists in N with both of the asserted properties. These difficulties can be removed by proving the "Recursion Theorem"—a theorem which, in quite general terms, establishes the validity of making definitions of the above type. We shall not prove this theorem, however, but will accept it and refer the interested reader to other more advanced texts for the proof. (For example, see page 48 of [5].) With our acceptance of the *existence* of the above operation of addition, it is now easy to prove that this binary operation must be *unique*. The proofs of both the existence of this binary operation (which we do not give) and its uniqueness (which we shall give) are based on the Principle of Mathematical Induction or Postulate **4**. A recursive definition of the above type is then called a *definition by induction*. Thus mathematical induction is useful not only for proving theorems but also for making definitions. To prove the uniqueness, let us suppose there exists another operation "$*$" with the same properties as those attributed to $+$: i.e., $m * 1 = m^+$ and $m * n^+ = (m * n)^+$. We now pick an arbitrary $m \in \mathbf{N}$ and consider it fixed, and define $S = \{k \in \mathbf{N} \mid m + k = m * k\}$. Since we are assuming that $m + 1 = m^+ = m * 1$, it follows that $1 \in S$. Moreover, if $n \in S$, then $m + n = m * n$ so that $m + n^+ = (m + n)^+ = (m * n)^+ = m * n^+$. Hence, $n^+ \in S$, and Postulate **4** implies that $S = \mathbf{N}$. The "two" operations $+$ and $*$ are then identical: since we recall that m also is arbitrary and this implies that $m + n = m * n$, for *any* $m, n \in \mathbf{N}$. There is then a *unique* operation $+$, subject to conditions **1** and **2**, and we shall call the unique number $m + n$ the *sum* of m and n. In the sequel, we shall usually write $m + 1$ for m^+, as is allowed by the definition.

We can give a similar definition of multiplication in $\mathbf{N}$.

Definition of Multiplication. With every pair of natural numbers m and n there is associated a unique natural number mn, such that:
1. $m1 = m$
2. $mn^+ = mn + m$.

The proof that this definition does in fact define the product mn of *any* two natural numbers m and n is quite like the corresponding proof for the case of addition. Since this definition is also recursive, we must again use the Recursion Theorem to guarantee the *existence* of such an operation, while the proof of its uniqueness is quite like that for addition.

As a result of these definitions we can derive the familiar *Laws of Arithmetic* which we now list as a theorem.

Theorem 2.12. *The following assertions are valid for arbitrary numbers* $k, m, n \in \mathbf{N}$.
1. *Associative Laws.*
   $k + (m + n) = (k + m) + n; k(mn) = (km)n.$
2. *Commutative Laws.*
   $m + n = n + m; mn = nm.$
3. *Distributive Laws.*
   $(k + m)n = kn + mn = n(k + m).$
4. *Cancellation Laws.*
   If $m + k = n + k$, *then* $m = n$; *if* $mk = nk$, *then* $m = n$.

We do not wish to burden our present discussion by presenting a complete proof of the above theorem, with all its component parts. These proofs, if they are desired, can be found in some of the references cited at the close of this chapter. However, we do wish to illustrate what can be done with our postulates, and with this objective in mind we shall confine our proofs to the *associative* and *commutative* laws of *addition*.

Proof. In order to prove the associative law of addition, let us define $S = \{p \in \mathbf{N} \mid m + (n + p) = (m + n) + p,$ for all $m, n \in \mathbf{N}\}$. We know, from the definition of addition, that $m + (n + 1) = m + n^+ = (m + n)^+ = (m + n) + 1$, and so $1 \in S$. Now, let us assume that $k \in S$; i.e., $(m + n) + k = m + (n + k)$, for arbitrary $m, n \in \mathbf{N}$. Then $m + (n + k^+) = m + (n + k)^+ = [m + (n + k)]^+ = [(m + n) + k]^+ = (m + n) + k^+$, so that k^+ is in S. It then follows by Postulate **4** that $S = \mathbf{N}$, and the associative law of addition holds in general in $\mathbf{N}$.

We shall phrase the proof of the commutative law of addition in $\mathbf{N}$ so as to use the First Principle of Induction rather than Postulate **4** directly, for the sake of variety. (Some people choose not to distinguish between the Principle and the Postulate, and we have, in fact, shown that the Principle is a direct consequence of the Postulate. However, we prefer to keep the two conceptually distinct.) We now give the proof and, for an arbitrary fixed $m \in \mathbf{N}$, let E_n represent the statement that $m + n = n + m$, where $n \in \mathbf{N}$. We must first show that $m + 1 = 1 + m$, a fact not immediately evident from the definition of addition. In order to establish this preliminary fact, we use an inductive argument and let F_m be the statement that $m + 1 = 1 + m$, for $m \in \mathbf{N}$. It is clear that F_1 is true, and let us assume that F_k is true, i.e., $k + 1 = 1 + k$, for $k \in \mathbf{N}$. Then, $k^+ + 1 = (k + 1) + 1 = (1 + k) + 1 = 1 + (k + 1) = 1 + k^+$, where we have used the associative law of addition, and so F_{k^+} is true. By the First Principle of Induction, it follows that F_m is true, i.e., $m + 1 = 1 + m$ for any natural number m, which is to say that E_1 is true. To continue our original proof, let us now assume that E_k is true, i.e., $m + k = k + m$, for the arbitrary—but considered fixed—natural number m, and arbitrary $k \in \mathbf{N}$. Then, $m + k^+ = (m + k)^+ = (k + m)^+ = k + m^+ = k + (m + 1) = k + (1 + m) = (k + 1) + m = k^+ + m$, which means that E_{k^+} is true. It follows from the First Principle of Induction that E_n is true for every natural number n. Since m was also arbitrary, we have shown that $m + n = n + m$ for *any* numbers $m, n \in \mathbf{N}$, as asserted. This completes the proof of the commutative law of addition and, as stated above, we shall leave the remaining portions of the proof of Theorem 2.12 to the student [see Problems 2, 3, 4, 12, 13]. It may be remarked, however, that the proofs are interdependent and so care must be taken in proving the various parts in the correct order. The proofs of the cancellation laws can be accomplished much easier after the material of § 2.2 has been presented. However, hints are provided in Problems 12 and 13 for these proofs solely on the basis of the material in this section. ∎

PROBLEMS 2–1

1. With reference to the proof of Theorem 2.11, how do we know that a non-successor exists in $\mathbf{N}$?

*2. Prove the distributive law in $\mathbf{N}$.

*3. Prove the associative law of multiplication in $\mathbf{N}$.

*4. Prove the commutative law of multiplication in $\mathbf{N}$.

5. Point out an instance where one of the Peano postulates, as we have stated them, implies another.

6. How could you characterize any statement or theorem whose truth might possibly be established by means of the First Principle of Induction?

**7. Prove that $n^+ \neq n$, for each $n \in \mathbf{N}$. (Hint: Let S be the set of natural numbers n such that $n^+ \neq n$.)

8. Use the First Principle of Induction to establish the familiar calculus formula: if $f(x) = x^n$, for any real number x and any natural number n, then $f'(x) = nx^{n-1}$. (Assume the formula for the derivative of a product of two functions.)

9. Use the First Principle of Induction to establish the following summation for any natural number n:

$$1^2 + 2^2 + 3^2 + \cdots + n^2 + \frac{n(n+1)(2n+1)}{6}.$$

10. Prove that $n + m \neq n$, for arbitrary $m, n \in \mathbf{N}$. (Hint: For any m, let S be the set of natural numbers such that $n + m \neq n$.)

11. Prove that if $m \neq n$, for $m, n \in \mathbf{N}$, *either* $m = n + p$, for *some* $p \in \mathbf{N}$ *or* $n = m + q$, for some $q \in \mathbf{N}$. (Hint: Consider n fixed and let $N_1 = \{n\}$, $N_2 = \{m \in \mathbf{N} \mid m = n + p,$ for some $p \in \mathbf{N}\}$, $N_3 = \{m \in \mathbf{N} \mid m + q = n,$ for some $q \in \mathbf{N}\}$, and use the Axiom of Induction to show that $\mathbf{N} = N_1 \cup N_2 \cup N_3$.)

12. Prove the cancellation law of addition. (Hint: Use an "indirect" proof by supposing that $m \neq n$, while $m + k = n + k$, and then apply the result in Problem 11.)

13. Use the method of Problem 12 to prove the cancellation law of multiplication in $\mathbf{N}$.

14. Use the Induction Principle to prove that $1 + 2 + \cdots + n = n(n+1)/2$, for $n \in \mathbf{N}$.

15. Use the Induction Principle to prove, for any $n \in \mathbf{N}$, that

$$\frac{1}{1 \cdot 2} + \frac{1}{2 \cdot 3} + \cdots + \frac{1}{n(n+1)} = \frac{n}{n+1}.$$

**16. Use the Induction Principle to prove that

$$1^2 + 3^2 + 5^2 + \cdots + (2n-1)^2 = \frac{n}{3}(2n-1)(2n+1),$$

for any $n \in \mathbf{N}$.

17. If $x \in \mathbf{N}$, use the method of "Definition by Induction" to define x^n, for any. $n \in \mathbf{N}$.

18. Use the Induction Principle and Problem 17 to prove that $x^m x^n = x^{m+n}$, for $m, n, x \in \mathbf{N}$.

19. Prove the *uniqueness* of the operation of multiplication (as we have defined it in the text), assuming its *existence* by the Recursion Theorem.
20. Without any reference to the Recursion Theorem, prove the *existence* in **N** of an operation satisfying the conditions for addition. (Hint: Let M be the subset of **N** (remember $\varnothing \subset$ **N**!) in which such an operation exists, and prove that $M = $ **N**.)
21. If $n \in$ **N** and $n \geq 4$, use mathematical induction to prove that $n! > 2^n$. (Caution: A slight alteration must be made in the form of the inequality, before *our* Induction Axiom can be applied. See also Problem 24.)
22. With reference to the Peano postulates and the set $M = \{1, 2, 3\}$, define the "successor" function on M so that only Postulate 2 fails.
23. Find a set of rational numbers r, with the understanding that $r^+ = r + 1$, such that *only* Postulate 4 of the Peano Postulates fails to hold in the set.
24. Use the Induction Axiom to obtain the following generalization: If a subset S of **N** contains a natural number $s \geq 1$, and also contains the natural number $r + 1$ whenever it contains r, then $S = \{n \in$ **N** $\mid n \geq s\}$. Give the corresponding statement of the Principle of Induction.

2.2. Order and the Second Principle of Induction

In the preceding section we have shown how the operations of addition and multiplication can be defined recursively in the set of natural numbers. The third basic concept in this system **N** is that of *order*, which can be defined now in terms of addition.

Definition. The order relation "is less than" ($<$), in the set **N**, can be defined as follows: for $m, n \in$ **N**, $m < n$ (or $n > m$) if and only if $m + k = n$ for some $k \in$ **N**.

It can be shown that the following properties of this relation follow from the definition:

1. For any natural numbers m and n, either $m = n$, $m < n$, or $m > n$ (*Trichotomy Law*).
2. If k, m, n are natural numbers such that $k < m$ and $m < n$, it follows that $k < n$ (*Transitive Law*).
3. In any nonempty set s of natural numbers, there exists a *least* number, i.e., a number l such that $l \leq s$, for each $s \in S$. (*Well-Ordering Principle*).

Since the Well-Ordering Principle is the basis for the Second Principle of Induction, to be given shortly, we shall include a proof of 3; but proofs of 1 and 2 will be left to the student [Problems 4, 5].

Proof of the Well-Ordering Principle. Let S be the given set of natural numbers and T be the subset of N, such that $t \leq s$ for each $s \in S$ and $t \in T$. It is clear that $1 \in T$ [Problem 1]. If s is any element of S, $s^+ > s$, and so $s^+ \notin T$. Hence, $T \neq N$, i.e., T is a proper subset of N. If $t^+ \in T$, for each $t \in T$, the Axiom of Induction would imply that $T = N$. Since $T \neq N$, there must exist some natural number $l \in T$, such that $l^+ \notin T$. This number l is the required number: because $l \leq s$, for each $s \in S$, since $l \in T$; and $l \in S$, since otherwise $l < s$, for each $s \in S$, and so $l^+ \leq s$ [Problem 2] in contradiction to the fact that $l^+ \notin T$. ∎

We are now in a position to state and prove the

SECOND PRINCIPLE OF INDUCTION

Let E_n be a statement involving the natural number n. Then, if the truth of E_m follows from the truth of E_k for all $k < m$, E_n is true for all $n \in N$.

Proof. (We note parenthetically that our hypothesis implies that E_1 is true, since E_k is explicitly or vacuously true according as $m > 1$ or $m = 1$.) Let $F = \{t \in N \mid E_t \text{ is false}\}$ and, if $F \neq \emptyset$, let q be its least number—as guaranteed by the Well-Ordering Principle. We know that $q > 1$, and the definition of F requires that E_p is true for all $p < q$, whereas E_q is false. This contradicts our inductive assumption, and our only alternative is to assert that F must be the empty set. Hence, E_n is true for every natural number n. ∎

The Second Principle of Induction is sometimes referred to as "strong" induction, while the earlier one—based directly on Axiom 4 of Peano—is called "weak." Actually, the Second Principle might appear to be the weaker of the two, since we are requiring "more" in its hypothesis, but it can be shown that the two are equivalent if n is a natural number. The "strength" of the Second Principle is due to the fact that it can be generalized to the Principle of Transfinite Induction, in which n may belong to a nondenumerable set in which an order relation has been defined. We shall not discuss this extension here, but it may be in order to comment that the two induction principles which we have discussed are sometimes called "finite"—to distinguish them from the "transfinite" one just mentioned. We shall see that it is usually easier to apply the First Principle of (Finite) Induction than the Second, but there are times when the Second is favored and the student should be familiar with both forms [see Problem 12 and the proof of Theorem 2.43].

The following theorem lists some well-known properties of the relation "is less than" in the set N.

Theorem 2.21. *If m and n are natural numbers such that $m < n$, then*: (i) $m + k < n + k$, *and* (ii) $mk < nk$, *for any $k \in N$. Conversely, if either* (i) *or* (ii) *holds for any $k \in N$, then $m < n$.*

Proof. Let $m < n$, so that $m + t = n$, for some $t \in N$. Then $(m + k) + t = (m + t) + k = n + k$, so that $m + k < n + k$, as required by (i). Also $mk + tk = (m + t)k = nk$, so that $mk < nk$, establishing (ii). For the converse, we use the trichotomy law. Let us assume that $m + k < n + k$, for some $k \in N$. By the trichotomy law either $m = n, m < n$, or $m > n$. If $m = n$, then $m + k = n + k$, which contradicts our assumption. If $m > n$ (or $n < m$), it follows from the first part of the theorem that $m + k > n + k$, which is again in contradiction with our assumption. Hence $m < n$, as asserted. We leave the proof of the multiplicative part of the converse to the student [Problem 3]. ∎

The set N of natural numbers, along with the operations of addition and multiplication, the order relation "is less than," and the "equality" relation, comprises the algebraic *system* of natural numbers. We shall see in subsequent chapters that this system contains certain subsystems, which provide us with simple examples of general systems of algebraic significance. Before we leave the set N, however, it may be well to emphasize again what we have been trying to do in these two sections. We have *not* tried to derive any new properties of the natural numbers. Our purpose has been to show how the *already-familiar* properties of these numbers *can* be derived from a set of simple postulates and definitions; for it is this spirit which characterizes the axiomatic approach to modern mathematics.

PROBLEMS 2–2

   *1. Prove that 1 is the least natural number, i.e., $1 < n$, for each natural number $n \neq 1$. (Hint: If $n \neq 1$, n is a successor.) Also show that $n < n^+$, for each $n \in N$.
  **2. If m and n are natural numbers such that $m < n$, show that $m^+ \leq n$.
   *3. If $mk < nk$, for natural numbers k, m, and n, prove that $m < n$, as required in the converse of Theorem 2.21.
   *4. Prove the trichotomy law. (Hint: Use Problem 10 of § 2.1 to show that only one of the relations can hold.)
   *5. Prove the transitive law for the relation $<$ in N.
    6. Decide which of the following subsets of Z are well ordered:
       (a) all even positive integers; (b) all odd negative integers; (c) all integers less than 1; (d) all integers greater than -2.
    7. Prove that any subset of a well-ordered set is also well ordered.

*8. Use the trichotomy law to prove the cancellation law of addition in **N** (cf. Problem 12 of § 2.1).

*9. Use the trichotomy law to prove the cancellation law of multiplication in **N** (cf. Problem 13 of § 2.1).

10. Using the natural ordering in **Q, find a subset of positive rational numbers which has no least member.

11. Suppose that S is a nonempty subset of **N** such that $s \leq n$ for some $n \in$ **N** and all $s \in S$. Then show that S contains a greatest element.

12. Use the Second Principle of Induction to prove the "generalized" associative law: Any product $a_1 a_2 a_3 \cdots a_n$ is independent of the position of parentheses.

13. Use induction to prove that $1 + 1/2^2 + 1/3^2 + \cdots + 1/n^2 \leq 2 - 1/n$, for every natural number n.

14. Use induction to prove that

$$\frac{1}{1 \cdot 2} + \frac{1}{2 \cdot 3} + \frac{1}{3 \cdot 4} + \cdots + \frac{1}{n(n+1)} < 1,$$

for every natural number n.

15. Use induction to prove that if the sum of the digits of a natural number is divisible by 9, so is the number.

16. Refer back to Chapter 1 and give a definition of the relation $<$ in **N**, as a subset of **N** $\times$ **N**.

17. If $m = np$, for natural numbers m, n, p with $p \neq 1$, prove that $m > n$.

18. Use Mathematical Induction to prove that $(1 + x)^n > 1 + nx$, for any real number $x > -1$ and all positive integers n.

19. Prove that the order relation $<$ is neither symmetric nor reflexive in **N**.

20. If $m < n$ and $p < q$, with m, n, p, $q \in$ **N**, prove that (a) $m + p < n + q$; (b) $mp < nq$.

21. Establish the "Division Algorithm" for natural numbers: For arbitrary numbers a, $b \in$ **N**, prove that either $a < b$, $a = pb$ for some unique $p \in$ **N**, or $a = pb + q$ for unique numbers p, $q \in$ **N**. (Hint: If neither of the first two alternatives holds, consider the set $\{a - pb \mid p \in$ **N**$\}$ and apply the Well-Ordering Principle.)

22. Look up the Axiom of Choice in another book and decide whether you are prepared to agree with the validity of this axiom. [For example, see [7] in the References of this chapter.]

23. Find the fallacy in the following inductive "proof": *All numbers in a set of n numbers are equal to each other.*

Proof. If we let E_n be the proposition, it is clear that E_1 is true. Let $\{n_1, n_2, \ldots, n_k, n_{k+1}\}$ be an arbitrary set of $k + 1$ numbers. Then if we assume that E_k is true, it follows that $n_1 = n_2 = \cdots = n_k$ and also $n_2 = n_3 = \cdots = n_{k+1}$. Since "things equal to the same thing are equal to each other," we have $n_1 = n_2 = \cdots = n_k = n_{k+1}$, and so E_{k+1} is true. Hence, by the First Principle of Induction, E_n is true for every natural number n. ∎

24. Use the Well-Ordering Principle to prove the First Principle of Induction.

2.3. The Rational Integers

It is quite likely that the *rational integers*—or *integers* as they are usually called—are just as familiar to the student as are the natural or "counting" numbers. However, it may be of interest to know that it is also possible to develop them axiomatically, using the foundation of the natural numbers. It is again not our purpose to derive any new results which are not already familiar, but merely to indicate what *can* be done. It is very easy to overload a brief survey like this with too complete a collection of proofs. And while such is necessary, of course, in any comprehensive development of our number system, our intention here is rather to point out the way and leave the details for more intensive courses on the subject. In this section it is appropriate that we accept the natural numbers N as a fully developed system, even though we left out many important steps in our brief development.

The need for the numbers which we call "integers" is apparent when we consider that some equations of the form $m + x = n$, with $m, n \in N$, are not solvable for $x \in N$. For example, the equation $5 + x = 2$ has no solution for x as a natural number. It is well known that the introduction of "signed," or "positive" and "negative," integers overcomes this deficiency in N, and the solution of the above equation would then be $x = -3$. In order to introduce these new numbers axiomatically, we use the product set $N \times N$ and define the desired operations and relations in this set of ordered pairs of natural numbers.

In our previous discussion of product sets, we defined two ordered pairs (m, n) and (r, s) to be *equal* provided $m = r$ and $n = s$. This has been referred to as the use of "equality" in the sense of "identity," a practice to which we shall generally subscribe. We have noted before that "equality" is an equivalence relation, but for our present purposes we need such a relation which is more inclusive—so that more ordered pairs will be *equivalent* than are *equal*. (If desired, we may think of this equivalence as a generalization of the basic notion of equality.) Intuitively, what we have in mind is that there are many ways to represent, say, the integer 6, a few of which are $7 - 1, 8 - 2, 9 - 3$, etc., and likewise the integer -4 can be represented by $1 - 5, 2 - 6, 3 - 7$, etc. Of course, we realize that we have not yet defined such an operation as subtraction, and so these representations are not really to be used—except as a guide to see what is going on "behind the scenes." With this preview, we now define the promised relation in $N \times N$ and designate it by $\sim$, in anticipation that it will, in fact, be an equivalence relation.

Definition. If (m, n) and (r, s) are elements of $N \times N$, we define $(m, n) \sim (r, s)$ provided $m + s = n + r$.

It is easy to see that the relation $\sim$, just defined, is an equivalence relation in $\mathbf{N} \times \mathbf{N}$. For instance, if $(m, n) \sim (r, s)$, then $m + s = n + r$ and, since this equation can be written $r + n = s + m$, we have shown that $(r, s) \sim (m, n)$. Hence, the relation is symmetric. We leave the verification of the other requirements of an equivalence relation to the student [Problem 1], and accept the accomplished fact. It now follows, from the basic property of any equivalence relation, that the elements of $\mathbf{N} \times \mathbf{N}$ are partitioned into disjoint classes of elements which are equivalent (*in the sense of our definition*) to each other. These equivalence classes are called *integers*, each class being identified with a particular integer. At first, these classes of ordered pairs of natural numbers may seem quite different from what we usually regard as integers—but consider what we said as an intuitive introduction before the definition! Is it not customary to regard $7 - 1$, $8 - 2$, $9 - 3$, etc. (which we are now writing more formally as $(7, 1)$, $(8, 2)$, $(9, 3)$, etc.), as merely different (but "equivalent") ways to represent the integer 6? Moreover, if we note that $7 + 2 = 1 + 8$, $8 + 3 = 2 + 9$, etc., we see that the pairs $(7, 1)$, $(8, 2)$, $(9, 3)$, etc., are equivalent *according to our definition above*. Thus, it should be apparent that we are not abandoning our intuition when we call the above classes "integers"; and our intuition also takes the lead in allowing us to designate *any* member of an equivalence class as a *representative* of that class. For instance, the pair $(7, 1)$ is a representative of the class identified with the integer which we usually call 6. In view of the determination of an equivalence class by *one* of its members, it is then appropriate to make this apparent by our notation: so we designate the class containing (m, n) by $\overline{(m, n)}$. In this notation, for example, the integer 6 could be designated as $\overline{(7, 1)}$ or $\overline{(8, 2)}$, etc.

We have now defined the integers *as elements* of a set, but before we claim to have produced the integers *as an algebraic system* we must verify that they can be endowed with the properties usually associated with these familiar numbers. This we shall now do and, in anticipation of the successful outcome of the project, we shall use the already-familiar $\mathbf{Z}$ to designate this system of integers. As was the case with $\mathbf{N}$, we shall not distinguish *notationally* between the *algebraic system* $\mathbf{Z}$ and the *set* $\mathbf{Z}$ of integers, even though the two should not be considered identical [Problem 23].

We introduce the operations of addition and multiplication in $\mathbf{Z}$ according to the following definitions, in which we use the corresponding operations already defined in $\mathbf{N}$.

Definition. If $x = \overline{(m, n)}$ and $y = \overline{(r, s)}$ are arbitrary integers, then

1. $x + y = \overline{(m + r, n + s)}$;
2. $xy = \overline{(mr + ns, ms + nr)}$.

If we keep in mind our *intuitive* notions of (m, n) and (r, s) as $m - n$ and $r - s$, respectively, it is clear that these definitions are reasonable and in agreement with our familiar concept of these operations. However, before we accept these definitions as valid, we must check that they are independent of the representatives used for the integers—even though representatives appear in the definitions. It certainly would be disastrous if we got different sums and/or products by using different representatives for the classes of integers! Thus, suppose that (m, n) and (m', n') belong to the same class, so that $m + n' = n + m'$; and similarly, both (r, s) and (r', s') are representatives of the same class, so that $r + s' = s + r'$. But then $m + r + n' + s' = m + n' + r + s' = n + m' + s + r' = n + s + m' + r'$, whence $\overline{(m + r, n + s)} = \overline{(m' + r', n' + s')}$. This proves that different representatives for any two integers still lead us to the same sum for the integers, and a similar proof can be made for multiplication [Problem 2]. We leave it for the student to verify that the equation $m + x = n$ is always solvable for $x \in \mathbf{Z}$, with arbitrary $m, n \in \mathbf{Z}$ [Problem 21], and so the deficiency noted in $\mathbf{N}$ has been remedied in $\mathbf{Z}$.

We now use the "natural" ordering of $\mathbf{N}$ to order the integers, according to the following definition.

Definition. If $\overline{(m, n)}, \overline{(r, s)} \in \mathbf{Z}$, then $\overline{(m, n)} < \overline{(r, s)}$ if $m + s < n + r$.

As was the case for the operations of addition and multiplication, before we may accept this as a valid definition, we must show that it is independent of the representatives of the integer classes. Thus, if (m', n') and (r', s') are elements from the same classes as (m, n) and (r, s), respectively, we know that $m' + n = m + n'$ and $r' + s = r + s'$. Now $m + s < n + r$ implies that $m + s + m' + r' < n + r + m' + r'$. But then $m + m' + r + s' < r + r' + m + n'$ and so, on cancellation of $m + r$, we obtain $m' + s' < r' + n'$. We have shown that $\overline{(m, n)} < \overline{(r, s)}$ implies that $\overline{(m', n')} < \overline{(r', s')}$, so that our definition of order is independent of the representatives selected from the classes.

The equivalence class in $\mathbf{N} \times \mathbf{N}$, all of whose members have the form (m, m) for some $m \in \mathbf{N}$, defines the integer 0, a number which can be easily shown to have its familiar properties [Problems 4, 18]. Now, $\overline{(m, n)} + \overline{(n, m)} = \overline{(m + n, m + n)} = 0$, from definition of 0. Hence, if $x = \overline{(m, n)}$, it will be in keeping with our intuition to let $-x = \overline{(n, m)}$. It follows from this that $-(-x) = x$. An integer x such that $0 < x$ is said to be *positive*, while x is *negative* if $x < 0$. The trichotomy law for $\mathbf{N}$ carries over to $\mathbf{Z}$, so that every integer is either zero, positive, or negative. Moreover, it is easy to show that $x < y$ for any negative integer x and any positive integer y.

It can be shown that the positive integers, as we have defined them, are in every way quite like the natural numbers, and so it is customary not to distinguish between these two kinds of numbers. For example, the number 2 can be regarded as either a natural number or a positive integer. We realize that what we mean by "like" is somewhat vague at this point, but we leave it to your imagination! In the next chapter, under the topic of isomorphism, our meaning will become more transparent. If we allow this identification of the natural numbers with the positive integers, the natural numbers can be considered to comprise a subsystem of the system of integers, while the latter is an extension of the former.

We complete this rather brief and sketchy development of the (rational) integers with definitions of two familiar notions. While "subtraction" is not essential in any discussion of numbers, it is nonetheless convenient to use, and we can define the *subtraction* of two integers x and y as follows: $x - y = x + (-y)$. The notion of *absolute value* $|x|$ of an integer x can be made precise in the following way: $|x| = x$, if $x \geq 0$; and $|x| = -x$, if $x < 0$. The absolute value of a nonzero integer is then defined to be a positive integer. In the following section we shall discuss several important properties of integers and show how the system of integers can be extended to the system of rational numbers.

PROBLEMS 2–3

   *1. Complete the verification that the relation $\sim$, which we defined in $\mathbf{N} \times \mathbf{N}$, is an equivalence relation.
   *2. Verify that the definition of multiplication of integers, given in this section, is independent of the class representatives and so is a valid definition.
   *3. Prove the associative law of addition for arbitrary integers.
   **4. Use the definition of 0 to prove that $0 + x = x = x + 0$, for any $x \in \mathbf{Z}$.
   *5. Prove the associative law of multiplication for arbitrary integers.
   *6. Prove the commutative law of addition for arbitrary integers.
   *7. Prove the commutative law of multiplication for arbitrary integers.
   *8. Prove the distributive law, $m(n + p) = mn + mp = (n + p)m$ for elements $m, n, p \in \mathbf{Z}$, assuming any results in the preceding problems.
   **9. Give a suitable definition for the integer 1, and prove that $x \cdot 1 = x = 1 \cdot x$, for arbitrary $x \in \mathbf{Z}$, assuming any results in the preceding problems.
   10. For arbitrary $x \in \mathbf{Z}$, prove that $x + (-x) = 0 = (-x) + x$, assuming any results in the preceding problems.
   11. Prove the trichotomy law for integers.
   12. Prove the transitive law for the relation $<$ in $\mathbf{Z}$.
   13. If z is positive and x is an arbitrary integer, prove that $xz < yz$ if and only if $x < y$.
   14. If z is negative and x is an arbitrary integer, prove that $xz < yz$ if and only if $x > y$.
   15. Prove, for arbitrary $x, y \in \mathbf{Z}$, that (a) $-(-x) = x$; (b) $(-x)y = -xy$.
   16. Prove, for arbitrary $x, y \in \mathbf{Z}$, that (a) $(-x)(-y) = xy$; (b) $(-x) + (-y) = -(x + y)$.
   17. Prove that $-|x| \leq x \leq |x|$, for any integer x.
   *18. Prove that $x \cdot 0 = 0 = 0 \cdot x$, for any $x \in \mathbf{Z}$.
   **19. Prove that the square of any nonzero integer is positive.

20. If $xy = 1$, for integers x, y, prove that $x = y = 1$ or $x = y = -1$.

*21. If m, n are given integers, prove that the equation $m + x = n$ has a unique solution in $\mathbf{Z}$ for x.

22. Prove the cancellation law of multiplication for integers. (Caution: The law is slightly different from the corresponding law in $\mathbf{N}$.)

23. Explain the difference between the *set* of all integers and the *algebraic system* of all integers.

2.4. Theorems on Integers

We have in mind two principal undertakings in the present section. One is to recall three very important and probably quite familiar theorems about rational integers. The other is to illustrate again the axiomatic method, which we have been emphasizing in the preceding sections, in the proof of these theorems. The theorems that we shall review are important tools in what is generally known as the *arithmetic* of integers. In view of our identification of the natural numbers with the positive integers, we shall feel entirely free to use, in our discussion of the positive integers, the axioms and any results that we have previously obtained or assumed for natural numbers. In particular, we shall use either Principle of Induction if it is useful in connection with the proof of any theorem about positive integers.

The elementary fact that any integer can be divided by any positive integer to yield a quotient and a nonnegative remainder is formally stated as Theorem 2.41. This result is often loosely referred to as the "Division Algorithm," although it is, of course, the *process* of obtaining the decomposition—rather than its *existence*—which is the actual "algorithm."

Theorem 2.41. (The Division Algorithm). *For any given integers a and b, b > 0, there exist unique integers q and r such that $a = bq + r$, where $0 \leq r < b$.*

Proof. Consider the subset of integers $S = \{a - bx \mid x \in \mathbf{Z}, a - bx \geq 0\}$. This subset contains at least one nonnegative integer $a + b|a|$ [Problem 1]. Now either $0 \in S$, or all elements of S are positive and the Well-Ordering Principle assures us of the existence in S of a least element. In either event, S contains a least *nonnegative* integer r. By definition of S, $r = a - bq$ for some $q \in \mathbf{Z}$, so that $a = bq + r$. We know that $r \geq 0$; but if $r \geq b$ it follows that $r - b = a - bq - b = a - b(q + 1) \geq 0$, while it is true that $a - bq - b < a - bq$. This is contrary to our choice of q so that r is the least element in S; hence $0 \leq r < b$, as desired. In order to establish uniqueness, suppose $a = bq + r = bq' + r'$, where $0 \leq r < b$ and $0 \leq r' < b$. Then $bq + r -$

$bq' - r' = 0$, and so $b(q' - q) = r - r'$. This implies that $r - r'$ is a multiple of b, but smaller in absolute value than b [Problem 2]. It follows that $r - r' = 0$ and $r = r'$, whence $q = q'$ and the proof is complete. ∎

If an integer a can be expressed in the form $a = bc$, we have been using the familiar language that b and c are "divisors" of a or "divide" a (written $b \mid a$ and $c \mid a$), and a is a "multiple" of b and c. We have seen before [Problem 9 of Problems 2–3] that 1 is a divisor of every integer, and a similar result could be established for -1. If an integer p is neither 0, 1, nor -1 and has no integral divisors except 1, -1, p, and $-p$, it is said to be *prime*. The *greatest common divisor* (g.c.d.) of two integers is a *positive* divisor which is "greatest" in the sense that it is divisible by any other common divisor. That is, if d is the g.c.d. of a and b while c is an integer such that $c \mid a$ and $c \mid b$, it follows from the definition that $c \mid d$. We shall have occasion in the sequel to refer to the "*Euclidean g.c.d.*" process or algorithm, which has as its culmination the representation of the g.c.d. of two integers as a sum of certain multiples of the integers. We first establish the existence of such a representation in the following theorem, and then briefly discuss the algorithm. The g.c.d. of two integers a and b will often be designated in the sequel by (a, b), where there is no danger of confusion with other meanings of an ordered pair.

Theorem 2.42. *Any two nonzero integers a and b have a greatest common divisor d, where $d = sa + tb$ for $s, t \in \mathbf{Z}$.*

Proof. The proof of this theorem involves a nice application of the Well-Ordering Principle. Thus, let D be the set of all integers that can be expressed in the form $xa + yb$, with $x, y \in \mathbf{Z}$. This set certainly contains *some* positive integers, and the Well-Ordering Principle assures us that there is a least positive integer $d = sa + tb$ in the set. By the division algorithm, $a = qd + r$ for integers q and r, $0 \le r < d$. Hence, $r = a - qd = (1 - qs)a + (-qt)b$, so that $r \in D$. Since d is the least positive integer in D, we must have $r = 0$ so that $d \mid a$. In a similar way we can show that $d \mid b$, so that d is a common divisor of a and b. To show that d is the g.c.d., let us suppose that some other integer c divides both a and b. Then $c \mid sa$ and $c \mid tb$, whence $c \mid (sa + tb)$ or $c \mid d$. It follows that $d = sa + tb$ is the greatest common divisor of a and b, as asserted. ∎

If a and b are positive integers (where we can assume that $a > b$), the division algorithm asserts that there exist integers q and r such that $a = qb + r$, where $0 \le r < b$. It can be seen quite easily [Problem 3] that the g.c.d. of a and b is also the g.c.d. of b and r. This fact can be readily utilized to derive the *g.c.d. algorithm* for obtaining the g.c.d. of any two positive integers, as outlined below for the integers 63 and 720. In this process the larger number is divided by the smaller, followed by the division of the divisor by the remainder;

and this procedure is repeated until a remainder 0 is obtained. The last divisor (which is 9 in the illustration) is then the desired g.c.d. [Problem 7].

$$
\begin{array}{r r r r}
 & 3 & 2 & 11 \\
 9 & \overline{27} & \boxed{63} & \boxed{720} \\
 & 27 & 54 & 63 \\
 & \overline{0} & \overline{9} & \overline{90} \\
 & & & 63 \\
 & & & \overline{27}
\end{array}
$$

It is possible to write the g.c.d. in the form $sa + tb$, if the successive remainders are expressed in terms of the original numbers a and b. In the above illustration, if we represent these remainders by r_1 and r_2, we see that:

$$r_1 = 27 = 720 - 11(63)$$

and

$$r_2 = \ 9 = \ 63 - \ 2(27).$$

Hence, $9 = 63 - 2[720 - 11(63)] = 23(63) + (-2)720$, which expresses 9 in the desired form with $s = 23$ and $t = -2$.

Our final theorem on integers is another very familiar one. We offer the proof of it as an illustration of the use of the Second Principle of Induction.

Theorem 2.43. (Fundamental Theorem of Arithmetic). *Any positive integer a is either 1, a prime, or can be expressed as a product of positive primes, this expression being unique except for the order of the prime factors.*

Proof. Let P_a be the assertion that the integer a is either 1, a prime, or can be expressed as a product of positive primes. If a is either 1 or a prime number, P_a is trivially true. On the other hand, if a is neither 1 nor prime, $a = bc$ for integers b and c such that $b < a$ and $c < a$. The inductive assumption of the Second Principle of Induction allows us to assume that P_b and P_c are true; i.e., $b = p_1 p_2 \cdots p_r$ and $c = q_1 q_2 \cdots q_s$, for prime integers $p_1, p_2, \ldots, p_r, q_1, q_2, \ldots, q_s$ with $r \geq 1$ and $s \geq 1$. But then $a = bc = p_1 p_2 \cdots p_r q_1 q_2 \cdots q_s$, so that P_a is true. An application of the Second Principle of Induction then allows us to conclude that P_n is true for every $n \in N$, i.e., every positive integer greater than 1 is either prime or can be expressed as a product of positive primes. In order to prove the uniqueness of the factors, we need the following two lemmas.

Lemma 1. *If a prime integer p divides the product ab of two integers a and b, then p divides either a or b.*

Proof. By definition of a prime, the only positive divisors of p are 1 and p. If p does not divide a, the only common positive divisor of p and a is 1, so that Theorem 2.42 asserts the existence of integers s and t such that $1 = sa + tp$. On multiplication of both members of this equation by b, we obtain $b = sab + tbp$. Inasmuch as p is a divisor of both terms of the right member of this latter equation, p is also a divisor of the left member, i.e., $p \mid b$, as desired.

The principle of mathematical induction can now be used to extend the result of Lemma 1 to obtain Lemma 2.

Lemma 2. *If a prime number p divides a product $a_1 a_2 \cdots a_n$ of n integers $a_1, a_2, \ldots, a_n$, then p must divide at least one of the a_i, $i = 1, 2, 3, \ldots, n$.*

Proof. For an inductive proof we let E_n be the statement of the proposition to be established. The details of the proof, however, will be left to the student [Problem 9].

Now to complete the proof of Theorem 2.43, let us suppose that $a = p_1 p_2 \cdots p_m = q_1 q_2 \cdots q_n$ are two factorizations of the positive integer a into primes. The argument that these two factorizations differ at most in the order of the factors can now proceed at an intuitive level, or at a more rigorous level involving mathematical induction. We shall give both types of argument! First, at an intuitive level, since p_1 divides a it follows from Lemma 2 that p_1 must divide one of the "q-factors," say, q_k. If we now cancel out p_1 and q_k from the indicated factorizations of a, we will be left with the equality of two products of prime factors—but each with one less factor than before. If we continue this process of identifying factors on both sides with a subsequent cancellation of these factors, ultimately at least one side of the equation will be reduced to 1. Since 1 cannot be expressed as a product of prime integers [Problem 8], it follows that the "p-factors" and "q-factors" must have been paired off as equal couples; and this is the result stated in the theorem. For a more sophisticated—and accurate—proof of the uniqueness of the factorization, we use the same argument as in the first part of the proof of the theorem. Thus, for $a \geq 1$, we let F_a denote the proposition that the factorization of the integer $a + 1$ into primes is *essentially unique*—i.e., unique except possibly for order. (Observe that we are not interested in any factorization of 1 at this time.) We now note that F_1 is true, and assume that F_k is true for $0 < k < a + 1$. If $a + 1 = p_1 p_2 \cdots p_r = q_1 q_2 \cdots q_s$ are two factorizations of $a + 1$ into prime numbers, we see that Lemma 2 implies that p_1, as a divisor of $a + 1$, must be a divisor of q_j, for some j between 1 and s. But p_1 and q_j are both primes and so $p_1 = q_j$, and these factors can be cancelled from the statement of equality of the two factorizations of $a + 1$. However, what remains after this cancellation is a statement of equality of two factorizations for a number *less* than $a + 1$, and it is our inductive assumption that these two factorizations are essentially unique. Since this smaller number differs from $a + 1$ only by the factor p_1 ($=q_j$), it follows that the two factorizations of $a + 1$ are essentially the same. The Second Principle of Induction now implies that F_a is true for all natural numbers (or positive integers) a; i.e., F_n is true for all positive integers $n \geq 2$. This completes the proof of the theorem. ∎

PROBLEMS 2–4

**1. If $a, b \in \mathbf{Z}$, with $b > 0$, prove that $a + b|a| \geq 0$.

*2. If $0 \leq r < b$ and $0 \leq r' < b$, prove that $0 \leq |r - r'| < b$.

*3. If a, b, q, r are positive integers such that $a = qb + r$, prove that the g.c.d. of a and b is also the g.c.d. of b and r.

4. Use the g.c.d. process illustrated in this section to determine the g.c.d. of each of the following pairs of numbers, and express each g.c.d. in the form $sa + tb$ of Theorem 2.42:

$$\text{(a) } 4078, 814; \text{ (b) } 982, 363; \text{ (c) } 48, 128.$$

5. Prove that the only integer divisible by every integer is 0.

6. Prove that if a and b are positive integers such that $a \mid b$ and $b \mid a$, then $a = b$.

*7. Prove that the " last divisor " in the g.c.d. process illustrated in this section is actually the g.c.d. of the original pair of numbers.

*8. Prove that 1 cannot be expressed as a product of prime integers.

9. Complete the inductive proof of Lemma 2.

10. Express each of the following integers as a unique power product of ascending primes, in accordance with Theorem 2.43: (a) 52920; (b) 1404.

11. Let us define the l.c.m. (*least common multiple*) of two integers a, b to be an integer $[a, b]$ such that $a \mid [a, b]$, $b \mid [a, b]$, and $[a, b] \mid x$ for any integer x such that $a \mid x$ and $b \mid x$. Then prove that $[a, b]$ exists, and that $[a, b] = ab/(a, b)$.

12. Use the results of Problems 4 and 11 to determine the l.c.m. of each pair of numbers in Problem 4.

13. If we wish to check whether a given positive integer n is prime, show why it is sufficient to check that n is not divisible by any prime p, where $p \leq \sqrt{n}$.

14. If each of two relatively prime integers divides an integer x, prove that the product of the integers also divides x.

15. If a and b are integers such that $[a, b] = m$ [see Problem 11], prove that $(m/a, m/b) = 1$.

16. If a and b are positive integers, prove that $[a, b] = ab$ if and only if $(a, b) = 1$ [see Problem 11].

**17. If a and b are positive integers, prove that $[a, b] = (a, b)$ if and only if $a = b$ [see Problem 11].

18. Use the Fundamental Theorem of Arithmetic to prove that the equation $m^2 = xn^2$, with $m, n \in \mathbf{Z}$, has no solution for x as a prime in $\mathbf{Z}$.

19. If $n \in \mathbf{Z}$, and p is a prime number such that $p \mid (n! + 1)$, prove that $p > n$. Then deduce that there are infinitely many primes in $\mathbf{Z}$.

20. Let $n > 0$ be a fixed integer, and define $a \equiv b \pmod{n}$ if $n \mid (a - b)$, for integers a, b. Prove that this defines an equivalence relation in $\mathbf{Z}$, and that the resulting set $\overline{Z}_n$ of equivalence classes has n members. This type of equivalence relation is called a *congruence*, integers in the same class are said to be *congruent mod n*, while the members of $\overline{Z}_n$ are called *residue* or *congruence classes (mod n)* of Z. Various ramifications of this system of classes will appear in the sequel.

21. Refer to Problem 20 and describe the members of $\overline{Z}_n$ for (a) $n = 2$; (b) $n = 3$; (c) $n = 5$.

22. With reference to Problem 20, if a, b and c, d are, respectively, in the same equivalence classes of $\overline{Z}_n$, prove that $a + c$ and $b + d$ are also in the same equivalence class. Prove that a similar result holds for ac and bd.

23. Refer to the definition in Problem 20 and prove that $a^p \equiv a(\bmod p)$, for any integer a and any prime number p.

2.5. The Rational, Real, and Complex Numbers

The discussion which we have given for the integers can now be largely imitated to give a development of the *rational numbers*, i.e., numbers usually written in the form a/b, where a and b ($\neq 0$) are integers. We prefaced our axiomatic development of Z by noting that it is not always possible to solve a simple equation like $m + x = n$ for x, with $m, n, x \in N$. Such equations can always be solved for $x \in Z$ [see Problem 21 of § 2.3]. However, there are still serious deficiencies in Z, in spite of its improvement over N, because "universal" division is not possible: for example, the quotient 2/3 does not exist as an element of Z; i.e., no solution in Z exists for the equation $3x = 2$ [see Problem 6]. It is partly to overcome this deficiency of *division by nonzero numbers* that we develop the system of rational numbers, and we remind the student that we have already used the symbol Q (for "quotient") to designate both these numbers *and* the system.

Let Z_0 be the set of nonzero integers. Then, for the development of Q, we use the product set $Z \times Z_0$ as our basic set (corresponding to $N \times N$ in the development of Z) and define our operations and relations in an appropriate manner. (Why do we not use $Z \times Z$ for the basic set?) Intuitively, it is helpful to think of each ordered pair $(m, n) \in Z \times Z_0$ as the fraction m/n, and then with this in mind the following "generalized equality" or equivalence relation will seem reasonable for an evolvement of the rational numbers.

Definition. If $(m, n), (r, s) \in Z \times Z_0$, we define $(m, n) \sim (r, s)$ provided $ms = nr$.

It is easy to check that the relation above is an equivalence relation [Problem 7], and our next step is to identify the equivalence classes with the *rational numbers.* For instance, we shall identify the class containing the fractions 1/2, 2/4, 3/6, ... with the rational number 1/2. We note that 1/2 is actually a "representative" of this class, but we are "begging the issue" just a bit by using the intuitive notation 1/2 instead of (1, 2) for a class member! In general, however, each equivalence class of $Z \times Z_0$ is determined by *any one* of its members, and so if (m, n) belongs to a class we may designate the class by $\overline{(m, n)}$. For the example above, the class containing (1, 2)—intuitively 1/2—is then designated $\overline{(1, 2)}$. We remark that we are using exactly the same notation as we did in our development of Z, but *this time* the components of our ordered pairs are in Z rather than in N. We have now obtained the *set* Q of rational numbers, and there remains only to define the operations of addition and multiplication, as well as the order relation <, in order to make Q into a *system* which has the properties usually associated with rational numbers.

Definition. If $\overline{(m, n)}, \overline{(r, s)} \in Q$, then

1. $\overline{(m, n)} + \overline{(r, s)} = \overline{(ms + nr, ns)}$;
2. $\overline{(m, n)}\,\overline{(r, s)} = \overline{(mr, ns)}$.

This definition introduces the familiar operations of addition and multiplication—in abstract notation—into the set of rational numbers. That these operations are adequately defined above is left for the student to verify [Problems 8, 9].

Before introducing the relation < in Q, it is appropriate to make the following preliminary definition: The rational number $\overline{(m, n)}$ is *positive* or $\overline{(m, n)} > 0$, if $mn > 0$, where we note, of course, that $mn \in Z$. Since this definition too—as has been the case so frequently in this chapter—is *formally* dependent on the representative selected to represent an element of Q, the validity of our definition rests on our showing that this "dependency" is merely in notation and not in fact. We leave this verification to the student [Problem 10], and now introduce the order relation in Q.

Definition. If $\overline{(m, n)}, \overline{(r, s)} \in Q$, then $\overline{(m, n)} < \overline{(r, s)}$ provided $\overline{(r, s)} - \overline{(m, n)}$ is positive.

We are assuming in this definition, of course, that "subtraction" has been given its usual meaning: If a and b are *rational numbers*, by $a - b$ we mean the rational number x such that $b + x = a$. It is easy to verify the existence of such a number for arbitrary rational numbers a, b [Problem 11].

At this point, if our development of Q were to be thorough, it would be necessary to establish all the familiar properties of rational numbers from the definitions. As we said earlier, however, it is not our intention to carry out the details of such a program, but in the problems we shall suggest that the student verify some of the properties. In view of our desire to be brief on this somewhat lengthy subject, we shall be content at this point with merely recalling two very important properties of $\mathbf{Q}$: (1) if a and $b(\neq 0) \in \mathbf{Q}$, it is possible to solve the equation $bx = a$ for $x \in \mathbf{Q}$; (2) it can be shown that the rational numbers of the form $\overline{(m, 1)}$ perform "in every way" just like the integers m. (Compare a similar remark made relative to the *positive* integers and the natural numbers, as a result of which we asserted that $\mathbf{N} \subset \mathbf{Z}$.) If we then agree to identify these rational numbers with the associated integers, we can say that $\mathbf{Z} \subset \mathbf{Q}$—and, in view of the parenthetical remark—that $\mathbf{N} \subset \mathbf{Z} \subset \mathbf{Q}$.

The student is doubtless familiar with the fact that there exist numbers like π, e (the base for natural logarithms), $\sqrt{2}$, etc., which are "real" but not rational, and so it is necessary to make a further extension of $\mathbf{Q}$ if we are to obtain all real numbers. The transition from $\mathbf{Q}$ to real numbers $\mathbf{R}$ is quite different from the transition from $\mathbf{N}$ to $\mathbf{Z}$ or from $\mathbf{Z}$ to $\mathbf{Q}$, since new notions are found to be necessary at this point. We do not propose to give even a brief development of $\mathbf{R}$, but shall be content with merely taking note of the characteristic property that distinguishes $\mathbf{R}$ from $\mathbf{Q}$. This is the property of "completeness," a property concerned with "bounds" to sets of numbers. If S is a set of numbers in which the usual order relation $<$ has been defined, an *upper bound* of S is a number which is not less than any number in S, while a *lower bound* is a number which is not greater than any number in S. That is, u is an upper bound of S if $s \leq u$, for any $s \in S$; and l is a lower bound of S if $l \leq s$, for any $s \in S$. For example, if $S = \{1, 2, 3, 4, 5\}$, an upper bound of S might be 5, $5\frac{1}{2}$, 9, $\sqrt{40}$, etc., while a lower bound might be $1, 0, -4, -51.3, -\sqrt{5}$, etc. We note that there is nothing unique about an upper (or lower) bound, provided one exists. However, for the collections of *all* upper and *all* lower bounds for a given set of numbers, the existence of a *greatest* lower bound and a *least* upper bound is what distinguishes the real numbers from the rationals. This is the "completeness" property, and we make it more precise with the following definition.

Definition. The real numbers $\mathbf{R}$ are said to be *complete* in the sense that any nonempty subset of $\mathbf{R}$ which has an upper (lower) bound has a least upper (greatest lower) bound.

For the particular set S above, it is clear that the least upper and greatest lower bounds are, respectively, 5 and 1. However, to grasp the essential notion of completeness, consider the more complicated set $\{1, 1.4, 1.41, 1.414, \ldots\}$, consisting of all finite decimal (and therefore rational) approximations of $\sqrt{2}$. This set clearly has an upper bound, for example 2, but there is no *rational* number which is a *least* upper bound [Problem 12]. However, the real (irrational) number $\sqrt{2}$ is the least upper bound of the set, and it is the existence of such minimal or maximal bounds for bounded subsets which is the distinguishing characteristic of real numbers.

For the convenience of the student, and for our possible reference later, we shall now list the basic properties of the system **R** of real numbers without proofs. The *real numbers* **R** comprise a set in which two binary operations (addition and multiplication) and two relations (equality and order) have been defined, subject to the following conditions in which x, y, z designate arbitrary elements of **R**, unless otherwise indicated:

1. *Closure laws: $x + y \in$ **R**; $xy \in$ **R**.* (In reality, these are redundant with our definition of an operation, and so they are not needed.)
2. *Associative laws: $(x + y) + z = x + (y + z)$; $(xy)z = x(yz)$.*
3. *Commutative laws: $x + y = y + x$; $xy = yx$.*
4. *Existence of identities: $0 + x = x$; $1(x) = x$.*
5. *Distributive law: $x(y + z) = xy + yz$.*
6. *Existence of inverses: $x + (-x) = 0$; $x(x^{-1}) = 1$, provided $x \neq 0$.*
7. *Trichotomy law:* either $x = y$, $x < y$, or $x > y$.
8. *Transitive law of order: $x < y$ and $y < z$ implies that $x < z$.*
9. *Cancellation laws of order: $x + z < y + z$ if and only if $x < z$; $xz < yz$ if and only if $x < y$ and $z > 0$ or $x > y$ and $z < 0$.*
10. *Completeness:* Any nonempty subset of real numbers bounded above (below) has a least upper (greatest lower) bound.

It can be shown not only that these properties are possessed by the real numbers, but that any number system which possesses them is "essentially" the system of real numbers. The proofs of these remarks are outside the scope of this book, but they may be found in [1] or [4].

There remains one more familiar number system—an extension of **R**— on which we shall make a very brief comment. This is the system **C** of *complex* numbers. The need for such an extension can be motivated by the desire that all polynomial equations with coefficients in a given number system have its solutions in the system. For we know that such a simple equation as $x^2 + 1 = 0$ has no solution in **R**! It is possible to axiomatize the complex numbers in a manner somewhat similar to the procedure used to obtain **Z** from **N** and **Q** from **Z**, and for this purpose we would use the product set **R** × **R** as the basic set. The development of **C** can be found in many books —such as [1]—but we omit it here. It is probably appropriate to remark, however, that any complex number can be expressed in the form $+a\,bi$, involving a "new" number i, with $a, b \in$ **R** and $i^2 = -1$. The system of complex numbers also possesses the first six properties of real numbers, as listed in the preceding paragraph. However, it is noteworthy that it is not possible to introduce an order relation $<$, unless we are willing to sacrifice some of the usual properties of this relation. Hence, $\mathbf{C}$ is not an ordered system. The complex numbers of the form $a + bi$, with $b = 0$, comprise a subsystem which can be identified with $\mathbf{R}$, and so we have the following chain of set inclusions: $\mathbf{N} \subset \mathbf{Z} \subset \mathbf{Q} \subset \mathbf{R} \subset \mathbf{C}$.

PROBLEMS 2–5

1. Use Lemma 2 of Theorem 2.43 (or Problem 18 of § 2.4) to prove that $\sqrt{3}$ is not a rational number.

2. List two upper and two lower bounds for the set $S = \{-2, 0, 1, 3\}$, none of which belong to S.

3. What are the unique upper and lower bounds of the set S in Problem 2, which belong to S?

4. What is the greatest lower bound of the set $\{1, 1/2, 1/3, \dots\}$ in $\mathbf{R}$?

5. Identify the greatest lower bound and least upper bound for (a) the *open interval* $\{x \in \mathbf{R} \mid 1 < x < 2\}$; (b) the *closed interval* $\{x \in \mathbf{R} \mid 1 \leq x \leq 2\}$.

6. Explain why the equation $3x = 2$ has no solution for $x \in \mathbf{Z}$.

*7. Prove that the relation used in this section to define the rational numbers is an equivalence relation.

*8. Verify that the definition of addition of rational numbers, as given in this section, is valid.

*9. Verify that the definition of multiplication of rational numbers, as given in this section, is valid.

*10. Verify that the definition, which we have given in this section for a *positive* rational number, is valid.

11. Verify that the equation $b + x = a$ always has a solution for x, if $a, b, x \in \mathbf{Q}$.

12. Explain why the set of finite decimal approximations of $\sqrt{2}$ has no rational least upper bound.

13. Prove, for arbitrary $x, y, z \in \mathbf{Q}$: (a) $(x + y) + z = x + (y + z)$; (b) $(xy)z = x(yz)$.

**14. Verify that the class $\overline{(0, a)}$, for any $a (\neq 0) \in \mathbf{Z}$, is the zero rational number.

15. Prove the following, for $x, y \in \mathbf{Q}$: (a) $x + y = y + x$; (b) $xy = yx$.

*16. Verify that the class $\overline{(a, a)}$, for any $a (\neq 0) \in \mathbf{Z}$, is the identity element 1 of $\mathbf{Q}$.

**17. Prove that any nonzero rational number has a multiplicative inverse [see Problem 16], and use this to show that the equation $bx = a$ is solvable for $x \in \mathbf{Q}$, and arbitrary $a, b (\neq 0) \in \mathbf{Q}$.

18. If $ab = 0$, for $a, b \in \mathbf{Q}$, prove that $a = 0$ or $b = 0$.

19. If r and s are any positive rational numbers, prove that $nr > s$ for some integer n. (This is known as the "Archimedean" property of $\mathbf{Q}$.)

20. Assume the "Archimedean" property for $\mathbf{R}$ [see Problem 19], and prove the existence of a rational number between any two real numbers.

21. Let us *try* to order the complex numbers by asserting that $a_1 + b_1 i < a_2 + b_2 i$, if $a_1 < a_2$ and $b_1 < b_2$. Which of the usual properties of $<$ fail for this relation?

22. Use the directions in Problem 21, but change the definition of $<$ so that $a_1 + b_1 i < a_2 + b_2 i$, if $a_1^2 + b_1^2 < a_2^2 + b_2^2$.

References

[1] BIRKHOFF, G. and MACLANE, S.: *A Survey of Modern Algebra*, Third Edition (New York, Macmillan, 1965).

[2] CROUCH, R. and WALKER, E.: *Introduction to Modern Algebra and Analysis* (New York, Holt, 1962).

[3] EVES, H. and NEWSOM, C.: *An Introduction to the Foundations and Fundamental Concepts of Mathematics* (New York, Holt, 1957).

[4] GRAVES, L. M.: *The Theory of Functions of Real Variables* (New York, McGraw-Hill, 1946).

[5] HALMOS, P. R.: *Naive Set Theory* (Princeton, N. J., Van Nostrand, 1960).

[6] JOHNSON, R.: *First Course in Abstract Algebra* (Englewood Cliffs, N. J., Prentice-Hall, 1953).

[7] WILDER, R. L.: *An Introduction to the Foundations of Mathematics* (New York, Wiley, 1952).

Selected Readings from The American Mathematical Monthly

ALBERT, R. G.: *A Paradox Relating to Mathematical Induction*, **57** (1950), 31–32.

BUCK, R. C.: *Inductive and Recursive Definitions*, **70** (1963), 128–135.

GONZALEZ, M. O. and MANCILL, J. D.: *On the System of Natural Numbers*, **57** (1950), 104–112; *Remarks on Natural Numbers*, **58** (1951), 186–188.

HENKIN, L.: *On Mathematical Induction*, **67** (1960), 323–338.

JUNGCK, G.: *Interval Induction*, **73** (1966), 295–297.

MARGARIS, A.: *Successor Axioms for the Integers*, **68** (1961), 441–444.

ROSSER, J. B.: *Problems on Natural Numbers*, **57** (1950), 353–354.

3 *General Algebraic Systems*

3.1. Groupoids and Semigroups

We have already characterized an *algebraic system* as a set of elements in which certain operations and relations have been defined. The fewer there are of these operations and relations, and the smaller the number of other requirements to be satisfied, the simpler the system is. However, it should be recognized that the simplest systems are not necessarily the most familiar.

We recall that a binary operation or composition in a set S is a mapping of the product set $S \times S$ into S. Thus, with any two (distinct or equal) elements of S taken in a definite order there is associated a third, well-defined element of S. In systems with one algebraic operation, it is customary to use multiplicative terminology and symbolism: that is, we refer to the operation as "multiplication" and the image under the mapping of any pair (a, b) as their "product" ab. It happens sometimes, however, that additive notation is more convenient, in which case we refer to the operation as "addition" and designate the "sum" of a and b by $a + b$. It is to be understood, of course, that these operation symbols do not of necessity have any of the properties familiarly associated with them in ordinary arithmetic.

It is part of the definition which we have given for a binary operation that it is single valued and maps *any* ordered pair of elements of the set S in which it has been defined. Moreover, it should be noted that the image elements under such a mapping are all in S. If a and b are elements of a subset H of S, it may or may not happen that $ab \in H$. But if $ab \in H$, for arbitrary elements $a, b \in H$, the subset is said to be *closed* under the operation. We wish to point out that it is implicit in our definition of an operation defined in a set S, that

43

S itself is always closed under the operation. From our point of view, if the underlying set is not closed, the " operation " has not been properly defined in the set, although it may be in some subset. Inasmuch as $S \times S$ is a set of *ordered* pairs, the order of the elements in such a pair is usually of importance in stating the rule of composition for any operation in S. That is, if a and b are elements of S, the mapped image of (a, b) may be different from that of (b, a). In the symbolism adopted, we are saying that ab (or $a + b$) may be different from ba (or $b + a$). If it is known that ab (or $a + b$) is the same as ba (or $b + a$) for arbitrary elements a and b of the system, the operation is said to be *commutative* and the system is known as a *commutative* system; otherwise, the operation and the system are *noncommutative*. If the (binary) operation of a system is known to be commutative, it is usually preferred to use the symbol of addition $(+)$ rather than the symbol of multiplication, but there are many exceptions to this usage.

Definition. A set of elements in which a (binary) operation has been defined is known as a groupoid.*

We now make a remark which is essentially a repetition of one made in the more specialized context of Chapter 2: Although an algebraic system is not to be identified with the underlying set of elements, we shall often find it convenient to use *the same symbolism for both*. In particular, we shall speak of an algebraic *system* S and also an *element* $a \in S$. In the latter case, we are referring in reality to S as the set of elements of the system; but this duplication in the meaning of the symbol should cause no confusion, and will eliminate the use of cumbersome notations like $\langle S, + \rangle$ or $\langle S, \cdot \rangle$ for the system whose set of elements is S.

It is easy to find examples of a groupoid, though most of the familiar ones are also examples of more complex systems. The natural numbers, with either ordinary addition or ordinary multiplication as the operation, form a groupoid. However, the set of odd natural numbers with ordinary addition and the set of real numbers with ordinary division do not satisfy the definition. (Why?) The set of integers with the operation of ordinary subtraction provides us with an example of a groupoid with a noncommutative operation or a *noncommutative groupoid*. A subset of a groupoid, which is closed under the operation of the groupoid, is a *subgroupoid*. It is important to understand in this definition—as in the definition of any subsystem—that the same rule of composition applies to the subset as to the set. It may be possible to define an operation in a subset so that the rule of composition is quite different from that of the operation in the set. Under such a circumstance, the subset would comprise an algebraic system but *would not be a subsystem* of the original.

---

* Some authors use this word for a different concept. See page 31 of *The Theory of Groups* by Zassenhaus (New York, Chelsea, 1958).

The definition of a groupoid does not require that the operation be *associative*. That is, for arbitrary elements a, b, c of the set, it is not necessarily true that $(ab)c = a(bc)$ [or $(a + b) + c = a + (b + c)$]. However, the groupoid of natural numbers under either ordinary addition or ordinary multiplication is easily seen to be both associative and commutative. We have noted previously that the groupoid of integers under subtraction is not commutative, and it can also be seen that it is not associative. Anyone who is familiar with the multiplication of vectors in physics will note that this system of vectors, with the operation of vector multiplication, provides us with another example of a nonassociative groupoid.

Definition. An associative groupoid is known as a *semigroup*.

In recent years, a great deal of study has been devoted to semigroups. This is due, in part, to the fact that many of the results of group theory carry over to this more general system, and partly because other familiar systems—such as rings—can be more easily described in terms of semigroups. A groupoid is too general a system to allow a very extensive theoretical analysis, but it now appears that groups—which have been studied for many years—have more conditions on them than are necessary for a worthwhile theory. The intermediate system, the semigroup, has an adequate amount of structure to provide an interesting study.

The set of natural numbers under either ordinary addition or ordinary multiplication is a familiar example of a (commutative) semigroup. In Chapter 1, we included a brief discussion of the idea of a mapping of a set S into itself, as well as the products of such mappings. If α, β, and γ are three mappings of a set S into itself, it will be recalled that the definition of a product of mappings requires that $\alpha(\beta\gamma) = (\alpha\beta)\gamma$, and so this mapping operation is associative. Hence, the mappings of S into S provide us with a simple example of a semigroup, the product operation for mappings being the operation defined in this semigroup.

For a semigroup, it is unambiguous to speak of the product abc of any three elements a, b, c of the system; but, for a general groupoid, this could mean either of the products $(ab)c$ or $a(bc)$. It is somewhat intuitive—and we omit the proof—that if the associative law holds for any three elements, it will hold for an arbitrary finite number: i.e., the product $a_1a_2a_3 \cdots a_n$ will have an unambiguous meaning, regardless of how the elements in the product are grouped. (However, see Problem 12 of § 2.2 for a suggestion for a proof of this "generalized" associative law in the semigroup of natural numbers under multiplication. A similar proof could be given for the operation of addition.) In this case, if $a_1 = a_2 = a_3 = \cdots = a_n = a$, we may designate the product conveniently by a^n. (If additive notation is used, we designate the sum of n elements, each of which is a, by na; i.e., $na = a + a + a + \cdots + a$, where there are n summands.) If a subset of a semigroup is closed under the operation, the subset comprises a *subsemigroup*.

Example 1. If we define a "star" operation in **R** by $a * b = a + 2b$, it is easy to see that the resulting system is a groupoid but not a semigroup. For, with arbitrary $a, b, c \in \mathbf{R}$, $a * (b * c) = a + 2(b * c) = a + 2(b + 2c) = a + 2b + 4c$, while $(a * b) * c = (a + 2b) + 2c = a + 2b + 2c$. Hence, the "star" operation is not associative, and the system is not a semigroup.

Example 2. If we revise the "star" operation in **R**, as given in Example 1, so that $a * b = a$, the resulting system can be easily seen to be a semigroup. For, in this case, $a * (b * c) = a * b = a$, and also $(a * b) * c = a * c = a$, so that this "star" operation is associative.

PROBLEMS 3–1

1. If a and b are elements of the groupoid of integers under ordinary multiplication, determine ab where (a) $a = 5$, $b = -6$; (b) $a = -2$, $b = 8$.

2. Apply the directions of Problem 1 to the groupoid of integers under ordinary addition, where we identify the abstract product ab with $a + b$.

3. Apply the directions of Problem 1 to the groupoid of integers under ordinary subtraction, where we identify the abstract product ab with $a - b$.

4. Let us define a binary composition in the set **Z of rational integers as follows: $a \circ b = a + b - ab$, for arbitrary $a, b \in \mathbf{Z}$. (This composition is known as the *circle* composition.) Show that **Z** is a semigroup under the circle composition.

5. Let us define a binary composition in the set **N** of natural numbers as follows: $a * b = a + b + ab$, for arbitrary $a, b \in \mathbf{N}$. Show that **N** is a semigroup under this *star* composition.

6. In the set P_S of all subsets of a set S, let set-theoretic union be the composition. Show that P_S is a semigroup under this composition.

7. If union is replaced by intersection in Problem 6, is the resulting system a semigroup?

8. Let **N** be considered a semigroup under ordinary addition. Now define a binary operation on the even natural numbers so that the resulting system is also a semigroup but not a subsemigroup of **N**.

9. With reference to Problem 8, how would one define the operation on the even numbers if the new system is to be a subsemigroup of **N**?

10. Prove the generalized commutative law in a semigroup $\mathcal{S}$, if it is known that $ab = ba$, for arbitrary $a, b \in \mathcal{S}$. That is, prove that a product of n elements $a_1, a_2, \ldots, a_n$ of $\mathcal{S}$ is independent of the order in which these elements are arranged for multiplication.

11. Prove that the set-theoretic intersection of any collection of subsemigroups of a semigroup $\mathcal{S}$ is also a subsemigroup of $\mathcal{S}$.

12. Let X be a subset of a semigroup $\mathcal{S}$, and prove that the intersection of all subsemigroups containing X is also a subsemigroup $[X]$ of $\mathcal{S}$. X is called

a *generating set* or set of *generators* of [*X*], while [*X*] is called the sub-semigroup *generated* by *X*. (How do we know that the above intersection is not ∅?)

13. With reference to Problem 12, decide whether a set of generators of a semigroup is or is not unique. Could the set of all elements in the semigroup be considered a generating set?

14. Establish the following "laws of exponents" for any semigroup S: (a) $x^m x^n = x^{m+n}$; (b) $(x^m)^n = x^{mn}$, for any $x \in S$ and arbitrary positive integers m, n.

15. Without reference to the "generalized" associative law, prove that $(ab)(cd) = a(bc)d$, with a, b, c, d arbitrary elements of a semigroup S in which we assume the basic 3-element associative law.

**16. Find the smallest set of generators [see Problem 12] for the semigroup of natural numbers under ordinary addition.

17. Apply the directions given in Problem 16 to the semigroup of natural numbers under ordinary multiplication.

18. A "multiplication table" for a finite algebraic system with one operation (multiplication) is a square array which indicates all possible products in the system. The left factors are displayed to the left of the array, while the right factors are displayed above. Decide whether the 2-elements systems, whose multiplication tables are given below, are semigroups:

(a)

	a	b
a	a	b
b	a	b

(b)

	a	b
a	a	b
b	b	a

19. Refer to Problem 18, and determine whether the 3-element groupoid, with the multiplication table displayed below, is a semigroup.

	a	b	c
a	a	b	c
b	b	a	c
c	c	c	c

20. Refer to Problem 18 and decide whether the multiplication table of a semigroup has any obvious properties which will distinguish the system from a groupoid—which is not a semigroup.

21. Refer to Problem 18 and fill in the blanks in the following multiplication table so that the 3-element groupoid defined is a semigroup.

	a	b	c
a	a	b	c
b		b	a
c	c		c

22. A *cancellation groupoid* **G** is one in which the left and right cancellation laws hold; i.e., $ab = ac$ (or $ba = ca$) implies that $b = c$. Prove that the multiplication table of such a **G**, with a finite number of elements, is characterized by the property that each element of **G** occurs exactly once in each of its rows and columns.

23. With X a set of symbols, let us define a *word* as a *formal* product $x_1 x_2 \cdots x_n$, with $x_i \in X, i = 1, 2, \ldots, n$. If we define the product of two words as the word resulting from the orderly juxtaposition of the symbols comprising the words, show that the system of words is a semigroup. This is called the *free semigroup on X*. What can be said about the cardinality of *any* free semigroup? Describe this semigroup if $X = \{x\}$. Why is a free semigroup, in general, not commutative?

24. If we were to define a *free groupoid* in a manner patterned after that of a free semigroup in Problem 23, how would the two systems differ?

3.2. Monoids and Groups

It sometimes happens that an algebraic system has a *neutral* or *identity* element, i.e., an element e such that $ae = ea = a$, for an arbitrary element a in the system. However, if there is an identity element, this element is the *only one* which has this property. For if f is another identity element, we must have $ef = e$ and also $ef = f$, from the definition of an identity element, so that $e = f$. It is customary to designate this unique identity element as 1 in the multiplicative notation and as 0 in the additive notation. To reemphasize a point which we made earlier, however, these elements should not be confused with integers, though in special cases they may actually be these familiar numbers.

Definition. A semigroup with an identity element is known as a *monoid*.

The set of integers under either ordinary addition or ordinary multiplication provides an example of a monoid, with 0 or 1 playing its familiar role of identity element in the system. The semigroup of mappings of a set S into itself is also a monoid, the identity mapping—in which each element maps onto itself—being the identity element. The set of integers under subtraction is an example of a groupoid which is not associative (as we noted before), nor does it have an identity element. The integer 0 is not an identity element because while $a - 0 = a$, for any integer a, it is not true in general that $0 - a = a$. The semigroup of natural numbers under ordinary addition and the semigroup of even integers under ordinary multiplication are other examples of a semigroup without an identity element. A subset of a monoid is, of course, a *submonoid* if the subset contains the identity of the monoid and is closed under the operation of the monoid. It may happen, however, that a subsemigroup of a monoid S contains an identity element but one which is different from the identity of the monoid. In such a case, the subsemigroup is a monoid but not a submonoid of S.

In elementary arithmetic, it is customary to speak of subtraction as an operation which is "inverse" to addition, and division as an operation which is "inverse" to multiplication. This terminology is a colloquialism which is meaningful, if we think of an operation as a procedure: for an "inverse" operation is then one which "undoes" the results of the original operation. However, it is more "mathematical" to consider an operation in a set S as a mapping of $S \times S$ into S; and unfortunately the "inverse" operation would then *not* be any "reasonable" reverse mapping of S into $S \times S$, such as one might want. Hence mathematicians prefer not to apply the adjective "inverse" to *operations* at all, but rather attach it to *elements* of the algebraic system: the results of an "inverse operation" are then accomplished by applying the basic operation of the system with the use of certain "inverse" elements. When subtraction is first encountered in grade school, the pupil is taught that subtraction of integers can be accomplished by "adding the negative of the subtrahend," and we do essentially the same thing in our present more abstract environment.

Let us then consider a multiplicative semigroup with an identity element 1, i.e., a monoid, and in particular the equations $ax = 1$ and $ya = 1$, for an arbitrary element a of the monoid. If $x = b$ is a solution of the first equation, then $ab = 1$ and we speak of b as a *right inverse* of a. Similarly, if $y = c$ is a solution of the second equation, then $ca = 1$ and c is referred to as a *left inverse* of a. An element a may be called *right regular* or *left regular* according as a right inverse or a left inverse exists for a. In case a is both right and left regular, it is not difficult to show [Problem 8] that any left inverse is equal to any right inverse, so that there exists a unique [Problem 9] element, denoted by a^{-1}, such that $aa^{-1} = a^{-1}a = 1$. The element a^{-1} is called the *inverse* of a, and a may be said to be *regular, invertible*, or *a unit*. (It possibly should be pointed out that some people use the terminology "unit element" for what we have called the "identity element" but, while this element is in fact a unit, there are usually many *other* units in a monoid.) If we happen to be using the additive notation in a monoid, with identity element 0, it is customary to designate the inverse of an element a as $-a$.

If we wish to solve an equation $ax = b$ (or $a + x = b$) in a monoid, it is important to know whether a is a regular element. For if a is regular, then a^{-1} (or $-a$) exists, and so $a^{-1}(ax) = (a^{-1}a)x = 1x = x = a^{-1}b$ (or $-a + (a + x) = (-a + a) + x = 0 + x = x = -a + b$) with the solution of the equation displayed. A similar remark applies to the equation $ya = b$ (or $y + a = b$).

Definition. A monoid in which every element is a unit is called a *group*, and will usually be designated $\mathfrak{G}$.

This means that a group is a set in which a binary operation (which we shall indicate as multiplication) has been defined, such that the following three conditions hold:

1. $(ab)c = a(bc)$, for arbitrary elements a, b, c in the set;
2. There exists an (identity) element 1 such that $a1 = 1a = a$, for an arbitrary element a in the set;
3. For each element a in the set, there is an associated (inverse) element a^{-1} in the set, such that $aa^{-1} = a^{-1}a = 1$.

It follows from the remark made just before the Definition that if a and b are *arbitrary* elements of a group $\mathfrak{G}$, the equations $ax = b$ and $ya = b$ are always solvable for x and y in $\mathfrak{G}$. The solutions of these equations are, in general, different. However, if the group is known to be *commutative* or *abelian* (i.e., $g_1 g_2 = g_2 g_1$ for arbitrary $g_1, g_2 \in \mathfrak{G}$), it is clear that the solutions will be the same. In order to illustrate the solvability of equations, let us consider the equation $ax = b$ (or $a + x = b$) with a, b in the monoid of ordinary integers under multiplication (or addition). It is clear in the multiplicative case that the equation is not always solvable: for example, there is no integral solution of $2x = 3$. On the other hand, it is always possible to solve the equation $a + x = b$ in the additive monoid of integers, the solution being $x = b - a$. If we examine the equation in the additive monoid of nonnegative integers, however, we shall find again that a solution may fail to exist: for example, in this monoid there is no solution to $5 + x = 2$. Actually, the astute student will have noted that the additive monoid of integers is actually a group— because every integer has an inverse—while the monoid of nonnegative integers is not. We are devoting Chapter 4 to a further study of groups, contenting ourselves here with a few preliminary remarks.

Example 1. It is possible to illustrate the system which we have called a monoid, by using a subset of integers and making slight changes in the ordinary operations of addition and multiplication. For any fixed positive integer $n > 1$, let $\mathbf{Z}'_n$ be the set of nonnegative integers less than n and define the sum and product of any two such integers as the *remainder* or *residue* when the ordinary sum or product is divided by n. For the case $n = 4$, the addition and multiplication tables are given below, the numbers added or multiplied occurring along the borders, as explained in Problem 18 of § 3.1.

+	0	1	2	3
0	0	1	2	3
1	1	2	3	0
2	2	3	0	1
3	3	0	1	2

·	0	1	2	3
0	0	0	0	0
1	0	1	2	3
2	0	2	0	2
3	0	3	2	1

It is not difficult [Problem 13] to see that both of these operations are associative in $\mathbf{Z}'_n$, and that 0 is the identity of addition while 1 is the identity of multiplication. The elements in $\mathbf{Z}'_n$ then form a monoid under either addition or multiplication: It is known, respectively, as the *additive* and *multiplicative monoid of integers mod n* [cf. Problem 20 of § 2.4 and see Problem 12 of § 3.3]. It is clear that both monoids are commutative.

Example 2. The *additive* monoid $\mathbf{Z}'_n$ of integers mod n [see Example 1] is actually a group. Because, if c is any number in $\mathbf{Z}'_n$ and we remember our definition of addition, we see that $c + (n - c) = (n - c) + c = 0$ [Problem 14], verifying that $n - c$ is the inverse of c. If we consider the existence of inverses in the *multiplicative* monoid $\mathbf{Z}'_n$, however, the presence of 0 makes it impossible for all numbers in this monoid to have inverses: $a0 = 0a = 0$ for any number $a \in \mathbf{Z}'_n$, so that 0 would fail to have a multiplicative inverse. In the case where $n = p$ is prime, however, one can use Theorem 2.42 to show that all numbers in $\mathbf{Z}'_p$ *except* 0 do have inverses. For if c is any such number, c is prime to p, and Theorem 2.42 assures the existence of integers r and s such that $1 = rc + sp$, where we recall that 1 is the g.c.d. of c and p. But, in the multiplicative monoid under discussion, $sp = 0$, so that $rc = cr = 1$. If $r > 0$, r is the desired inverse; if $r < 0$, the inverse can be taken to be $p + r$, as a simple check will verify [Problem 15]. We shall have many occasions in the future to consider the systems of integers mod n, for they are of fundamental importance in the theory of other algebraic systems.

In this book we are going to be concerned only with associative systems, although a great deal of study has recently been devoted to nonassociative systems. We merely remark, in passing, that a *quasigroup* is a (nonassociative) groupoid each element of which has an inverse; if the quasigroup has an identity element, the system is known as a *loop*.

PROBLEMS 3–2

1. Solve the equation $ya = b$ for y in the monoid of positive integers under multiplication if: (a) $a = 2$, $b = 10$; (b) $a = 1$, $b = 4$. Could you solve the equation for y if $a = 4$ and $b = 2$?
2. In the groupoid of integers under subtraction, solve the equation $ya = b$ for y if ya is identified with $y - a$ and (a) $a = 2$, $b = 5$; (b) $a = 8$, $b = -4$.

3. In the groupoid of integers under subtraction, solve the equation $ax = b$ for x if ax is identified with $a - x$ and (a) $a = 2$, $b = 5$; (b) $a = 8$, $b = -4$. Compare the results of Problems 2 and 3.

4. Identify the algebraic system that is formed by the set of (a) rational numbers under addition; (b) irrational numbers under addition; (c) irrational numbers under multiplication.

**5. Explain why the mappings of a set into itself comprise a monoid, with the usual composition of mappings as the operation.

6. If one were to define " subtraction " in an additive monoid S as a mapping of $S \times S$ into S, how would the definition be worded?

7. Is it possible to prove the uniqueness of a right inverse for an element of a monoid, in the absence of any further information? Is the situation changed if the cancellation law is assumed?

*8. In a monoid, prove that any left inverse of an element is equal to any right inverse of the same element. Can you prove this without using the associative law, i.e., in a groupoid with identity?

*9. Why does it follow from Problem 8 that inverse elements in a monoid are unique, provided they exist?

10. Prove that any monoid in which the equations $ax = b$ and $ya = b$ can be solved for x and y, with a and b arbitrary elements of the monoid, must have an identity element.

11. Prove that each element of a monoid, subject to the conditions of Problem 10, has an inverse. Hence try to give an alternate definition of a group, and prove it equivalent to the one given in the text.

**12. Prove that a *finite* monoid (i.e., with a finite number of elements) is a group if any solutions of $ax = b$ and $ya = b$ which exist must be unique. (Note that we do not *assume* here the existence of solutions for all these equations.)

13. Prove that the operations in the monoids described in Example 1 are associative and commutative.

14. In Example 2, explain why $c + (n - c) = 0$.

15. If $r < 0$ in Example 2, explain why the inverse of c is $p + r$.

16. If X is a set of two or more elements, and an operation is defined in X by $ab = a$, for arbitrary a, $b \in X$, prove that the system is a noncommutative semigroup without an identity element.

17. Refer to Example 1, and give the addition and multiplication tables for the semigroup (a) Z_5' ; (b) Z_6' .

18. Refer to the tables in Problem 17, and find a nonzero element in Z_6' which has no multiplicative inverse. Are there any of this kind in Z_5' ?

19. Prove that the intersection of any collection of submonoids of a monoid is also a submonoid.

20. Let S be the system of even integers regarded as a multiplicative semigroup, with S' the monoid resulting when the integer 1 is adjoined to S. Explain why S is not a submonoid of S'. More generally, let S be any monoid, and suppose an element $e(\notin S)$ be adjoined to S to produce the system S', where $e^2 = e$ and $es = se = s$, for any $s \in S$. Then show that S is not a submonoid of S'.

21. If a, b, c are arbitrary elements of a group, prove that the equation $axba = bc$ has a unique solution for x in the group.

22. (Del Franco) Let $X = \{A, B, C, D, E, F, G\}$, with the relation "precedes" defined in X to mean "is adjacent to and on the left of," as in the order of piano keys. (This implies that G "precedes" A.) We now define two operations on X: $x_i * x_j = x_k$, where x_k precedes x_j; $x_i \circ x_j = x_j$.

   (a) Decide whether X is a semigroup relative to either or both operation(s).
   (b) Prove that an arbitrary $x \in X$ is a left identity in $\langle X, \circ \rangle$ but that this system has no right identity.
   (c) Prove that $\langle X, * \rangle$ has no left or right identity, but that each $x \in X$ has a unique right identity associated with it (elementwise).

3.3. Isomorphism

It is an historical fact that often independent studies have been made of two or more algebraic systems, and later these systems have been recognized to be "algebraically" the same. We refer to such systems as being "isomorphic" or say that we have established an "isomorphism"—a particular type of mapping—between them. Let us first consider the notion from an intuitive viewpoint. A set may be considered an algebraic system in which we have defined no operations or relations apart from the *identity* (or "equals") relation. In this simple case the idea of isomorphism is the same as that of cardinal number, which means for finite sets that they have the same number of elements. Notice that we do not consider any of the properties which the elements of either set may have—and these may well be different for the two sets—but we consider merely the question of cardinality. For instance, a set of 10 points on a line, a set of 10 people in a room, and a set of 10 words are isomorphic *sets*. (We have also said such sets are "equivalent.")

The situation is a little more complex in the case of systems in which we have defined operations and/or other relations. However, the basic idea is still the same: Two systems are isomorphic if their associated sets are isomorphic *and*—in very loose language—any deduction in one of the systems can be translated into an equally correct deduction in the other. As we have already noted, the elements of the two sets may be different, the rules of composition may be different, and the relations may be defined in entirely different ways; but if the systems are isomorphic they are algebraically indistinguishable. We are now ready to give a precise definition of the concept, for the case of algebraic systems with one operation and no relations but equality.

Definition. Let S and S' be two algebraic systems (groupoids), each with one operation for which we shall use the same multiplicative notation. Then these systems are *isomorphic*, and we write $S \cong S'$ if:

1. there is a one-to-one correspondence between the elements of S and of S', this correspondence being conveniently indicated by $a \leftrightarrow a'$, for $a \in S$ and $a' \in S'$; and

2. the operation is "preserved" by the correspondence, i.e., if $a \leftrightarrow a'$ and $b \leftrightarrow b'$, with $a, b \in S$ and $a', b' \in S'$, it follows that $ab \leftrightarrow a'b'$.

It is sometimes helpful to represent the above conditions pictorially, as shown in the arrangement below

$$
\begin{array}{ccc}
\underline{S} & & \underline{S'} \\
a & \longleftrightarrow & a' \\
b & \longleftrightarrow & b' \\
ab & \longleftrightarrow & (ab)' = a'b'.
\end{array}
$$

The groupoid of even natural numbers under addition is isomorphic to the groupoid of all natural numbers N under addition. For, let us establish a one-to-one correspondence—as required by **1**—whereby each even number $2k$ corresponds to the number $k \in N$. It is immediate that this correspondence is one-to-one. Furthermore, in addition to $2k \leftrightarrow k$, let us assume that $2m \leftrightarrow m$, so that $2k + 2m = 2(k + m)$ and $2(k + m) \leftrightarrow k + m$. But this means that the correspondent of the sum of $2k$ and $2m$ is the sum of their respective correspondents, which is the statement (in additive notation) that condition **2** is satisfied. Hence the two groupoids are isomorphic.

A slightly less elementary example of an isomorphism is provided by the groupoid of positive real numbers P under multiplication and the groupoid of all real numbers R under addition. In this case, we can set up a one-to-one correspondence by associating each positive real number in P with its common logarithm in R. Each positive real number has a unique, well-defined, common logarithm, and each real number—positive, negative, or zero—is the common logarithm of some unique, well-defined, positive number. Hence the correspondence is one-to-one as desired. If a and b are arbitrary positive real numbers, the following correspondences show that the systems are isomorphic.

$$
\begin{array}{ccc}
\mathbf{P} & & \mathbf{R} \\
a & \longleftrightarrow & a' = \log a \\
b & \longleftrightarrow & b' = \log b \\
ab & \longleftrightarrow & (ab)' = \log ab = \log a + \log b = a' + b'.
\end{array}
$$

It should be noted in this example that not only are the two sets distinct, but the operation in one case is addition, and in the other it is multiplication—thus illustrating an earlier remark.

It is sometimes convenient to use a slightly different language in discussing isomorphic systems. Thus, the one-to-one correspondence or bijective mapping that is associated with two isomorphic systems may be said to define an *isomorphism* of one system with the other. In the language and terminology of mappings, we may say that a mapping ψ of a groupoid S onto a groupoid S' is an *isomorphism* if the following conditions are satisfied:

1. ψ is a bijection from S to S'.
2. If $a\psi = a'$ and $b\psi = b'$, then $(ab)\psi = a'b'$; i.e., $(ab)\psi = (a\psi)(b\psi)$ for arbitrary $a, b \in S$.

Let us reemphasize a point which we noted above, that the elements and defining rules for the operations and relations of two isomorphic systems can be quite different, and yet the two systems are not to be distinguished *as to their algebraic structures*. This implies that any result which can be proved about one of the systems and which does not refer to the nature of its elements, remains true in the other system. It is assumed, of course, that the operations and/or relations of two isomorphic systems are of the *same kind*. For example, it would be impossible for a groupoid to be isomorphic to an algebraic system with one *ternary* operation involving a triple of elements of the latter system; and it would not be possible for one ordered groupoid to be " order " isomorphic to another ordered groupoid if the rules governing the two ordering relations happen to be different. In the latter connection, however, whenever we refer to an order relation—without further qualification—we shall always mean a (simple) order subject to the three rules given in § 2.2. In view of what we have said, it is not necessary to make independent studies of isomorphic systems. Only in examples will it be desirable to speak of sets of specific elements and operations that depend on the properties of these elements.

It can be shown that if two groupoids are isomorphic, the validity of the associative or commutative law in one system entails its validity in the other [Problems 3, 4]. Moreover, if one system S has an identity element 1, the correspondent of 1 in the other system S' is the identity element of S'. For let $1'$ in S' be the correspondent of 1 in S. Then if a' is an arbitrary element of S', the correspondent of which is a in S, the equation $a1 = 1a = a$ in S implies that the equation $a'1' = 1'a' = a'$ is valid in S'. But this means that $1'$ is the identity element of S', as asserted. It can also be shown that if the elements in one of two isomorphic systems have inverses, the same is true of the elements in the other system [Problem 5]. This should be expected, of course, along with the other properties just mentioned, in view of our algebraic identification of isomorphic systems.

An isomorphism of a system S with a system S' is said to be an *automorphism* if S and S' are the same system. Intuitively, we can think of an automorphism as a shuffling of the elements of a system, but with the operations and relations in the system remaining unaltered. We caution that it is quite possible for two systems to have the same elements—and so be equal as sets—but be different algebraic systems. Such systems may possibly not even be isomorphic. For a simple example of an automorphism, consider the system of complex numbers $a + bi$, where $a, b \in \mathbf{R}$. If we think of this system as an additive group—i.e., with addition as the group operation—it is easy to verify that the mapping $a + bi \to a - bi$ of every complex number onto its conjugate is an automorphism of the system [Problem 7].

It possibly should be pointed out that, while it is relatively easy to check whether a given mapping is an isomorphism, it is considerably more difficult to decide whether two systems of the same kind are isomorphic. Because, in the latter instance, one must discover the isomorphic mapping and it is this "discovery" problem which can be very difficult—especially if the system has a large or infinite number of elements. We conclude this section with two more illustrative examples of how to establish an isomorphism and, in the case of Example 2, to validate an assumption made in Chapter 2.

Example 1. It is almost trivial to show that the real numbers constitute a monoid, under either addition or multiplication, which is isomorphic to a submonoid of the monoid of all complex numbers under the operation with the same name. However, let us sketch a brief outline of the proof.

1. The mapping $a \to a + 0i$, for any $a \in \mathbf{R}$, is the "obvious" candidate for the isomorphism. It is certainly one-to-one: for if $a + 0i \neq b + 0i$, it follows that $a \neq b$.

2. Let us suppose that: $a \to a + 0i$
$$b \to b + 0i.$$
Then $a + b \to a + b + 0i$, by the rule of the mapping, and it is immediate that $a + b + 0i = (a + 0i) + (b + 0i)$. If we designate the mapping by ψ, this result may be abbreviated to $(a + b)\psi = (a\psi) + (b\psi)$, and this completes the proof of the isomorphism for the additive case. For the case of multiplication, we have merely to note that $(a + 0i)(b + 0i) = ab + 0i$, so that $(a\psi)(b\psi) = (ab)\psi$, and the proof is complete.

Example 2. In §2.3 we gave an axiomatic development of the rational integers, and stated that the positive integers are "in every way quite like" the natural numbers. In the earlier section we promised a later clarification of this remark, and we do this now in part by showing that the semigroup of natural numbers under addition (multiplication) is isomorphic to the semigroup of positive rational integers under addition (multiplication). As usual, we let $\mathbf{N}$ designate the natural numbers and $\mathbf{P}$ the positive integers, a typical element of $\mathbf{P}$ being designated by $\overline{(r + x, r)}$ with x a fixed and r an arbitrary natural number [Problem 1]. The following schema then outlines the desired proof of the existence of an isomorphic mapping $N \to P$.

1. $x \to \overline{(r + x, r)}$, for any $r \in N$.
   This mapping is clearly one-to-one of N onto P, i.e., a bijection.
2. If further,
   $y \to \overline{(s + y, s)}$, for any $s \in N$, then
   $x + y \to \overline{(m + x + y, m)}$, for any $m \in N$.
   However,

$$\overline{(r + x, r)} + \overline{(s + y, s)} = \overline{(r + s + x + y, r + s)} = \overline{(m + x + y, m)}$$

if we let $m = r + s$. This is the second requirement for the isomorphism of the additive systems.
3. Moreover, $xy \to \overline{(n + xy, n)}$, for any $n \in N$, and a little computation shows that

$$\overline{(r + x, r)}\,\overline{(s + y, s)} = \overline{(rs + ry + sr + sx + xy, rs + ry + sr + sx)}$$

$$= \overline{(n + xy, n)}$$

if we let $n = rs + ry + sr + sx$ [Problem 2].

As in Example 1, if we designate the mapping by ψ, we have shown that $(x + y)\psi = (x\psi) + (y\psi)$ and $(xy)\psi = (x\psi)(y\psi)$, and so have completed the proof of the isomorphism of both the additive and the multiplicative systems. It is noteworthy that the fact that the additive system is a semi-group, while the multiplicative system is a monoid, is irrelevant as far as the isomorphism of the systems is concerned.

PROBLEMS 3–3

1. Explain why $\overline{(r + x, r)}$ is a typical positive integer, as asserted in Example 2.
2. Carry out the computation referred to in Example 2.
**3. Prove that if one of two isomorphic groupoids is commutative, so is the other.
*4. Prove that if one of two isomorphic groupoids is associative, so is the other.
5. Prove that if each element in one of two isomorphic groupoids has an inverse, the same is true of the elements in the other groupoid.
6. Prove that "is isomorphic to" is an equivalence relation in the set of all groupoids.
**7. Prove that the mapping $a + bi \to a - bi$ of each complex number onto its conjugate is an automorphism of the additive group of C.

8. Let S and S' be, respectively, the additive groupoids of positive integers and positive even integers. If these integers are ordered by the usual "less than" relation, prove that S and S' are isomorphic as *ordered* groupoids. (Hint: Is the order relation "preserved" by the mapping?)

9. Let $f: \mathcal{G} \to \mathcal{G}$ be a mapping of a group $\mathcal{G}$ defined by $f(a) = a^{-1}$, $a \in \mathcal{G}$.
   (a) Show that f is a bijection.
   (b) Show that f is an isomorphism if and only if $\mathcal{G}$ is commutative.
   (c) Exhibit this isomorphism explicitly for the case where $\mathcal{G}$ is the additive group $\mathbf{Z}'_6$.

10. If two 5-element groupoids are being considered for possible isomorphism, what is the maximum number of mappings to be examined before a definite conclusion can be reached?

11. Show that any semigroup can be isomorphically imbedded in a monoid [see Problem 20 of § 3.2].

12. Show that the *set* $\mathbf{Z}'_n$ of "remainders" or integers mod n, as described in Example 1 of § 3.2, is cardinally equivalent to the set $\overline{\mathbf{Z}}_n$ of residue classes mod n, as described in Problem 20 of § 2.4. Try to define both an additive and a multiplicative operation in $\overline{\mathbf{Z}}_n$ so that $\mathbf{Z}'_n$ and $\overline{\mathbf{Z}}_n$ are isomorphic both as additive and as multiplicative monoids. (See Example 1 of § 3.5 for a further elaboration on this.)

13. If ψ is an isomorphic mapping of a groupoid S onto a groupoid S', prove that the inverse of ψ is also an isomorphic mapping of S' onto S. (When we speak of an isomorphism "between" two systems, we are actually assuming that the mapping can go either way.)

14. Prove that the automorphisms of a semigroup S comprise a monoid under the usual composition of mappings.

15. Prove that the monoid in Problem 14 is a submonoid of the monoid of all functions from S to S.

16. Let S_1 be a subsemigroup of a semigroup S. Then if ψ is an isomorphic mapping of S onto a semigroup S', prove that the *restriction* $\psi \mid S_1$ of ψ to S_1 is an isomorphism of S_1 into S'—i.e., onto a subsemigroup of S'.

17. Let $\psi: S \to S'$ be an isomorphism for semigroups S and S'. Then if X is a subset of S, prove that the "images" under ψ of the subsemigroup $[X]$ generated by X is the subsemigroup generated in S' by the "images" of the elements of X, i.e., $[X]\psi = [X\psi]$.

18. Refer to Problem 23 of § 3.1 and prove that the free semigroup with one generator is isomorphic to the additive semigroup of natural numbers.

19. Let $f: \theta \to e^{i\theta}$ be a mapping of the additive group $\mathbf{R}$ onto the multiplicative group of complex numbers of absolute value 1. Decide (with a reason!) whether f is an isomorphism.

20. Let $\psi: \mathcal{G}_1 \to \mathcal{G}_2$ designate an isomorphism of a group $\mathcal{G}_1$ onto a group $\mathcal{G}_2$, where $a_1\psi = a_2$, with $a_1 \in \mathcal{G}_1$ and $a_2 \in \mathcal{G}_2$. Then prove that the mappings $a_1^{-1} \to a_2^{-1}$ also define an isomorphism of $\mathcal{G}_1$ onto $\mathcal{G}_2$.

21. Show by actual demonstration that any group with three elements has an automorphism apart from the identity. Try to prove this for any group.

3.4. Homomorphism

The idea of isomorphism or isomorphic mapping, as discussed in the preceding section, is a special case of the more general idea of *homomorphism*. In the case of a homomorphism or homomorphic mapping we simply drop the condition that the mapping be bijective. To be specific, we give the following definition.

Definition. Let S and S' be two groupoids, the operation in each case being indicated as multiplication. A *homomorphism* of S into S' is then a mapping $\psi : S \to S'$ such that $(ab)\psi = (a\psi)(b\psi)$, for arbitrary $a, b \in S$.

As just noted, an isomorphism is then a homomorphism in which the mapping is a bijection. In the definition above, if S and S' are the same *system* [see Problem 1], we call ψ an *endomorphism*. The system $S\psi$, onto which S is mapped by ψ, is called the *homomorphic image* of S under ψ, and we note that $S\psi$ is usually a *proper* subsystem of S'.

While homomorphic images often share many of the properties of the original system, the two systems cannot be considered equivalent unless the homomorphism is an isomorphism [see Problem 3]. We shall consider a few examples of homomorphic mappings.

Example 1. Let S be the groupoid of integers under addition, and S' the groupoid consisting of the two integers 1 and -1 with multiplication as the operation. Then, if $x' = x\psi = 1$ or -1 according as x is even or odd, the mapping ψ is a homomorphism of S onto S'. For, if both a and b are even, $a' = a\psi = 1$ and $b' = b\psi = 1$, while $(a + b)' = (a + b)\psi = 1$ since $a + b$ is even; and so $(a + b)' = a'b'$, as required. If a is odd and b is even, $a' = a\psi = -1$, and $b' = b\psi = 1$, and so $(a + b)' = (a + b)\psi = -1$, since $a + b$ is odd. But then $(a + b)' = -1 = (-1)(1) = a'b'$, as before. Similar arguments for the other cases (a even and b odd, both a and b odd) will completely establish the fact that $(a + b)' = a'b'$, as is required in the definition of a homomorphism.

Example 2. Another example of a homomorphism is supplied by the ordinary plane line-vectors of physics and the projections of these vectors on a straight line. In this case we let S be the groupoid of the plane vectors emanating from the origin, with ordinary vector addition as the operation; and we let S' be the groupoid of all horizontal vectors emanating from the origin. If ψ maps S onto S' so that $x' = x\psi$ is the horizontal projection of x, for any x in S, we see that ψ is a homomorphism of S onto S'. For the projection of the sum of two vectors is the sum of their projections; and this is the same thing as saying that $(x + y)' = (x + y)\psi = x\psi + y\psi = x' + y'$ for arbitrary x, $y \in S$, as required in the definition.

It can be shown, just as in the case of an isomorphism, that if an operation in a groupoid is associative or commutative, these properties are inherited by any homomorphic image of the system [Problems 5, 6]. It is also true that if a semigroup has an identity element, so has any homomorphic image [Problem 7]. These remarks are equivalent to the statement that any homomorphic image of a (commutative) semigroup or monoid is, respectively, a (commutative) semigroup or monoid. In the case of monoids, however, one must be careful! For, if ψ is a homomorphism of a monoid S into a monoid S', it is true that $S\psi$ [or $\psi(S)$] is a monoid *but* it is not necessarily a submonoid of S': the identity elements of $S\psi$ and S' do not necessarily coincide. For example, it is easy to see that $x\psi = 0$, for all $x \in \mathbf{Z}$, defines an endomorphism of the multiplicative monoid $\mathbf{Z}$ of ordinary integers, but since $1\psi = 0$—and 0 is not the multiplicative identity of $\mathbf{Z}$—the image system $\mathbf{Z}\psi$ is not a submonoid of $\mathbf{Z}$. Is $\mathbf{Z}\psi$ a monoid [Problem 8]? A homomorphism of a monoid S into a monoid S', such that the identity element of S maps onto the identity element of S', is sometimes said to be *proper*. In other words, if $\psi : S \to S'$ is a proper homomorphism, for monoids S and S', $S\psi$ is a submonoid of S' [Problem 14].

We have just noted that the properties of commutativity, associativity, and existence of an identity element carry over from a groupoid to any homomorphic image, but the same cannot be said for the existence of inverse elements: it is not possible to prove generally that the defining equations for inverses in an image system have *unique* solutions [see Problems 9, 10, 11]. It *is* possible to prove, however, that if an equation is solvable in a monoid, the "corresponding" equation in a homomorphic image system also *has a solution*. For let us suppose that ψ is a homomorphic mapping of a groupoid S onto a groupoid S', with the operation in each system being indicated as multiplication (i.e., juxtaposition). Then, assuming solvability of equations in S, if a' and b' are arbitrary elements of S', we must consider the existence of solutions of the equations $a'x = b'$ and $ya' = b'$ in S'. Since ψ is a surjective mapping, there exist elements a and b in S such that $a' = a\psi$ and $b' = b\psi$. We are assuming that the equation $ax = b$ has a solution $x = c \in S$, and the definition of a homomorphism implies that $a'c' = b'$, where $c' = c\psi$. Hence c' is a solution of $a'x = b'$, as asserted. However, inasmuch as a and b are not necessarily unique, it cannot be inferred that c and c' are unique. A similar argument applies to the solution for y of the equation $ya' = b'$. We shall prove in the next chapter that any homomorphic image of a group is a group, and so for this important type of algebraic system, the "existence of inverses" is a property which is carried over to any image system.

While we have seen that most properties of a groupoid are inherited by a homomorphic image, there is very little that we can say in the other direction. It is quite possible for a homomorphic image to be associative and/or commutative without the original system having either of these properties. Neither are we able to infer the existence of an identity or inverse elements in a groupoid from their existence in a homomorphic image. However, the next theorem is important and of interest in this connection. We remarked in Chapter 1 that, while we would use "right" symbolic mappings for the most part, we would use "left" mappings if these seemed more convenient. In this theorem we shall then use "left" mappings, and let $\psi(A)$ be the image of a system A under a homomorphism ψ. Moreover, even though the inverse ψ^{-1} of ψ does not necessarily exist as a mapping, it will be convenient to use $\psi^{-1}(B)$ to designate the "inverse image" of a system B under ψ; i.e., $\psi^{-1}(B)$ is the set of elements which are mapped by ψ onto B.

Theorem 3.41. *Let $\psi : S \rightarrow S'$ be a homomorphism, with S and S' groupoids. Then, if A is a subgroupoid of S and B is a subgroupoid of S', $\psi(A)$ is a subgroupoid of S' and $\psi^{-1}(B)$ is a subgroupoid of S. Moreover, the theorem remains true if the words "groupoid" and "subgroupoid" are replaced, respectively, by "semigroup" and "subsemigroup."*

Proof. We first prove that $\psi(A)$ is a subgroupoid, and to this end we pick arbitrary elements a', b' in $\psi(A)$. There exist (not necessarily unique) elements a, $b \in A$ such that $\psi(a) = a'$ and $\psi(b) = b'$ and, since we are assuming that A is a groupoid, we know that $ab \in A$. But $a'b' = \psi(a)\psi(b) = \psi(ab) \in \psi(A)$, and so $\psi(A)$ is closed and a groupoid. For the proof that $\psi^{-1}(B)$ is closed, we let a, b in S be arbitrary elements of $\psi^{-1}(B)$. Then, for (possibly not distinct) elements a', $b' \in B$, $\psi(a) = a'$ and $\psi(b) = b'$. The fact that ψ is a homomorphism now assures us that $\psi(ab) = \psi(a)\psi(b) = a'b'$, and this latter product is in B since B is a subgroupoid. Hence $ab \in \psi^{-1}(B)$, and so $\psi^{-1}(B)$ is a groupoid. The final remark in the theorem is immediate, if we assume that S and S' are semigroups [see also Problem 7]. ∎

If ψ is a *proper* homomorphism of a monoid S into a monoid S', the subset of elements of S which map onto the identity of S' constitute an important submonoid of S [Problem 14]. (For the case where S is a group, the homomorphism is in fact determined "up to an isomorphism" by this subsystem—as we shall see later.) This submonoid of S is called the *kernel of ψ*, and is designated Ker ψ. We have already seen that any homomorphic image of a monoid is a monoid, and the image monoid, for any homomorphism ψ, is then designated as Im ψ.

PROBLEMS 3–4

1. Review the distinction between two groupoids S and S' being the same *system* and having the same *set* of elements. Give an example in which S and S' form distinct systems with the same elements.

*2. Complete the argument needed to show that the mapping in Example 1 is a homomorphism.

3. Let A be a subsemigroup of a semigroup S, and define the "inclusion" homomorphism $i : A \to S$ by $i(x) = x$, for $x \in A$. (Note "left" mapping, for variety!) Then prove that i is a homomorphism of A into S and the "identity" isomorphism of A onto a subsemigroup of S. This illustrates the fact that a homomorphism *into* a system S can be an *isomorphism onto* a subsystem of S.

4. Give an example to illustrate the fact that a homomorphism *onto* a system need not be an isomorphism.

*5. Prove that any homomorphic image of an associative groupoid is associative.

*6. Prove that any homomorphic image of a commutative groupoid is also commutative.

*7. If ψ is a homomorphic mapping of a monoid S, prove that $\psi(S)$ has an identity element.

8. Decide whether the additive system, made up of the real number 0 and the usual addition, satisfies the requirements of a monoid.

9. The equation $3 + x = 5$ has the unique solution $x = 2$ in the additive groupoid $\mathbf{Z}$. If $\mathbf{Z}$ is mapped, as in Example 1, solve the "corresponding" equation in the image system. Do all equations $ax = b$ and $ya = b$, with a and b in the image system, have unique solutions?

10. Prove that the mapping, in which each rational integer is mapped onto its remainder when divided by 4 [see Example 1 of § 3.2], is a homomorphism of $\mathbf{Z}$ onto $\mathbf{Z}_4'$, each considered an additive monoid. Decide whether equations of the form $a + x = b$, for arbitrary $a, b \in \mathbf{Z}_4'$, have unique solutions.

11. Use the directions of Problem 10, but with the multiplicative monoids $\mathbf{Z}$ and $\mathbf{Z}_4'$ and the equations of the form $ax = b$.

12. If S is a commutative additive semigroup and n a natural number, it is customary to define nx, for any $x \in S$, to be the sum $x + x + \cdots + x$ with n summands. (Note, in particular, that nx is not a multiplication of n and x, but is merely a convenient notation for a certain sum.) Prove that the mapping α defined on S by $x\alpha = nx$, for each $x \in S$, is an endomorphism of S.

**13. If $f_1 : S_1 \to S_2$ and $f_2 : S_2 \to S_3$ designate homomorphisms, for semigroups S_1, S_2, S_3, prove that $f_1 f_2$ is also a (right) homomorphism of S_1 into S_3, under the usual composition of mappings.

14. Prove that a homomorphism $h : S \to S'$ is proper, for monoids S and S', if and only if $h^{-1}(e')$ is a submonoid of S, and e' is the identity element of S'. (Note the "left" mapping here!)

15. Let α and β be mappings of the integers $\mathbf{Z}$ into $\mathbf{Z}$, defined by $x\alpha = x + 1$ and $x\beta = 2x$, for each integer x [see Problem 12]. Then show that (a) α is not an endomorphism of the additive monoid $\mathbf{Z}$; (b) β is an endomorphism of the additive monoid $\mathbf{Z}$; (c) $\alpha\beta \neq \beta\alpha$.

**16. If S is any semigroup, prove that the endomorphisms of S constitute a sub-monoid of the monoid of all functions from S to S, using the usual composition of functions for the operation.

17. A homomorphism $\psi : S_1 \to S_2$, for semigroups S_1 and S_2, is said to be a *monomorphism* if its mapping is injective [see § 1.4]. Prove that the following mappings are monomorphisms: (a) the homomorphism described in Problem 3; (b) the mapping of $\mathbf{Z}$ into $\mathbf{Z}$, defined by $x \to nx$, for any $x \in \mathbf{Z}$ and fixed $n \in \mathbf{N}$.

18. A homomorphism $\psi : S_1 \to S_2$, for semigroups S_1 and S_2, is said to be an *epimorphism* if its mapping is surjective [see § 1.4]. Prove that the homomorphisms, described in Examples 1 and 2 and in Problems 10 and 11, are epimorphisms.

19. Let $f_1 : S_1 \to S_2$ and $f_2 : S_2 \to S_3$ designate homomorphisms, for semigroups S_1, S_2, S_3. Then, using " right " mappings and the usual rule of composition for mappings, prove that if $f_1 f_2$ is an epimorphism, so is f_2.

20. With the symbolism of Problem 19, prove that if $f_1 f_2$ is a monomorphism, so is f_1.

21. The mapping sequence $A \xrightarrow{f_1} B \xrightarrow{f_2} C$, with f_1 and f_2 homomorphisms and A, B, and C monoids, may be said to be *exact* if $\operatorname{Im} f_1 = \operatorname{Ker} f_2$. Then prove that the homomorphism $f : A \to B$ is an epimorphism if $A \xrightarrow{f} B \to 0$ is an exact sequence [see Problem 18], with 0 the " zero " monoid.

22. Refer to Problems 17 and 21 and prove that the homomorphism f is a monomorphism if $0 \to A \xrightarrow{f} B$ is an exact sequence.

23. A *character* of a semigroup S is a homomorphism ψ of S into the multiplicative semigroup of complex numbers, with the proviso that $1\psi \neq 0$, in case S has an identity element. If characters of S are multiplied "pointwise" (i.e., $s(\psi_1\psi_2) = (s\psi_1)(s\psi_2)$, for characters ψ_1, ψ_2, and $s \in S$) prove that the characters of S form a semigroup S^*. Moreover, if S^{**} is the character semigroup of S^*, prove that the mapping $s \to h_s$, where $\psi h_s = s\psi$, for each $\psi \in S^*$, is a homomorphism of S into S^{**}.

24. If X is a set of generators [see Problem 12 of § 3.1] of a semigroup S, and F is the free semigroup on X [see Problem 23 of § 3.1], show that S is a homomorphic image of F. This is usually given as the defining property of a free semigroup—and there is an obvious extension of the concept to any algebraic system with one binary operation.

3.5. Fundamental Homomorphism Theorem

While a given groupoid S may have many distinct homomorphic images, it is possible to use the notion of a partition to obtain *all* of these—except for isomorphic duplicates. We shall call a partition " regular " if the class to which a product ab belongs depends only on the classes to which the elements a and b of S belong. The following definition makes this notion precise.

Definition. A partition of a set comprising the elements of a groupoid is *regular* if, for arbitrary elements a_1 and a_2 of one class and arbitrary elements b_1 and b_2 of another class, the elements $a_1 b_1$ and $a_2 b_2$ belong to the same class.

We recall from § 1.3 that if an equivalence relation is defined on a set, the set is partitioned into a collection of equivalence classes known as the *quotient set* relative to the given relation. However, at that time, no operation had been defined on either the set or its quotient sets—also known as *factor sets*. In the case of a *regular* partition, however, we are working with a groupoid—a set with a binary operation—and it is easy to define an operation on the factor set of the groupoid to produce what we call a *factor groupoid*. In fact, the definition of "regular" was formulated with this new operation in mind: if A and B are any two classes of a regular partition of a groupoid, we define the product AB to be the class that contains the product ab, for arbitrary elements $a \in A$ and $b \in B$. The factor set with this operation is then a groupoid $\bar{S}$, and it is easy to see that the mapping which associates each element of S with its class in $\bar{S}$ is a homomorphism. [Problem 2.] This mapping is called the *natural homomorphism* of S onto $\bar{S}$, with $\bar{S}$ the *factor* or *quotient* groupoid of S with respect to the regular partition. That these factor groupoids exhaust all possible homomorphisms, up to isomorphisms, is the content of the theorem in this section. We are then supplied with some quantitative information on the number of homomorphic images possible for a given groupoid. First, however, let us look at some examples of regular partitions of groupoids along with their associated factor systems.

Example 1. In this example, we actually give some of the details requested in Problem 12 of § 3.3. For a fixed integer $n > 1$, the integers $\mathbf{Z}$ are partitioned into equivalence classes $\bar{\mathbf{Z}}_n$; all integers in any one class have the same remainder when divided by n or, equivalently, n divides the difference between any two integers of any one class. If $\mathbf{Z}$ is considered an additive (multiplicative) groupoid, we see that the partition is regular: for, if $\bar{r}$ and $\bar{s}$ are the classes of integers with remainders on division by n of r and s, respectively, the sum (product) of an element of $\bar{r}$ and an element of $\bar{s}$ will belong to the same class—regardless of which elements are chosen [Problem 6]. Since $r \in \bar{r}$ and $s \in \bar{s}$, we can then define $\bar{r} + \bar{s} = \overline{r+s}$ and $\bar{r} \cdot \bar{s} = \overline{rs}$, and this makes the *set* $\bar{\mathbf{Z}}_n$ of classes into the *factor groupoid* $\bar{\mathbf{Z}}_n$—which is additive or multiplicative, as desired. Since $\bar{0}$ is the additive identity (or zero) while $\bar{1}$ is the multiplicative identity, $\bar{\mathbf{Z}}_n$ is actually a monoid when regarded as either an additive or multiplicative system. With each integer r, $0 \le r < n$, there is associated a unique class $\bar{r}$ of integers, and this sets up a one-to-one correspondence between the elements of $\mathbf{Z}_n'$ and the elements of the "remainder" system $\overline{Z}_n$—as discussed in Example 1 of § 3.2. We leave it for the student to verify that the two systems $\overline{Z}_n$ and Z'_n are actually isomorphic, as either additive or multiplicative monoids [Problem 14]. This means, of course, that it is "algebraically" unimportant whether we work with the monoid of *classes* $\overline{Z}_n$ or the monoid of *remainders* Z'_n. In practice, it is customary to combine certain features of each of these two systems and obtain another one which is essentially equivalent to both. In the new system, we discard the cumbersome symbolism of classes and work with integers themselves—being cognizant, of course, that there are only n of these which are distinct mod n. And, in fact, these "representative" integers are usually taken to be the n elements of Z'_n. For example, $3 + 5 \equiv 2 \pmod 6$; and $2 \cdot 5 \equiv 3 \pmod 7$. We shall label this somewhat "composite" system simply as Z_n, and refer to it in what follows as the *system of integers mod n*. We leave it at this time as an additive or multiplicative monoid, but at a later time we shall see that it may be given a more complex structure.

Example 2. Let us consider the 6-element groupoid, the multiplication table of which is shown below.

	a	b	c	d	e	f
a	a	b	e	e	c	d
b	b	b	f	f	c	d
c	e	f	c	d	a	b
d	e	f	d	d	b	a
e	c	c	a	b	e	f
f	d	d	b	a	f	f

It is immediate that the system is a groupoid, and it may be checked that the subsets $A = \{a, b\}$, $B = \{c, d\}$, $C = \{e, f\}$ are the members of a regular partition [Problem 8]. A glance at the multiplication table shows that the 3-element factor groupoid has the following multiplication table:

	A	B	C
A	A	C	B
B	C	B	A
C	B	A	C

We now proceed to the statement and proof of the Fundamental Homomorphism theorem.

Theorem 3.51. *For each homomorphic image S' of a groupoid S, there exists a regular partition of S, such that S' is isomorphic to the factor groupoid $\overline{S}$ of S with respect to this partition.*

Proof. If ψ is the homomorphism that maps S onto S', we obtain the desired partition of S by collecting in the same classes all elements of S whose images under ψ coincide. This partition is regular, for suppose a_1 and a_2 are in one class while b_1 and b_2 are in another. Then $a_1\psi = a_2\psi = a' \in S'$, and $b_1\psi = b_2\psi = b' \in S'$; and the definition of a homomorphism requires that $(a_1b_1)\psi = (a_1\psi)(b_1\psi) = a'b' = (a_2\psi)(b_2\psi) = (a_2b_2)\psi$. Hence a_1b_1 and a_2b_2 are in the same class, and so the partition is regular. We now construct the factor groupoid $\bar{S}$, as described above, and assert that $S' \cong \bar{S}$. If a' is an arbitrary element of S', let $A \in \bar{S}$ be the set of elements $a \in S$ such that $a\psi = a'$. The definition of A assures us that the correspondence $a' \leftrightarrow A$ between S' and $\bar{S}$ is one-to-one. Now let a_1', a_2' be elements of S' which are associated under this correspondence with A_1 and A_2 in $\bar{S}$, respectively. Then if $a_1 \in A_1$ and $a_2 \in A_2$, so that $a_1\psi = a_1'$ and $a_2\psi = a_2'$, the class A_1A_2 contains the element a_1a_2 and so $a_1'a_2' \leftrightarrow A_1A_2$, as required by the definition of an isomorphism. This completes the proof. ∎

In Example 1 above, the *natural* homomorphism, relative to the given regular partition, is the mapping $r \to \bar{r}$, for any $r \in \mathbf{Z}$. In the case of Example 2, it is necessary to write out the actual mapping for each element of the system: $a \to A$, $b \to A$, $c \to B$, $d \to B$, $e \to C$, $f \to C$. We leave it for the student to verify [Problems 7, 9] that each of these mappings is in fact a homomorphism.

PROBLEMS 3–5

1. Explain why it is important that a partition of a groupoid be regular if a factor groupoid is to be constructed.
**2. If a factor groupoid is constructed from any regular partition of a groupoid S, prove that the mapping that associates each $a \in S$ with the class containing it is a homomorphism.
3. State the maximal number of isomorphically distinct homomorphisms conceivable for a groupoid of (a) 3 elements; (b) 5 elements. (By "conceivable" we mean plausible but not necessarily possible!)
4. Construct an abstract groupoid S containing 3 elements [see Example 2], and determine the different possible factor groupoids $\bar{S}$.
5. Explain why any groupoid has at least one homomorphic image.
6. Explain why the partition in Example 1 is regular.
7. Give the proof that the natural mapping in Example 1 is a homomorphism.
8. Verify that the partition in Example 2 is regular.
9. Prove that the natural mapping in Example 2 is a homomorphism.
10. Construct a 5-element groupoid [see Example 2] and determine its factor groupoid relative to some regular partition.
11. We have seen before (§ 3.4) that the mapping ψ of $\mathbf{Z}$, such that $a\psi$ is 1 or -1 according as a is even or odd, is a homomorphism of the additive groupoid of integers onto the multiplicative groupoid of the set $\{1, -1\}$.

(a) Describe the partition of **Z** that is associated by Theorem 3.51 with ψ.

**(b) Prove that the partition described in (a) is regular.

(c) What elements of the partition in (a) correspond to 1 and -1 in the isomorphism asserted by Theorem 3.51?

12. Consider the homomorphism of the plane vectors, as discussed in § 3.4, and prove that the associated partition of the basic groupoid of vectors is regular.

13. Let $\{a, b, c\}$ be the set of elements of a groupoid S', onto which the ordinary integers **Z** are mapped according to the following rule: for $x \in \mathbf{Z}$, $x \to a$, if $2 \mid x$; $x \to b$, if $3 \mid x$ and $(x, 2) = 1$; $x \to c$, for all other x. Describe the partition of **Z** determined by this mapping.

14. Give the details of the proof that $\overline{\mathbf{Z}}_n$ and $\mathbf{Z}'_n$ are isomorphic, as either additive or multiplicative monoids.

15. Give reasons why the partition of **Z**, described in Problem 13, is or is not regular, if **Z** is considered (a) an additive groupoid; (b) a multiplicative groupoid. If the partition is regular in either (a) or (b) or both, give the composition table(s) of $\overline{\mathbf{Z}}$ thereby determined.

16. State the theorem that corresponds to Theorem 3.51 for both semigroups and monoids. In view of what has gone before—in the text and problems—explain why the conclusions of these theorems follow directly from the theorem in this section. Why does the extension of Theorem 3.51 to groups *not* follow from previous material in the text?

17. Let S be the set of all polynomials of degree 2 or less in a symbol x, with integral coefficients, and having $x - 2$ as a factor. If ordinary addition and multiplication of polynomials is assumed, decide whether S is an additive and/or multiplicative semigroup (monoid). Try to find a homomorphic image of S into **Z**—apart from the trivial one in which each polynomial is mapped onto 0.

18. Let S be the additive semigroup of all polynomials with integral coefficients in a symbol x. Determine at least one partition of S which is regular with respect to the composition in S. If the composition in S is changed to multiplication, would your partition still be regular?

19. Return to Problem 19 of § 3.3 and find the kernel of the mapping f—which is a homomorphism. Then use Theorem 3.51 to determine the factor groupoid which is isomorphic to the "image" groupoid $f(\mathbf{R})$.

References

[1] BRUCK, R.H.: *A Survey of Binary Systems* (Berlin, Springer-Verlag, 1958).

[2] CHEVALLEY, C.: *Fundamental Concepts of Algebra*, Chapter 1 (New York, Academic Press, 1957).

[3] KUROSH, A.: *Theory of Groups*, Vol. 1, pp. 21–31 (New York, Chelsea, 1955).

Selected Readings from The American Mathematical Monthly

DE SUA, F. C.: *A System Isomorphic to the Reals*, **67** (1960), 900–903.

DOYLE, P. H.: *Some Properties of Groupoids*, **70** (1963), 1051–1057.

ETHERINGTON, I. M. H.: *Groupoids with Additive Endomorphisms*, **65** (1958) 596–601.

FRINK, O.: *Symmetric and Self-Distributive Systems*, **62** (1955), 697–707.

MULCRONE, T. F.: *Semigroup Examples in Modern Algebra*, **69** (1962), 296–301.

SCHENKMAN, E.: *A Certain Class of Semigroups*, **63** (1956), 242–243.

4 Groups

4.1. Equivalent Definitions

We climaxed our discussion of general algebraic systems in Chapter 3 with the introduction of a very important one known as a *group*. This system was defined as a monoid which has the additional characteristic that *each* element has an "inverse" associated with it in the system. If it so happens that $ab = ba$, for arbitrary elements a and b of the group, the system is commutative and is known as a *commutative* or *abelian group*—the latter name in honor of the great mathematician Abel (1802–1829). It is possible, of course, that $ab = ba$ for *certain* elements a and b of a nonabelian group, and in such cases we say that these particular elements *commute* or *are permutable*. The *order* of a group is the number of its elements, and a group is *finite* if its order is a finite number [cf. Problem 12 of § 3.2]. If a subset of a group is closed under the group operation and also satisfies all the other requirements of a group by itself, this subset comprises a *subgroup*. It would be possible at this time to establish the existence of groups of any order and discover many other interesting properties of a group, but we prefer to postpone this study until after we have presented some equivalent formulations for a group.

Our postulate that a group be a monoid requires the existence of an identity element, and it was shown in Chapter 3 that this identity element (usually designated 1) must be *unique*. We have required in our definition of a group that each element be a "unit" or have an "inverse" associated with it, and it was suggested in Problems 8 and 9 of § 3.2 that the student prove that these inverse elements are also unique. However, in view of the importance of this property, we shall give the proof here in the form of an elementary theorem.

Theorem 4.11. *If an element a of a monoid has both a right inverse and a left inverse, these elements are the same and constitute the unique inverse of a.*

Proof. If S is a monoid with identity element 1, the definition of right and left inverses requires the existence of elements a' and a'' in S such that $aa' = a''a = 1$. However, by associativity in S, $a''aa' = a''(aa') = a''(1) = a''$, and also $a''aa' = (a''a)a' = (1)a' = a'$, so that $a'' = a'$. Hence, *any* left inverse of a is equal to *any* right inverse of a and, since an inverse is both a right inverse and a left inverse, this implies the uniqueness of the inverse of any element. We have been designating this unique inverse of an element $a \in S$ by a^{-1}. ∎

Corollary. *Each element of a group has a unique inverse.*

It is then a consequence of our earlier definition of a group that this algebraic system has a *unique* identity element and, associated with each element of the group, a *unique* inverse. The existence of an identity element and inverse elements is so important in the structure of a group that it seems desirable to rephrase our definition of a group with these elements in a more central position. It will be noted in the definition below that we are not assuming uniqueness of the identity and inverse elements in the *definition*, but this can be inferred from what we have just shown.

Definition. A *group* is an algebraic system G, with one binary operation indicated as multiplication for convenience, such that the following postulates are in effect:

1. *Closure.* The product $ab \in G$ provided $a, b \in G$. (This is actually assumed in our definition of a binary operation in G.)
2. *Associative Law.* For arbitrary $a, b, c \in G$, it is true that $(ab)c = a(bc)$.
3. *Existence of an Identity Element.* There exists an element $1 \in G$ such that $a1 = 1a = a$, for each $a \in G$.
4. *Existence of Inverses.* For each $a \in G$ there exists an inverse element $a^{-1} \in G$, such that $aa^{-1} = a^{-1}a = 1$.

It should be clear that, while formally this definition of a group may be somewhat different from that given in Chapter 3, the two definitions are actually equivalent. For the first three postulates simply require the system to be a monoid, while Postulate **4**—in the light of the discussions on "uniqueness" earlier in this section—requires that each element of the monoid be a unit. The postulates which we have given are somewhat stronger than necessary, and in Problem 15 we suggest how Postulates **3** and **4** can be relaxed while the system remains a group.

There is another somewhat different way of formulating the definition of a group which, while usually not so easy to use, is still worthy of mention. This definition was suggested in Chapter 3, as Problem 11 of § 3.2. We shall state this definition, and assert its equivalence to the one above, in the form of a theorem.

Theorem 4.12. *A nonempty semigroup* S *is a group if and only if the equations* $ax = b$ *and* $ya = b$ *have (unique) solutions in* S *for x and y, with a and b arbitrary elements of* S.

Proof. If S is a group, the equations $ax = b$ and $ya = b$ have solutions. For $x = a^{-1}b$ and $y = ba^{-1}$ are certainly (unique) solutions of the given equations [Problem 4]. Conversely, let a be an arbitrary element of the nonempty semigroup S. By the condition in the theorem, there exists $e \in S$ such that $ae = a$, so that e is a *right identity for a*. In order to prove it is a right identity for S, let s be an arbitrary element of S. Again by the condition in the theorem, there exists $t \in S$ such that $ta = s$, whence $se = (ta)e = t(ae) = ta = s$. Hence, e is a right identity for each and every element of S. The existence of a right inverse for a follows immediately from the fact that the equation $ax = e$ has a solution in S for x. If we now accept the result stated in Problem 15, we have shown that the solvability of the two given equations implies the existence of an identity element, and also of an inverse associated with each element of S, and so the system is a group according to our four postulates above. ∎

Throughout the book, we shall continue to designate the unique identity element of a group by either 1 or 0, according as the multiplicative or additive notation is used. Similarly, for the two cases, we shall designate the unique inverse of an element a by either a^{-1} or $-a$. In this beginning section of our chapter on groups, we are leaving a group as an essentially abstract concept, although the student may find examples occurring to him. In the following section, we shall illustrate the abstract concept with a number of very concrete examples.

PROBLEMS 4–1

1. Explain why the "closure" postulate, which we have listed in our definition of a group, is actually a redundancy.
*2. Explain why the Corollary follows directly from Theorem 4.11.
*3. Review the argument given in Chapter 3 to establish the uniqueness of the identity element of a monoid—and so of a group.
*4. Check that $a^{-1}b$ and ba^{-1} are solutions, respectively, of the equations $ax = b$ and $ya = b$, for a and b in a group.
5. Think of at least three illustrations of the group concept. Are they all commutative?
6. Think of one illustration of a nonabelian group.
7. If $a^0 = 1$, for any element a of a group, prove the familiar "laws of

exponents" for groups: $a^m a^n = a^{m+n}$ and $(a^m)^n = a^{mn}$, for any nonnegative integers m and n [cf. Problem 14 of § 3.1].

8. If we define $a^{-t} = (a^{-1})^t$, for any positive integer t, prove the "laws" stated in Problem 7 for *all* integers m and n.

9. Refer to Problem 8, and prove that $(ab)^n = a^n b^n$ for arbitrary elements a and b of an abelian group, and any integer n.

10. If you did not do it before (!) in Problem 12 of § 2.2, prove the generalized associative law for a group, assuming the associativity of three elements as asserted in Postulate **3** of this section.

**11. If we assume the existence of a left identity and left inverses in a semigroup, show that the left cancellation law also holds. (That is, show that $ab = ac$ implies that $b = c$, for arbitrary elements a, b, c in the semigroup.)

12. In Problem 11, replace the word "left" by "right" in each of its three occurrences, and prove the revised assertion.

13. Use the conditions and result in Problem 12 to prove that a left identity of a semigroup is also a right identity.

14. Use the conditions in Problem 11 and the results in Problems 11 and 12 to prove that any left inverse is also a right inverse in a semi-group.

15. Combine the results in Problems 11–14 to show that Postulates **3 and **4** of a group may be weakened to assume the existence of only left (right) inverses and a left (right) identity.

*16. Prove that if e is a left (right) identity for a given element a of a group, then e is the identity element. (That is, show that $ea = a$ (or $ae = a$) implies that $e = 1$.)

*17. An element a of a group is *idempotent* if $a^2 = a$. Prove that the only idempotent element of a group is the identity element.

18. Express the results of Problems 16 and 17 in additive notation.

*19. Without exhibiting any solution, explain why any existing solution of $ax = b$ (or $ya = b$), with all elements in a group, must be unique.

20. (Del Franco). Explain why the system, whose multiplication table is given below, is not a group. Note that e is a left identity and each element has a left inverse. Does this contradict the result in Problem 15?

	e	a	b	c
e	e	a	b	c
a	b	c	e	a
b	a	b	c	e
c	e	c	a	b

4.2. Some Simple Examples of a Group

In this section we shall collect some simple examples of a group, though in most cases we shall leave to the student the major portion of the verification that the system actually is a group. This verification can be accomplished most conveniently with the help of the four postulates given in the preceding section.

1. The set of all integers forms a group under ordinary addition, the so-called *additive group of integers.* Since the sum of any two integers is an integer, and addition is an associative operation, Postulates **1** and **2** are satisfied. The identity element is 0, while the inverse of any integer n is $-n$, so that Postulates **3** and **4** are satisfied, and the system is a group. (What is the inverse of $-n$ in this group?) The sets of rational numbers, real numbers, and complex numbers also provide familiar examples of an additive group, and each of these contains the additive group of integers as a subgroup.

2. By an *integral multiple* of a given number a we shall mean na, where $na = a + a + \cdots + a$ (n summands). If we assume the familiar properties of such multiples, including $n(a + b) = na + nb$, it can be seen that all integral multiples of a given number form a group under addition. (What is the identity element of such a group?) The group of integers in Example 1 can be considered the special case of this where $a = 1$, and the subgroup of *even* integers the case where $a = 2$. We note in this connection, however, that the set of all *odd* integers and the set of all nonnegative integers do not comprise groups. (Why?)

3. The set of all nonzero rational numbers forms a group under multiplication, the so-called *multiplicative group of nonzero rational numbers.* The identity element of this group is the integer 1 (or 1/1), while the inverse of the rational number m/n is n/m. The subset of *positive* rational numbers also forms a multiplicative group, a subgroup of the larger group. (It may be well to remark, parenthetically, that we shall continue the practice begun in Chapter 3 of referring to the natural numbers, integers, rational numbers, real numbers, and complex numbers by **N**, **Z**, **Q**, **R**, and **C**, respectively, *without regard to the algebraic system that they are considered to form at the time.* For instance, we would refer to the group in Example 1 as the *additive group* **Z** *of integers.*)

4. An example of a finite group is provided by the set $\{1, -1\}$ of integers, with ordinary multiplication as the operation. This group is also a subgroup of the principal group in Example 3.

5. The complex nth roots of unity form a group under ordinary complex multiplication. In order to see this, it should be recalled that if ω is a primitive nth root of unity, a complete set of nth roots is $\omega, \omega^2, \omega^3, \ldots, \omega^n = 1$. (A primitive nth root of unity has the property that its nth power, but not any smaller positive integral power, is 1.) Since n is an arbitrary positive integer, and there are n complex nth roots of unity, this example shows that *there exists at least one group with an arbitrary finite order.*

6. The set of complex numbers with absolute value 1 is a group under ordinary complex multiplication. These numbers can be associated with points

on a unit circle, and in the verification of the group postulates it will be helpful to recall the polar representation of a complex number.

7. The rotations of a plane figure, through multiples of 45° about a point, form a group, in which the *product* of two rotations is the rotation resulting from *performing in succession* the two rotations. If we consider two rotations to be *equal* if all points of the figure are in identical positions after each rotation, it is easy to see that there are only 8 distinct elements in the set of rotations. These may be designated, with an obvious symbolism, as: $R_0, R_{45}, R_{90}, R_{135}, R_{180}, R_{225}, R_{270}, R_{315}$. The identity element of this group is R_0, the rotation through 0°; and it should be noted that the inverse of each element is in the set. For example, the inverse of R_{45} is R_{315}, since $R_{45}R_{315} = R_{315}R_{45} = R_0$. Rotations through negative multiples of 45° are present in the set, in the form of equivalent positive rotations. For instance, a rotation through $-45°$ is equivalent to the rotation designated as R_{315}.

8. Consider a square so oriented that its center is at the origin and its sides are parallel to the axes of a rectangular coordinate system. The square can be carried into itself as the result of any of the following 8 *rigid motions*:

   I: the identity "motion" in which the square remains fixed.
   H: the reflection of the square in the horizontal axis.
   V: the reflection of the square in the vertical axis.
   D: the reflection of the square in the diagonal of quadrants 1 and 3.
   D': the reflection of the square in the diagonal of quadrants 2 and 4.
   R: a clockwise rotation of the square about the origin through 90°.
   R': a clockwise rotation of the square about the origin through 180°.
   R'': a clockwise rotation of the square about the origin through 270°.

As in Example 7, we shall consider two rigid motions to be equal if each point of the square is carried into an identical position by the two motions. If we again define the *product* of two rigid motions to be the resultant of the motions performed in succession, it can be shown that the set of "symmetries" just listed comprises a group, known as the *group of symmetries of the square* —otherwise known as the *dihedral* group of order 8 [see Problem 8 of § 4.3]. This group is nonabelian since, for instance, $VD = R$ while $DV = R''$. If we border a square mesh with the 8 symmetries of a square, as shown in Table 1, and place the product ab of two elements a and b opposite a on the left and below b, the result is the *multiplication table* of the group. (Multiplication tables of this sort were mentioned earlier, in particular, in the problems of § 3.1.) The multiplication table of a finite group is also known as a *Cayley square*, in honour of the mathematician A. Cayley (1821–1895). The student is urged to fill in the spaces left blank in the Cayley square exhibited in Table 1 (Problem 5). A reference to an interesting commentary on the group in Example 8 is given in Problem 8 of § 4.3.

	I	R	R'	R"	H	V	D	D'
I	I	R	R'	R"	H	V	D	D'
R	R	R'		I				H
R'	R'		I	R				D
R"	R"			R'				V
H	H	D'	V	D	I	R'	R"	R
V	V			D'		I	R	R"
D	D			V		R"	I	R'
D'	D'	V	D	H	R"	R	R'	I

Table 1

PROBLEMS 4–2

**1. Use a Cayley square to exhibit the complete multiplication table of the group in Example 4.

*2. Use the directions of Problem 1 for the group in Example 5 with $n = 4$.

*3. Show that the system in Example 6 is closed under the operation.

*4. In the symbolism of Example 7, how would we represent a rotation of (a) $450°$; (b) $-270°$; (c) $-135°$; (d) $-360°$?

*5. Fill in the blank spaces of the multiplication table in Example 8.

*6. Use Table 1, as completed in Problem 5, to determine each of the following products: (a) $R(VD')$; (b) $(HV)D$; (c) $(R'D)(R"H)$.

*7. With reference to Example 7, express each of the following products as one of the basic set elements:

$$\text{(a) } R_{45}R_{180}; \quad \text{(b) } R_{180}R_{270}; \quad \text{(c) } R_{225}(R_{135}R_{270}).$$

*8. Explain why the rule $n(a + b) = na + nb$, for any natural number n and arbitrary elements a, b of an algebraic system, is valid if the system is both commutative and associative.

9. Use a noncommutative semigroup S of idempotent elements ($a^2 = a$, for each $a \in S$) to show that the rule in Problem 8 can hold without the assumption that the system is commutative. Can it hold in a nonassociative system?

10. Use Example 8 as a model, and determine the group of symmetries of an equilateral triangle.

11. Use Example 8 as a model and determine the group of symmetries of a rectangle which is not a square.

12. Verify that the group of symmetries of a cube has order 48. These symmetries are called the *isometries* of the cube. (Hint: Any vertex can be carried onto any of the 8 vertices.)

13. Determine the order of the group of symmetries of a regular tetrahedron.

14. Determine any proper subgroups (i.e., distinct from the whole group) of the group in Example 8. (See § 3.1 for a discussion of general subsystems.)

15. Prove that the set of all continuous real functions defined on the real interval [0, 1] comprises a group under the usual operation of addition of functions. (That is, if f and g are functions, then $(f + g)(x) = f(x) + g(x)$, $x \in [0, 1]$.)

16. A "translation" of the point (x_0, y_0) of the Cartesian plane is a mapping of (x_0, y_0) onto a point $(x_0 + \alpha, y_0 + \beta)$, for real α and β. Use the usual definition of product for two mappings, and prove that the set of all translations of (x_0, y_0) forms an abelian group.

17. Prove that the semigroup, whose multiplication table [see Problem 18 of § 3.1] is given below, is a group:

	e	a	b	c
e	e	a	b	c
a	a	b	c	e
b	b	c	e	a
c	c	e	a	b

18. Consider the set of all deformations—without "breaking"—of the line segment joining two points P and Q. If we regard the "product" of two deformations as the two deformations performed in sequence, prove that the set of all these deformations forms a group. This is called the group of *homeomorphisms* of the segment PQ.

**19. Let the elements of a set $\mathcal{G}$ be: t, $1 - t$, $1/t$, $1/(1 - t)$, $(t - 1)/t$, $t/(t - 1)$. Prove that $\mathcal{G}$ constitutes a group, if the "product" of two elements is obtained by substituting the second member of the product for t in the first. (This group is a representative set of the "cross ratios" of four points, a group which is invariant under projection—the key notion of "projective" geometry.)

20. If $\mathcal{S}_1$ and $\mathcal{S}_2$ are semigroups, we define the sum $f + g$ of two homomorphisms f and g of $\mathcal{S}_1$ into $\mathcal{S}_2$ by the rule that $(f + g)(x) = f(x) + g(x)$, for $x \in \mathcal{S}_1$. Prove that the set of all such homomorphisms forms an additive group.

21. Assuming the usual product or composition of two mappings, prove that the automorphisms of a semigroup form a multiplication group.

22. Any mapping of the points of a plane which preserves distance is known as a "rigid motion" of the plane [cf. Examples 7–8]. Prove that the set of rigid motions of a plane forms a group under the usual composition of mappings. Is the group abelian?

4.3. Two Important Groups

In this section we conclude our list of examples of a group with two very important types. One of these is of the abelian variety and one is not. The group of permutations on a finite set of elements, which we describe first, is so basic that it illustrates the very beginning of the theory of groups.

1. A *permutation* is a *bijective mapping of a finite set to itself,* and it is custom- ˈ
ary to describe a permutation by actually designating the image of each
element under the mapping. For example, the permutation on the first n
natural numbers such that each number i is mapped onto the number a_i,
can be indicated by $\begin{pmatrix} 1 & 2 & 3 \cdots n \\ a_1 & a_2 & a_3 \cdots a_n \end{pmatrix}$. The *identity element*—or *identity per-*
mutation—is the permutation in which each element is mapped onto itself,
and can be designated as $\begin{pmatrix} 1\,2\,3 \cdots n \\ 1\,2\,3 \cdots n \end{pmatrix}$ or more simply as (1) or 1. The
inverse of a permutation is simply the reverse mapping: if α is the
permutation $\begin{pmatrix} 1 & 2 & 3 \cdots n \\ a_1 & a_2 & a_3 \cdots a_n \end{pmatrix}$, the *inverse* α^{-1} of α is the permutation
$\begin{pmatrix} a_1 & a_2 & a_3 \cdots a_n \\ 1 & 2 & 3 \cdots n \end{pmatrix}$. In particular, if α is the permutation on the first five
natural numbers designated as $\begin{pmatrix} 1\,2\,3\,4\,5 \\ 4\,1\,5\,2\,3 \end{pmatrix}$, it follows that $\alpha^{-1} = \begin{pmatrix} 1\,2\,3\,4\,5 \\ 2\,4\,5\,1\,3 \end{pmatrix}$.
It should be noted that the order in which the elements are listed on the top
line of an indicated permutation is of no importance. For example, the
permutation α, just cited, could also have been designated as $\begin{pmatrix} 3\,1\,5\,4\,2 \\ 5\,4\,3\,2\,1 \end{pmatrix}$
and in many other ways, for it is only the *mappings* which matter in the
definition of a permutation. Moreover, in the description of a permutation
α, it is customary to omit any symbols that are left unchanged, if $\alpha \neq 1$. For
instance, the permutation $\begin{pmatrix} 1\,2\,3\,4\,5 \\ 1\,3\,4\,2\,5 \end{pmatrix}$ would generally be designated more
simply as $\begin{pmatrix} 2\,3\,4 \\ 3\,4\,2 \end{pmatrix}$. If we define the *product* of two permutations to be the
resultant of the two mappings, it can be seen quite readily that the set of all
permutations on a finite set forms a group with 1 as the identity element.
This group has order $n!$, if there are n elements in the set, and is labeled
S_n—the *symmetric group of degree n.* That is, the symmetric group of
degree n is the group of all permutations on n symbols. It is easy to see that
the symmetric group is, in general, nonabelian. For example, consider the
elements $\begin{pmatrix} 1\,3\,4 \\ 3\,4\,1 \end{pmatrix} = \alpha_1$ and $\begin{pmatrix} 3\,5\,6 \\ 6\,3\,5 \end{pmatrix} = \alpha_2$ of S_6. With $\alpha_1\alpha_2$ defined as the
resultant of α_1 followed by α_2, the permutation $\alpha_1\alpha_2$ maps 1 onto 3 and 3
onto 6, so that $1(\alpha_1\alpha_2) = 6$. Similarly, $2(\alpha_1\alpha_2) = 2$; 3 is mapped onto 4 by
α_1, while 4 is unchanged by α_2, so that $3(\alpha_1\alpha_2) = 4$; and, in like manner,
$4(\alpha_1\alpha_2) = 1$, $5(\alpha_1\alpha_2) = 3$, $6(\alpha_1\alpha_2) = 5$. We have shown that $\alpha_1\alpha_2 =$
$\begin{pmatrix} 1\,3\,4\,5\,6 \\ 6\,4\,1\,3\,5 \end{pmatrix}$, while a similar analysis shows that $\alpha_2\alpha_1 = \begin{pmatrix} 1\,3\,4\,5\,6 \\ 3\,6\,1\,4\,5 \end{pmatrix}$, so
that $\alpha_1\alpha_2 \neq \alpha_2\alpha_1$.

2. Our other example of a group, to be introduced at this time, is an especially important one, since it arises in connection with many different topics of mathematics. It is the basis for what is usually known as a study of *congruences*. This group is the *additive group of integers mod n*, for any integer $n(>1)$—which is often called the "modulus." Actually, the student has already encountered this system, as the additive monoid in Example 1 of § 3.5, but we now show that this system is a group. In view of the importance of the example, we shall review it at the risk of some duplication with what has gone before.

The equivalence relation of "congruence" ($\equiv$) is first defined in the set $\mathbf{Z}$ of integers, so that $a \equiv b \pmod{n}$ if $a - b$ is divisible by n or, equivalently [Problem 9], if a and b have the same remainder on division by n. There then results a partition [Problem 20 of § 2.4] of $\mathbf{Z}$ into disjoint classes of congruent integers—i.e., all integers in any one class are congruent to each other. For example, for the case $n = 5$, the following chains of congruences illustrate the disposition of all integers in the various congruence classes:
$$\cdots \equiv -10 \equiv -5 \equiv 0 \equiv 5 \equiv 10 \equiv \cdots \pmod{5}; \cdots \equiv -9 \equiv -4 \equiv 1 \equiv 6$$
$$\equiv 11 \equiv \cdots \pmod{5}; \cdots \equiv -8 \equiv -3 \equiv 2 \equiv 7 \equiv 12 \equiv \cdots \pmod{5}; \cdots \equiv$$
$$-7 \equiv -2 \equiv 3 \equiv 8 \equiv 13 \equiv \cdots \pmod{5}; \cdots \equiv -6 \equiv -1 \equiv 4 \equiv 9 \equiv 14 \equiv$$
$\ldots \pmod{5}$. In the general case, there are n congruence classes, and in the earlier problem referred to above we have designated these classes by $\overline{\mathbf{Z}}_n$. Each of these classes is uniquely determined by any one of its members; and if we select the smallest positive integer in each class to represent it—and work with these representatives alone—we have the set of "remainders" as discussed in Example 1 of § 3.2. If $n = 5$, this complete set of remainders is $\{0, 1, 2, 3, 4\}$, and every integer is congruent mod 5 to one of these integers.

We now use the procedure and symbolism of Example 1, § 3.5, to define an operation of addition in the set $\overline{\mathbf{Z}}_n$ of congruence classes. Thus, if $\bar{r}$ and $\bar{s}$ are the classes which contain the integers r and s, respectively, we define $\bar{r} + \bar{s} = \overline{r + s}$, where, of course $\overline{r + s}$, is the class containing $r + s$. That this does define addition in a valid manner was a matter discussed in the earlier example. We have now reached the stage of this example, and have exhibited $\overline{\mathbf{Z}}_n$ as an additive groupoid: but it is easy to see that this system is a group. The associative law in $\mathbf{Z}$ allows us to assert that $r + (s + t) = (r + s) + t$, and so $\bar{r} + (\bar{s} + \bar{t}) = \overline{r + (s + t)} = \overline{(r + s) + t} = (\bar{r} + \bar{s}) + \bar{t}$, so that addition is associative in $\overline{\mathbf{Z}}_n$. Since $\bar{0} + \bar{r} = \bar{r} = \bar{r} + \bar{0}$, for any $\bar{r} \in \overline{\mathbf{Z}}_n$, we see that $\bar{0}$ is the additive identity for $\overline{\mathbf{Z}}_n$. We note finally that $\bar{r} + \overline{n - r} = \overline{n - r + r} = \bar{n} = \bar{0}$, for any, $\bar{r} \in \overline{\mathbf{Z}}_n$ so that each element of the system of classes has an inverse. Hence, $\overline{\mathbf{Z}}_n$ is a group—the *additive group of* (*congruence classes of*) *integers mod n*. To illustrate these group properties for $\overline{\mathbf{Z}}_5$, we see that $\bar{3} + \bar{4} = \bar{7} = \bar{2}$ and $\bar{4} + \bar{2} = \bar{6} = \bar{1}$; the additive identity element, of course, is $\bar{5}$ or $\bar{0}$; and the inverse of $\bar{3}$ is $\overline{5 - 3}$ or $\bar{2}$, while the inverse of $\bar{4}$ is $\bar{1}$.

The arithmetic of $\overline{\mathbf{Z}}_n$, as we have outlined it above, is an arithmetic of *classes*—i.e., the elements of the system are classes. In practice it is usually preferred to replace this arithmetic of classes by an equivalent "modular" arithmetic whose elements are integers. In this modular arithmetic, instead of the class equality $\bar{a} = \bar{b}$, we write $a \equiv b \pmod{n}$, thereby considering all integers in the same class as *congruent mod n*. It is often convenient to think of "congruence" as a "generalized equality," but it would violate our announced usage of the sign of *equality* to indicate *identity* if we were to use $=$ here in place of $\equiv$. One can always select the smallest nonnegative integer as the representative of any congruence class, and, if we do this, we are working in the isomorphic system of "remainders"—as outlined in Example 1 of § 3.2. The two systems are, however, conceptually distinct: for $\mathbf{Z}_n'$ contains only n integers as its complete membership, while $\overline{\mathbf{Z}}_n$ contains n classes of congruent integers—each class containing infinitely many integers. It will be the system of congruent classes to which we shall most often refer in the sequel and—as already pointed out in Example 1 of § 3.5—we shall designate it simply as $\mathbf{Z}_n$—the *system of integers mod n*.

One of the characteristic properties of a group is that "linear" equations are always solvable in the group. In the case of the additive group $\mathbf{Z}_n$, this means that every equation $x + b = c$, with $b, c \in \mathbf{Z}_n$, is solvable for $x \in \mathbf{Z}_n$. We illustrate with an example, using the notation of congruences.

Example. Solve the congruence $x + 3 \equiv 2 \pmod{4}$, for $x \in \mathbf{Z}$.

Solution. We are searching for integers x such that $(x + 3) - 2$ or $x + 1$ is divisible by 4. But these integers have the form $-1 + 4k$, for any integer k, and so the set of solutions to the congruence is $\{\ldots, -5, -1, 3, \ldots\}$. In the notation used earlier, we would designate this class solution as $\bar{3}$; or, if we are working in the "remainder" system, the unique solution is the integer 3.

The case of $\mathbf{Z}_n$ illustrates what *can* be done with *any* additive abelian group $\mathcal{G}$ in which an equivalence relation has been defined—provided the resulting partition is regular. That is, given an additive factor group, it is always possible to build up a "modular" arithmetic which involves the *elements* of $\mathcal{G}$. When we discussed factor systems in Chapter 3, our attention was focused on the *equivalence classes* as the elements of the system—rather than on the elements of the parent system from which the factor system was derived. It is the spirit of the example of $\mathbf{Z}_n$, however, to see that is is possible to keep in mind *both* the elements of the group $\mathcal{G}$ *and* the elements of any factor group of $\mathcal{G}$: the elements of any one class are merely regarded as "equivalent" to each other. If $\sim$ is an equivalence relation defined in $\mathcal{G}$, we might even extend the symbolism of $\mathbf{Z}_n$ and write $a \equiv b \pmod{\sim}$ whenever a and b are in the same equivalence class. Moreover, if the resulting partition of $\mathcal{G}$ is regular, we can then develop an additive arithmetic " modulo $\sim$," which is quite analogous to that of $\mathbf{Z}_n$. For, if $a_1 \equiv b_1 \pmod{\sim}$, and $a_2 \equiv b_2 \pmod{\sim}$, it follows that $a_1 + a_2 \equiv b_1 + b_2 \pmod{\sim}$; and it is easy to see [Problem 14] that the group of representative elements of the equivalence classes of $\mathcal{G}$, with addition performed " mod $\sim$," is isomorphic to the factor group of $\mathcal{G}$ relative to $\sim$.

We remarked at the beginning of this section that the two groups to be discussed here were of great importance. It will be shown later that *every* finite group is isomorphic to a group of permutations—as described in Example 1; and the arithmetic of the group $\mathbf{Z}_n$ will be expanded in the next chapter so that the resulting system is a *ring*—an important algebraic system with *two* binary operations. Both examples will keep recurring from time to time in the sequel.

PROBLEMS 4–3

*1. Use a Cayley square to exhibit the complete addition table for the group of integers mod 5, discussed in Example 2.

2. Perform each of the following additions within the additive group of integers mod 7: (a) $4 + 4$; (b) $6 + 4$; (c) $5 + 6$; (d) $4 + 4 + 4$.

3. Determine the inverse of each of the following elements in the additive group of integers mod 7: (a) 4; (b) 2; (c) 0; (d) 6.

*4. List all the members of the symmetric group S_3, and associate each of these with its inverse.

5. Show that $\alpha\beta \neq \beta\alpha$, where α and β are members of S_5 defined as follows:

$$\alpha = \begin{pmatrix} 1 & 3 & 4 \\ 4 & 1 & 3 \end{pmatrix} \quad \text{and} \quad \beta = \begin{pmatrix} 1 & 2 & 3 & 4 & 5 \\ 3 & 4 & 1 & 5 & 2 \end{pmatrix}.$$

**6. If $\alpha = \begin{pmatrix} 1 & 3 & 4 \\ 4 & 1 & 3 \end{pmatrix}$, $\beta = \begin{pmatrix} 1 & 2 & 3 & 6 \\ 3 & 6 & 1 & 2 \end{pmatrix}$, and $\gamma = \begin{pmatrix} 1 & 4 & 5 & 6 \\ 5 & 6 & 4 & 1 \end{pmatrix}$ are elements of S_6, determine each of the following products: (a) $\alpha(\beta\gamma)$; (b) $\alpha(\gamma\beta)\alpha$; (c) $\alpha^2\beta$; (d) $\gamma^2\beta$.

7. Use the notation of Problem 6 to determine each of the following: (a) $\alpha^{-1}\beta^{-1}$; (b) $\gamma^{-1}\alpha^2$; (c) $\beta^2\gamma^{-1}$.

**8. Label the vertices of a square as indicated below. Then use Example 8 of § 4.2 to represent the eight " rigid motions " of the square as a subgroup of S_4. [See p. 1127 of *The American Mathematical Monthly*, Vol. 72, No. 10 (December, 1965), for an interesting commentary on this group. Also see Problems 21, 22 29, of § 4.5 below.]

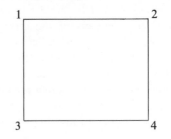

9. Explain why two integers have the same remainder when divided by a positive integer n if and only if their difference is divisible by n.

10. With α and β defined as in Problem 5, solve each of the following equations for $x \in S_5$: (a) $x\alpha = \beta$; (b) $\alpha x = \beta$; (c) $x\beta = \alpha$; (d) $\beta x = \alpha$.

11. Use the directions of Problem 10, with α and β defined as in Problem 6.

12. Solve each of the following congruences for $x \in \mathbf{Z}$: (a) $x + 5 \equiv 2 \pmod 7$; (b) $x + 4 \equiv 6 \pmod 7$.

13. Solve each of the following congruences for $x \in \mathbf{Z}$: (a) $x + 8 \equiv 1 \pmod{10}$; (b) $x + 5 \equiv 4 \pmod{10}$.

14. Let $\sim$ be defined in an additive abelian group $\mathcal{G}$, with a regular partition being effected in $\mathcal{G}$. Then prove that the factor group $\overline{\mathcal{G}}$, determined by $\sim$, is isomorphic to the group of representatives of the equivalence classes, addition in the latter group being defined as in $\mathcal{G}$ but "mod $\sim$."

15. With α, β, and γ defined as in Problem 6, solve each of the following equations for $x \in S_6$: (a) $\alpha x\beta = \gamma$; (b) $\alpha x\alpha^{-1} = \beta$.

16. Use the directions of Problem 15 for the following equations: (a) $\alpha x\beta^{-1} = 1$; (b) $\beta^{-1}x\gamma = \alpha\beta$.

17. With α and β defined as $\alpha = \begin{pmatrix} 1 & 3 & 4 \\ 4 & 1 & 3 \end{pmatrix}$ and $\beta = \begin{pmatrix} 1 & 2 & 4 \\ 4 & 1 & 2 \end{pmatrix}$, determine a solution in S_5 of the equation $x^{-1}\alpha x = \beta$.

18. List all the members of the symmetric group of permutations of $\{1, 2, 3, 4\}$. Prove that the permutations which leave the symbol 1 invariant is a subgroup of S_4, and determine its members.

19. State and prove a theorem which generalizes the assertion in the second sentence of Problem 18.

20. If we use multiplication instead of addition in Example 2, and assume that $n = p$ is a prime, the multiplicative system of *nonzero* integers mod p is a group. Prove this result with the help of Theorem 2.42.

21. Refer to Problem 20 and prove that the additive group $\mathbf{Z}_4$ is isomorphic to the multiplicative group of nonzero elements of $\mathbf{Z}_5$. (Two groups are isomorphic if they are isomorphic *as groupoids*. Try the mapping: $\bar{0} \to \bar{1}$, $\bar{1} \to \bar{3}$, $\bar{2} \to \bar{4}$, $\bar{3} \to \bar{2}$; also find another.)

22. Use the directions of Problem 21, with $\mathbf{Z}_4$ and $\mathbf{Z}_5$ replaced by $\mathbf{Z}_6$ and $\mathbf{Z}_7$, respectively, ignoring the mapping given in the hint.

23. Accept the result of Problem 20, and solve each of the following congruences in the multiplicative group of nonzero integers mod 5: (a) $3x \equiv 2 \pmod 5$; (b) $2x \equiv 4 \pmod 5$.

24. Accept the result of Problem 20, and solve each of the following congruences in the multiplicative group of nonzero integers mod 7 : (a) $3x \equiv 5 \pmod 7$; (b) $2x \equiv 1 \pmod 7$.

25. If we use multiplication instead of addition in Example 2, the result is the multiplicative semigroup of integers mod n. In this system, prove the following results concerning solutions x of a congruence $ax \equiv b \pmod n$, with a and b in the system: (a) If there is a solution for x, then (a, n) divides b. (b) If (a, n) divides b, there is a solution for x.

26. By "trial and error," solve the congruence $3x \equiv 9 \pmod{14}$ for x in the multiplicative semigroup of integers mod 14.

27. By "trial and error," solve the congruence $2x \equiv 6 \pmod{14}$ in the multiplicative semigroup of integers mod 14. From the number of solutions of this congruence which are distinct mod 14, what can you conclude about the semigroup?

28. If $(c, n) = 1$, prove that $ac \equiv bc \pmod{n}$ implies that $a \equiv b \pmod{n}$, for $a, b, c \in \mathbf{Z}$ and any positive modulus $n \neq 1$.

4.4. Elementary Properties of Groups

In this section we discuss some of the very elementary but basic properties of groups, and we list them as theorems for the sake of future reference. The first two have been established earlier, but we repeat them in the interest of completeness.

Theorem 4.41. *A group has* only one *identity element, usually designated* 0 *or* 1 *according as the additive or multiplicative notation is used.*

Theorem 4.42. *A group has* only one *inverse associated with each element of the group. The unique inverse of an element a will be designated* $-a$ *in the additive notation and* a^{-1} *in the multiplicative notation.*

Theorem 4.43. *The inverse of a product of elements from a group is the product of the inverses of the elements in reverse order.*

Proof. For consider a product $a_1 a_2 a_3 \cdots a_n$, with each element a_i in the group. Then it is clear that $(a_1 a_2 a_3 \cdots a_n)(a_n^{-1} a_{n-1}^{-1} a_{n-2}^{-1} \cdots a_1^{-1}) = (a_1 a_2 \cdots a_{n-1})(a_n a_n^{-1})(a_{n-1}^{-1} a_{n-2}^{-1} \cdots a_1^{-1}) = (a_1 a_2 \cdots a_{n-1})(a_{n-1}^{-1} a_{n-2}^{-1} \cdots a_1^{-1}) = \cdots = a_1 a_1^{-1} = 1$, and similarly $(a_n^{-1} a_{n-1}^{-1} a_{n-2}^{-1} \cdots a_1^{-1})(a_1 a_2 \cdots a_n) = 1$. Inasmuch as the inverse of any group element is unique by Theorem 4.42, it follows that $(a_1 a_2 a_3 \cdots a_n)^{-1} = a_n^{-1} a_{n-1}^{-1} a_{n-2}^{-1} \cdots a_1^{-1}$, as desired. We note in passing that in the additive notation, this theorem asserts that $-(a_1 + a_2 + \cdots + a_n) = -a_n - a_{n-1} - \cdots - a_1$. ∎

Theorem 4.44. (Cancellation Law). *If* a, b_1, *are elements of a group, such that* $ab_1 = ab_2$ *or* $b_1 a = b_2 a$, *it follows that* $b_1 = b_2$.

Proof. For we can multiply both members of the first equation on the left, or of the second equation on the right, by a^{-1} and the result follows immediately. ∎

Theorem 4.45. *Any homomorphic image of a group is a group.*

Proof. A group $\mathcal{G}$ is a monoid, and if $\mathcal{G}$ is mapped homomorphically onto a system $\mathcal{G}'$ we have seen before [Theorem 3.41, and Problem 7 of § 3.4], that $\mathcal{G}'$ is a monoid. Hence, $\mathcal{G}'$ has an identity element, and we must show that each element $a' \in \mathcal{G}'$ has an inverse. If a is an element of $\mathcal{G}$ that is mapped onto a' (Why does such an a exist?), there exists $a^{-1} \in \mathcal{G}$ such that $aa^{-1} = a^{-1}a = 1$. It follows from the basic property of a homomorphic mapping that $a'(a^{-1})' = (a^{-1})'a' = 1'$, where $1'$ is the identity element of $\mathcal{G}'$. Hence, $(a^{-1})'$ is the inverse of a', and the postulates of a group (as given in this chapter) then imply that $\mathcal{G}'$ is a group. ∎

It may be recalled that we were not able to prove the uniqueness of solutions of the defining equations for an inverse, in a homomorphic image of a groupoid, even though this uniqueness was assumed in the original system. In view of Theorem 4.45, however, solutions *are* unique in a homomorphic image if the groupoid is in fact a group. We have seen earlier that the factor groupoid of any groupoid with respect to a regular partition is a homomorphic image of the groupoid. It then also follows from Theorem 4.45 that any factor groupoid of a group $\mathcal{G}$, with respect to a regular partition, is a group known as a *factor* or *quotient* group of $\mathcal{G}$. (The reader will note that a special case of this was discussed in Example 2 of § 4.3.) Our earlier result [Theorem 3.51] then implies that every *homomorphic image of a group is isomorphic to one of its factor groups.*

We have previously used the notation a^n for the product of n elements each equal to a. That is, $a^2 = aa$, $a^3 = aaa$, etc., and such products are unambiguously defined in view of the associative property of the group operation. We now *define* [cf. Problem 8 of § 4.1] negative integral powers of a to be the inverses of the corresponding positive powers: i.e., $a^{-n} = (a^n)^{-1}$ for any integer $n > 0$. Inasmuch as $(aaa \cdots a)(a^{-1}a^{-1}a^{-1} \cdots a^{-1}) = 1$, where each of the indicated factors contains the same number of elements, it follows that $(a^n)^{-1} = (a^{-1})^n$, and so $a^{-n} = (a^n)^{-1} = (a^{-1})^n$. If we *define* $a^0 = 1$, we have given meaning to every integral power of a group element. In case the notation is additive, we write multiples na instead of a^n and $(-n)a$ instead of a^{-n}; and so we have shown that $(-n)a = -(na)$, a multiple which we can designate more simply by $-na$. It is now easy to verify the following theorem.

Theorem 4.46. *For any group element a and arbitrary integers m and n, we have* $a^m a^n = a^{m+n}$ *and* $(a^m)^n = a^{mn}$. *(In case the notation is additive, these become* $ma + na = (m+n)a$ *and* $n(ma) = (mn)a$.)

Proof. We leave the verification of this result to the student. ∎

If all powers of an element a are distinct elements of the group to which it belongs, a is said to be of *infinite* order. On the other hand, if $a^m = a^k$ where $m > k$, it follows that $(a^m)(a^{-k}) = a^{m-k} = 1$, as a result of Theorem 4.46 and the definition of an inverse. Hence some positive power of a is the identity element. If n is the smallest positive integer such that $a^n = 1$, we say that a is *of finite order* with *order* n. In the sequel we shall use $o(a)$ to denote the order of the group element a, and $o(\mathcal{G})$ to denote the order of a group $\mathcal{G}$.

If a group element a has order n, the elements $a^0 = 1$, $a^1 = a$, a^2, a^3, ..., a^{n-1} are all distinct, by definition of order. Moreover, every power of a is equal to one of these: for suppose m is an arbitrary integer. Then $m = nq + r$, for integers q, r such that $0 \le r < n$, and so $a^m = a^{nq}a^r = (a^n)^q a^r = a^r$, as asserted. In particular, we see that if $a^m = 1$, it follows that m is divisible by its order n. We note that the inverse of a is a^{n-1}, since $aa^{n-1} = a^{n-1}a = a^n = 1$.

It is clear that every element of a finite group must have finite order, or the group could not be finite. If every element of a group has finite order, the group is said to be *periodic*. There are also groups whose elements—apart from the identity element—all have infinite order, and these are known as *torsion-free* or *locally infinite* groups. The ordinary additive group of integers is an example of a torsion-free group, while any group of permutations is a periodic group.

PROBLEMS 4–4

   *1. Show that the multiplication table for a finite group contains each group element once, and only once, in each of its rows and columns.

   2. Use the result of Problem 1 to prove that there is only one possible multiplication table for a group of order 3.

   3. Construct all possible abstract groups of order 4, using the result of Problem 1. (Note that the existence of a multiplication table does not in itself establish a group, for there are 4 postulates for a group! Moreover, two multiplication tables may be quite different, whereas the associated groups may actually be isomorphic.)

   4. If a and b are elements of a finite abelian group, prove that the order of ab is a divisor of the least common multiple (l.c.m.) of the orders of a and b.

   5. The integers 1, 3, 5, 7 comprise a group under *multiplication and reduction modulo* 8. (That is, replace each ordinary product by its remainder after division by 8.) Exhibit the proper mapping to show that this group is isomorphic to one of the groups discovered in Problem 3.

   *6. Prove that a group is abelian if every element except the identity has order 2.

   7. For the purposes of this problem, we recall that a *function* was defined in Chapter 1 as a *mapping*. The *sum* $f + g$ of two functions f and g is defined so that $x(f+g) = xf + xg$, for each x in the common domain of f and g. Show that the set of all real-valued continuous functions on **R is a group with this additive operation.

   8. Use the definition of addition given in Problem 7, and show that the set of all real-valued differentiable functions on **R** comprises an additive group.

9. Prove that the mapping α, where $n\alpha = i^n$ for any integer n, is a homomorphism of the additive group of $\mathbf{Z}$ into $\mathbf{C}$. Describe the homomorphic image, and identify its elements with those of the isomorphic quotient group whose existence was asserted following Theorem 4.45.

10. Let the mapping β of the additive group of $\mathbf{R}$ into the multiplication group of $\mathbf{C}$ be defined so that $x\beta = e^{ix}$, for each real number x. Show that β is a homomorphism of $\mathbf{R}$ onto a group $\mathbf{C}'$, and describe $\mathbf{C}'$.

11. Which of the following mappings of the multiplicative group of all nonzero real numbers into itself are homomorphisms? In each of these cases, describe the homomorphic image. (a) $x \rightarrow -x$; (b) $x \rightarrow |x|$; (c) $x \rightarrow 1/x$; (d) $x \rightarrow 3x$; (e) $x \rightarrow x^2$; (f) $x \rightarrow -1/x$.

12. Prove that the set of nth roots of unity, i.e., all complex numbers of the form $e^{(2\pi ki)/n}$, for $k \in \mathbf{Z}$, is a group under ordinary complex multiplication.

13. Show that the mapping $k \rightarrow e^{(2\pi ki)/n}$ of Problem 12, for a fixed positive integer n, is a homomorphism from the additive group $\mathbf{Z}$ of integers to the group in the problem. Describe the subset of integers which are mapped onto the identity of this group.

14. Explain why each element of a finite group must have finite order. If each element of a group has finite order, is the group necessarily finite? Supply either a proof or a counterexample for the query.

15. In this problem [cf. Problem 7], let us use the more usual notation of "left mappings" and define the sum $f + g$ of two functions on a common domain D by $(f+g)(x) = f(x) + g(x)$, for any $x \in D$. Then prove that the set of all functions f on $\mathbf{R}$, such that $f(2) = 0$, make up an additive group.

16. Use the notation suggested in Problem 15 and prove that the set S of functions (including the zero function) on $\mathbf{R}$, such that $fg \neq 0$ for all *nonzero* functions $f, g \in \mathsf{S}$, comprises an additive group.

17. Refer to the group described in Problem 19 of § 4.2, and use Theorem 4.43 to determine $(ab)^{-1}$, where $a = 1 - t$ and $b = 1/t$.

**18. Refer to the symmetric group S_6 [see Example 1 of § 4.3 for a description of S_n], and use Theorem 4.43 to determine $(\alpha\beta)^{-1}$, where $\alpha = \begin{pmatrix} 1 & 2 & 3 & 4 \\ 3 & 4 & 1 & 2 \end{pmatrix}$ and $\beta = \begin{pmatrix} 1 & 3 & 5 \\ 5 & 1 & 3 \end{pmatrix}$.

19. Use the directions of Problem 18 for the case where $\alpha = \begin{pmatrix} 1 & 2 & 3 & 4 & 5 \\ 3 & 1 & 5 & 4 & 2 \end{pmatrix}$ and $\beta = \begin{pmatrix} 2 & 4 & 5 & 6 \\ 4 & 6 & 2 & 5 \end{pmatrix}$.

20. If the "cancellation law" of Theorem 4.44 holds in a semigroup S, is S necessarily a group? (Hint: either prove that S is a group or find a counterexample.)

21. In any group G, with $a \in \mathsf{G}$, let T_a be the function ("*left multiplication*") from G to G, such that $gT_a = ag$, for all $g \in \mathsf{G}$. Prove that the set of T_a, for all $a \in \mathsf{G}$, forms a group isomorphic to G, with the usual composition of functions.

22. Prove the following "weak converse" to Theorem 4.44: if S is a finite commutative semigroup such that the cancellation law of Theorem 4.44 holds, then S is a group.

23. Prove that any groupoid S with an identity element is a semigroup if we assume the equality of two arbitrary (but fixed) distinct bracketings of $a_1 a_2 \cdots a_n$, with $a_1, a_2, \ldots, a_n \in S$.

4.5. Subgroups

If a subset of a group is closed under the group operation and satisfies all the other requirements of a group in its own right, we have previously referred to the subset as a *subgroup*. It is perhaps conceivable that the identity element of a subgroup might be different from that of the original group. However, if we note that the identity element of a group must also serve as an identity element for any of its subgroups, and that the identity element of any group or subgroup is unique, this "conceived" possibility is untenable. The identity element of a group *must* coincide with the identity element of any of its subgroups. The uniqueness of the inverse elements in a group also implies that the inverse of any element *in a subgroup* must be the same element as the inverse in the whole group. We shall not discuss the difficult problems of determining the number of subgroups of a given group $\mathcal{G}$ and how to find them. If $\mathcal{G}$ is finite, these matters can be answered, of course, by "brute force," and there are theoretic results—some of which we shall mention later—which do throw light on these problems. However, we shall merely hint at the difficulty by stating that the symmetric group S_4 of order 24 has 28 subgroups, while the unique group of order 23 has none but the trivial ones—the whole group and the subgroup consisting only of the identity! The following theorem is a convenient criterion for deciding whether a subsystem of a group is a subgroup.

Theorem 4.51. *A nonempty subset $\mathcal{H}$ of a group $\mathcal{G}$ is a subgroup if and only if $ab^{-1} \in \mathcal{H}$ (or $a - b \in \mathcal{H}$, if the group is additive), for arbitrary $a, b \in \mathcal{H}$.*

Proof. Suppose that $\mathcal{H}$ is a subgroup with $a, b \in \mathcal{H}$. Then $b^{-1} \in \mathcal{H}$, and the closure postulate requires that $ab^{-1} \in \mathcal{H}$. On the other hand, let us consider $\mathcal{H}$ to be a subset of $\mathcal{G}$, such that $ab^{-1} \in \mathcal{H}$ for arbitrary $a, b \in \mathcal{H}$. Then, if $a \in \mathcal{H}$, we have $aa^{-1} = 1 \in \mathcal{H}$, where 1 is the identity element of $\mathcal{G}$. Also, if $b \in \mathcal{H}$, we have $1b^{-1} = b^{-1} \in \mathcal{H}$. Hence, if $a, b \in \mathcal{H}$, it then follows that $a(b^{-1})^{-1} = ab \in \mathcal{H}$, and this gives us the closure property. Thus $\mathcal{H}$ is a subgroup, as asserted. $\blacksquare$

Before proceeding further with the developments in this section, it seems advisable to introduce some notation which will be useful both here and in later sections of the chapter. If X and Y are arbitrary subsets of a group $\mathcal{G}$, we define the indicated set-products as follows:

$$XY = \{xy \mid x \in X \text{ and } y \in Y\};$$
$$XY^{-1} = \{xy^{-1} \mid x \in X \text{ and } y \in Y\};$$
$$X^{-1} = \{x^{-1} \mid x \in X\}.$$

There are, of course, other analogous notations for similar products involving two or more sets. A slight but useful variant of this notation occurs when one of the sets involved in a product is a singleton. For example, if $X = \{x\}$, we simply write xY instead of XY, with a similar interpretation being given, of course, to Yx. Thus, for any given $x \in \mathcal{G}$, $xY = \{xy \mid y \in Y\}$. In the notation just introduced, it would then be possible to phrase Theorem 4.51 as follows: *A nonempty subset $\mathcal{K}$ of a group $\mathcal{G}$ is a subgroup if and only if $\mathcal{K}\mathcal{K}^{-1} \subset \mathcal{K}$.* There is, of course, the usual change in notation if the group $\mathcal{G}$ is considered to be additive.

We now consider the notion of a *cyclic* group. If a is any element of a group $\mathcal{G}$, the set $\mathcal{K}$ of elements $\{ \cdots, a^{-3}, a^{-2}, a^{-1}, a^0 = 1, a^1 = a, a^2, a^3, \cdots \}$ comprises a subgroup. For let $x = a^m$ and $y = a^n$ be arbitrary elements of $\mathcal{K}$, where m and n are integers. We recall that all integral powers of a group element have been defined in § 4.4, and that Theorem 4.46 asserts that $a^m a^n = a^{m+n}$, for arbitrary integers m and n. Then $y^{-1} = (a^n)^{-1} = a^{-n}$, and so we have $xy^{-1} = a^m a^{-n} = a^{m-n} \in \mathcal{K}$. It then follows from Theorem 4.51 that $\mathcal{K}$ is a subgroup of $\mathcal{G}$, as asserted. The element a is said to be a *generator* of $\mathcal{K}$; and $\mathcal{K}$ is said to be the *cyclic subgroup generated by* a, and may be designated by $[a]$. Of course, it can happen that $\mathcal{K} = \mathcal{G}$, and in this case the whole group $\mathcal{G}$ is cyclic with a as a generator. We will frequently designate this abstract cyclic group of order n—as well as any isomorphic copy of it—by C_n.

If $\mathcal{G}$ is a finite group, not all powers a^t of any of its elements a are distinct. In fact, $o(a)$ must be some positive integer n, so that $a^n = 1$, and it is clear that $(a^t)^{-1} = a^{n-t}$ for any integer $t > 0$: hence, in this case, the subgroup generated by a must contain only the set $\{a^0 = 1, a, a^2, \ldots, a^{n-1}\}$ of n elements. A cyclic group is always abelian, and so we see that it is quite a common occurrence for a nonabelian group to contain abelian subgroups.

Theorem 4.52. *If S is any collection of subgroups of a group $\mathcal{G}$, the intersection of these subgroups is also a subgroup of $\mathcal{G}$.*

Proof. Let a and b be elements of the intersection. Then a and b are in each subgroup of the collection and, by Theorem 4.51, it follows that ab^{-1} is in each of these subgroups. But then ab^{-1} is in the common intersection and so this intersection is a subgroup of $\mathcal{G}$, as asserted. ∎

We are now able to generalize the notion of a cyclic subgroup. For if M is *any* nonempty subset of a group $\mathcal{G}$, consider the set of subgroups of $\mathcal{G}$ that contain M. Since this set contains $\mathcal{G}$, it is not empty, and by Theorem 4.52 the intersection of all its members is a subgroup of $\mathcal{G}$. This group is known as the subgroup *generated by the set M*, and will be denoted by $[M]$; the elements of M will be referred to as the *generators* of the subgroup. [cf. Problem 12 of Problems 3–1]. If $M = \{a_1, a_2, \ldots, a_n\}$, we shall write $[a_1, a_2, \ldots, a_n]$ instead of $[M]$. It is clear that $[M]$ can be characterized as the "smallest" subgroup of $\mathcal{G}$ that contains M, in the sense that any other subgroup of $\mathcal{G}$ that contains M also contains $[M]$. The elements of $[M]$ are just the finite products $a_1 a_2 a_3 \cdots a_r$, where each a_i is either an element of M or the inverse of such an element. To see this, let $\mathcal{K}$ be the collection of all such products, for all positive integers r. Then, if $a = a_1 a_2 a_3 \cdots a_m \in \mathcal{K}$ and $b = b_1 b_2 b_3 \cdots b_n \in \mathcal{K}$, we have $b^{-1} = b_n^{-1} b_{n-1}^{-1} b_{n-2}^{-1} \cdots b_1^{-1} \in \mathcal{K}$, and it follows that $ab^{-1} = a_1 a_2 a_3 \cdots a_m b_n^{-1} b_{n-1}^{-1} b_{n-2}^{-1} \cdots b_1^{-1} \in \mathcal{K}$. Hence, by Theorem 4.51, $\mathcal{K}$ is a subgroup of $\mathcal{G}$ which contains M. But any subgroup that contains M must contain every element of $\mathcal{K}$, and so $\mathcal{K} = [M]$. If $M = \{a\}$, the group $[M]$ is the cyclic group $[a]$, as discussed before.

PROBLEMS 4–5

1. Prove that I, D, D', R' comprise the elements of a subgroup $\mathcal{H}$ of the group of symmetries of the square [see Example 8 of § 4.2].

2. If $x = R''$ in the group of symmetries of the square, list the elements of $\mathcal{H}x$ where $\mathcal{H}$ is the subgroup described in Problem 1.

3. Using the notation of Problem 2, list the members of $\mathcal{H}x$ and compare this set with $x\mathcal{H}$.

4. Refer to Problem 8 of § 4.3 and express the subgroup in Problem 1 as a subgroup of S_4.

5. With reference to the group of symmetries of the square, described in Example 8 of § 4.2, find (a) two subgroups of order 4, different from $\mathcal{H}$ in Problem 1; (b) five subgroups of order 2.

6. If $\alpha = \begin{pmatrix} 1 & 2 & 3 & 4 & 5 \\ 4 & 3 & 5 & 2 & 1 \end{pmatrix}$, determine the cyclic subgroup $[\alpha]$ of S_5.

*7. Determine all the subgroups of the group of symmetries of the square [see Example 8 of § 4.2].

*8. Prove that a semigroup $\mathcal{S}$, contained in a group $\mathcal{G}$, is a subgroup of $\mathcal{G}$ if and only if $\mathcal{S}^{-1} \subset \mathcal{S}$.

*9. If $\mathcal{S}$ is a nonempty subset of a group $\mathcal{G}$, prove that the semigroup generated in $\mathcal{G}$ by $\mathcal{S} \cup \mathcal{S}^{-1}$ is a group and is identical with the subgroup of $\mathcal{G}$ generated by $\mathcal{S}$.

*10. Prove that the subset of invertible elements of a monoid comprises a group.

11. In the group S_4 of permutations of $\{1, 2, 3, 4\}$ determine the subgroup which (a) leaves the *elements* 1 and 2 invariant; (b) leaves the *set* $\{1, 2\}$ invariant; (c) leaves all elements *invariant modulo 2*—i.e., as elements of $\mathbf{Z}_2$.

*12. If $\mathcal{S} \subset \mathcal{G}$, for a semigroup $\mathcal{S}$ and finite group $\mathcal{G}$, prove that $\mathcal{S}$ is a subgroup of $\mathcal{G}$ if $\mathcal{S}\mathcal{S} \subset \mathcal{S}$. Give a *verbal* statement of this latter condition.

*13. Prove that a finite semigroup is a group if the cancellation law is known to hold in the semigroup.

*14. Prove that any finite subsemigroup of a group is a subgroup.

**15. If g is a fixed element of a group $\mathcal{G}$, the set C_g of all elements of $\mathcal{G}$ which commute with g is known as the *centralizer* of g. Prove that C_g is a subgroup of $\mathcal{G}$.

*16. The subset of all elements of a group $\mathcal{G}$ which commute with all the elements of $\mathcal{G}$ is known as the *center* of $\mathcal{G}$. Prove that the center of a group is a subgroup.

17. Determine the center of the group of symmetries of the square [see Example 8 of § 4.2], using the representation of this group as a subgroup of S_4 [see Problem 8 of § 4.3].

*18. Let H be a subset of a group $\mathcal{G}$, with $k \in \mathcal{G}$. We first extend the symbolism introduced in § 4.5 so that $k^{-1}Hk$ designates the set of elements of $\mathcal{G}$ of the form $k^{-1}hk$, with $h \in H$. Prove that $\{k \in \mathcal{G} \mid k^{-1}Hk = H\}$ is a subgroup of $\mathcal{G}$, known as the *normalizer* of H in $\mathcal{G}$. In the sequel we shall designate this group as N_H or, if $H = \{g\}$, by N_g.

19. If $\mathcal{H}$ and $\mathcal{K}$ are subgroups of a group $\mathcal{G}$, prove that $\mathcal{H}\mathcal{K}$ is a subgroup of $\mathcal{G}$ if and only if $\mathcal{H}\mathcal{K} = \mathcal{K}\mathcal{H}$.

20. Prove that the elements of finite order in any commutative group form a subgroup.

**21. Determine the subgroup $[\alpha, \beta]$ of S_4, where (a) $\alpha = \begin{pmatrix} 1 & 2 & 3 & 4 \\ 2 & 1 & 4 & 3 \end{pmatrix}$, $\beta = \begin{pmatrix} 1 & 3 & 2 & 4 \\ 3 & 1 & 4 & 2 \end{pmatrix}$; (b) $\alpha = \begin{pmatrix} 1 & 2 \\ 2 & 1 \end{pmatrix}$, $\beta = \begin{pmatrix} 3 & 4 \\ 4 & 3 \end{pmatrix}$. Verify that the group in (a) represents the group of symmetries of the rectangle shown below [see Problem 22 below, and cf. Problem 8 of § 4.3].

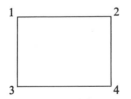

*22. Prove that the subgroups in (a) and (b) of Problem 21 are isomorphic to each other, with each isomorphic to the group $[a, b]$, where $a^2 = b^2 = 1$ and $ab = ba$. A group with this structure is called the *four-group* and is usually designated V (F. Klein's "Vierergruppe").

*23. Determine the subgroup $[\alpha, \beta]$ of S_4, where (a) $\alpha = \begin{pmatrix} 1 & 2 \\ 2 & 1 \end{pmatrix}$, $\beta = \begin{pmatrix} 1 & 2 & 3 \\ 2 & 3 & 1 \end{pmatrix}$ (b) $\alpha = \begin{pmatrix} 1 & 3 & 4 \\ 3 & 4 & 1 \end{pmatrix}$, $\beta = \begin{pmatrix} 2 & 3 & 4 \\ 3 & 4 & 2 \end{pmatrix}$.

24. Prove that a nonempty subset $\mathcal{H}$ of a finite group $\mathcal{G}$ is a subgroup of $\mathcal{G}$ if and only if $\mathcal{H}\mathcal{H} = \mathcal{H}$ [cf. Problem 12].

25. Prove that $o(ab) = o(ba)$, for elements a and b of a finite group.

*26. Prove that any subgroup of a cyclic group is cyclic. (Hint: If $\mathcal{G} = [a]$ and $\mathcal{H}$ is a subgroup of $\mathcal{G}$, show that the set $S = \{m \in \mathbf{Z} \mid a^m \in \mathcal{H}\}$ is closed under addition and subtraction, and hence contains at least one positive integer.

Then use the Well-Ordering Principle [see § 2.2] and Theorem 2.41 to prove that $S = \{kr\}$, for a fixed positive integer r, and $k \in \mathbf{Z}$, and so $\mathcal{K} = [a^r]$, as asserted.)

*27. Determine all subgroups of a cyclic group $\mathcal{G}$ if (a) $o(\mathcal{G})$ is infinite; (b) $o(\mathcal{G}) = p^n$ for some prime p and positive integer n [see Problem 26].

28. If $\mathcal{G}$ is the group of symmetries of the square [Example 8 of § 4.2], verify that $\mathcal{G} = [R, D]$.

29. Prove that the group of symmetries of the square, as represented in Problem 8 of § 4.3, is isomorphic to the abstract group $[a, b]$, with $a^4 = b^2 = 1$ and $ab = ba^3$. (Hint: Let $a \leftrightarrow R$ and $b \leftrightarrow H$, with R and H as in Example 8 of § 4.2.)

4.6. Important Results on Permutation Groups

In Example 1 of § 4.3, we discussed the notion of a group of permutations on n symbols, and designated the group of all such permutations as the *symmetric group S_n* of *degree n*. While the basic set in that example was the set of the first n natural numbers, it should be emphasized that this was merely a convenient choice: for a permutation can be performed on the elements of *any* set. To introduce a point of history, group theory dealt at first *only* with groups of permutations, and abstract groups were introduced at a later date for a more complete understanding of permutation groups. The importance of permutation groups in the general theory, however, stems at least in part from the following theorem, due to Cayley.

Theorem 4.61 (Cayley). *Every finite group of order n is isomorphic to a permutation group, a subgroup of the symmetric group of degree n.*

Proof. Let $\mathcal{G}$ be a group of n elements which we may list as $a_1, a_2, a_3, \ldots, a_n$. If b is an arbitrary element of $\mathcal{G}$, the products $a_i b$ ($i = 1, 2, 3, \ldots, n$) are all distinct (Why?), and so we can associate with b the mapping or permutation π_b such that $a_i \pi_b = a_i b$. This permutation is often referred to as the *right multiplication* of $\mathcal{G}$ by b and, in our earlier notation for permutations, can be designated by $\begin{pmatrix} a_1 & a_2 & a_3 \cdots a_n \\ a_1 b & a_2 b & a_3 b \cdots a_n b \end{pmatrix}$. Now let π_c be the permutation associated with $c \in \mathcal{G}$, so that $a_i \pi_c = a_i c$, $i = 1, 2, 3, \ldots, n$. Then π_{bc} is the permutation associated with bc, and $a_i \pi_{bc} = a_i(bc) = (a_i b)c = (a_i \pi_b)\pi_c = a_i(\pi_b \pi_c)$, so that $\pi_{bc} = \pi_b \pi_c$. It follows that the mapping $b \to \pi_b$ is a homomorphism of $\mathcal{G}$ into the symmetric group S_n, and an application of Theorem 4.45 allows us to assert that this homomorphic image is a subgroup of S_n. Moreover, two distinct elements of $\mathcal{G}$ give rise to distinct permutations in S_n: for if $a\pi_b = a\pi_b'$, for any $a \in \mathcal{G}$, we have $ab = ab'$ and the cancellation law [Theorem 4.44] requires that $b = b'$. Hence the elements of the homomorphic image in S_n are in a one-to-one correspondence with the elements of $\mathfrak{G}$, and so the homomorphism is in fact an isomorphism. We have shown that $\mathfrak{G}$ is isomorphic to a subgroup of S_n, as asserted in the theorem. ∎

The isomorphism $b \to \pi_b$ is sometimes known as the *right regular realization* or *representation* of $\mathfrak{G}$ as a permutation group. By means of left multiplication it is possible, in a similar manner, to obtain a *left regular realization* (*representation*) of a finite group as a group of permutations. However, in this case, the mapping is not an isomorphism, but what is known as an "anti-isomorphism," a notion which we prefer not to discuss further. (It should be emphasized, of course, that we have been using our preferred notation of "right mappings," as discussed in § 1.4, and a change to the notation of "left mappings"—as is usually the case when one deals with sets of real functions—would result in a reversal in the terminology just introduced.) Since a finite group—such as S_n—has only a finite number of subgroups, it follows from the Cayley theorem that there exists only a finite number of nonisomorphic groups of any given order.

Example 1. To illustrate Cayley's theorem, let us refer to Example 8 of § 4.2 and determine the right regular representation of the group of symmetries of the square. (In Problem 8 of § 4.3, the student was asked to represent this group as a subgroup of S_4, the procedure to be used being based directly on the geometric interpretation of the various mappings.) The basic set of elements involved here is $\{I, R, R', R'', H, V, D, D'\}$ and, assuming that Table 1 of § 4.2 has been completely filled out, we obtain our desired permutations from a strict application of the procedure given for the right realization of any finite group, For example, if we desire the permutation which is associated with R' in this isomorphism, we need merely note from the table that $IR' = R'$, $RR' = R''$, $R'R' = I$, $R''R' = R$, $HR' = V$, $VR' = H$, $DR' = D'$, $D'R' = D$. The permutation, associated with R', is then $\begin{pmatrix} I & R & R' & R'' & H & V & D & D' \\ R' & R'' & I & R & V & H & D' & D \end{pmatrix}$ and, in a like manner, we can obtain all the other permutations which constitute the right regular representation of the group of symmetries under discussion. If we wish to determine a group of permutations on four symbols [as in Problem 8 of § 4.3] which shall be isomorphic to this group of symmetries, it is best to proceed directly—as suggested above—and without reference to the Cayley theorem. Thus, if we label the vertices of a square 1, 2, 3, 4, as in Figure 1, it is clear geometrically that R' maps 1 onto 4, 2 onto 3, 3 onto 2, and 4 onto 1, and so R' is associated with the permutation $\begin{pmatrix} 1 & 2 & 3 & 4 \\ 4 & 3 & 2 & 1 \end{pmatrix}$. It is easy to obtain the other seven permutations in S_4 which constitute the desired group—a job already done by those students who have completed Problem 8 of §4.3. This representation of the group of symmetries of the square will be a subgroup of S_4, whereas the representation discussed at the beginning of this example is a subgroup of S_8, thereby illustrating an important point: it may be possible to represent a finite group isomorphically as a subgroup of

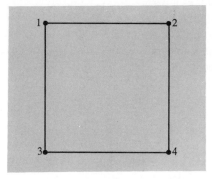

Figure 1

S_n in more than one way and for different numbers n. The Cayley method is often not the easiest way of doing this—as in the latter portion of the example just discussed—but it does give us a definite procedure or *modus operandi* for accomplishing the job in at least one way.

Before leaving Example 1, it may be well to make two comments. (1) We have been using the words "represent" and "representation" in the sense of an isomorphic map. There exists considerable theory on what is known as the "Representation Theory" of groups, in which a "representation" is a more general homomorphism. We will not use this more technically accurate terminology, but will continue to confine our meaning of "represent" to what is essentially a colloquialism or—if you prefer—a special case of the general meaning. (2) In the example, we did not actually prove that the two permutation groups are isomorphic to the given group of symmetries, but merely determined the representations of these symmetries as permutations. Of course, in the case of the *regular* representation, the isomorphism follows from the Cayley theorem. In the case involving S_4, the isomorphism property is intuitively evident but, to be mathematically accurate, it would be necessary to check that the mapping does preserve the operations. To do this completely would require 64 separate checks, and we do not wish to do this! However, it is suggested in Problem 23 that the student do some of this actual checking.

Let us now consider some of the simple properties of permutations on a set of n symbols, which *for convenience* we shall designate as the natural numbers $\{1, 2, 3, \ldots, n\}$. It should be understood, of course, that no special properties of this basic set of natural numbers are to be used in this discussion, for they are merely serving as convenient symbols. If $k\pi \neq k$, for a permutation π, the symbol k is said to be "moved" by π; otherwise k is "left invariant" by π. A permutation π, which permutes the elements of a subset $\{a_1, a_2, a_3, \ldots, a_r\}$ of the basic set such that $a_i\pi = a_{i+1}$ ($i = 1, 2, 3, \ldots, r - 1$), $a_r\pi = a_1$, and leaves invariant all other elements of $\{1, 2, 3, \ldots, n\}$, is known as a *cycle* of *length r*, and we write $\pi = (a_1a_2a_3 \cdots a_r)$. Two cycles are *disjoint* if they move disjoint sets of elements, and it is clear that disjoint permutations commute with one another. A more convenient but equivalent [Problem 8] definition of a cycle is now given.

Definition. A permutation π is called *cyclic* or *a cycle* if, for any two symbols moved by π, each is carried into the other by some power of π.

A cycle of length 2 is a *transposition*. For example, the transposition (56) interchanges 5 and 6 but leaves all other elements of the set $\{1, 2, 3, \ldots, n\}$ invariant. Every cycle of length r can be written as a product of $r - 1$ transpositions, for $(a_1a_2a_3 \cdots a_r) = (a_1a_2)(a_1a_3) \cdots (a_1a_r)$, an equality which can be verified by actually comparing the images under both of these mappings of each element of the set $\{1, 2, 3, \ldots, n\}$. However, we have the following general result for any permutation.

Theorem 4.62. *Every permutation π can be written as a product of disjoint cycles which is unique apart from the order of the factors.*

Proof. Let a and b be arbitrary elements of the set $\{1, 2, 3, \ldots, n\}$. Then we define an equivalence relation in this set so that $a \sim b$ provided a is carried into b by some power of π. Since both positive and negative powers of π are defined, it can be easily checked that this relation is in fact an equivalence relation [Problem 5]. The set $\{1, 2, 3, \ldots, n\}$ then splits up into disjoint classes, called the *orbits* of π, according to a familiar property of any equivalence relation. Each class consists of elements which can be carried into each other by some power of π, and so π generates a cycle on the elements of each class. Since every element of $\{1, 2, 3, \ldots, n\}$ is in some one of these classes, and cycles on disjoint sets of elements have no connection with each other, it follows that the permutation π is a product—in any order—of the disjoint cycles associated with the equivalence classes. ∎

It is easy on inspection to write a given permutation as a product of disjoint cycles. For example, consider the permutation

$$\pi = \begin{pmatrix} 1 & 2 & 3 & 4 & 5 & 6 & 7 \\ 4 & 3 & 2 & 5 & 1 & 7 & 6 \end{pmatrix}.$$

We notice that this permutation maps 1 onto 4, 4 onto 5, and 5 onto 1, thereby completing one of its component cycles. The effect of π on the elements $\{1, 4, 5\}$ is then the same as (145). In like manner we see that π on $\{2, 3\}$ is identical with (23), while on $\{6, 7\}$ it is the same as (67). It follows that $\pi = (145) (23) (67)$.

The notion of an "orbit" of a permutation α, as introduced in the proof of Theorem 4.62, is an interesting and useful one. If α operates on a set S, our definition implies that an orbit of α is a subset of S with the property that each of its members can be mapped onto any of its members by some power of α. An element x in S is then "fixed by α" if the orbit of α that contains x is a singleton, i.e., if x is the sole member of one of the orbits of α on S. In the language of orbits, a permutation $\alpha \neq (1)$ is a cycle if it has only one orbit with more than one element—i.e., only one nontrivial orbit. If all the orbits of a permutation have the same number of elements, the permutation is sometimes said to be "regular" [see Problem 15]. If $\mathcal{G}$ is a group of permutations on a set S, the idea of an orbit of a permutation α can be extended to an "orbit of $\mathcal{G}$." An equivalance relation can be defined on S so that two elements are "$\mathcal{G}$-equivalent" provided one can be mapped onto the other by some member of $\mathcal{G}$. (See Problem 6 for the proof that this defines an equivalence relation.) The equivalence classes of S which result from this relation are now called the *orbits of* $\mathcal{G}$. If $\mathcal{G} = [\alpha]$ is a cyclic group, it is clear that the "orbits of $\mathcal{G}$" are the same as the "orbits of α," and the two definitions coincide. If $\mathcal{G}$ is not cyclic. however, the orbits of $\mathcal{G}$ do provide us with a generalization of the more elementary concept of the orbits of a permutation. We shall be referring to both types of orbits in the sequel.

PROBLEMS 4-6

*1. Express each of the following permutations as a product of disjoint cycles:

(a) $\begin{pmatrix} 1 & 2 & 3 & 4 & 5 & 6 & 7 & 8 \\ 3 & 6 & 4 & 1 & 8 & 2 & 5 & 7 \end{pmatrix}$; (b) $\begin{pmatrix} 1 & 2 & 3 & 4 & 5 & 6 & 7 \\ 4 & 5 & 6 & 7 & 2 & 3 & 1 \end{pmatrix}$;

(c) (2345) (346); (d) (1437) (2537) (1567).

*2. Express each of the following cycles as product of transpositions: (a) (134675); (b) (24631); (c) (364289).

3. Express each of the cycles in Problem 2 as a product of transpositions with two additional factors.

4. If α, β, and γ are, respectively, the permutations given in (a), (b), and (c) of Problem 1, determine in simplest form the permutation (a) $\alpha\beta$; (b) $\alpha^2\beta$; (c) $\beta\gamma$.

5. Prove that the relation introduced in the proof of Theorem 4.62 is an equivalence relation.

6. Prove that "$\mathcal{G}$-equivalence" does satisfy the requirements of an equivalence relation on a set S containing n elements, with $\mathcal{G} \subset S_n$.

7. Explain why the orbits of a permutation α are the same as the orbits of the cyclic group $\mathcal{G} = [\alpha]$.

*8. Prove that the formal definition which we gave for a cycle is equivalent to the earlier, more intuitive one.

9. Obtain the right regular representation of S_3 as a permutation group.

10. Use a Cayley square to write out the complete multiplication table of S_3.

**11. Determine the right regular representation of the additive group of integers modulo 4.

*12. Prove that any two permutations which move disjoint sets of symbols are commutative.

13. Prove that the order of any permutation is the least common multiple of the orders of its disjoint cycles.

14. Prove that the permutations of $\{1, 2, 3, 4\}$, which leave invariant the polynomial $x_1 x_2 + x_3 + x_4$ is a subgroup of order 4 of S_4. Write down the multiplication table for this so-called *group of the polynomial*.

15. Prove that a permutation $\alpha \in S_n$ is regular if and only if α is some power of a cycle on n elements.

16. If $\pi = (1364)$, determine the members of the cyclic group $[\pi]$, both as a subgroup of S_4 and a subgroup of S_6. Explain the relationship of these two subgroups to each other.

17. Determine the membership of the group $[\alpha, \beta]$, as a subgroup of S_5, where $\alpha = (154)$ and $\beta = (23)$.

18. Use the directions given in Problem 17 for the case where $\alpha = (154)$ and $\beta = (12)$.

*19. List all members of the symmetric group S_4.

**20. Find the subgroup $[\alpha, \beta]$ of S_4, where $\alpha = (12)$ and $\beta = (13)(24)$.

21. Find the subgroup $[\alpha, \beta, \gamma]$ of S_4, where $\alpha = (12)$, $\beta = (24)$, and $\gamma = (34)$.

*22. Express each element of the four-group [see Problem 22 of Problems 4.5]—except the identity—as a product of transpositions in S_4.

23. If ψ is the mapping of the group of symmetries of the square into S_4 [see Example 1 above and Example 8 of § 4.2], prove that $(xy)\psi = (x\psi)(y\psi)$ where (a) $x = R$, $y = D$; (b) $x = R'$, $y = V$.

24. Prove that S_4 can be generated by the transpositions (12), (23), and (34). Generalize this result to S_n.

25. Prove that S_4 can be generated by the cycle (1234) and *any* transposition, say (12). Generalize this result to S_n.

26. Let $f: X \to Y$ be a one–to–one mapping of a set X onto a set Y, with S_X and S_Y the respective groups of all permutations of their elements. Then, if $\alpha \in S_X$, prove that $\alpha \to f^{-1}\alpha f$ is an isomorphism of S_X onto S_Y.

27. Prove that the additive group of rational numbers is generated by the set $S = \{1, 1/2, 1/6, 1/24, \ldots, 1/n!, \ldots\}$, but by no proper subset of S.

28. Prove that the multiplicative group of positive rational numbers is generated by the set of all prime numbers.

29. Find the orbits in the set $\{1, 2, 3\}$ of the transposition α where (a) $\alpha = (12)$; (b) $\alpha = (23)$.

30. If $\pi = (143)$ is considered a permutation in S_4, determine the orbit of α which contains (a) (13)(24);   (b) (1423).

4.7. The Uniqueness Theorem

Since every permutation can be written as a product of disjoint cycles, and every cycle can be written as a product of transpositions, it follows that every permutation can be written as a product of transpositions. In fact, we have noted before that any cycle of length r can be written as a product of $r - 1$ transpositions. Hence, if we can express a permutation on n symbols as a product of k disjoint cycles (including possibly some cycles of length 1), it is quite easy to see that we can write the permutation as a product of $n - k$ transpositions. To illustrate this argument, let us suppose that we have already written some permutation as (123) (4) (567) (89). But (123) = (12) (13) and (567) = (56) (57), so that we can express the permutation in the form (12) (13) (56) (57) (89). In this case $n = 9$, and $k = 4$, so that $n - k = 5$ and we note that there are 5 transpositions in our representation of the given permutation. The number of transpositions in the various representations of a permutation is, of course, not unique: for example, we could include (25) (25) as a pair of additional factors which would not affect the permutation given in the illustration. However, while the number of these transpositions is not unique, it is always even or always odd. This is essentially the assertion of the following theorem, due to Cauchy (1789–1857).

Theorem 4.71 (Cauchy). *If a permutation π on n symbols can be factored into k disjoint cycles, the number of transpositions in any representations of π as a product of transpositions is either always even or always odd, accordingly as $n - k$ is even or odd.*

Proof. Since each cycle of length r can be written as a product of $r - 1$ transpositions, it is possible to express π as a product of $n - k$ transpositions, as was shown above. We recall that, in obtaining $n - k$, we are allowing that some of the k cycles may have length 1, and so will contribute nothing to the set of transpositions. It will be convenient to refer to $n - k$ as $N(\pi)$, and we shall show that the parity of this number is an invariant of π, not dependent on the particular representation of the permutation as a product of disjoint cycles—thereby partially justifying the notation. We shall then show that if $N(\pi)$ is even (odd), then *any* factorization of π as a product of transpositions contains an even (odd) number of factors. The validity of the two following formulas can be readily checked for any permutation π_1.

1. If $\pi_1 = (ba_1 \cdots a_2 ca_3 \cdots a_4)$, then $\pi_1(bc) = (ba_1 \cdots a_2)(ca_3 \cdots a_4)$.

2. If $\pi_1 = (ba_1 \cdots a_2)(ca_3 \cdots a_4)$, then $\pi_1(bc) = (ba_1 \cdots a_2 ca_3 \cdots a_4)$.

In the case of **1**, the elements b and c lie in the same cycle of π_1, and multiplying π_1 by (bc) increases the number of cycles in the permutation by 1. In the case of **2**, the elements b and c lie in different cycles of π_1, and multiplying π_1 by (bc) decreases the number of cycles in the permutation by 1. Since k is the number of cycles in the original representation of π as a product of disjoint cycles, it follows that $N(\pi)$ is decreased or increased by 1 on the multiplication of π by a transposition, according as the elements of the transposition lie in the same or in different cycles of π. Now suppose that π is written as a product of m transpositions, say $\pi = (ab)(cd) \cdots (pq)$. Since any transposition is its own inverse, this implies that $\pi(pq) \cdots (cd)(ab) = (1)$, where (1) is the identity permutation. Since $N(1) = 0$, we must have $0 = N(\pi) \pm 1 \pm 1 \cdots \pm 1$, where there are m terms of ± 1. It follows that m must be even or odd, according as $N(\pi)$ is even or odd, as asserted in the theorem. ∎

A permutation π is called *even* or *odd* according as any factorization of π as a product of transpositions contains an even or an odd number of factors. This definition implies [Problem 1] that the inverse of an even permutation is even, and that the product of two even permutations is even. It is then an immediate consequence of Theorem 4.51 that the set of all even permutations on n symbols is a subgroup of the symmetric group S_n. This subgroup is known as the *alternating group on n symbols*, and will be designated in the sequel as A_n.

PROBLEMS 4–7

*1. Explain why the inverse of a permutation π is even if and only if π is even.

2. Express each of the following permutations as a product of transpositions in two ways:

(a) $\begin{pmatrix} 1 & 2 & 3 & 4 & 5 & 6 \\ 5 & 4 & 6 & 1 & 2 & 3 \end{pmatrix}$;   (b) $\begin{pmatrix} 1 & 2 & 3 & 4 & 5 & 6 \\ 3 & 1 & 4 & 2 & 6 & 5 \end{pmatrix}$.

3. Express the inverse of each of the following permutations in S_6 as a product of transpositions:

(a) $(123)(56)$; (b) $(12)(34)(56)$.

4. Decide whether the following permutations are even or odd:
(a) $(123)(456)(214)$; (b) $(12)(2356)(1342)$.

5. If α and β are, respectively, the permutations in Problems 2(a) and 2(b), determine (a) α^4; (b) β^3; (c) $\alpha^2\beta^2$; (d) $\alpha^3\beta^2\alpha\beta$.

6. If α and β are, respectively, the permutations in Problems 3(a) and 3(b), determine the subgroup of S_6 symbolized as (a) $[\alpha]$; (b) $[\alpha, \beta]$.

7. Express the inverse of each of the following permutations as a product of transpositions: (a) $(156)(23)$; (b) (12345).

**8. In the symmetric group S_4, show that there are 6 distinct cycles on two symbols and 8 distinct cycles on three symbols.

*9. In the symmetric group S_4, show that there are 6 distinct cycles on four symbols, and 3 permutations expressible as a product of two distinct transpositions.

*10. Include the identity permutation (1) and use the results of Problems 8 and 9 to list all the elements of S_4.

*11. Use the result of Problem 10 to obtain a listing of the elements in the alternating group A_4.

**12. Prove that the alternating group A_n has $n!/2$ members.

13. Prove that a cycle of length r is even or odd according as r is odd or even.

*14. Give the complete proof that the set of even permutations on n symbols forms a subgroup of S_n. Consider the set of odd permutations in a similar manner.

15. Show that the mapping, which associates each even permutation in S_n with 1 and each odd permutation in S_n with -1, is a homomorphism of S_n onto the group in Example 4 of § 4.2.

16. If $\alpha = (1234)$ and $\beta = (12)(34)$, determine the permutation symbolized as $\beta^{-1}\alpha\beta$.

17. Generalize the result in Problem 16 as follows: If $\alpha, \beta \in S_n$, and $\beta = (a_1a_2 \cdots a_m)$, prove that $\alpha^{-1}\beta\alpha = (a_1'a_2' \cdots a_m')$, where $a_i' = a_i\alpha, i = 1, 2, \ldots, m$. (Hint: Consider the map of $a_i\alpha$ under $\alpha^{-1}\beta\alpha$.)

18. Use the result in Problem 17 to show how *any* two cycles on the same number of symbols are related.

19. Prove that the order of any permutation is the l.c.m. of the lengths of its disjoint cycles.

20. Refer to Problem 8 of § 4.3 and Problem 22 of § 4.6 to represent each element of the group $\mathfrak{G}$ of symmetries of the square and the group V of symmetries of the rectangle as a product of transpositions. Use your result to show that V is a subgroup of A_4.

21. If $P = \prod_{i<j} (x_i - x_j)$, $i = 1, 2, \ldots, n-1$, $j = 2, 3, \ldots, n$, show that any transposition (rs) of two subscripts in P changes it into $-P$. Hence, use Theorem 4.71 to obtain a new definition of "even" and "odd" as applied to a permutation.

22. A polynomial in $x_1, x_2, \ldots, x_n$ is "symmetric" if it is invariant under the symmetric group of permutations of its subscripts. Find all symmetric polynomials for the case $n = 3$ (cf. Problem 14 of § 4.6).

4.8. Cosets and Lagrange's Theorem

We shall see in this section that any subgroup of a group gives rise to a partition of the group into disjoint subsets known as "cosets." If $\mathcal{G}$ is the group and $\mathcal{H}$ is an arbitrary subgroup, we shall accomplish this by defining an equivalence relation in $\mathcal{G}$ as follows: $a \sim b$, for $a, b \in \mathcal{G}$, provided $a^{-1}b \in \mathcal{H}$. It is a routine matter to verify that this is an equivalence relation, but we include the details. Since $a^{-1}a = 1 \in \mathcal{H}$, the relation is reflexive; if $a^{-1}b \in \mathcal{H}$, it follows that $(a^{-1}b)^{-1} = b^{-1}a \in \mathcal{H}$, and so the relation is symmetric; and since $a^{-1}b \in \mathcal{H}$ and $b^{-1}c \in \mathcal{H}$ imply that $(a^{-1}b)(b^{-1}c) = a^{-1}c \in \mathcal{H}$, the relation is transitive. Hence the relation is an equivalence relation, and so it induces a partition of $\mathcal{G}$ into disjoint subsets [see § 1.3]. We have seen earlier (in the proof of the result just referred to) that a class of equivalent elements can be identified with the class of elements that are equivalent to *any one* of its members. It follows, in the present case, that if a is a member of an equivalence class, the class consists of all elements b of the form $b = ah$, with h an arbitrary element of $\mathcal{H}$. This class is $a\mathcal{H}$, in the notation introduced in § 4.5, and we have shown that each class of the partition has this form, for some $a \in \mathcal{G}$. A set $a\mathcal{H}$ is known as a *left coset* (some call this a *right coset*) of $\mathcal{H}$ in the group $\mathcal{G}$. We note further that each left coset of $\mathcal{H}$ has the same number of elements as $\mathcal{H}$. For, if $ah_1 = ah_2$, with $h_1, h_2 \in \mathcal{H}$, the cancellation law for groups would require that $h_1 = h_2$. Hence there is a one-to-one correspondence between the elements of $\mathcal{H}$ and the elements of any left coset of $\mathcal{H}$. This leads us to the following important theorem due to Lagrange (1736–1813).

Theorem 4.81. (Lagrange). *The order of each subgroup of a finite group $\mathcal{G}$ is a divisor of the order of $\mathcal{G}$.*

Proof. Let m be the order of a subgroup $\mathcal{H}$ of a group $\mathcal{G}$ of order n. We have seen that $\mathcal{G}$ can be partitioned into disjoint left cosets of $\mathcal{H}$, each of which has m elements. Since every element of $\mathcal{G}$ is in some coset, if there are r left cosets in the decomposition we must have $n = mr$. Hence $m \,|\, n$, as asserted. ∎

It is clear that, if we define the equivalence relation to require that $ab^{-1} \in \mathcal{H}$ instead of $a^{-1}b \in \mathcal{H}$, we would encounter the notion of *right cosets* of the form $\mathcal{H}b$. This time we would obtain a partition of $\mathcal{G}$ into disjoint right cosets, and, if s is the number of these cosets, the equation $n = ms$ would arise. It follows that $s = r$, and so the number of right cosets of a given subgroup is equal to the number of its left cosets, in any coset decomposition of a group.

This common number is called the *index* of the subgroup in the group, according to the following definition.

Definition. The *index* of a subgroup $\mathcal{H}$ in a group $\mathcal{G}$ is the number of cosets in either (left or right) coset decomposition of $\mathcal{G}$ with respect to $\mathcal{H}$. This index is often designated $[\mathcal{G} : \mathcal{H}]$.

It is an important point, in the proof of Lagrange's theorem, that the *product of the order of a subgroup and its index in the group is equal to the order of the group*.

While $\mathcal{H} = 1\mathcal{H} = \mathcal{H}1$ is clearly a coset in either the left or right coset decomposition of $\mathcal{G}$ with respect to $\mathcal{H}$, the other cosets in the two decompositions are usually distinct. Any element ah of the left coset $a\mathcal{H}$ has its inverse $(ah)^{-1} = h^{-1}a^{-1}$ in the right coset $\mathcal{H}a^{-1}$. It follows that the left and right cosets of $\mathcal{H}$ can be put in a one-to-one correspondence, in such a way that the elements of the cosets in one decomposition are the inverses of the elements of the corresponding coset in the other. In the case of abelian groups, of course, it is unnecessary to distinguish between left and right cosets. Let us now consider a few illustrations of coset decompositions.

1. If **Z** is the additive group of integers, and $\mathcal{H}$ is the subgroup of integers divisible by 4, two integers a and b are in the same coset if $a - b$ is divisible by 4. There are then four cosets in the decomposition of **Z** with respect to $\mathcal{H}$: the coset $\mathcal{H}$, and the three sets of integers which have the remainders 1, 2, 3, respectively, on division by 4. Since **Z** is commutative, we do not distinguish between left and right cosets here.

2. If we decompose the symmetric group S_n with respect to its alternating subgroup A_n, there are two cosets: the coset A_n of even permutations, and the coset of odd permutations. For if a and b are two permutations in S_n, it is clear that ab^{-1} is even when a and b are both even or both odd. In this case, there is only one left or right coset in addition to A_n, and so again the left and right decompositions are identical—even though the group S_n is not commutative.

3. As an example of two distinct coset decompositions, let us consider the decomposition of S_3 with respect to the cyclic subgroup $\mathcal{H} = [(12)]$, generated by (12). In this case, two permutations a and b are in the same left coset provided $a^{-1}b \in \mathcal{H}$. It can be shown that there are three cosets in this left decomposition: the coset $\mathcal{H}$, consisting of (1) and (12); the coset (13)$\mathcal{H}$, consisting of (13) and (132); the coset (23)$\mathcal{H}$ consisting of (23) and (123). On the other hand, two permutations a and b are in the same right coset provided $ab^{-1} \in \mathcal{H}$, and in this case we discover the following three right cosets: the coset $\mathcal{H}$; the coset $\mathcal{H}$(13), consisting of (13) and (123); the

coset $\mathcal{H}(23)$, consisting of (23) and (132). We note that the two decompositions are different, in this case.

4. For a final example, let us consider the decomposition of **C**, the additive group of all complex numbers, with respect to the subgroup **R** of all real numbers. In this case, two complex numbers are in the same coset provided their difference is real, i.e., their "pure imaginary" components are equal. If we identify the complex numbers with the points of a plane, with the real numbers along the x axis, the cosets are then the points comprising the lines parallel to the x (or real) axis. We close this section with two elementary consequences of the theorem of Language.

Theorem 4.82. *Every group of prime order is cyclic.*

Proof. For each element a of a group generates a subgroup $[a]$ whose order must divide the order of the group. Since the order of the group is prime, *each* of its elements different from the identity must generate the whole group, and so the group is cyclic. ∎

Theorem 4.83. *If $\mathcal{G}$ is a finite group of order n, then $a^n = 1$ for each $a \in \mathcal{G}$.*

Proof. For each element $a \in \mathcal{G}$ generates a cyclic subgroup $[a]$ of some finite order m. Then $a^m = 1$, and $n = mr$ for some integer r, by Lagrange's theorem. Hence $a^n = a^{mr} = (a^m)^r = 1$, as asserted. ∎

PROBLEMS 4–8

*1. Prove that the only left (right) coset of a subgroup $\mathcal{H}$ in a group $\mathcal{G}$, which is also a subgroup of $\mathcal{G}$, is $\mathcal{H}$ itself.

2. Let $\mathcal{H}$ be a subgroup of a finite group $\mathcal{G}$. Then prove directly (i.e., without reference to the properties of an equivalence relation) that, if $a\mathcal{H}$ and $b\mathcal{H}$ have one element in common, they must be identical cosets.

3. Determine the coset decompositions of S_3 with respect to the subgroup $[(13)]$.

**4. Show that the permutations $\{(1), (123), (132)\}$ form a subgroup of S_3, and determine the coset decomposition of S_3 with respect to this subgroup.

5. Use Lagrange's theorem to prove the Fermat theorem: if a is an integer and p is a prime integer, then $a^p \equiv a \pmod{p}$. (Hint: The multiplicative group of nonzero integers modulo p has $p - 1$ members.)

6. Determine the coset decomposition of the group of symmetries of the square with respect to the subgroup $[I, D]$ [see Example 8 of § 4.2].

7. Prove that any abelian group of order pq, p and q distinct prime integers, is necessarily cyclic.

8. Determine the left coset decomposition of S_4 with respect to the four-group in Problem 22 of § 4.6.

9. Determine the right coset decomposition of S_4 with respect to the four-group in Problem 22 of § 4.6, and compare with the result in Problem 8.

10. Determine the left coset decomposition of S_4 with respect to the subgroup $[\alpha, \beta]$ in Problem 23(a) of § 4.5.

11. Determine the right coset decomposition of S_4, with respect to the subgroup $[\alpha, \beta]$ in Problem 23(a) of § 4.5, and compare with the result in Problem 10. Do these two decompositions have the same characteristic as those found in Problems 8 and 9?

12. Use the directions in Problem 10 for the subgroup in Problem 23(b) of § 4.5.

13. Use the directions in Problem 11, but with reference to the subgroup referred to in Problem 12.

14. Use the result in Problem 11 of § 4.7 to obtain the coset decomposition of S_4 with respect to A_4.

**15. Determine the coset decomposition of the additive group of integers $\mathbf{Z}$ with respect to the subgroup of integers divisible by 6.

16. Use Theorems 4.81 and 4.82 to describe the nature of any proper subgroup—if any exists—of a group of order (a) 6; (b) 15.

17. If π_a is the permutation defined as "right multiplication by a" in a group $\mathcal{G}$, with $a \in \mathcal{G}$, prove that the orbits of π_a are the left cosets of $[a]$ in $\mathcal{G}$ [see (Cayley's) Theorem 4.61].

18. If $\mathcal{G}$ is a finite group, prove that each "right multiplication" π_a of (Cayley's) Theorem 4.61 is a regular permutation [see § 4.6]. Note that the same argument applies to a "left multiplication," and so the designation "regular" of the representations of $\mathcal{G}$ as permutation groups by Cayley's theorem is justified.

19. Let $\mathcal{G}$ be a group containing more than one element. Then prove that $\mathcal{G}$ contains no subgroup—except $\mathcal{G}$ and the identity—if and only if $\mathcal{G}$ is a finite group of prime order.

20. Prove the following basic theorem on indexes: If $\mathcal{K} \subset \mathcal{H} \subset \mathcal{G}$, for groups $\mathcal{K}, \mathcal{H}, \mathcal{G}$, then $[\mathcal{G} : \mathcal{H}][\mathcal{H} : \mathcal{K}] = [\mathcal{G} : \mathcal{K}]$.

4.9. Normal or Invariant Subgroups

Inasmuch as a subgroup of $\mathcal{G}$ induces a partition of $\mathcal{G}$ into cosets, it is natural to ask under what conditions such a partition is regular. For we recall the close connection between regular partitions and homomorphisms of a group. It will turn out that a partition induced by a subgroup is regular if and only if the subgroup is "normal" or "invariant," a notion explained in the following definition.

Definition. A subgroup $\mathcal{H}$ of a group $\mathcal{G}$ is *normal* (*invariant, self-conjugate*) in $\mathcal{G}$ if $a\mathcal{H} = \mathcal{H}a$, for each $a \in \mathcal{G}$.

In other words, a subgroup is normal if it permutes, *as a subset*, with each element of the group. However, it should be recognized that the actual elements of a normal subgroup do not necessarily commute with all elements of the group. It follows directly from the definition that if $\mathcal{H}$ is a normal subgroup of $\mathcal{G}$, the left and right cosets of $\mathcal{H}$ in $\mathcal{G}$ are identical. Of course, all subgroups of an abelian group are normal [Problem 6].

It is possible to arrive at the definition of a normal subgroup in a different way. Two elements a and b in $\mathcal{G}$ are said to be *conjugate in* $\mathcal{G}$ if there exists $g \in \mathcal{G}$ such that $b = g^{-1}ag$ (or $a = g^{-1}bg$). It is not difficult to show [Problem 13] that the set of all conjugates of the elements of a subgroup $\mathcal{H}$ by a fixed $g \in \mathcal{G}$ is also a subgroup of $\mathcal{G}$. That is, $g^{-1}\mathcal{H}g$ is a subgroup of $\mathcal{G}$. However, if $\mathcal{H}$ is normal in $\mathcal{G}$, $\mathcal{H}g = g\mathcal{H}$ for any $g \in \mathcal{G}$, and so for this type of subgroup $g^{-1}\mathcal{H}g = \mathcal{H}$. Hence if we designate $g^{-1}\mathcal{H}g$ as a *conjugate* subgroup of $\mathcal{H}$, we see that a normal subgroup has the property that it is *equal to all of its conjugates* in $\mathcal{G}$, or is *self-conjugate*.

In order to justify the use of the word "invariant" as a synonym for "normal," we first recall that any isomorphism of a system onto itself is known as an *automorphism*. It is evident that $a^{-1}\mathcal{G}a = \mathcal{G}$, for any $a \in \mathcal{G}$, so that the whole group $\mathcal{G}$ is self-conjugate. This means that there is a one-to-one correspondence between the elements of $\mathcal{G}$ and itself such that $g \in \mathcal{G}$ corresponds to $a^{-1}ga \in \mathcal{G}$. But then $g \rightarrow a^{-1}ga$ defines a mapping of $\mathcal{G}$ onto $\mathcal{G}$, and it can be shown directly that this mapping is an automorphism of $\mathcal{G}$ [Problem 14], a so-called *inner* automorphism. However, if $\mathcal{H}$ is a normal subgroup of $\mathcal{G}$, we have just seen that $a^{-1}\mathcal{H}a = \mathcal{H}$, for any $a \in \mathcal{G}$, and so we can characterize a normal subgroup as one which is *invariant under all inner automorphisms* of $\mathcal{G}$.

At this point it is appropriate to recall a concept which we introduced in Problem 18 of § 4.5. This concept is too important for us to assume that the student did do this earlier problem, and so—at the risk of going over something already familiar to the reader—we reintroduce the concept in slightly more general terms and explore it further.

Definition. If H is a nonempty subset of a group $\mathcal{G}$, and $\mathcal{K}$ a subgroup of $\mathcal{G}$, the set $N_{\mathcal{K}}(H) = \{k \in \mathcal{K} \mid k^{-1}Hk = H\}$ is called the *normalizer of H in $\mathcal{K}$*. In case $\mathcal{K} = \mathcal{G}$, we usually call $N_{\mathcal{G}}(H)$ the *normalizer of H* and designate it simply $N(H)$. If $H = \{a\}$ is a singleton, for some $a \in \mathcal{G}$, we speak of the *normalizer of a* in $\mathcal{K}$ or $\mathcal{G}$, as appropriate, rather than the "normalizer of H," and write $N_{\mathcal{K}}(a)$, $N_{\mathcal{G}}(a)$ or $N(a)$ [cf. Problem 18 of § 4.5].

The proof that $N_{\mathcal{K}}(H)$ is a subgroup of $\mathcal{K}$ is essentially the proof that was requested in the earlier problem to which we referred, but we suggest in Problem 2 that the student review the details. It is an immediate consequence of our definition that, if $\mathcal{H}$ is a subgroup of $\mathcal{G}$, the normalizer $N(\mathcal{H})$ of $\mathcal{H}$ is *the largest subgroup of $\mathcal{G}$ in which $\mathcal{H}$ is normal*, thereby justifying the use of the word "normalizer." A similar interpretation can be applied to the case $N_{\mathcal{K}}(\mathcal{H})$, where $\mathcal{K} \neq \mathcal{G}$ [Problem 3]. If we use the abbreviated notation $\mathcal{H}^g$ for the set $g^{-1}\mathcal{H}g$, it follows that $\mathcal{H}^g$ and $\mathcal{H}$ are identical if $\mathcal{H}$ happens to be a normal subgroup of $\mathcal{G}$. This is not necessarily the case, of course, if $\mathcal{H}$ is an arbitrary subgroup or subset of $\mathcal{G}$, but we nevertheless have the following result which is of interest even for this general case.

Lemma. *For any subset $H \subset \mathcal{K}$, with $\mathcal{K}$ a subgroup of a group $\mathcal{G}$, the sets H^k and H have the same cardinality for any $k \in \mathcal{K}$.*

Proof. If $h \in H$, let us consider the mapping $h \to k^{-1}hk = h'$ of H onto H^k, for any fixed $k \in \mathcal{K}$. The definition of H^k implies that the mapping is surjective or "onto" [Problem 4], while it can be seen similarly that the mapping $h' \to kh'k^{-1} = k(k^{-1}hk)k^{-1} = h$ is a surjection of H^k to H. Since the composite of these two mappings—in either order—is the identity, they are the respective inverses of each other; and we conclude from this that the mapping $h \to h'$ sets up a one-to-one correspondence between H and H^k, whence these sets have the same cardinality. ∎

The set H^k is called a *conjugate* of H, and the collection of all these conjugates, for arbitrary $k \in \mathcal{K}$, is called *the set of conjugates of H under $\mathcal{K}$*. We may also rephrase this idea slightly differently and state that two subsets H and H' of $\mathcal{G}$ are *conjugate under a subgroup $\mathcal{K}$ of $\mathcal{G}$* if $H' = H^k$, for some $k \in \mathcal{K}$. The preceding lemma then asserts that any two conjugates of H under $\mathcal{K}$ have the same cardinality. We emphasize, of course, that everything that we have said with reference to $\mathcal{K}$ remains valid if $\mathcal{K} = \mathcal{G}$.

It has been noted that, if $\mathcal{H}$ is a normal subgroup of $\mathcal{G}$, there does not exist a conjugate of $\mathcal{H}$ in $\mathcal{G}$—or, *a fortiori* in a subgroup $\mathcal{K}$—which is distinct from $\mathcal{H}$. On the other hand, it would be unreasonable to expect that *all* the conjugates H^k, $k \in \mathcal{K}$, would be distinct for an arbitrary subset $H \subset \mathcal{G}$. The question of how many distinct conjugates there are of H under $\mathcal{K}$ is answered in the following important result.

Theorem 4.91. *Let H be a subset and $\mathcal{K}$ a subgroup of a group $\mathcal{G}$. Then the set of conjugates H^k, for $k \in \mathcal{K}$, has the same cardinality as the set of cosets of $N_{\mathcal{K}}(H)$ in $\mathcal{K}$. If $\mathcal{G}$ is a finite group, this result can be phrased more simply as follows*: The number of conjugates of H under $\mathcal{K}$ is the index of the normalizer of H in $\mathcal{K}$, i.e., $[\mathcal{K} : N_{\mathcal{K}}(H)]$.

Proof. Let us suppose that $H^{k_1} = H^{k_2}$, i.e., $k_1^{-1}Hk_1 = k_2^{-1}Hk_2$, for some $k_1, k_2 \in \mathcal{K}$. Then $H = (k_2k_1^{-1})^{-1}H(k_2k_1^{-1})$, so that $k_2k_1^{-1} \in N_{\mathcal{K}}(H)$ whence $k_2 \in [N_{\mathcal{K}}(H)]k_1$. But this argument implies that two conjugates H^{k_1} and H^{k_2} are equal if and and only if k_1 and k_2 belong to the same right coset, and so there must be a one-to-one correspondence between distinct conjugates of H under $\mathfrak{K}$ and distinct right cosets of $N_{\mathfrak{K}}(H)$ in $\mathfrak{K}$. Since the number of these cosets—in the case of a finite $\mathfrak{G}$—is the index of $N_{\mathfrak{K}}(H)$ in $\mathfrak{K}$, the proof of the theorem is complete. ∎

If the set H in the preceding discussions consists of a single element h, the set of "conjugates of h" will arise in a natural way. However, it may be more intuitive to think of "conjugation" as an equivalence relation defined in $\mathfrak{G}$ as follows: two elements a and b in $\mathfrak{G}$ are *conjugate* if there exists $g \in \mathfrak{G}$ such that $a = g^{-1}bg$. It is an elementary matter to check that this does define an equivalence relation [Problem 5], and so partitions the set $\mathfrak{G}$ into disjoint equivalence classes of conjugate elements. These equivalence classes are sometimes referred to as simply the "classes" of $\mathfrak{G}$. As for *any* partitioning of a set, each element of $\mathfrak{G}$ belongs to one unique class and the union of all the classes is the set $\mathfrak{G}$. In Problem 16 of § 4.5, the *center* of a group $\mathfrak{G}$ was defined as the subgroup of $\mathfrak{G}$, each element of which commutes with every element of $\mathfrak{G}$. In symbols, if c is in the center of $\mathfrak{G}$, $cg = gc$ for every $g \in \mathfrak{G}$. Moreover, it is an elementary but important fact [Problem 19] that the center of a group is a *normal* subgroup. The characteristic property of the center of a group would then require each element of the center to be the unique member of the (conjugate) class to which it belongs, while the other classes would necessarily have at least two members [Problem 15]. The following "counting principle" may then be regarded as a corollary to Theorem 4.91.

Corollary. *If a group $\mathfrak{G}$ has order n, and its center has order c_0, then $n = c_0 + \sum_{i=1}^{r} n_i$, where there are r distinct conjugate classes of elements in $\mathfrak{G}$ not in the center, n_i is the order of the ith of these conjugate classes, and $n_i \mid n$.*

Proof. We have already remarked that each element of $\mathfrak{G}$ is accounted for either in the center or in one of the conjugate classes of elements not in the center; and that the center and these conjugate classes are disjoint sets. (Note, of course, that the center itself is not a conjugate class, but is the union of the "singleton" classes.) Hence, all that we need to prove is that $n_i \mid n$, $i = 1, 2, \ldots, r$. But n_i is the number of conjugates of some element $g \in \mathfrak{G}$ and so, by Theorem 4.91, n_i is the index in $\mathfrak{G}$ of the normalizer $N(g)$. By the proof of (Lagrange's) Theorem 4.81, $n_i \mid n$ as asserted. The equation given in the corollary, which in a sense "counts" the elements of $\mathfrak{G}$, is known as the *class equation* of the group. ∎

If A and B are subsets of a group $\mathfrak{G}$, we have already defined the *product AB* (see § 4.5) and have noted that "set commutativity" ($AB = BA$) does not necessarily imply "element commutativity" ($ab = ba$, for arbitrary $a \in A$,

$b \in B$). More generally, we can state that while this multiplication of subsets of a group is an associative operation [Problem 1], it is not necessarily commutative; of course, for certain subsets A and B it *can* happen that $AB = BA$, and this always happens if $\mathcal{G}$ is an abelian group. Even if $\mathcal{H}$ and $\mathcal{K}$ are subgroups of $\mathcal{G}$, it is not necessarily the case that $\mathcal{H}\mathcal{K}$ is also a subgroup, but the student was asked to show earlier [Problem 19 of § 4.5] that this is true if and only if $\mathcal{H}\mathcal{K} = \mathcal{K}\mathcal{H}$, However, the subgroup *generated by subsets A and B*, i.e., the intersection of all subgroups of $\mathcal{G}$ containing A and B, does exist and we shall extend an earlier symbolism to let $[A, B]$ designate this subgroup. The following theorem, which we need at a later stage in the book, can now be established.

Theorem 4.92. *If $\mathcal{H}$ and $\mathcal{K}$ are normal subgroups of a group $\mathcal{G}$, the subgroup* $[\mathcal{H}, \mathcal{K}]$, *generated by $\mathcal{H}$ and $\mathcal{K}$, coincides with the product $\mathcal{H}\mathcal{K}$.*

Proof. Since $[\mathcal{H}, \mathcal{K}]$ contains all products ab, with $a \in \mathcal{H}$ and $b \in \mathcal{K}$, it is clear that $[\mathcal{H}, \mathcal{K}] \supset \mathcal{H}\mathcal{K}$. Conversely, let ab and $a'b'$ be any two elements of $\mathcal{H}\mathcal{K}$, where $a, a' \in \mathcal{H}$ and $b, b' \in \mathcal{K}$. Then $(ab)(a'b') = (aa')(a'^{-1}ba'b')$ and $(ab)^{-1} = b^{-1}a^{-1} = (b^{-1}ab)^{-1}b^{-1}$. But since $\mathcal{H}$ and $\mathcal{K}$ are normal in $\mathcal{G}$, it follows that $a'^{-1}ba' \in \mathcal{K}$ and $b^{-1}ab \in \mathcal{H}$; hence, $\mathcal{H}\mathcal{K}$ is closed under the group operation, and contains the inverse of every element in $\mathcal{H}\mathcal{K}$. Thus, $\mathcal{H}\mathcal{K}$ is a subgroup of $\mathcal{G}$, and $[\mathcal{H}, \mathcal{K}] \subset \mathcal{H}\mathcal{K}$. In view of the previous reversed inclusion, it follows that $[\mathcal{H}, \mathcal{K}] = \mathcal{H}\mathcal{K}$, as asserted in the theorem. ∎

PROBLEMS 4–9

*1. Prove that set multiplication is associative, i.e., $A(BC) = (AB)C$, for arbitrary subsets A, B, C of a group.

2. In the notation of this section, prove that $N_{\mathcal{K}}(H)$ is a subgroup of the group $\mathcal{G}$, for any nonempty subset H of $\mathcal{G}$.

3. If $\mathcal{H} \subset \mathcal{K} \subset \mathcal{G}$, for subgroups $\mathcal{H}$ and $\mathcal{K}$ of $\mathcal{G}$, explain why $N_{\mathcal{K}}(\mathcal{H})$ is the largest subgroup of $\mathcal{K}$ in which $\mathcal{H}$ is normal.

4. If H is a subset and $\mathcal{K}$ a subgroup of a group $\mathcal{G}$, prove that the mapping $h \rightarrow k^{-1}hk$ of H to H^k for $h \in H$ and any fixed $k \in \mathcal{K}$, is surjective.

*5. Prove that "conjugation" is an equivalence relation in a group.

6. Show that any subgroup of an abelian group is normal. Either try to prove the converse or find a counterexample—i.e., a nonabelian group all of whose subgroups are normal.

7. Prove that any two permutations in S_n are conjugate if and only if they have the same cycle structure.

8. Determine all the conjugates under the four-group $V \subset S_4$ of the cycle (123) [see Problem 22, § 4.6].

9. If $H = [\alpha, \beta]$, where $\alpha = (12)$ and $\beta = (34)$, determine all the conjugates under the four-group V of the subgroup $\mathcal{H} \subset S_4$ [see Problem 8].

*10. If $\mathcal{W}$ is the subgroup of S_4 generated by (12)(34), prove that $\mathcal{W}$ is normal in the four-group V [see Problem 8], but not normal in the alternating group A_4. This illustrates the fact that "normality" is not a transitive property.

**11. If $\mathcal{K} \subset \mathcal{H} \subset \mathcal{G}$, for subgroups $\mathcal{K}$ and $\mathcal{H}$ of $\mathcal{G}$, prove that $\mathcal{K}$ is normal in $\mathcal{H}$ if $\mathcal{K}$ is normal in $\mathcal{G}$ [cf. Problem 10].

12. If a and b are elements of a finite group, use the fact that ab and ba are conjugates to prove that these composite elements have the same order [cf. Problem 25, § 4.5].

*13. If $\mathcal{H}$ is a subgroup of a group $\mathcal{G}$, prove that $g^{-1}\mathcal{H}g$ is also a subgroup for any $g \in \mathcal{G}$.

*14. If a is any fixed element of a group $\mathcal{G}$, prove that the mapping $g \to a^{-1}ga$, $g \in \mathcal{G}$, is an automorphism of $\mathcal{G}$.

15. If a group $\mathcal{G}$ is decomposed into its (conjugate) classes, explain why any class containing an element not in the center of $\mathcal{G}$ must contain at least two elements.

*16. Prove that the four-group [see Problem 8] is a normal subgroup of A_4.

17. Prove that the alternating group A_n is a normal subgroup of the symmetric group S_n.

18. Prove that any subgroup of index 2 is normal in the group.

**19. Prove that the center of a group is a normal subgroup.

20. Prove that the set of inner automorphisms of a group $\mathcal{G}$ comprises a normal subgroup of the group of all automorphisms of $\mathcal{G}$.

21. Refer to Problem 20 and determine the group of inner automorphisms of the group of symmetries of the square [see Example 8, § 4.2].

*22. If $\mathcal{H}$ and $\mathcal{K}$ are subgroups of a group $\mathcal{G}$, prove that $\mathcal{H}\mathcal{K}$ is also a subgroup if *either* $\mathcal{H}$ or $\mathcal{K}$ is normal in $\mathcal{G}$.

*23. For the subgroups in Problem 22, prove that $[\mathcal{H}, \mathcal{K}] = \mathcal{H}\mathcal{K}$ [cf. Theorem 4.92].

24. If both subgroups $\mathcal{H}$ and $\mathcal{K}$ in Problem 22 are normal in $\mathcal{G}$, prove that the subgroup $\mathcal{H}\mathcal{K}$ is also normal in $\mathcal{G}$.

25. If $\mathcal{H}$ and $\mathcal{K}$ are subgroups of a group $\mathcal{G}$, with $\mathcal{H}$ normal in $\mathcal{G}$, prove that $\mathcal{H} \cap \mathcal{K}$ is a normal subgroup of $\mathcal{K}$—but not necessarily normal in $\mathcal{G}$.

26. If both subgroups $\mathcal{H}$ and $\mathcal{K}$ in Problem 25 are normal in $\mathcal{G}$, prove that $\mathcal{H} \cap \mathcal{K}$ is also normal in $\mathcal{G}$.

27. If $n \geq 3$, prove that no proper normal subgroup of A_n contains a cycle of length 3.

28. If $n \geq 5$, show that every normal subgroup of A_n—except the identity—must contain a cycle of length 3. Then use Problem 27 to conclude that A_n contains no normal subgroups except itself and the identity. Such a group as A_n, $n \geq 5$, with this property is said to be *simple*.

29. If a and b are elements of a group $\mathcal{G}$, the element $a^{-1}b^{-1}ab$ is called the *commutator* of a and b, since $ab = ba(a^{-1}b^{-1}ab)$. Prove that the subgroup generated by the commutators of all pairs of elements in $\mathcal{G}$ is normal in $\mathcal{G}$. This normal subgroup is called the *derived* group of $\mathcal{G}$. (Note: The product of two commutators is not necessarily a commutator!)

30. Decompose the group of symmetries of the square [see Example 8, § 4.2], into its conjugate classes, and check the validity of the class equation in this instance.

31. Prove that the group of symmetries of the square, considered a subgroup of S_4 [see Problem 8 of § 4.3] is normal in S_4.

4.10. Normal Subgroups and Homomorphisms

We are now able to obtain the result, referred to at the beginning of the preceding section, which connects normal subgroups with regular partitions.

Theorem 4.101. *The decomposition of a group $\mathfrak{G}$ into cosets of a normal subgroup $\mathfrak{H}$ is a regular partition of $\mathfrak{G}$. Conversely, if a regular partition of $\mathfrak{G}$ is given, the class that contains the identity element is a normal subgroup $\mathfrak{H}$ of $\mathfrak{G}$, and all other classes of the partition are cosets of $\mathfrak{H}$.*

Proof. Suppose two cosets of a normal subgroup $\mathfrak{H}$ are given. If a and b are *arbitrary* elements of the respective cosets, these cosets can be designated as $a\mathfrak{H}$ and $b\mathfrak{H}$. Then $(a\mathfrak{H})(b\mathfrak{H}) = a(b\mathfrak{H})\mathfrak{H} = ab\mathfrak{H}$, and so the product of *any* two elements of the cosets is in the coset $ab\mathfrak{H}$. This shows that the partition of $\mathfrak{G}$ is regular. For the converse, let A be the class in a given regular partition which contains the identity element 1 of $\mathfrak{G}$. If $a_1, a_2 \in A$, then $a_1 a_2$ must be in the same class as $1 \cdot 1 = 1$ (by the definition of a regular partition), and so $a_1 a_2 \in A$. For an arbitrary element $a \in A$, $aa^{-1} = 1$ must be in the same class as $1a^{-1} = a^{-1}$, and so $a^{-1} \in A$. Hence A is a subgroup of $\mathfrak{G}$. If b is an arbitrary element of $\mathfrak{G}$, and $a \in A$, then $b^{-1}ab$ must be in the same class as $b^{-1}1b = 1$. It follows that $b^{-1}ab \in A$, and so A is normal in $\mathfrak{G}$. Finally, let B be an arbitrary class of the given regular partition. If $a \in A$ and $b \in B$, the product ba must be in the same class as $b1 = b$, and so $bA \subset B$. If c is an arbitrary element of B, inasmuch as b and c lie in the same class, so do the products $b^{-1}c$ and $b^{-1}b = 1$. But then $b^{-1}c \in A$ and $c \in bA$, so that $B \subset bA$. In view of the reversed inclusion obtained before, we have $B = bA$, and so every class of the partition is a coset, as asserted in the theorem. ∎

As a result of this theorem, we see that there is a one-to-one correspondence between the regular partitions of a group and its normal subgroups. In each case, the normal subgroup appears as the class of the regular partition that contains the identity element of the group. Of course, it is a property of any regular partition that its members comprise a factor or quotient group. Hence the cosets of a normal subgroup $\mathfrak{H}$ of a group $\mathfrak{G}$ constitute a factor group, the group products of which, we have seen before, are defined by: $(a\mathfrak{H})(b\mathfrak{H}) = ab\mathfrak{H}$, for $a, b \in \mathfrak{G}$. It is customary not to use the symbolism which we introduced in connection with partitions, but instead we designate the factor group induced by a normal subgroup $\mathcal{H}$ of $\mathcal{G}$ by $\mathcal{G}/\mathcal{H}$.

In order to connect the notion of a homomorphism with normal subgroups and factor groups, we need one further definition [cf. § 3.4].

Definition. The *kernel* of a homomorphism of a group $\mathcal{G}$ onto a group $\mathcal{G}'$ is the subset of $\mathcal{G}$ that is mapped onto the identity element of $\mathcal{G}'$.

We have seen before that any homomorphism of $\mathcal{G}$ induces a regular partition [Theorem 3.51] and also maps the identity element onto the identity element of the image group $\mathcal{G}'$. It follows from Theorem 4.101 that the kernel of a homomorphism is a normal subgroup, since the kernel certainly contains the identity of $\mathcal{G}$. On the other hand, any normal subgroup of $\mathcal{G}$ is the class that contains the identity element in some regular partition. But since this class is mapped onto the identity element of the image group $\mathcal{G}'$ by the induced natural homomorphism [see § 3.5], we see that the given normal subgroup is the kernel of this homomorphism. This establishes the following important result.

Theorem 4.102. *The normal subgroups, and only these, are the kernels of the homomorphisms of a group.*

For any normal subgroup $\mathcal{H}$ of a group $\mathcal{G}$, the [Problem 3] homomorphism $a \to a\mathcal{H}$ of $\mathcal{G}$ onto the factor group $\mathcal{G}/\mathcal{H}$ is said to be *natural*. The following very important *isomorphism theorem* is also an immediate consequence of the preceding results and Theorem 3.51, if we note that the isomorphism of two groups follows from their isomorphism *as groupoids*.

Theorem 4.103. (First Isomorphism Theorem). *If $\mathcal{G}'$ is the image of a group $\mathcal{G}$ under a homomorphism with kernel $\mathcal{H}$, then $\mathcal{G}' \cong \mathcal{G}/\mathcal{H}$.*

As a consequence of the preceding theorems, we now have the following quantitative information concerning homomorphic images of a group: there is exactly the same number of isomorphically-distinct homomorphic images of a group $\mathcal{G}$ as there are isomorphically-distinct normal subgroups of $\mathcal{G}$.

Examples

(1) Probably one of the simplest illustrations of the preceding theorem occurs when we consider the additive group $\mathbf{Z}_n$, for some natural number n, to be a homomorphic image of the additive group $\mathbf{Z}$ of integers. The homomorphic mapping is the one used in the definition of $\mathbf{Z}_n$, and which maps each integer onto its remainder on division by n. The *kernel* of this homomorphism is the set of all integral multiples of

n, a (normal) subgroup of $\mathbf{Z}$ which may be designated in earlier notation as $[n]$. The theorem then asserts that $\mathbf{Z}_n \cong \mathbf{Z}/[n]$, a result which is essentially Problem 12 of § 3.3 with $\mathbf{Z}$ and $\mathbf{Z}_n$ regarded as monoids.

(2) The multiplicative group of positive rational numbers can be mapped homomorphically onto the additive group $\mathbf{Z}$ of integers, as follows: Each positive rational number r can be expressed as $r = 2^n r'$, for some integer n and rational fraction r' with numerator and denominator odd, so that the mapping $r \to n$ is a homomorphism of the kind asserted [Problem 8]. The *kernel* of this homomorphism is the set of rational fractions which, if reduced to lowest terms, have both numerators and denominators odd. If we designate the original multiplicative group by $\mathbf{Q}^+$ and the kernel of the homomorphism by D, we can then assert on the basis of the theorem that $\mathbf{Q}^+/D \cong \mathbf{Z}$, with $\mathbf{Z}$ considered additive. For this example, since the operations play an important role, it might be wise to designate the original group by $\langle \mathbf{Q}^+, \cdot \rangle$ and the isomorphic image by $\langle \mathbf{Z}, + \rangle$, in which case our final conclusion would be that $\langle \mathbf{Q}^+, \cdot \rangle/D \cong \langle \mathbf{Z}, + \rangle$.

(3) The four-group $V = \{(1), (12)(34), (13)(24), (14)(23)\}$ of Problem 22, § 4.5 is known [Problem 16] to be a normal subgroup of S_4, and so V determines a homomorphism of S_4 in which V is the kernel. By the theorem, this homomorphic image is isomorphic to S_4/V, and it is not difficult to determine that the elements of this factor group are: V, $V(123)$, $V(132)$, $V(12)$, $V(13)$, $V(14)$. This factor group in turn can be seen [Problem 18] to be isomorphic to S_3.

(4) In the notation of Example 8, § 4.2, the subgroup $[R]$ generated by R can easily be seen to be normal [Problem 19] in the (dihedral) group $\mathcal{G}$ of symmetries of the square. Since $[R]$ has order 4 and $\mathcal{G}$ has order 8, there are only two cosets in the decomposition of $\mathcal{G}$ under $[R]$, and these may be seen to be $[R]$ and $[R]D$. If $[R]$ is taken as the *kernel* of a homomorphism of $\mathcal{G}$, it follows that $\mathcal{G}/[R]$ must be a 2-element cyclic group.

We close this section with the statements of two more "isomorphism" theorems, which are of frequent use in the theory of groups.

Theorem 4.104. (Second Isomorphism Theorem). *If $\mathcal{H}$ and $\mathcal{K}$ are subgroups of a group $\mathcal{G}$, with $\mathcal{K}$ normal in $\mathcal{G}$, then $\mathcal{H} \cap \mathcal{K}$ is normal in $\mathcal{H}$ and $\mathcal{H}/\mathcal{H} \cap \mathcal{K} \cong \mathcal{H}\mathcal{K}/\mathcal{K}$.*

Proof. We leave the proof to the student in Problem 22, merely noting at this point that $\mathcal{H}\mathcal{K}$ is a group by Problem 22 of § 4.9.

Theorem 4.105. (Third Isomorphism Theorem). *Let $\mathcal{K} \subset \mathcal{H} \subset \mathcal{G}$, with both $\mathcal{K}$ and $\mathcal{H}$ normal subgroups of $\mathcal{G}$. Then $\mathcal{H}/\mathcal{K}$ is a normal subgroup of $\mathcal{G}/\mathcal{K}$ and $(\mathcal{G}/\mathcal{K})/(\mathcal{H}/\mathcal{K}) \cong \mathcal{G}/\mathcal{H}$.*

Proof. We leave the proof to the student in Problem 24.

PROBLEMS 4–10

*1. Make direct use of the definitions to prove that the kernel of any homomorphism of a group is a normal subgroup.

**2. Determine the left and right coset decomposition of S_3, with respect to the cyclic subgroup $[(12)]$, and use this decomposition to verify that $[(12)]$ is not normal in S_3.

3. If $\mathcal{H}$ is a normal subgroup of $\mathcal{G}$, explain why the mapping $a \to a\mathcal{H}$, for each $a \in \mathcal{G}$, is a homomorphism of $\mathcal{G}$ onto $\mathcal{G}/\mathcal{H}$.

4. Let $\mathcal{G}$ be the multiplicative group of complex numbers with absolute value 1. Prove that the mapping $e^{i\theta} \to e^{ki\theta}$, $k \in \mathbf{Z}$, is a homomorphism of $\mathcal{G}$ and determine its kernel.

5. Explain why a homomorphic mapping of a group is one-to-one if and only if the kernel of the mapping consists of the identity alone.

6. What can be said about any homomorphic image of a group of prime order?

7. Explain why any homomorphic image of a cyclic group is cyclic.

8. Verify that the mapping $r \to n$ in Example 2 is a homomorphism.

9. Determine all the factor groups of the cyclic group of order 30.

*10. Prove that the set of all automorphisms of a group is a group, and that the set of all inner automorphisms is a normal subgroup of this group of all automorphisms.

11. Prove that the only 4-element groups are the cyclic group of order 4 and the four-group V.

12. Determine all the subgroups of S_3, and check each for normality.

13. The additive group $\mathbf{Z}$ is mapped onto the additive group $\mathbf{Z}_8$ of remainders on division by 8. Verify that the mapping is a homomorphism and determine its kernel. Use this example to illustrate the isomorphism asserted in Theorem 4.103.

14. The symmetric group S_n is mapped onto the multiplicative group, consisting of the integers 1 and -1, in such a way that each even permutation is mapped onto 1 and each odd permutation is mapped onto -1. Prove that the mapping is a homomorphism, determine its kernel, and describe the isomorphism asserted in Theorem 4.103 for this case.

15. If $f : \mathcal{G} \to \mathcal{G}'$ is a homomorphism, for groups $\mathcal{G}$ and $\mathcal{G}'$, with $\mathcal{H}'$ a subgroup of $\mathcal{G}'$, prove that $f^{-1}(\mathcal{H}')$ is a subgroup of $\mathcal{G}$ which contains the kernel of f.

16. Verify that the four-group V, expressed as the permutations in Example 3, is a normal subgroup of S_4. (Hint: Determine the 20 permutations α in S_4 but not in V, and show that $V = \alpha^{-1}V\alpha$ for each α.)

17. Use the results in Problem 16 to determine the coset decomposition of S_4 under V, and hence determine the elements of the factor group S_4/V.

18. Use the six cosets found in Problem 17 to verify that S_4/V is isomorphic to S_3. (Hint: Designate the cosets $V_1 = V$, V_2, V_3, V_4, V_5, V_6 and determine the multiplication table for these elements.)

19. Use the notation in Example 8 of § 4.2 to verify that the subgroup $[R]$ of the (dihedral) group $\mathcal{G}$ of symmetries of the square is normal in $\mathcal{G}$.

20. Do the verification requested in Problem 19, but use the representation of $\mathcal{G}$ as the subgroup of S_4 described in Problem 8 of § 4.3.

21. Verify that $\mathcal{H} = \{(1), (13)(24)\}$ is an invariant subgroup of the four-group V [see Problem 21(a) of § 4.5], and determine the elements of the factor group $V/\mathcal{H}$.

22. Prove Theorem 4.104. (Hint: In the natural homomorphism of $\mathcal{H}\mathcal{K}$ onto $\mathcal{H}\mathcal{K}/\mathcal{K}$, the subgroup $\mathcal{H}$ is mapped *onto* this whole factor group. (Why?) Then use the First Isomorphism Theorem.)

23. Illustrate the Second Isomorphism Theorem (Theorem 4.104) by taking $\mathcal{H} = [3]$ and $\mathcal{K} = [5]$ in the additive group $\mathbf{Z}$ of integers.

24. Prove Theorem 4.105. (Hint: Define the mapping $f : \mathcal{G}/\mathcal{K} \to \mathcal{G}/\mathcal{H}$ so that $f(a\mathcal{K}) = a\mathcal{H}$, for each $a \in \mathcal{G}$. Then prove that f is a homomorphism with kernel $\mathcal{H}/\mathcal{K}$, and apply the First Isomorphism Theorem.

25. Let $\mathcal{K}$ be the group of symmetries of the square, a group already known [Problem 31, § 4.9] to be normal in S_4. Illustrate Theorem 4.105 by exhibiting the correspondence $\mathcal{H}/\mathcal{K} \leftrightarrow \mathcal{H}$, where $\mathcal{H}/\mathcal{K}$ is a normal subgroup of $S_4/\mathcal{K}$, and $\mathcal{H}$ is a normal subgroup of S_4 containing $\mathcal{K}$.

26. Let $\mathcal{G}$ and $\mathcal{G}'$ be groups, with $\mathcal{K}$ a normal subgroup of $\mathcal{G}$. Then prove that every homomorphism $f : \mathcal{G} \to \mathcal{G}'$, with kernel $\mathcal{K}$, induces a homomorphism $f_* : \mathcal{G}/\mathcal{K} \to \mathcal{G}'$ such that $f = \pi f_*$, where $\pi : \mathcal{G} \to \mathcal{G}/\mathcal{K}$ is the natural homomorphism in which $a\pi = a\mathcal{K}$, for each $a \in \mathcal{G}$. (Note that we are not assuming here that $\mathcal{G}'$ is the image of $\mathcal{G}$ under f.)

**27. Prove that every infinite cyclic group is isomorphic to the additive group $\mathbf{Z}$ of integers, and that every cyclic group of order n is isomorphic to the additive group $\mathbf{Z}_n$ of integers mod n.

28. Let $\mathcal{G}$ and $\mathcal{G}'$ be arbitrary groups, with $\mathcal{H}$ and $\mathcal{H}'$ normal subgroups of $\mathcal{G}$ and $\mathcal{G}'$, respectively. Then prove that each homomorphism $f : \mathcal{G} \to \mathcal{G}'$, which maps $\mathcal{H}$ into $\mathcal{H}'$, induces a homomorphism $f_* : \mathcal{G}/\mathcal{H} \to \mathcal{G}'/\mathcal{H}'$. (Hint: For each $g \in \mathcal{G}$, show that $f(g\mathcal{H}) \subset f(g)\mathcal{H}'$.)

29. Refer to Problem 23 of § 3.1, and try to construct a *free group* on a set X of symbols. Check your result against pp. 124–127 of [5].

30. *If you have done Problem 29*, prove that every group is isomorphic to a factor group of a free group. (Hint: Every group has a set of generators: for example, the set of all elements of the group. Set up a one-to-one correspondence between this set and a set of symbols which generate a free group, and apply Theorem 4.103.)

4.11. Direct Products

One of the most fruitful ways to study the structure of a complicated algebraic system is to reduce it in some manner to one or more simpler systems: a study of these simpler systems may then throw light on the original system. This is one of the reasons for studying homomorphic images—and in particular factor systems—since these usually have a simpler structure than the given system. There are two other methods of analysis available to us in the case of groups, that of "direct products" and "composition series", and it is to the first of these that we direct our attention in this section, leaving our brief discussion of composition series to a later section. While all of these analytical methods can be discussed within the context of general algebraic systems, we shall, of course, confine our present comments to groups.

There are two kinds of direct products—*internal* and *external*—but, while they are conceptually distinct, the resulting groups will be seen to be isomorphic. For this reason, the importance of distinguishing between the two kinds is not great. An *external* direct product is a new group derived from a given collection of abstract groups, while an *internal* direct product is a decomposition of a given group in terms of certain of its subgroups. The idea in forming an external product of groups is not too different from that of forming products in arithmetic, the resulting product group being of more complex structure than that of any of the original; while the process of decomposing a group into an internal direct product of subgroups is more like the arithmetic process of factoring. Moreover, just as factoring is generally more difficult than multiplying, so is the representation of a group as an internal direct product—even if possible—more difficult generally than the construction of the external direct product of a set of groups. There are theoretical advantages in defining *external* products first, but it should be clear even from the very brief comments above that it is the *internal* product which is the important one in the analysis of a given group. Hence we prefer to follow the lead of Kurosh in [5] and put *internal* direct products in the central position, relegating external direct products to a mere "passing" comment. In this way we are able to state most of our useful results on group decomposition with the use of the sign of "equality" rather than that of "isomorphism." We emphasize again, however, that the two versions of direct products do yield groups which are isomorphic, and the only really important matter is that of priority.

If H and K are subsets of a group $\mathcal{G}$, the set product HK has been defined earlier as the collection of all products hk, with $h \in H$ and $k \in K$. In general HK is merely a subset of $\mathcal{G}$, and this is usually the case even if both H and K happen to be groups [see Problems of § 4.5]. However, if $\mathcal{H}$ and $\mathcal{K}$ are normal subgroups of $\mathcal{G}$, it is asserted in Theorem 4.92 that the set product $\mathcal{HK}$ is in fact a subgroup of $\mathcal{G}$. It is conceivable that $\mathcal{HK}$ is the whole group $\mathcal{G}$ and if, in addition, $\mathcal{H}$ and $\mathcal{K}$ are "sufficiently distinct" so as to have only the identity element in common, we have obtained the desired *internal* decomposition of $\mathcal{G}$ in terms of $\mathcal{H}$ and $\mathcal{K}$. This is made more precise in the following definition.

Definition. *Let $\mathcal{H}$ and $\mathcal{K}$ be subgroups of a group $\mathcal{G}$. Then we say that $\mathcal{G}$ is the* internal direct product *of $\mathcal{H}$ and $\mathcal{K}$, and write $\mathcal{G} = \mathcal{H} \times \mathcal{K}$, provided:* (1) $\mathcal{H}$ *and $\mathcal{K}$ are normal subgroups of $\mathcal{G}$;* (2) $\mathcal{HK} = [\mathcal{H}, \mathcal{K}] = \mathcal{G}$; (3) $\mathcal{H} \cap \mathcal{K} = 1$.

If $\mathcal{G}$ is written additively, we speak of the direct sum $\mathcal{H} \oplus \mathcal{K}$; in (2), we would replace $\mathcal{H}\mathcal{K}$ by the corresponding additive composition $\mathcal{H} + \mathcal{K}$ and, in (3), 1 would be replaced by 0.

In view of our announced emphasis on this type of product, we shall usually drop the adjective "internal" and refer simply to a *direct product*.

Example 1. In Problem 22 of § 4.5, the Klein four-group V was described in abstract form as a group consisting of the four elements $\{1, a, b, ab\}$, where $a^2 = b^2 = 1$ and $ab = ba$. Since V is abelian, all subgroups are normal, so that the subgroups $[a]$ and $[b]$ certainly satisfy condition (1) for a direct product. Moreover, it is evident [Problem 1] that the other two conditions are also satisfied, so that $V = [a] \times [b]$. If the more usual additive notation of abelian groups is used, with ab replaced by $a + b$, we would write $V = [a] \oplus [b]$. It may be well to make a comment on notation here. In indicating a direct *product*, we prefer *not* to put a circle around the sign $\times$, since this circled symbol $\otimes$ is used for another ("tensor") product. However, in the case of additive notation, we do need the circled symbol $\oplus$ to be distinguished from the ordinary sum of two groups [Problem 3]—and there is no ambiguity in this usage of the symbol $\oplus$.

The definition which we gave above for the direct decomposition of a group $\mathcal{G}$ is a special case of the following more general situation.

Definition. A group $\mathcal{G}$ is the *direct product* of its subgroups $\mathcal{H}_1, \mathcal{H}_2, \ldots, \mathcal{H}_n$, and we write $\mathcal{G} = \mathcal{H}_1 \times \mathcal{H}_2 \times \ldots \times \mathcal{H}_n$, if either of the following sets of conditions is satisfied:

   (A) (1) The subgroups $\mathcal{H}_1, \mathcal{H}_2, \ldots, \mathcal{H}_n$ are normal in $\mathcal{G}$.
        (2) $\mathcal{H}_1\mathcal{H}_2 \ldots \mathcal{H}_n = [\mathcal{H}_1, \mathcal{H}_2, \ldots, \mathcal{H}_n] = \mathcal{G}$.
        (3) $\mathcal{H}_i \cap (\mathcal{H}_1 \ldots \mathcal{H}_{i-1}\mathcal{H}_{i+1} \ldots \mathcal{H}_n) = 1$, $i = 1, 2, \ldots, n$.
   (B) (1′) $h_i h_j = h_j h_i$, for arbitrary $h_i \in \mathcal{H}_i$ and $h_j \in \mathcal{H}_j$, $i \neq j$, $i, j = 1, 2, \ldots, n$.
        (2′) Each $g \in \mathcal{G}$ has a unique representation as a product $g = h_1 h_2 \ldots h_n$, where $h_i \in \mathcal{H}_i$, $i = 1, 2, \ldots, n$.

If $\mathcal{G}$ is written additively, there will be, of course, the usual change in symbolism for the above definition. Our first theorem here asserts that the two sets of conditions (A) and (B) are equivalent.

Theorem 4.111. *Conditions* (A) *and* (B), *for the direct decomposition of a group $\mathcal{G}$, are equivalent.*

Proof. (a) *(A) implies (B).* Let $h_i \in \mathcal{K}_i$ and $h_j \in \mathcal{K}_j$, $i \neq j$, so that, by (1), $h_j^{-1} h_i h_j \in \mathcal{K}_i$ and $h_i^{-1} h_j h_i \in \mathcal{K}_j$. But then the ("commutator") element $h_j^{-1} h_i^{-1} h_j h_i = (h_j^{-1} h_i^{-1} h_j) h_i = h_j^{-1} (h_i^{-1} h_j h_i)$ is in both $\mathcal{K}_i$ and $\mathcal{K}_j$, whence $h_j^{-1} h_i^{-1} h_j h_i \in \mathcal{K}_i \cap \mathcal{K}_j$. It follows from (3) that $h_j^{-1} h_i^{-1} h_j h_i = 1$, $h_j h_i = h_i h_j$, and we have established (1'). In order to obtain a proof of (2'), our first observation is that condition (2) implies directly a representation of each $g \in \mathcal{G}$ in the form $g = h_1 h_2 \cdots h_n$, $h_i \in \mathcal{K}_i$, $i = 1, 2, \ldots, n$. Let us tentatively assume two representations $g = h_1 h_2 \cdots h_n = h_1' h_2' \cdots h_n'$, with $h_i' \in \mathcal{K}_i$, $i = 1, 2, \ldots, n$. If $h_i = h_i'$, $i = 1, 2, \ldots, r-1$, but $h_r \neq h_r'$, then an application of the cancellation law and other group properties to the above equality, along with (1'), yield us $h_r'^{-1} h_r = (h_{r+1}' \cdots h_n')(h_{r+1} \cdots h_n)^{-1} = (h_{r+1}' h_{r+1}^{-1}) \cdots (h_n' h_n^{-1}) \neq 1$, which is in contradiction to (3). Hence each representation of g as specified in (2') is unique.

(b) *(B) implies (A).* Of course, (1') and (2') imply (2) at once. For the proof of (3), let us assume that $b \in \mathcal{K}_i \cap (\mathcal{K}_1 \cdots \mathcal{K}_{i-1} \mathcal{K}_{i+1} \cdots \mathcal{K}_n)$, $b \neq 1$. Then, b is at the same time an element of both $\mathcal{K}_i$ and $(\mathcal{K}_1 \cdots \mathcal{K}_{i-1} \mathcal{K}_{i+1} \cdots \mathcal{K}_n)$, contrary to (2'). Hence, $\mathcal{K}_i \cap (\mathcal{K}_1 \cdots \mathcal{K}_{i-1} \mathcal{K}_{i+1} \cdots \mathcal{K}_n) = 1$. In order to obtain (1), we let $g \in \mathcal{G}$ and $h_i' \in \mathcal{K}_i$, for any $i = 1, 2, \ldots, n$. Then, since $g = h_1 h_2 \cdots h_n$, by (2'), an application of (1') gives us $g^{-1} h_i' g = h_i^{-1} h_i' h_i \in \mathcal{K}_i$. Hence $\mathcal{K}_i$ is normal in $\mathcal{G}$, and the proof is complete. ∎

Example 2. Let $\mathcal{G} = [a]$ be the cyclic group of order 6, so that $a^6 = 1$. The elements $\{1, a^2, a^4\}$ comprise a (multiplicative) cyclic subgroup C_3 of order 3, and the elements $\{1, a^3\}$ make up a (multiplicative) cyclic subgroup C_2 of order 2. It is clear that the elements of C_3 and C_2 commute with each other, since they all belong to the cyclic group $\mathcal{G}$. Moreover, each element of $\mathcal{G}$ has a unique representation in the form hk, with $h \in C_3$ and $k \in C_2$: $1 = 1 \cdot 1$, $a = a^4 \cdot a^3, a^2 = a^2 \cdot 1, a^3 = 1 \cdot a^3, a^4 = a^4 \cdot 1, a^5 = a^2 \cdot a^3$ [see Problem 4]. Hence, by conditions (B) of our definition, $\mathcal{G} = C_3 \times C_2$. Again, if additive notation were used in $\mathcal{G}$, we would write $\mathcal{G} = C_3 \oplus C_2$.

It may not have escaped notice by the reader that both of our examples of direct decomposition have been of an abelian group. To help "explain" this, it may be of interest to know that the smallest nonabelian group, with a nontrivial (i.e., neither factor the identity subgroup) decomposition, has order 12, and such a group would have [see Problem 17] a multiplication table with 144 entries! Before proceeding with further results, two comments are in order in connection with direct products: (a) In view of property (1') of (B), the subgroups in a direct decomposition can be permuted in any order desired. In particular, if $\mathcal{G} = \mathcal{K} \times \mathcal{K}$, then also $\mathcal{G} = \mathcal{K} \times \mathcal{K}$. (b) The associative property of a group operation eliminates the necessity for parentheses in any direct decomposition of a group. Hence, if $\times$ (or $\oplus$) is considered an "operation" symbol, the operation is both commutative and associative.

The role of factor groups in an analysis of a group is pointed out by the following important theorem.

Theorem 4.112. *If* $\mathcal{G} = \mathcal{H} \times \mathcal{K}$, *for subgroups* $\mathcal{H}$ *and* $\mathcal{K}$ *of a group* $\mathcal{G}$, *then* $\mathcal{K} \cong \mathcal{G}/\mathcal{H}$ *(and* $\mathcal{H} \cong \mathcal{G}/\mathcal{K}$*).*

Proof. Let $\mathcal{H}g$ be a coset of $\mathcal{G}/\mathcal{H}$, where we have written $\mathcal{H}g$ instead of $g\mathcal{H}$ for variety. By the defining property of $\mathcal{G}$, $g = hk$, for $h \in \mathcal{H}$ and $k \in \mathcal{K}$, so that $k \in \mathcal{H}g$. Inasmuch as k is the only element of $\mathcal{K}$ in $\mathcal{H}g$ (Problem 7), there is a one-to-one correspondence between the elements of $\mathcal{K}$ and the cosets of $\mathcal{G}/\mathcal{H}$. We leave the rest of the verification of the isomorphism of $\mathcal{K}$ with $\mathcal{G}/\mathcal{H}$ to the reader [Problem 8]. ∎

The definition of a direct decomposition of a group tells us that any direct factor must be a normal subgroup, while the above theorem supplies the additional information that each factor must also be a homomorphic image of the group. The general problem of determining whether a given group can be decomposed in a nontrivial fashion is difficult and at present unsolved, but the preceding results are of use—especially in the case of finite groups. If we regard the natural homomorphism of $\mathcal{G}$ onto $\mathcal{G}/\mathcal{H}$ (or $\mathcal{G}$ onto $\mathcal{G}/\mathcal{K}$) as the mapping f, the result in Theorem 4.112 can be stated in the slightly different form of the following corollary.

Corollary. *Let* $\mathcal{G} = \mathcal{H} \times \mathcal{K}$, *for subgroups* $\mathcal{H}$ *and* $\mathcal{K}$ *of a group* $\mathcal{G}$. *Then if* f *is a homomorphism of* $\mathcal{G}$ *with either* $\mathcal{H}$ *or* $\mathcal{K}$ *as its kernel, the other factor is isomorphic to the image and we can write* $\mathcal{G} \cong \operatorname{Im} f \times \operatorname{Ker} f$.

The following theorem, which is a partial converse to the preceding result, is useful in some applications.

Theorem 4.113. *If* $\mathcal{G}$ *is a group such that a homomorphism* f *of* $\mathcal{G}$ *induces an isomorphism of a normal subgroup* $\mathcal{H}$ *onto* $\operatorname{Im} f$, *then* $\mathcal{G} = \mathcal{H} \times \operatorname{Ker} f$. *In other words, the existence of a homomorphism* f, *which induces an isomorphism of a normal subgroup onto* $\operatorname{Im} f$, *implies that* $\operatorname{Ker} f$ *will "split off" as a direct factor.*

Proof. We know from Theorem 4.102 that $\operatorname{Ker} f$ is a normal subgroup, so that both $\mathcal{H}$ and $\operatorname{Ker} f$ are normal. In order to show that $\mathcal{G} = \mathcal{H} \cdot \operatorname{Ker} f$, we let g be an arbitrary element of $\mathcal{G}$. If we let $f(g) = y$, the isomorphism of $\mathcal{H}$ implies the existence of an element $a \in \mathcal{H}$ such that $f(a) = y$. If we now define $b = a^{-1}g$, we see that $f(b) = f(a^{-1}) \cdot f(g) = [f(a)]^{-1}f(g) = y^{-1}y = 1$. Hence $g = ab$, and we have shown that $\mathcal{G} = \mathcal{H} \cdot \operatorname{Ker} f$. Finally, let $c \in \mathcal{H} \cap \operatorname{Ker} f$. The definition of $\operatorname{Ker} f$ then implies that $f(c) = 1$, while the isomorphism induced on $\mathcal{H}$ by f now requires that $c = 1$. Hence, $\mathcal{H} \cap \operatorname{Ker} f = [1]$, and we have verified conditions (1), (2), (3) of a direct product, i.e., $\mathcal{G} = \mathcal{H} \times \operatorname{Ker} f.$ ∎

We conclude this section with a brief comment on the *external* direct product of two or more abstract groups, as promised earlier. In this case, the given groups are not necessarily subgroups of one group—so that no common group operation can be assumed. However, if we regard the groups as sets, it is possible to form the Cartesian product of these sets and endow the elements of the product with a component-wise operation. In particular, for the case of two groups $\mathcal{H}$ and $\mathcal{K}$, the Cartesian product of the *sets* $\mathcal{H}$ and $\mathcal{K}$ is the collection of ordered pairs $\{(h, k)\}$, with $h \in \mathcal{H}$ and $k \in \mathcal{K}$. If (h_1, k_1) and (h_2, k_2) are two such pairs, we can define their product as follows: (h_1, k_1) $(h_2, k_2) = (h_1 h_2, k_1 k_2)$. (We note that a product *is* defined in each component, because the elements involved in such a product belong to the same group.) It is not difficult to verify [Problem 11] that the Cartesian product of $\mathcal{H}$ and $\mathcal{K}$ is now a group—the *external direct product* of $\mathcal{H}$ and $\mathcal{K}$—also designated as $\mathcal{H} \times \mathcal{K}$. It is easy to see that this type of product, if regarded as an operation, is commutative and associative—up to an isomorphism [see Problems 12,13]. The connection between the internal and external direct products is clarified when we observe that if $\mathcal{G} = \mathcal{H} \times \mathcal{K}$ is an external direct product of groups $\mathcal{H}$ and $\mathcal{K}$, $\mathcal{G}$ contains subgroups $\mathcal{H} \times 1$ and $1 \times \mathcal{K}$ isomorphic, respectively, to $\mathcal{H}$ and $\mathcal{K}$, *and $\mathcal{G}$ is the internal direct product of these two of its subgroups.* Hence the distinction between the two types of products dissolves if we agree to identify groups which are isomorphic.

PROBLEMS 4–11

*1. Complete the verification in Example 1 that the group V is the indicated direct product.

2. Explain why our definition of an *internal* direct product would be meaningless unless we assume the groups to be subgroups of some given group.

*3. Review what we mean by the "ordinary" sum $\mathcal{H} + \mathcal{K}$ of subgroups $\mathcal{H}$ and $\mathcal{K}$ of an additive group $\mathcal{G}$. What are some circumstances under which this sum is a group [see Problems of § 4.5]?

4. Verify that the representations of the group elements in Example 2 are unique, for the manner specified.

5. Explain the relationship between the order of a group, expressible as a direct product, and the orders of its factors.

6. If $C_6 = [a]$, $a^6 = 1$, is the cyclic group of order 6, list three distinct representations of the identity element as a product of two elements of C_6.

**7. In the proof of Theorem 4.112, explain why k is the only element of $\mathcal{K}$ in $\mathcal{H}g$.

*8. Complete the verification of the isomorphism asserted in Theorem 4.112.

9. State what the actual "converse" of Theorem 4.112 would be, and explain wherein it would differ from Theorem 4.113.

10. If $\mathcal{G} = [a] \times [b]$, where $a^3 = b^3 = 1$, use a multiplication table for $\mathcal{G}$ to verify that $\mathcal{G}$ is not the cyclic group of order 9.

*11. Verify that the *external* direct product of two groups is a group.

*12. If *external* direct products are understood, explain why $\mathcal{K}_1 \times (\mathcal{K}_2 \times \mathcal{K}_3) \cong (\mathcal{K}_1 \times \mathcal{K}_2) \times \mathcal{K}_3$, for groups $\mathcal{K}_1$, $\mathcal{K}_2$, $\mathcal{K}_3$.

*13. Explain why the *external* products $\mathcal{K} \times \mathcal{\bar{K}}$ and $\mathcal{\bar{K}} \times \mathcal{K}$ of groups $\mathcal{K}$ and $\mathcal{\bar{K}}$ are isomorphic.

14. Show that there are only two isomorphically distinct groups of order 4: the cyclic group $C_4 = [a]$, $a^4 = 1$; and the four-group V, shown in Example 1 to be the direct product of two cyclic groups of order 2.

**15. Prove that there can be only one noncyclic group of order 6: a nonabelian group $[a, b]$, where $a^3 = b^2 = (ab)^2 = 1$.

16. Verify that the group in Problem 15 is isomorphic to the symmetric group S_3, by exhibiting the isomorphic mapping.

17. Use the group in Problem 15 to construct a nonabelian group $\mathcal{G}$ of order 12, such that $\mathcal{G} = \mathcal{K} \times \mathcal{\bar{K}}$, with $\mathcal{K}$ and $\mathcal{\bar{K}}$ subgroups of $\mathcal{G}$ of orders 6 and 2, respectively.

18. Exhibit the multiplication table for a group of order 8, expressible as the direct product of three (cyclic) groups of order 2.

19. Exhibit the multiplication tables for the two groups of order 8, each of which has at least one cyclic direct factor of order 2.

20. By "trial and error" show that the group in Problem 15 has only the trivial direction decomposition.

21. If $\mathcal{G} = \mathcal{K}_1 \times \mathcal{K}_2 \times \cdots \times \mathcal{K}_n$, verify that the mappings $\pi_i : \mathcal{G} \to \mathcal{K}_i$, $i = 1, 2, \ldots, n$, are homomorphisms, where $g\pi_i = h_i$, $g = h_1 h_2 \cdots h_n \in \mathcal{G}$, $h_i \in \mathcal{K}_i$. This type of homomorphism is called a *projection*.

22. If $\mathcal{N}$ is a normal subgroup of $\mathcal{G} = \mathcal{K} \times \mathcal{\bar{K}}$, for subgroups $\mathcal{K}$ and $\mathcal{\bar{K}}$ of $\mathcal{G}$, prove that $\mathcal{N}$ is abelian or has a nontrivial intersection with either $\mathcal{K}$ or $\mathcal{\bar{K}}$.

23. If $\mathcal{G} = \mathcal{K} \times \mathcal{\bar{K}}$, for subgroups $\mathcal{K}$ and $\mathcal{\bar{K}}$ of $\mathcal{G}$, verify the existence of homomorphisms i, j, p, q, as indicated in the diagram below, such that ij is the identity on $\mathcal{K}$ and pq is the identity on $\mathcal{\bar{K}}$. Verify, moreover, that iq and pj are the zero homomorphisms on $\mathcal{K}$ and $\mathcal{\bar{K}}$, respectively.

$$\mathcal{K} \overset{i}{\underset{j}{\rightleftarrows}} \mathcal{G} \overset{q}{\underset{p}{\rightleftarrows}} \mathcal{\bar{K}}.$$

*24. Assuming the usual notation for cyclic groups, prove that $C_{mn} = C_m \times C_n$, provided $(m, n) = 1$.

25. Refer to Problems 14 and 24, and prove that $C_{p^2} \neq C_p \times C_p$, for any prime p. (The two groups C_p are, of course, isomorphic but distinct here.]

26. If $\mathcal{G} = \mathcal{K} \times \mathcal{\bar{K}}$ is considered an external product, verify that $\mathcal{K} \times 1$ is a normal subgroup of $\mathcal{G}$ and isomorphic to $\mathcal{K}$. Similarly examine $1 \times \mathcal{\bar{K}}$, and show that the two subgroups generate $\mathcal{G}$.

27. If $\mathcal{G} = \mathcal{K} \times \mathcal{\bar{K}}$ ir an *internal* direct product, prove that $\mathcal{G}$ is isomorphic to an *external* direct product of groups isomorphic to $\mathcal{K}$ and $\mathcal{\bar{K}}$ [cf. Problem 26].

28. If $\mathcal{G} = \mathcal{K} \times \mathcal{\bar{K}}$, for subgroups $\mathcal{K}$ and $\mathcal{\bar{K}}$ of $\mathcal{G}$, prove that the center of $\mathcal{G}$

[see Problem 16 of § 4.5] is the direct product of the center of $\mathcal{H}$ and the center of $\mathcal{K}$.

29. Let $\{\mathcal{H}_i\}$, $i \in \mathbf{N}$, designate a denumerably infinite number of groups. The Cartesian product of the *sets* $\mathcal{H}_i$ can be defined as the collection of all sequences $(h_1, h_2, \ldots)$, $h_i \in \mathcal{H}_i$, where each sequence has only a finite number of components different from the identities of the associated groups. Now use a componentwise multiplication, and verify that the resulting " direct product " of infinitely many groups is also a group.

30. If $\mathcal{G} = \mathcal{H} \times \mathcal{K}$, prove that any normal subgroup of $\mathcal{H}$ (or $\mathcal{K}$) is also normal in $\mathcal{G}$.

4.12. Abelian Groups

The theory of abelian groups, one of the most important classes of groups, is quite well developed—even though an infinite abelian group may have a very complicated structure. As an illustration of this latter fact, we might note that the nonzero complex numbers form a multiplicative group, and this abelian group contains elements of every finite order as well as elements of infinite order. In this section we shall give a very brief introduction to abelian groups, including the most important structure theorems, but we note parenthetically that whole books (see [3] and [5]) have been written on this topic. As is customary in dealing with abelian groups, we shall use additive notation and language, speaking of direct *sums* instead of products, the *n-multiple na* instead of the *n*th *power* a^n, for *a* in the group, and refer to the " zero " subgroup 0 instead of the identity subgroup 1. It will be convenient to continue to use the notation $\mathcal{G}/\mathcal{H}$ for a factor group of an abelian group $\mathcal{G}$ [some write $\mathcal{G}-\mathcal{H}$ instead of $\mathcal{G}/\mathcal{H}$ and call it a " difference " group], even though we shall use $g + \mathcal{H}$ to designate a coset belonging to this factor group.

The idea of *order*, both for a group and its individual elements, has already been well established. If each element of a group $\mathcal{G}$ has finite order, $\mathcal{G}$ has been called *periodic*, but it is easy to see that a periodic group may have infinite order [Problem 29]. At the other extreme from the periodic groups we find the *aperiodic* or *torsion-free* groups, and in these groups only the zero element has finite order. It is not difficult to prove [Problem 6] that the subset of elements of finite order in an abelian group $\mathcal{G}$ forms a subgroup—usually known as the *torsion* subgroup of $\mathcal{G}$. We note that all subgroups of an abelian group, including the torsion subgroup, are normal and so factor groups can be formed with any subgroup. The following theorem may be seen to be of importance in any analysis of abelian groups.

Theorem 4.121. *If $\mathcal{G}$ is any abelian group, with $\mathcal{T}$ its torsion subgroup, the factor group $\mathcal{G}/\mathcal{T}$ is torsion-free.*

Proof. We use an indirect proof and assume tentatively the existence of a nonzero element $x \in \mathcal{G}/\mathcal{T}$ of finite order m. If, in the natural homomorphism $\mathcal{G} \to \mathcal{G}/\mathcal{T}$, we have $u \to x$, for $u \in \mathcal{G}$, then $mu \to mx = \mathcal{T}$, from which we conclude that $mu \in \mathcal{T}$ and has some finite order n. But then $n(mu) = (nm)u \to (nm)x = \mathcal{T}$, so that u is of finite order and $u \in \mathcal{T}$. But $u \to x$ and since x was chosen to be nonzero in $\mathcal{G}/\mathcal{T}$, $x \neq \mathcal{T}$, and we have reached a contradiction. Hence $\mathcal{G}/\mathcal{T}$ is torsion-free as asserted. ∎

As a result of this theorem, the study of abelian groups is essentially reduced to the separate studies of periodic and torsion-free groups, along with a study of how to construct a group $\mathcal{G}$, which contains a *given* periodic group $\mathcal{T}$ as a subgroup, such that the quotient group $\mathcal{G}/\mathcal{T}$ is isomorphic to a *given* torsion-free group. This latter problem is a special case of the more general "Extension Problem" of group theory, a problem which is very difficult and in general unsolved. On the other hand, the study of periodic groups is the simplest and, at least for the finite case, the theory is quite complete. No study of the Extension Problem, even for abelian groups, will be attempted here.

In any study of periodic groups we have need of the following two lemmas, results which are valid whether the group is abelian or nonabelian. We shall use multiplicative notation for these lemmas.

Lemma 1. *Let g be an element of order mn in a group $\mathcal{G}$, where $(m, n) = 1$. Then g has a* unique *representation in the form $g = yz = zy$, where y has order m, z has order n, and both y and z are powers of g.*

Proof. By the Euclidean algorithm, $sm + tn = 1$ for certain integers s and t, and so $g = g^{sm+tn} = g^{sm}g^{tn}$. If we now let $g^{tn} = y$ and $g^{sm} = z$, then clearly $g = yz = zy$ and $y^m = (g^{tn})^m = 1$, $z^n = (g^{sm})^n = 1$. It follows that the order of y is m_1, where $m_1 \mid m$; and the order of z is n_1, where $n_1 \mid n$. Since $g = yz = zy$, the order of g must divide $m_1 n_1$ but, since $o(g) = mn$, we must have $m_1 = m$ and $n_1 = n$. In order to establish uniqueness, let us suppose that $g = y_1 z_1 = z_1 y_1$ for elements y_1 and z_1 (possibly different from y and z) of orders m and n, respectively. We first observe that y_1 and z_1 permute with g [Problem 7], and from this we conclude that they also permute with y and z—since these are known to be powers of g. From the equality $g = yz = y_1 z_1$ we deduce that $y_1^{-1}y = v = z_1 z^{-1}$, with v defined by this equation, and where y and y_1 are permuting elements of order m while z and z_1 are permuting elements of order n. But then $v^m = 1 = v^n$ and, since $(m, n) = 1$, this yields $v = 1$. Hence, $y_1 = y$ and $z_1 = z$, and there is a unique representation of g in the form asserted. ∎

Lemma 2. *Let g be an element of order $n = n_1 n_2 \cdots n_r$, where $n_1, n_2, \ldots, n_r$ are relatively prime in pairs. Then g has a unique representation in the form $g = y_1 y_2 \cdots y_r$, where y_i is of order n_i and y_i is a power of g, $i = 1, 2, \ldots, r$.*

Proof. The proof is by induction on r, and is left to the student [Problem 15]. ∎

In a given abelian group, the collection of elements whose orders are some power of a fixed prime p may be readily seen [Problem 8] to form a subgroup called the *Sylow* subgroup $S(p)$. We are now able to state our first structure theorem on finite periodic groups.

Theorem 4.122. *Any finite abelian group $\mathcal{G}$ is the direct sum of its Sylow subgroups $S(p)$.*

Proof. If $p_1, p_2, \ldots, p_t$ are the various prime numbers appearing as factors of the orders of the elements of $\mathcal{G}$, it is immediate that the direct sum $S(p_1) \oplus S(p_2) \oplus \cdots \oplus S(p_t)$ is a subgroup of $\mathcal{G}$. But if $x \in \mathcal{G}$, an application of Lemma 2 shows that $x = x_1 + x_2 + \cdots + x_t$, where $x_i \in S(p_i)$, $i = 1, 2, \ldots, t$. Hence every element of $\mathcal{G}$ belongs to the direct sum, and so $\mathcal{G} = S(p_1) \oplus S(p_2) \oplus \cdots \oplus S(p_t)$, as asserted. ∎

We have restricted the statement of the above theorem to finite groups for the simple reason that our discussion of direct products (sums) was restricted to the case of a finite number of direct factors (summands). If the idea of direct sums is extended in a natural way to include infinitely many summands [see Problem 29 of § 4.11], the statement and proof of Theorem 4.122 will carry over to any periodic abelian group $\mathcal{G}$ with only the changes resulting from the presence of an infinite number of distinct prime factors in the orders of the group elements [see Problem 16].

We now come to the fundamental decomposition theorem, sometimes known as the " Basis Theorem," of *finitely generated* abelian groups (see footnote on page 142 of [6]). Of course, finite groups are included within the domain of this theorem, but the resulting decomposition is, in general, different from the Sylow decomposition in Theorem 4.122. The proof we give is due to Rado [*J. London Math. Soc.*, **26** (1951), pp. 74–75], and is based on the following lemma.

Lemma 3. *If $\mathcal{G} = [a_1, a_2, \ldots, a_k]$ is an abelian group with k generators, and $n_1, n_2, \ldots, n_k$ are k relatively prime integers, the group can also be described as $\mathcal{G} = [b_1, b_2, \ldots, b_k]$ for generators $b_1, b_2, \ldots, b_k$, where $b_1 = n_1 a_1 + n_2 a_2 + \cdots + n_k a_k$.*

Proof. Our proof will be by induction on n, where $n = |n_1| + |n_2| + \cdots + |n_k|$. If $n = 1$, the second system of generators is identical with the first, and so there is nothing to prove. We now assume the "induction hypothesis" that the lemma is established for the case of k relatively prime integers, *the sum of whose absolute values is less than n.* Since $n_1, n_2, \ldots, n_k$ are relatively prime, at least two—say n_1 and n_2— of the n_i are not zero, and there is no loss in generality if we assume that $|n_1| \geq |n_2| > 0$. Then either $|n_1 + n_2| < |n_1|$ or $|n_1 - n_2| < |n_1|$, so that $|n_1 \pm n_2| + |n_2| + \cdots + |n_k| < n$ for one of the choices of signs in the first term. Moreover, it is clear [Problem 9] that $\mathcal{G} = [a_1, a_2, \ldots, a_k] = [a_1, a_2 \mp a_1, a_3, \ldots, a_k]$. It is easy to check that the numbers $n_1 \pm n_2, n_2, \ldots, n_k$ are relatively prime [Problem 10], and so our induction hypothesis implies that $\mathcal{G} = [b_1, b_2, \ldots, b_k]$, where $b_1 = (n_1 \pm n_2)a_1 + n_2(a_2 \mp a_1) + n_3 a_3 + \cdots + n_k a_k = n_1 a_1 + n_2 a_2 + \cdots + n_k a_k$, and the proof of our lemma is complete. ∎

Theorem 4.123 (The Basis Theorem). *Any finitely generated abelian group is the direct sum of a finite number of cyclic groups of infinite and/or finite orders.*

Proof. There is nothing unique about the number of elements in a set of generators of a group $\mathcal{G}$, for, in fact, the set of all elements of $\mathcal{G}$ may be said to constitute a rather trivial generating set [Problem 1]. However, let us suppose that $\mathcal{G}$ has a generating system of k elements, so that $\mathcal{G} = [g_1, g_2, \ldots, g_k]$. Now, with k fixed, we consider all k-element generating systems of $\mathcal{G}$, and select one $\{a_1, a_2, \ldots a_k\}$ which is minimal relative to a lexicographical ordering of the elements with respect to their orders. The meaning of this property is that $o(a_1) \leq o(a_2) \leq \cdots \leq o(a_k)$, and for no generating system $\{b_1, b_2, \ldots, b_k\}$ is it the case that $o(b_1) = o(a_1)$, $o(b_2) = o(a_2)$, $\ldots$, $o(b_{j-1}) = o(a_{j-1})$, but $o(b_j) < o(a_j)$, for some j, $1 \leq j \leq k$. These generating systems may contain zeros (considered to have "order" 0) and other repeated elements as well as elements of infinite order, the latter appearing to the right of all generating elements of finite order in any system. (The finite orders occurring here are called the *torsion coefficients* of $\mathcal{G}$) We now *assert* that $\mathcal{G} = [a_1] \oplus [a_2] \oplus \cdots \oplus [a_k]$, where each of the summands designates, of course, a cyclic subgroup of $\mathcal{G}$. In view of the abelian nature of $\mathcal{G}$, the proof of this assertion consists in establishing the "unique representation" property for direct summands. If the expression of an element of $\mathcal{G}$ in terms of $a_1, a_2, \ldots, a_k$ is not unique, there would result [Problem 11] an equation of the form $t_1 a_1 + t_2 a_2 + \cdots + t_k a_k = 0$, with not all terms equal to zero. Let us suppose that $t_1 a_1 = t_2 a_2 = \cdots = t_{j-1}a_{j-1} = 0$, but $t_j a_j \neq 0$, $j \geq 1$. It is no restriction to assume that $0 < t_j < o(a_j)$ [Problem 12]. If t is the g.c.d. of $t_j, t_{j+1}, \ldots, t_k$, we can write $t_i = t m_i$, $i = j, j+1, \ldots, k$, and the numbers $m_j, m_{j+1}, \ldots, m_k$ are relatively prime. If we now apply the pre-

ceding lemma to the subgroup $[a_j, a_{j+1}, \ldots, a_k]$, we see that we can assert
that $[a_j, a_{j+1}, \ldots, a_k] = [b_j, b_{j+1}, \ldots, b_k]$, where $b_j = m_j a_j + m_{j+1} a_{j+1}$
$+ \cdots + m_k a_k$. However, $t b_j = 0$ [Problem 13], and so $\mathcal{G} = [a_1, a_2, \ldots,$
$a_{j-1}, a_j, \ldots, a_k] = [a_1, a_2, \ldots, a_{j-1}, b_j, \ldots, b_k]$, where $o(b_j) \le t \le t_j$
$< o(a_j)$. Since this contradicts our choice of the system $\{a_1, a_2, \ldots, a_k\}$ as
the one which is lexicographically "first," we must conclude that $t_1 = t_2 =$
$\cdots = t_k = 0$, and the uniqueness of the representation of g is established.
The proof of the theorem is now complete. ∎

Corollary. *If $\mathcal{G}$ is a finitely generated abelian group, $\mathcal{G} = \mathcal{T} \oplus \mathcal{F}$, where $\mathcal{T}$ is the
torsion subgroup of $\mathcal{G}$ and $\mathcal{F}$ is torsion-free.*

Proof. The proof is immediate, and is left to the student [Problem 14]. ∎

Group elements, such as $a_1, a_2, \ldots, a_k$ in the proof of the above theorem,
which have the property that all representation of elements of the group in the
form $n_1 a_1 + n_2 a_2 + \cdots + n_k a_k$ are unique, with $0 \le n_i < o(a_i)$, $i = 1, 2, \ldots,$
k, are sometimes said to be *independent*. If, moreover, every element of $\mathcal{G}$ has
such a representation, these generators constitute what is called a *basis* for $\mathcal{G}$
[see Problem 17]. ∎

An *infinite* cyclic group cannot be decomposed into a direct sum, because
any two of its nontrivial subgroups [see Problem 27 of § 4.5] have a nonzero
intersection [Problem 23]. It is also true that finite cyclic groups of prime
power orders are also *indecomposable*, in the sense that no such group can be
expressed as a nontrivial direct sum of subgroups. For, if $\mathcal{G} = [a]$, where the
order of a is p^n, with p a prime, the only nonzero subgroups of $\mathcal{G}$ are $[a]$, $[pa]$,
$[p^2 a], \ldots, [p^{n-1} a]$, and each of these contains the next one in the order listed
[Problem 24]. A *cyclic* group of prime power order is said to be *primary* and is
a special kind of *p-group*—a group whose elements have orders which are
powers of the prime p. We are now able to obtain a better decomposition
result for *finite cyclic* groups than the Sylow decomposition of Theorem 4.122
and one which, in addition, gives more precise information than Theorem
4.123.

Theorem 4.124. *A finite cyclic group $\mathcal{G}$ of order $n = p_1^{n_1} p_2^{n_2} \cdots p_r^{n_r}$, with $p_1, p_2,$
$\ldots, p_r$ distinct primes and $r \ge 2$, splits into the direct sum of r primary cyclic
groups of orders $p_1^{n_1}, p_2^{n_2}, \ldots, p_r^{n_r}$.*

Proof. Let $\hat{p}_i = p_1^{n_1} \cdots p_{i-1}^{n_{i-1}} p_{i+1}^{n_{i+1}} \cdots p_r^{n_r}$, $i = 1, 2, \ldots, r$. If $\mathcal{G} = [a]$, the
cyclic subgroup $[\hat{p}_i a]$ has order $p_i^{n_i}$, $i = 1, 2, \ldots, r$. An analysis of the
orders of the elements involved [Problem 21] shows that $[\hat{p}_i a] \cap ([\hat{p}_1 a] +$
$\cdots + [\hat{p}_{i-1} a] + [\hat{p}_{i+1} a] + \cdots + [\hat{p}_r a]) = 0$, $i = 1, 2, \ldots, r$, and so the sum

of the subgroups $[\hat{p}_i a]$, $i = 1, 2, \ldots, r$, is direct. (This is *implied* by conditions (A) for a direct product.) However, since the order of the direct sum of r finite groups is the product of the orders of the groups [Problem 5 of § 4.11], the order of this direct sum is n—the order of $\mathcal{G}$. Hence $\mathcal{G} = [a] = [\hat{p}_1 a] \oplus [\hat{p}_2 a] \oplus \cdots \oplus [\hat{p}_r a]$. ∎

The following results follow immediately from Theorem 4.124, and so the details of their proofs are left to the student. The first gives a stronger form of our Basis Theorem, while the second is a special case of the first "Sylow" theorem to be discussed in the next section.

Corollary 1. *Every finitely generated abelian group is the direct sum of a finite number of indecomposable cyclic groups, some of which may be infinite while others may be finite and primary.*

Corollary 2. *Every finite abelian group is the direct sum of a finite number of cyclic groups of prime power order* [See Problems 31, 32].

Corollary 3. *If the order of an abelian group is divisible by a prime p, the group contains an element of order p.*

Let us give a few illustrations of the preceding theorems, using for this purpose some special cases of an abelian group $\mathcal{G}$.

Example 1. *Let* $\mathcal{G} = [a]$, where the order of a is 8. In this case, since $\mathcal{G}$ is cyclic and $8 = 2^3$ is a prime power, the group $\mathcal{G}$ is not decomposable.

Example 2. If $\mathcal{G}$ is an abelian group of order $12 = 2^2 \cdot 3$, there are two possibilities:

(a) $\mathcal{G} = C_{12}$ is cyclic. In this case, $\mathcal{G} = C_4 \oplus C_3$ [see Problem 24 of § 4.11], with C_4 indecomposable.
(b) If $\mathcal{G}$ is not cyclic, the Basis Theorem assures us of a decomposition of $\mathcal{G}$ into a direct sum of cyclic groups. The only possibility—in order to be distinct from (a)—is that $\mathcal{G} = C_2 \oplus C_2 \oplus C_3$. [The two groups C_2 are distinct, but isomorphic] In this case, $C_2 \oplus C_2$ is the Klein four-group which, in turn, may be identified with the Sylow subgroup $S(2)$ of Theorem 4.122; the subgroup C_3 is $S(3)$.

Example 3. Let $\mathcal{G} = [2, \omega]$ be considered a subgroup of the multiplicative group of nonzero complex numbers, with ω a primitive cube root of unity. Then the order of 2 is infinite, while the order of ω is 3. The Basis Theorem assures us of a direct decomposition of $\mathcal{G}$, and it is easy to see [Problem 22] that $\mathcal{G} = [2] \times [\omega] \cong \mathbf{Z} \oplus C_3$, with $\mathbf{Z}$ and C_3 considered additive groups.

PROBLEMS 4–12

1. Explain why the set of *all* elements of a group $\mathcal{G}$ may be said to comprise a generating set for $\mathcal{G}$.
2. Describe the possible structure of an abelian group of order (a) 5; (b) 9; (c) 10; (d) 18.
3. Describe the possible structure of a cyclic group of order (a) 16; (b) 20; (c) 36; (d) 60.
4. Describe the subgroup of the multiplicative group of complex numbers generated by $\{3, \omega_1, \omega_2\}$, where ω_1 is a primitive cube root of unity and ω_2 is a primitive fifth root of unity.
5. Do Problem 4 if ω_2 is a primitive (a) sixth root of unity; (b) ninth root of unity.
*6. Prove that the subset of elements of finite order in an abelian group forms a subgroup. Is your proof valid for an arbitrary group?
*7. In the proof of Lemma 1, show why y_1 and z_1 permute with z.
*8. In an abelian group, prove that the subset of elements whose orders are powers of a fixed prime forms a subgroup.
*9. In the proof of Lemma 3, explain why a_2 may be replaced in the original generating system for $\mathcal{G}$ by $a_2 \mp a_1$.
*10. If $n_1, n_2, \ldots, n_k$ are relatively prime integers, explain why $n_1 \pm n_2, n_2, \ldots, n_k$ are also relatively prime.
11. In the proof of Theorem 4.123, explain why the equation $t_1 a_1 + t_2 a_2 + \cdots + t_k a_k = 0$ results from the "unique representation" property of a direct sum.
*12. In the proof of Theorem 4.123, why may we assume $0 < t_j < o(a_j)$?
*13. Explain why $t b_j = 0$ in the proof of Theorem 4.123.
*14. Supply the proof of the Corollary to Theorem 4.123.
*15. Prove Lemma 2 as indicated in the text.
16. Extend the proof of Theorem 4.122, as suggested in the text, to include the case where $\mathcal{G}$ is infinite.
17. Show that a maximal number of independent elements of an abelian group does not necessarily generate the group. (Hint: If $\mathcal{G} = [a]$, consider the element ka, where $1 < k < o(a)$.)
*18. Prove Corollary 1 to Theorem 4.124.
*19. Prove Corollary 2 to Theorem 4.124.
*20. Prove Corollary 3 to Theorem 4.124.
*21. In the proof of Theorem 4.124, explain why $[\hat{p}_i a]$ has only the zero intersection with $[\hat{p}_1 a] + \cdots + [\hat{p}_{i-1} a] + [\hat{p}_{i+1} a] + \cdots + [\hat{p}_r a]$.
22. In Example 3, explain why the Basis Theorem gives the decomposition $\mathcal{G} = [2] \times [\omega]$.
**23. Explain why any two nontrivial subgroups of an infinite cyclic group have a nonempty intersection.
24. If $\mathcal{G} = [a]$ is a cyclic group of order p^n, with p a prime, explain why $[a] \supset [pa] \supset [p^2 a] \supset \cdots \supset [p^{n-1} a]$.

**25. Show that an abelian group of order n must have at least one subgroup whose order is an arbitrary factor m of n. This is the converse of the theorem of Lagrange for finite *abelian* groups.

26. If $\mathcal{H}$ is a subgroup of a finite abelian group $\mathcal{G}$, prove that $\mathcal{G}$ contains a subgroup isomorphic to $\mathcal{G}/\mathcal{H}$.

27. If $\mathcal{G}_1$, $\mathcal{G}_2$, $\mathcal{G}_3$ are finite abelian groups, prove that $\mathcal{G}_1 \oplus \mathcal{G}_2 \cong \mathcal{G}_1 \oplus \mathcal{G}_3$ if and only if $\mathcal{G}_2 \cong \mathcal{G}_3$. Regard the sums here as *external* direct sums.

28. Look up the proof of Theorem 4.123 as given on pages 37–39 of [4], and compare with the proof given in this section.

29. Let $\mathcal{G}$ be the "additive group of rational numbers modulo 1;" i.e., $\mathcal{G}$ is the set of rational numbers x, such that $0 \leq x < 1$, with "addition" defined in $\mathcal{G}$ by ignoring the integral part of "ordinary" sums. Then show that $\mathcal{G}$ is an example of an infinite periodic group.

30. With addition defined as in Problem 29, let $\mathcal{G}$ be the "additive group of real numbers modulo 1." Find the torsion subgroup $\mathcal{T}$ of $\mathcal{G}$, and decide whether $\mathcal{G}$ is isomorphic to $\mathcal{T} \oplus \mathcal{G}/\mathcal{T}$.

*31. Prove that every finite abelian group can be expressed as the direct sum of cyclic groups of orders $n_1, n_2, \ldots, n_t$, such that $n_i \mid n_{i+1}$, $1 \leq i < t, t \geq 1$.

32. Use the following suggestions to obtain another proof of Corollary 2 to Theorem 4.124: apply Theorem 4.122 and select $a \in S(p)$, for some p, such that a has maximal order p^k in $S(p)$; let $\mathcal{H}$ be the maximal subgroup such that $\mathcal{H} \cap [a] = 0$; prove that $\mathcal{H} + [a] = \mathcal{H} \oplus [a]$; use an indirect proof to show that $\mathcal{H} \oplus [a] = \mathcal{G}$, noting that if $x \in \mathcal{G}$ and $x \notin \mathcal{H} \oplus [a]$, we may assume that $px \in \mathcal{H} + [a]$; since $o(\mathcal{H}) < o(\mathcal{G})$, the process of "splitting off" direct summands terminates with the desired decomposition.

33. A group $\mathcal{K}$ is said to be a *free abelian group on* $\{a_k\}$ if $\mathcal{K}$ is the direct sum of the infinite cyclic groups $[a_k]$, the elements a_k being a *basis* for $\mathcal{K}$. Prove the "unique representation" property for this basis, and then prove that every finitely generated abelian group is isomorphic to a factor group of a free abelian group.

4.13. The Sylow Theorems

The prime motivation of this section is the matter of how much of the converse to Lagrange's theorem can be preserved. We recall that this theorem states that if $\mathcal{G}$ is any finite group, the order of any subgroup of $\mathcal{G}$ divides the order of $\mathcal{G}$. It would be nice—and group theory would be much easier—if there existed a subgroup of order m for every divisor m of the order of a group! We have already seen that this converse *does* hold for abelian groups [Problem 25, § 4.12], but the example of the alternating group A_4 shows that the converse does not hold in general: A_4 has subgroups of orders 2, 3, and 4, but none of order 6 [Problem 22]. The three Sylow theorems [after L. Sylow (1832–1918)], however, do give us information about *prime power* subgroups, and this information is both qualitative and quantitative. The proofs which we present here or refer to in the problems following, while not original, are not the ones found in most texts. Some of these " usual" proofs make use of more elaborate "machinery" than we have developed, and most use a type of induction which, while completely valid, is somewhat elusive and mysterious to the beginning student. Any discussion of the Sylow theorems must be prefaced by some preliminary discussion of *p-groups*, and we recall from § 4.12 that these are groups of elements whose orders are powers of a prime *p*. Our first (Cauchy) theorem is the extension to the nonabelian case of Corollary 3 to Theorem 4.124—the basis theorem for finite cyclic groups. The proof is a brief, charming one, due to McKay [*American Mathematical Monthly*, **66** (1959), page 119]. In this section, we revert to multiplicative notation.

Theorem 4.131 (Cauchy). *If the order of a finite group $\mathcal{G}$ is divisible by a prime, p, then $\mathcal{G}$ contains an element of order p.*

Proof. Let $\mathcal{G}$ have order n, and consider the set of p-tuples $S = \{(a_1, a_2, \ldots, a_p) \mid a_i \in \mathcal{G}, a_1 a_2 \cdots a_p = 1\}$. Since each row of the multiplication table of a finite group contains exactly one identity element 1, the set S has n^{p-1} members. An equivalence relation is now defined on S by asserting that two p-tuples are *equivalent* if one is the result of a cyclic permutation on the other [Problem 7]. If all the components of a p-tuple are equal, it is the unique member of its equivalence class; and otherwise there are p members in any equivalence class. Let r be the number of solutions in $\mathcal{G}$ to the equation $x^p = 1$, so that r is the number of equivalence classes of S which contain only one member. We know, of course, that $r \geq 1$, since the trivial solution arising from $a_1 = a_2 = \cdots = a_p = 1$ is always present. If s is the number of equivalence classes with p members, then $r + sp = n^{p-1}$, whence $p \mid r$ and so the number of elements of order p is, in fact, a nontrivial multiple of p. ∎

Corollary. *A finite group $\mathcal{G}$ is a p-group if and only if the order of $\mathcal{G}$ is a power of p.*

Proof. If $\mathcal{G}$ is a p-group, let us suppose that $q \mid o(\mathcal{G})$ and $(p, q) = 1$. But then, by the theorem, there must exist an element in $\mathcal{G}$ of order q, contrary to the definition of a p-group. The converse is a direct consequence of Lagrange's theorem. ∎

The first Sylow theorem is concerned with the *existence* of p-subgroups of a finite group, and may be seen to be a generalization of (Cauchy's) Theorem

4.131. The proof we give is due to Wielandt, appearing in the journal *Archiv der Mathematik*, **10** (1959), pp. 401–402, but more recently pointed out by Herstein [*Topics In Algebra*, Boston: Ginn , 1964, p. 78].

Theorem 4.132 (First Sylow Theorem). *If $p^r \mid n$, where n is the order of a group $\mathcal{G}$, then $\mathcal{G}$ has a subgroup of order p^r.*

Proof. We are assuming that $n = p^r m$, where m is an integer which *may* be divisible by some nontrivial power of p. For definiteness, let us suppose that p^t is the *maximal* power of p dividing m, where $t \geq 0$. The idea of the proof is an application of elementary number theory to a simple combinatorial argument: we consider all subsets of $\mathcal{G}$ containing p^r elements, and discover one which has the necessary (and sufficient) closure property to be a group!

The initial point is a number-theoretic one, and we leave it to the student to verify: with p, t, r, and n defined as above, p^t *does* but p^{t+1} *does not* divide the binomial coefficient $\binom{p^r m}{p^r}$ [Problem 8]. Now, let M be the collection of the $\binom{p^r m}{p^r}$ subsets of $\mathcal{G}$, each containing p^r elements. In this collection of subsets, we define an equivalence relation so that $M_i \sim M_j$, for M_i, $M_j \in M$, provided $M_i = M_j g$ for some $g \in \mathcal{G}$ [Problem 9]. The number of set-elements in these equivalence classes may vary, but we claim that p^{t+1} does not divide *all* of these cardinalities: for if p^{t+1} did divide them all, p^{t+1} would divide the number of subsets which comprise M, i.e., $\binom{p^r m}{p^r}$, contrary to what was discovered above. Hence, we may assume the existence of an equivalence class $\{M_1, M_2, \ldots, M_k\}$ of k elements, where p^{t+1} does not divide k. The definition of equivalence implies, for $i = 1, 2, \ldots, k$ and $g \in \mathcal{G}$, that $M_i g = M_j$, for some $j = 1, 2, \ldots, k$. It will happen that $j = i = 1$, for certain g, and we let $\mathcal{K} = \{g \in \mathcal{G} \mid M_1 g = M_1\}$. The set $\mathcal{K}$ is easily seen to be a sub-group of $\mathcal{G}$ [Problem 10], and we shall show that $\mathcal{K}$ is a subgroup of the type desired, its order $o(\mathcal{K})$ being p^r. The sets $M_1, M_2, \ldots, M_k$ are non-overlapping [Problem 11], are all of the same cardinality [Problem 12], and together contain all the elements of $\mathcal{G}$. Hence, $k \cdot o(\mathcal{K}) = n = p^r m$. Inasmuch as p^{t+1} *does not* divide k, and p^{t+r} *does* divide $n = p^r m$, it follows that $p^r \mid o(\mathcal{K})$, whence $o(\mathcal{K}) \geq p^r$. On the other hand, if $m_1 \in M_1$, $m_1 h \in M_1$ for all $h \in \mathcal{K}$, and these elements are distinct; and so there are at least $o(\mathcal{K})$ distinct elements in M_1. Hence $p^r \geq o(\mathcal{K})$, and the two inequalities yield $o(\mathcal{K}) = p^r$, so that $\mathcal{K}$ is a subgroup of the desired order. ∎

Corollary. *If n is the order of a group $\mathcal{G}$, where $n = p^r m$ and $(m, p) = 1$, then $\mathcal{G}$ has a subgroup of order p^r.*

A maximal p-subgroup of this kind is called a *Sylow p-subgroup* (or *p-Sylow subgroup* or *p-sylow subgroup*), and so *the corollary asserts the existence of Sylow p-subgroups for any prime p dividing the order of a finite group.* We do not give proofs for the other two Sylow theorems, but the hints toward their proofs—which we include in the problem set following—capitalize on the notion of *orbits*, as introduced in § 4.6. If $\mathcal{G}$ is a permutation group on a set X, we recall that the *orbits* of $\mathcal{G}$ are various disjoint subsets of X, each consisting precisely of elements which can be carried into each other by permutations of $\mathcal{G}$. In addition, we remind the reader that, if α is a single permutation on X, the *orbits* of α are identified with the orbits of the cyclic group $[\alpha]$. The *stabilizer* S_x of an element $x \in X$ is the subset of $\mathcal{G}$ which keeps x fixed, and it is an easy matter to prove [cf. Problem 11 of § 4.5] that S_x is a subgroup of $\mathcal{G}$ [Problem 13]. These notions are used in the proofs of the other two Sylow theorems, the statements of which we now give.

Theorem 4.133 (Second Sylow Theorem). *All Sylow p-subgroups of a finite group are conjugate to each other, and so belong to the same conjugate class of the group.*

Proof. See Problem 33.

Theorem 4.134 (Third Sylow Theorem). *The number of Sylow p-subgroups of a group of order n is r, where $r \mid n$ and $r \equiv 1$ (mod p).*

Proof. See Problem 33.

The Sylow theorems are extremely useful in discovering the possible structure of a group of given order. Such a structural analysis increases in complexity, of course, with the number of distinct prime factors of this order, but it is fairly easy if the number is small. The remainder of this section will be devoted mainly to two examples which illustrate the applications of the Sylow theorems to structure problems. We know that any group of prime order must be cyclic, but another type of group which keeps recurring when even-ordered groups are being discussed, is the *dihedral* group D_n of order $2n$. We have referred many times in the past to D_4, since it is the group of symmetries of the square, as well as to D_2, a group which we have previously called the four-group V or the group of symmetries of a "nonregular" rectangle. In general, D_n can be defined as a group $[a, b]$, where $a^n = b^2 = 1$, and $bab = a^{-1}$. The identification of D_4 with the group of symmetries of the square is not uniquely characteristic of the case $n = 4$, because it can be easily shown that, if $n > 2$, D_n is isomorphic to the group of symmetries of a regular polygon with n sides: in this isomorphism, a can be identified with a rotation of the polygon, about its center, through an angle of $2\pi/n$ radians, while b can be regarded as a reflection of the polygon about a line passing through the center and one vertex [see Problem 29 of § 4.5, and Problem 14 below]. In this and the following sections, it will be convenient to write $H \lhd \mathcal{G}$ to indicate that H is a *normal subgroup* of G.

Example 1. *If p is an odd prime, any group $\mathcal{G}$ of order $2p$ is either cyclic or dihedral.* For (Cauchy's) Theorem 4.131 asserts the existence of an element x of order p and an element y of order 2 in $\mathcal{G}$. If $\mathcal{H} = [x]$, we note that $[\mathcal{G}:\mathcal{H}] = 2$ so that $\mathcal{H} \lhd \mathcal{G}$. A characteristic property of normality requires that $y^{-1}xy = yxy = x^i$, for some $i = 1, 2, \ldots, p$. But then $x = y^2xy^2 = y(yxy)y = yx^iy = x^{i^2}$, so that $i^2 \equiv 1 \pmod{p}$ and, since p is prime, $i = \pm 1$. In the case of $i = 1$, $xy = y^{-1}x = yx$, $\mathcal{G}$ is abelian and $\mathcal{G} = C_2 \oplus C_p$: in the case $i = -1$, we have the multiplication table for the dihedral group D_p. This result then gives us the structure of all possible groups of orders 6, 10, 14, 22, etc.

Our next example illustrates how the Second and Third Sylow theorems can be used in an analysis of group structure.

Example 2. *Let $o(\mathcal{G}) = pq$, for some group $\mathcal{G}$, where p and q are primes and $p < q$. Then either $\mathcal{G}$ is cyclic, or $\mathcal{G} = [a, b]$, where $a^p = b^q = 1$, $a^{-1}ba = b^r$ in which $r \not\equiv 1 \pmod{q}$ and $r^p \equiv 1 \pmod{q}$.* We first note the existence of a Sylow p-subgroup $\mathcal{H} = [a]$, $a^p = 1$, and of a Sylow q-subgroup $\mathcal{K} = [b]$, $b^q = 1$. The Third Sylow theorem tells us that the number of subgroups conjugate to $\mathcal{K}$ is $1 + tq$, for some $t \geq 0$. But we know from Theorem 4.91 that $1 + tq = [\mathcal{G}:N(\mathcal{K})]$, and this number must divide $o(\mathcal{G}) = pq$. Inasmuch as $(1 + tq, q) = 1$, $1 + tq$ must divide p; since $p < q$, $t = 0$ and $\mathcal{K} \lhd \mathcal{G}$ [Problem 16]. A similar argument shows us that the number of subgroups of $\mathcal{G}$, conjugate to $\mathcal{H}$, is $1 + sp$, for some $s \geq 0$, and $1 + sp$ must divide q. Since $q > p$, there are two possibilities now: (1) $s = 0$; (2) $s \neq 0$, so that $1 + sp = q$. In Case (1), the argument is identical to the preceding, so that here $\mathcal{H} \lhd \mathcal{G}$, and $\mathcal{G} = \mathcal{H} \times \mathcal{K}$ [Problem 17]. Moreover, since the orders of $\mathcal{H}$ and $\mathcal{K}$ are p and q, respectively, with $(p, q) = 1$, $\mathcal{G}$ is cyclic. In Case (2), there exist q subgroups of order p, and, in particular, a nonnormal subgroup $[a]$ of order p. Since $[b]$ is normal, however, $a^{-1}ba = b^r$, for some $r \geq 1$. If $r \equiv 1 \pmod{q}$, $ba = ab$, so that this is the abelian case already discussed in (1). If $r \not\equiv 1 \pmod{q}$, it is easy to see that $a^{-1}b^ia = b^{ir}$, for any i and, with $i = r$, we have $a^{-2}ba^2 = a^{-1}b^ra = b^{r^2}$. A simple inductive proof will show [Problem 18] that $a^{-j}b^ra^j = b^{r^j}$, for any j and, with $j = p$, we see that $b = a^{-p}ba^p = b^{r^p}$. Hence $r^p \equiv 1 \pmod{q}$, as asserted. A special case of this result if of interest: *if q does not divide $p - 1$, then $\mathcal{G}$ is cyclic.* For instance, all groups of orders 15 or 35 are cyclic., but this assertion does not allow us to make a judgment concerning a group of order 21.

The group Q of *quaternions* may be defined as the group $[a, b]$, where

$a^4 = 1$, $b^2 = a^2$ and $b^{-1}ab = a^{-1}$ [see Problem 19]. It can be shown [Problem 21] that the only nonabelian groups of order 8 are D_4 and Q, and with this information we are able to make a complete listing of all possible groups $\mathfrak{G}$ with $o(\mathfrak{G}) \le 10$.

$o(\mathfrak{G})$	Distinct groups of order $o(\mathfrak{G})$
2	C_2
3	C_3
4	C_4, $C_2 \oplus C_2 \cong D_2$
5	C_5
6	C_6, $D_3 \cong S_3$
7	C_7
8	C_8, $C_4 \oplus C_2$, $C_2 \oplus C_2 \oplus C_2$, Q, D_4
9	C_9, $C_3 \oplus C_3$
10	C_{10}, D_5

PROBLEMS 4–13

1. Describe the structures possible for a group whose order is (a) 11; (b) 33; (c) 55; (d) 77.
2. Use the Sylow theorems to rediscover the structures of all possible groups of order 4.
3. Find the Sylow 2-subgroups and 3-subgroups of S_3 and S_4.
4. Show that A_4 has one Sylow subgroup of order 4 and four Sylow subgroups of order 3.
5. Prove that a group of order 108 must contain a normal subgroup of order either 9 or 27.
6. Verify that the quaternion group Q is *hamiltonian*; i.e., every subgroup of Q is normal.
*7. Verify that the relation, defined in the set S in the proof of Theorem 4.131, is an equivalence relation.
*8. If p is any prime number, show that p^t divides $\binom{p^r m}{p^r}$ if and only if p^t divides m.
*9. Verify that the relation, defined in the set M in the proof of Theorem 4.132, is an equivalence relation.
*10. Prove that the subset $\mathfrak{K}$, described in the proof of Theorem 4.132, is a subgroup of $\mathfrak{G}$.
*11. With reference to the proof of Theorem 4.132, explain why the sets $M_1, M_2, \ldots, M_k$ are nonoverlapping.

*12. Explain why the sets in Problem 11 must have the same cardinality.

13. If $\mathcal{G}$ is a group of permutations acting on a set X, prove that the stabilizer S_x of an element $x \in X$ is a subgroup of $\mathcal{G}$.

*14. Show why D_n is isomorphic to the group of symmetries of a regular n-sided polygon.

15. Find the center of D_5, by first expressing each element in the form of a product $a^i b^j$.

*16. Explain why the presence of a unique Sylow p-subgroup $\mathcal{K}$ in a group $\mathcal{G}$ requires that $\mathcal{K} \lhd \mathcal{G}$.

**17. If every Sylow p-subgroup of a finite group $\mathcal{G}$ is normal, prove that $\mathcal{G}$ is the direct product of these subgroups [cf. Theorem 4.122].

18. Give the induction argument requested in Example 2.

19. Quaternions are frequently described as the algebraic system of 8 elements $\{\pm 1, \pm i, \pm j, \pm k\}$, which are combined according to the rules $i^2 = j^2 = k^2 = -1, ij = -ji = k, jk = -kj = i, ki = -ik = j$, along with the usual rules of multiplication for ± 1. Prove that this system is a group and that it is isomorphic to Q, as described in the text.

20. Find the center of Q, referring to Problem 19 if desired.

21. Prove that the only nonabelian groups of order 8 are D_4 and Q.

22. Prove that A_4 has no subgroup of order 6.

23. If p is an arbitrary prime, prove that any group $\mathcal{G}$ of order p^2 is abelian by (a) using a Sylow theorem; (b) considering the center of $\mathcal{G}$.

24. Use Problem 23 to discover the structures of all groups of order (a) 9; (b) 25.

25. If $\mathcal{G}$ is a group of order p^n, explain why any subgroup of $\mathcal{G}$ of order p^{n-1} is normal.

26. Prove that any normal subgroup of order p, contained in a p-group $\mathcal{P}$ of order $p^n, n > 1$, is in the center of $\mathcal{P}$.

27. Prove that the center of any nontrivial p-group has more than one element. (Hint: consider the class equation.)

**28. Prove that there can exist no simple [see Problem 28 of § 4.9] group of order (a) 30; (b) 200.

29. If $\mathcal{P}$ is a Sylow p-subgroup of a group $\mathcal{G}$, prove that $N(\mathcal{P})/\mathcal{P}$ has no element $(\neq 1)$ whose order is a power of p.

30. Let $\mathcal{P}$ be a Sylow p-subgroup of a group $\mathcal{G}$, such that $a^{-1}\mathcal{P}a = \mathcal{P}$ for some element $a \in \mathcal{G}$. Then prove that $a \in \mathcal{P}$ if the order of a is a power of p. (Hint: consider the natural homomorphism $f: N(\mathcal{P}) \to N(\mathcal{P})/\mathcal{P}$, and use Problem 29.)

31. If $\mathcal{G}$ is a group of permutations on a set X, prove that the cardinality of each orbit of $\mathcal{G}$ divides the order of $\mathcal{G}$. (Hint: Consider $[\mathcal{G} : S_x]$, where S_x is the stabilizer of x.)

32. If $\alpha : \mathcal{P} \to S_n$ is a homomorphism of a p-group $\mathcal{P}$ into the symmetric group S_n, use the result in Problem 31 to show that the cardinality of each orbit of $\alpha(\mathcal{P})$ is a power of p.

33. Use the following plan, patterned after the presentation in [8], to prove the Second and Third Sylow theorems. We assume the First Sylow theorem, and the existence of a Sylow p-subgroup $\mathcal{P}$ of any group $\mathcal{G}$ of order n divisible by p.
    (a) Let $X = \{\mathcal{P} = \mathcal{P}_1, \mathcal{P}_2, \ldots, \mathcal{P}_r\}$ be the set of conjugates of $\mathcal{P}$ in $\mathcal{G}$, and

define the permutation $\alpha_a : X \to X$, where $\alpha_a(\mathscr{P}_j) = a^{-1}\mathscr{P}_j a$, $a \in \mathscr{G}$. Then prove that the mapping $\alpha : a \to \alpha_a$ is a homomorphism of $\mathscr{G}$ into S_r.

(b) The homomorphism α induces a homomorphism α' of $\mathscr{P}$ into S_r and, by Problem 32, the cardinality of each orbit of $\alpha'(\mathscr{P})$ is a power of p.

(c) Use Problem 30 to argue that there is a unique orbit of $\alpha'(\mathscr{P})$ with cardinality 1, all others cardinalities some nontrivial power of p. Hence, $r \equiv 1 \pmod{p}$.

(d) Tentatively assume the existence of a Sylow p-subgroup $\mathscr{P}' \neq \mathscr{P}_i$, $i = 1, 2, \ldots, r$, and consider the homomorphism $\alpha'' : \mathscr{P}' \to S_r$ induced by α on $\mathscr{P}'$. Argue that there is no orbit of $\alpha''(\mathscr{P}')$ with cardinality 1, whence $r \equiv 0 \pmod{p}$. This is a contradiction, and hence we have the Second Sylow theorem.

(e) Use Theorem 4.91 to see that $r \mid n$. Parts (c) and (e) complete the Third Sylow theorem.

4.14. A Brief Survey

In this final section of our chapter on elementary group theory, we wish to call attention to some further results, and make a few comments on the present status of the study of groups. The first of the topics, to which we make brief reference here, is that of *subinvariant series*; and it is this topic which, along with direct products, is often of use in the analysis of a given group—to follow up a remark made earlier.

Every group has at least two normal subgroups—the group itself and the subgroup consisting of the identity element alone. If a group has no other normal subgroups, we have called the group *simple*. The other extreme to a simple group is the case where every subgroup is normal, and we have called a group of this kind *hamiltonian*. The student was asked to verify, in Problem 6 of § 4.13, that *the quaternion group Q is hamiltonian* while it can be shown (for instance, see page 45 of [8]) that *the alternating group A_n is simple if $n \geq 5$*. A normal subgroup $\mathscr{K}$ of a group $\mathscr{G}$ is said to be *maximal* in $\mathscr{G}$ if $\mathscr{K} \lhd \mathscr{G}$, and no normal subgroup $\mathscr{K}$ of $\mathscr{G}$ exists such that $\mathscr{K} \lhd \mathscr{K} \lhd \mathscr{G}$. It can be shown rather easily that $\mathscr{K}$ is maximal in $\mathscr{G}$ if and only if the factor group $\mathscr{G}/\mathscr{K}$ is simple [Problem 13].

A *normal* series for a group $\mathscr{G}$ is a finite sequence of subgroups $\mathscr{G}_0 = \mathscr{G}$, $\mathscr{G}_1, \mathscr{G}_2, \ldots, \mathscr{G}_{r-1}, \mathscr{G}_r = 1$, such that $\mathscr{G} \rhd \mathscr{G}_1 \rhd \mathscr{G}_2 \rhd \cdots \rhd \mathscr{G}_{r-1} \rhd 1$, *with each subgroup normal in $\mathscr{G}$*. A less restrictive type of series arises if $\mathscr{G}_i$ is merely required to be normal in $\mathscr{G}_{i-1}, i = 1, 2 \ldots, r$, in which case it is said to be a *subnormal* or *subinvariant* series for $\mathscr{G}$. (The student is warned that some writers refer to this special kind of series as "normal".) The factor groups $\mathscr{G}/\mathscr{G}_1, \mathscr{G}_1/\mathscr{G}_2, \ldots, \mathscr{G}_{r-1}/1$ are called the *factors* of the above series. If each $\mathscr{G}_i$ is maximal in $\mathscr{G}_{i-1}$, the subinvariant series is called a *composition series*, i.e., a *composition series* is a subinvariant series which cannot be lengthened. Every group has at leat one subinvariant series—whose members are the whole group and the identity subgroup—but not every (infinite) group has a composition series. It is clear, of course, that every finite group does have a composition series. The following theorem, which we state without proof, is one of the important results in basic group theory.

Theorem 4.141. (*Jordan-Hölder*). *The number of terms in any two composition series for a given group is the same, and the factors of the two series are isomorphic in some order.*

Note that a group may have distinct composition series, but it is their *length* and *set of factors* which are the invariants of the group.

> ***Example.*** With V, as usual, designating the four-group and A_4 the alternating group on 4 symbols, we have seen before that $V \lhd A_4$ and $A_4 \lhd S_4$. Since V is abelian, and is the direct product of two cyclic subgroups of order 2—both of which are trivially normal in V—the following is an example of a subinvariant series: $1 \lhd C_2 \lhd V \lhd A_4 \lhd S_4$. In fact, if we note the index of each subgroup of this series in the next larger (sub)group, it is clear that this series is a composition series. The factors $C_2/1$, V/C_2, A_4/V, and S_4/A_4 are isomorphic, respectively, to C_2, C_2, C_3, and C_2 [Problem 3]. The Jordan-Hölder theorem then asserts that *any* composition series for S_4 must involve 5 terms, and the associated factor groups are: three which are isomorphic to C_2, and one which is isomorphic to C_3.

It should be clear that the existence of a composition series for a group makes the group somewhat more transparent, for we can see its internal structure more easily by examining its factors. If it should happen that the factors of any composition series of a group are all *cyclic* groups, the group belongs to a very select class of groups called *solvable*. (There is some variation in the usage of the word "solvable", and the reader should be aware of this.) From the analysis in the above example, it is clear that S_4 is a solvable group. One of the many beautiful applications of group theory is to the theory of equations, and it is to this application that the name "solvable" owes its origin. With every algebraic equation with real coefficients, there is associated a *group of automorphisms*—the so-called *galois group* of the equation. The mathematician Évariste Galois (1811–1832), before being vanquished in a duel over a love affair, was able to prove that an equation is solvable by radicals only if its galois group is a solvable group. The mathematics leading to this result is known as the *galois theory of equations* [See § 7.9]. It is possible to find a polynomial equation with rational coefficients, whose galois group is not solvable, for every degree in excess of 4. (This was shown by a contemporary of Galois, the mathematician Abel (1802–1829) for the case of degree

5.) Thus, we have the following important result: *Polynomial equations of degree n, with rational coefficients, are not, in general, solvable by radicals if* $n \geq 5$. It should be well known to the reader, of course, that there are many equations of degree 5 or greater which *are* solvable by radicals, but in essence the above result asserts that there can be no *formula*—similar to the "quadratic formula"—for such a solution, with the formula involving only radicals.

During our discussion of the decomposition of a group into an internal direct product in § 4.12, the astute student may have noted that we made no mention there of uniqueness. Our assertions were always of an "existence" type, leaving the possibility of different decompositions an open question. Actually, for the case of finite groups, the decompositions which we obtained in § 4.12 are unique, but this is the result of a somewhat difficult theorem beyond the scope of this book. The theorem applies to certain types of infinite groups, as well as to finite groups, but we restrict our statement of the theorem to the finite case.

Theorem 4.142 (Remak–Krull–Schmidt). *Let* $\mathcal{G} = \mathcal{H}_1 \times \mathcal{H}_2 \times \cdots \times \mathcal{H}_s = \mathcal{K}_1 \times \mathcal{K}_2 \cdots \times \mathcal{K}_t$ *be two decompositions of a finite group* $\mathcal{G}$ *into indecomposable groups. Then* $s = t$, *and it is possible to reindex the subgroups so that* $\mathcal{H}_i \cong \mathcal{K}_i$, *for all i, and* $\mathcal{G} = \mathcal{H}_1 \times \cdots \times \mathcal{H}_r \times \mathcal{K}_{r+1} \times \cdots \times \mathcal{K}_t$, *for* $1 \leq r \leq s$.

Note that the result does not state merely that the direct factors are uniquely determined up to an isomorphism: it is even possible to replace factors of one decomposition by factors of the other. The interested student can find a proof of this theorem in most of the books listed at the end of this chapter—for example, on page 81 of [8].

We have implied by earlier results that the theory of *finite* abelian groups is quite satisfactorily complete. However, the two recent books on general abelian groups (see [3] and [5]) indicate that the situation is somewhat different for abelian groups of the infinite variety. As for the theory of general abstract groups, the situation is again radically different, with many simply-stated problems still unvolved. For example, the following *Burnside* problem remains open, although considerable work has been done on it: is every finitely generated periodic group finite? Another unanswered query is: Do there exist infinite nonabelian groups whose proper subgroups are all finite? The theory of groups is currently a very active branch of mathematical research, and very recently an important "classical" problem was solved by Thompson and Feit [*Pac. J. Math.*, **13** (1963), 775–1029]: the order of any finite nonabelian simple group is an even number. We have only "scratched the surface" of group theory in this chapter, but the interested student is encouraged to consult one of the several fine references, which we list on this topic, for his further study.

PROBLEMS 4–14

1. Explain why the series in the Example is not a normal series for S_4.
2. Find a normal series for S_4, different from the trivial one: $1 \lhd S_4$ [see Problem 1].
*3. Verify that the factor groups in the Example are the indicated cyclic groups.
4. Write down an equation of degree 5, with rational coefficients, which is "solvable by radicals" with the introduction of exactly two "radicals."
5. While isomorphic groups clearly have isomorphic composition factors, if these exist, use an example to show that groups with isomorphic composition factors are not necessarily isomorphic. (Hint: consider groups of order 4.)
6. If a group $\mathcal{G}$ has a direct decomposition $\mathcal{G} = \mathcal{G}_1 \times \mathcal{G}_2 \times \mathcal{G}_3$, where $o(\mathcal{G}_1) = 2$, $o(\mathcal{G}_2) = 4$, $o(\mathcal{G}_3) = 5$, find two other direct decompositions of $\mathcal{G}$. Explain why this does not violate the Remak–Krull–Schmidt theorem.
7. Find a composition series, and its composition factors, for a cyclic group of order 8.
8. Find a composition series, and its composition factors, for a cyclic group of order 30.
9. Find a composition series, and its composition factors, for a cyclic group of order 36.
10. Find three direct decompositions of an abelian group of order 100 [see Problem 6].
11. Show that the additive group $\mathbf{Z}$ can have no composition series.
12. Explain why no infinite cyclic group can have a composition series [see Problem 11].
13. Prove that a normal subgroup $\mathcal{K}$ of a group $\mathcal{G}$ is maximal if and only if $\mathcal{G}/\mathcal{K}$ is simple.
**14. Check the truth of the Jordan-Hölder theorem by considering two distinct composition series for the cyclic group C_{30} [see Problem 8].
15. Explain why every cyclic group is solvable.
16. Explain why every abelian group of finite order is solvable. (An alternative definition of "solvable" requires only that the factors of any composition series be *abelian*.
17. It is known that A_n is simple for $n \geq 5$, so that a composition series for S_n is $1 \lhd A_n \lhd S_n$. Explain why this proves that S_n, $n \geq 5$, is not solvable.
**18. Prove that the factor group $\mathcal{G}/\mathcal{G}'$ is abelian, for any group $\mathcal{G}$ and its derived group or commutator subgroup $\mathcal{G}'$ [see Problem 29 of § 4.9]. Also show that, if $\mathcal{K}$ is a normal subgroup such that $\mathcal{G}/\mathcal{K}$ is abelian, $\mathcal{G}' \subset \mathcal{K}$.
19. Prove that every subgroup and every factor group of a solvable group is solvable.
20. If we extend the use of the words "permutation" and "alternating subgroup" to apply to denumerably infinite sets, verify that the permutations $b_i = (4i-3 \quad 4i-2)(4i-1 \quad 4i)$, $i = 1, 2, 3, \ldots$ generate an infinite abelian group which is a subgroup of the alternating group on the set of all natural numbers. If we accept the fact that this alternating group is simple [cf. Problem 17], show that we have illustrated the fact that a group can have a composition series while one of its subgroups does not. Explain why this does not violate the result in Problem 19.
21. Show that the "Thompson and Feit" result, referred to in the text, is equivalent to the statement that *every group of odd order is solvable*.

References

[1] BIRKHOFF, G., and MACLANE, S.: *A Survey of Modern Algebra,* Third Edition (New York, Macmillan, 1965).

[2] BURNSIDE, W.: *The Theory of Groups of Finite Order* (New York, Cambridge University Press, 1911).

[3] FUCHS, L.: *Abelian Groups* (Publishing House of The Hungarian Academy of Sciences, Budapest, 1958).

[4] HALL, M.: *The Theory of Groups* (New York, Macmillan, 1959).

[5] KAPLANSKY, I.: *Infinite Abelian Groups* (Ann Arbor, University of Michigan Press, 1954).

[6] KUROSH, A.: *Theory of Groups,* Vol. 1 (New York, Chelsea, 1955).

[7] LEDERMANN, W.: *The Theory of Finite Groups* (New York, Interscience Publishers, 1953).

[8] ROTMAN, J.: *The Theory of Groups* (Boston, Allyn and Bacon, 1965).

[9] SCOTT, W.: *Group Theory* (Englewood Cliffs, Prentice-Hall, 1964).

[10] WIELANDT, H.: *Finite Permutation Groups* (New York, Academic Press, 1964).

Selected Readings from The American Mathematical Monthly

BALL, R. W.: *On the Order of an Element in a Group,* **71** (1964), 784–785.

DESKINS, W. E. and HILL, J. D.: *On the Definition of a Group,* **68** (1961), 795–796.

EVANS, T.: *A Condition for a Group to be Commutative,* **68** (1961), 898–899.

HABER, S. and ROSENFELD, A.: *Groups as Unions of Proper Subgroups,* **66** (1959), 491–494.

JACOBSON, R. A.: *Absolutely Independent Axioms for Abelian Groups,* **72** (1965), 991–993.

JACOBSON, R. A. and YOCOM, K. L.: *Absolutely Independent Group Axioms,* **72** (1965), 756–758.

JOHNSON, C., Jr.: *A Mixed Non-Group,* **71** (1964), 785.

MCHAFFEY, R.: *Isomorphism of Finite Abelian Groups,* **72** (1965), 48–50.

MORGADO, J.: *A Single Axiom for Groups,* **72** (1965), 981–982.

ROSENBAUM, R. A.: *Some Simple Examples of Groups,* **66** (1959), 902–905.

SCHENKMAN, E.: *The Basis Theorem for Finitely Generated Abelian Groups,* **67** (1960), 770–771.

SCHENKMAN, E. and WADE, L. I.: *The Mapping which takes each Element of a Group onto its nth Power,* **65** (1958), 33–34.

SLATER, M.: *A Single Postulate for Groups,* **68**, (1961), 346–347.

WHITTAKER, J. V.: *On the Postulates Defining a Group,* **62** (1955), 636–640.

WYMAN, J. W.: *Another Mixed Nongroup,* **73** (1966), 397.

5 *Rings*

5.1. Definition and Examples

In this chapter we study an important type of algebraic system with two binary operations, which is known as a *ring*. Some of the examples, which we have used previously in illustrations of simpler systems, have actually been rings, but at that time we were interested in only one of their binary operations. The foremost example of this usage is the system of integers, with the two operations of ordinary addition and multiplication. A consideration of some of the properties of this system, and of others like it, leads us to the following definition.

Definition. A *ring* $\mathcal{R}$ is an algebraic system in which an identity relation (=) and two binary operations (designated as addition and multiplication) have been defined, such that
1. $\mathcal{R}$ is an additive abelian group;
2. $\mathcal{R}$ is a multiplicative semigroup;
3. the following distributive laws hold for arbitrary elements a, b, $c \in \mathcal{R}$:

$$a(b + c) = ab + ac;$$
$$(b + c)a = ba + ca.$$

If we regard $\mathcal{R}$ as simply an additive group, with no attention paid to the operation of multiplication, it is convenient to speak of this group as *the additive group of the ring* $\mathcal{R}$. It is easy to see that every abelian group $\mathcal{G}$ is the additive group of a ring: for we have merely to retain the (additive) group

138

operation and introduce a trivial operation of multiplication into $\mathcal{G}$ so that $ab = 0$, for arbitrary $a, b \in \mathcal{G}$. Since the distributive laws hold in this new system, it is a ring and its additive group is $\mathcal{G}$. Such a ring is sometimes called a *zero ring*, and these rings play a role in the theory of rings which parallels that of abelian groups in the theory of groups. A special case of this occurs when $\mathcal{R}$ contains the additive zero as its only element, and we shall refer to this trivial ring as *the zero ring* and designate it as 0. Our definition implies the existence in any ring $\mathcal{R}$ of the additive identity 0, and the additive inverse $-a$ for any $a \in \mathcal{R}$. If a subset of $\mathcal{R}$ is closed under both operations of $\mathcal{R}$, and also satisfies conditions **1, 2, 3** as a subsystem, this subsystem is called a *subring* of $\mathcal{R}$. Every ring contains 0 as one of its subrings.

We recall that $a - b$ is an equivalent notation for $a + (-b)$, and we have the following simple but important extension of Theorem 4.51.

Theorem 5.11. *A subset $\mathcal{B}$ of a ring is a subring of $\mathcal{R}$ if and only if $a - b$ and ab are in $\mathcal{B}$, for arbitrary elements a, b in $\mathcal{B}$.*

Proof. Since a subset of the additive group of a ring is a subgroup provided $a - b$ is in the subset, for arbitrary elements a, b in the subset, it follows that $\mathcal{B}$ is an additive subgroup as desired. We are postulating that $\mathcal{B}$ is closed under the multiplicative operation in $\mathcal{R}$, and since associativity of multiplication and the validity of the distributive laws are inherited from $\mathcal{R}$, it follows from our definition that $\mathcal{B}$ is a subring. ∎

Let us now develop some familiarity with the ring concept through the medium of a few examples.

1. We have previously referred to the most familiar example, that of the ring **Z** of rational integers under addition and multiplication. The rational, real, and complex numbers, with the usual operations, are other familiar rings. Moreover, in this chapter, we shall often refer to these number systems as rings without further verification [see Problem 7].

2. The set $\mathbf{Z}[\sqrt{2}]$ of real numbers of the form $a + b\sqrt{2}$, with a and b rational integers, is a ring with the usual operations of real numbers. Actually this system is a subring of **R**, as can be verified with the help of Theorem 5.11. For $(a + b\sqrt{2}) - (c + d\sqrt{2}) = (a - c) + (b - d)\sqrt{2}$ and $(a + b\sqrt{2})(c + d\sqrt{2}) = (ac + 2bd) + (bc + ad)\sqrt{2}$, for arbitrary integers a, b, c, d, and so the system is closed under subtraction and multiplication. The method used to show that the system in this example is a ring is an important one, and so we emphasize the point: in order to show that a subsystem of a ring is a subring, not all the postulates need be checked;

a simple application of Theorem 5.11 is all that is necessary. On the other hand, if the subsystem is *not* contained in what is known to be a ring, it will be necessary to check the complete set of postulates.

3. The set of all real-valued, continuous functions on **R** is a ring if we define addition and multiplication for arbitrary functions f and g of the set by $(f+g)(x) = f(x) + g(x)$ and $(fg)(x) = f(x) \cdot g(x)$, for $x \in \mathbf{R}$. The 0 of this ring is the function whose value at each real number is 0, and $-f$ is the function defined so that $(-f)(x) = -f(x)$. While in a complete and detailed discussion it would be necessary to check all the postulates to verify that this system is a ring, this verification should cause no difficulty [Problem 3].

4. The set of rational integers forms a ring $\mathbf{Z}_n$ under the operations of ordinary addition and ordinary multiplication followed by reduction modulo n, for any positive integer n [see Example 2 of § 4.3]. The verification that this is a ring is almost immediate [see Problem 4].

5. If $\mathcal{A}$ is an arbitrary ring, we can define the system $M_n(\mathcal{A})$ of all $n \times n$ (read "n by n") matrices from the ring $\mathcal{A}$. The matrices or elements of $M_n(\mathcal{A})$ are the arrays $[a_{ij}]$ of the form

$$[a_{ij}] = \begin{bmatrix} a_{11} & a_{12} & \dots & a_{1n} \\ a_{21} & a_{22} & \dots & a_{2n} \\ \dots & \dots & \dots & \dots \\ a_{n1} & a_{n2} & \dots & a_{nn} \end{bmatrix},$$

each of which consists of n (horizontal) *rows* and n (vertical) *columns* of elements a_{ij} from $\mathcal{A}$. The *order* of such a matrix is n. In this notation, a_{ij} is the entry in the matrix $[a_{ij}]$ that lies at the intersection of the ith row and jth column. For example, a_{11} is at the intersection of the first row and first column, while a_{21} is at the intersection of the second row and first column, etc.

Two matrices in $M_n(\mathcal{A})$ are *equal* if corresponding entries in the matrices are equal elements of $\mathcal{A}$. That is, $[a_{ij}] = [b_{ij}]$ if $a_{ij} = b_{ij}$, for all i and j from 1 to n. This is our customary usage of equality in the sense of identity.

We define the *addition* or *sum* of two matrices to be the matrix obtained by adding corresponding entries in the component matrices. This means that $[a_{ij}] + [b_{ij}] = [c_{ij}]$, where $c_{ij} = a_{ij} + b_{ij}$, for $i, j = 1, 2, 3, \dots, n$. It is then easy to see that $M_n(\mathcal{A})$ is an abelian group under addition. Since we have defined addition for any two $n \times n$ matrices, this operation is properly defined in $M_n(\mathcal{A})$; moreover, associativity of addition in $\mathcal{A}$ is carried over to $M_n(\mathcal{A})$ by the rule of operation. The additive identity, or *zero matrix*, is the matrix all of whose entries are 0; while the additive inverse of any matrix $[a_{ij}]$ is clearly the matrix whose entries are the respective negatives of the entries in $[a_{ij}]$. There is, of course, a different zero matrix associated with each n, but it is convenient to designate them all by 0 or, in case of confusion, by 0_n. We illustrate this symbolism in the 2×2 case below.

$$\text{If } [a_{ij}] = \begin{bmatrix} a_{11} & a_{12} \\ a_{21} & a_{22} \end{bmatrix} \text{ and } [b_{ij}] = \begin{bmatrix} b_{11} & b_{12} \\ b_{21} & b_{22} \end{bmatrix}, \text{ we have}$$

$$[a_{ij}] + [b_{ij}] = \begin{bmatrix} a_{11} + b_{11} & a_{12} + b_{12} \\ a_{21} + b_{21} & a_{22} + b_{22} \end{bmatrix}, \quad -[a_{ij}] = \begin{bmatrix} -a_{11} & -a_{12} \\ -a_{21} & -a_{22} \end{bmatrix},$$

$$\text{and } 0 = 0_2 = \begin{bmatrix} 0 & 0 \\ 0 & 0 \end{bmatrix}.$$

The product $[p_{ij}]$ of two $n \times n$ matrices $[a_{ij}]$ and $[b_{ij}]$ is defined so that $p_{ij} = a_{i1}b_{1j} + a_{i2}b_{2j} + \cdots + a_{in}b_{nj}$ is the element in the (i, j)-position. This is sometimes referred to as the "row by column" rule of matrix multiplication, since the elements of the rows of $[a_{ij}]$ are multiplied, respectively, by the corresponding elements of the columns of $[b_{ij}]$, and these products are then added to obtain the elements of the matrix product $[a_{ij}][b_{ij}]$. For example, in the system $M_3(\mathbf{Z})$ of 3×3 matrices with entries in the ring $\mathbf{Z}$ of integers, the following matrix product is obtained by applying this rule:

$$\begin{bmatrix} 1 & 3 & -1 \\ 2 & 1 & 0 \\ 3 & -1 & 2 \end{bmatrix} \begin{bmatrix} 2 & 0 & 1 \\ 3 & -2 & 0 \\ 1 & 1 & 1 \end{bmatrix} = \begin{bmatrix} 10 & -7 & 0 \\ 7 & -2 & 2 \\ 5 & 4 & 5 \end{bmatrix}.$$

It is easy to see that multiplication is associative, for consider the product $[a_{ik}]([b_{kl}][c_{lj}])$ of matrices $[a_{ik}]$, $[b_{kl}]$, and $[c_{lj}]$, where it has been convenient to change the indexing symbols in the manner indicated, The rule for multiplication shows that the entry of the product in the (i, j)-position is $\sum_{k, l=1}^{n} a_{ik}(b_{kl}c_{lj})$. The corresponding entry of the product $([a_{ik}][b_{kl}])[c_{lj}]$ is $\sum_{k, l=1}^{n} (a_{ik}b_{kl})c_{lj}$, and because multiplication is associative in $\mathcal{A}$, these two entries are the same. Hence $[a_{ik}]([b_{kl}][c_{lj}]) = ([a_{ik}][b_{kl}])[c_{lj}]$, so that the associative law holds for multiplication in $M_n(\mathcal{A})$. (If the student finds the notation for the above summations a little condensed, he should let $n = 3$, say, and actually write out several such sums in detail [Problem 1].) The distributive laws in $M_n(\mathcal{A})$ can be verified in a similar manner. For, if we consider the matrices $[a_{ik}]([b_{kj}] + [c_{kj}])$ and $[a_{ik}][b_{kj}] + [a_{ik}][c_{kj}]$, it can be seen that the entry in the (i, j)-position for the first matrix is $\sum_{k=1}^{n} a_{ik}(b_{kj} + c_{kj})$, while for the second matrix it is $\sum_{k=1}^{n} a_{ik}b_{kj} + \sum_{k=1}^{n} a_{ik}c_{kj}$. Since the distributive laws hold in $\mathcal{A}$, these two elements are equal, and so $[a_{ik}]([b_{kj}] + [c_{kj}]) = [a_{ik}][b_{kj}] + [a_{ik}][c_{kj}]$, thus showing that this distributive law also holds in $M_n(\mathcal{A})$. In a similar manner, it can be shown that $([b_{ik}] + [c_{ik}])[a_{kj}] = [b_{ik}][a_{kj}] + [c_{ik}][a_{kj}]$, so that the other distributive law also remains in effect in $M_n(\mathcal{A})$.

We have shown that $M_n(\mathcal{A})$ is an abelian group under addition and a semi-group under multiplication, with both distributive laws holding, so that $M_n(\mathcal{A})$ is a ring. Even if the multiplication semigroup of $\mathcal{A}$ is commutative, the ring $M_n(\mathcal{A})$ will not have this property, however, except when $n = 1$. It is easy to check the "probable" truth of this remark with a random pair of 3×3 matrices of integers.

PROBLEMS 5–1

*1. Write out each of the following sums completely:

   (a) $\sum\limits_{k,l=1}^{3} (a_{ik}b_{kl})c_{lj}$;   (b) $\sum\limits_{k,l=1}^{3} a_{ik}(b_{kl}c_{lj})$.

2. List the nine individual postulates for a ring.

*3. Verify that the system in Example 3 is a ring.

*4. Make addition and multiplication tables for the ring in Example 4, with $n = 4$.

5. Verify that the system containing two elements 0, 1, and having the following addition and multiplication tables, is a ring.

+	0	1		·	0	1
---	---	---		---	---	---
0	0	1		0	0	0
1	1	0		1	0	1

6. If we define multiplication in Example 3 by $(fg)(x) = f[g(x)]$, is the resulting system a ring?

*7. Verify that the complex numbers form a ring which contains the real numbers and rational numbers as subrings.

8. Prove that the system of even integers constitutes a subring of $\mathbf{Z}$.

9. Prove that the system of all integral multiples of *any* integer constitutes a subring of $\mathbf{Z}$.

10. Refer to Example 2, and prove that the system $\mathbf{Z}[\sqrt{3}]$ is a subring of both $\mathbf{Q}[\sqrt{3}]$ and $\mathbf{R}$.

11. If $a = \begin{bmatrix} 2 & 3 & 0 \\ 1 & 1 & 3 \\ -2 & 2 & -1 \end{bmatrix}$ and $b = \begin{bmatrix} -2 & 3 & 1 \\ 4 & 0 & 6 \\ 1 & 1 & 5 \end{bmatrix}$,

   determine both ab and ba.

12. If $c = \begin{bmatrix} 1 & 1 & 1 \\ -2 & 3 & 0 \\ 3 & 5 & 6 \end{bmatrix}$, use the matrices in Problem 11 to verify that

   $a(b + c) = ab + ac$ and $(b + c)a = ba + ca$.

**13. A Gaussian integer is a complex number $a + bi$, where a and b are rational integers. Show that the set of Gaussian integers forms a ring under ordinary addition and multiplication of complex numbers.

*14. An element a of a ring $\mathcal{R}$ is said to be *idempotent* if $a^2 = a$. If all elements of $\mathcal{R}$ are idempotent, prove that $xy = yx$ for any $x, y \in \mathcal{R}$. (Hint: Consider $(x + x)^2$ and $(x + y)^2$.]

15. Let $\mathcal{R}$ be a ring of idempotent elements [see Problem 14], such that if $2a = 0$, for some $a \in \mathcal{R}$, then $a = 0$. Prove that $\mathcal{R}$ consists of exactly one element.

16. If n is a positive integer, with a, b arbitrary elements of a ring $\mathcal{R}$, derive the " binomial expansion " for $(a + b)^n$.

17. If $\mathcal{A}$ and $\mathcal{B}$ are rings, prove that $\mathcal{A} \times \mathcal{B}$ is a ring if we define addition and multiplication in the product set as follows:
$$(a_1, b_1) + (a_2, b_2) = (a_1 + a_2, b_1 + b_2), (a_1, b_1)(a_2, b_2) = (a_1 a_2, b_1 b_2).$$

18. Prove that the subsystem of $M_n(\mathcal{A})$ in Example 5, consisting of all matrices $[a_{ij}]$ with $a_{ij} = 0$, $i \neq j$, is a subring of $M_n(\mathcal{A})$. This is the subring of *diagonal* matrices.

**19. For any ring $\mathcal{R}$, prove that $C(\mathcal{R}) = \{c \in \mathcal{R} \mid ca = ac, a \in \mathcal{R}\}$ is a subring of $\mathcal{R}$. This subring is called the *center* of $\mathcal{R}$.

20. Let $\mathcal{G}$ be an abelian group, and prove that the set of all endomorphisms $f: \mathcal{G} \to \mathcal{G}$ is a ring, using the usual rules for the addition and multiplication of two mappings. This ring is often designated Hom $(\mathcal{G}, \mathcal{G})$.

21. Let $\mathcal{R} = P(S)$ be the set of all subsets (i.e., the power set) of a set S. Then define $A + B = A \cup B - A \cap B$ and $AB = A \cap B$, for arbitrary subsets $A, B \in \mathcal{R}$, and prove that $\mathcal{R}$ is a ring.

22. Let $\mathcal{L}$ be the set of all complex-valued functions on $\mathbf{R}$, with $f \in \mathcal{L}$ said to be *absolutely integrable* if $\int_{-\infty}^{\infty} |f(t)| \, dt$ is finite. The *convolution* of two functions f and g is the function $f * g$ defined so that $(f * g)(t) = \int_{-\infty}^{\infty} f(t - \lambda) g(\lambda) \, d\lambda$, for each $t \in \mathcal{R}$. Prove that $\mathcal{L}$ is a ring under ordinary addition and the convolution of functions—the latter regarded as " multiplication "—*assuming* that $\mathcal{L}$ is closed under the operation of convolution [see Problem 23].

23. If the multiplication of two functions is defined as in Example 3, use an example to show that the set $\mathcal{L}$ in Problem 22 is not closed under *this* operation. (Hint: define f and g so that $f(t) = g(t) = 1/\sqrt{t}$, $0 < t \leq 1$; $f(t) = g(t) = 0$, otherwise.)

5.2. Some Elementary Properties of Rings

Several of the elementary properties of rings are consequences of the fact that a ring is a group under the operation of addition, and a semigroup under the operation of multiplication. We have already noted that every ring contains the element 0, and the additive inverses or " negatives " of elements of the ring. In addition, it is a consequence of the additive group properties that

$-(a + b) = -a - b$, and $-(a - b) = -a + b$. Also, since integral multiples in a ring are defined as for group elements in Chapter 4, it has been established that $n(a + b) = na + nb$, $(n + m)a = na + ma$, and $(nm)a = n(ma)$, for arbitrary ring elements a, b and arbitrary integers m, n. The following theorem lists some further simple properties of ring elements, properties which are familiar in the ring of integers.

Theorem 5.21. *The equations* $a0 = 0a = 0$, $(-a)b = a(-b) = -ab$, *and* $(-a)(-b) = ab$ *are valid for arbitrary elements* a, b *of a ring.*

Proof. If a is a ring element, the distributive laws imply that $a(0 + 0) = a0 + a0$, and also that $0a = (0 + 0)a = 0a + 0a$. Hence, $0a = a0 = 0$ [see Problem 7 of Problems 4.1]. If b is an arbitrary ring element, $[a + (-a)]b = 0 = ab + (-a)b$, so that $(-a)b = -ab$. In like manner we can show that $a(-b) = -ab$. A combination of these results then gives $(-a)(-b) = -a(-b) = -(-ab) = ab$. ∎

The notions of *homormophism*, *isomorphism*, *endomorphism*, *epimorphism*, *monomorphism*, and *automorphism*, as applied to a ring, are merely the applications of these familiar ideas to its underlying additive group and multiplicative semigroup. Thus we say that a mapping of a ring $\mathcal{R}$ into a ring $\mathcal{R}'$ is a *homomorphism* if both operations are preserved by the mapping. In our usual symbolism, we can indicate this as follows.

$\mathcal{R}$		$\mathcal{R}'$
a	$\longrightarrow$	a'
b	$\longrightarrow$	b'
$a + b$	$\longrightarrow$	$a' + b'$
ab	$\longrightarrow$	$a'b'$

If $\mathcal{R}$ and $\mathcal{R}'$ are the same algebraic system, the homomorphism is known as an *endomorphism*. In case a homomorphic mapping is bijective, the mapping is an *isomorphism* and the rings $\mathcal{R}$ and $\mathcal{R}'$ are *isomorphic*; if $\mathcal{R}$ and $\mathcal{R}'$ are identical systems, any isomorphic mapping of $\mathcal{R}$ onto $\mathcal{R}'$ (i.e., $\mathcal{R}$) is an *automorphism* of $\mathcal{R}$. The meanings of *epimorphism* and *monomorphism*, as applied to rings, are the same as in other algebraic systems and need not be repeated.

An algebraic system $\mathcal{S}$ is said to be *imbedded* in a system $\mathcal{S}'$, provided $\mathcal{S}$ is isomorphic to a subsystem of $\mathcal{S}'$. While we may not have used the word before, the idea of "imbedding" has arisen many times in the past: for example, each of the number systems **N**, **Z**, **Q**, **R**, **C**, is *imbedded* in those systems written to the right of it; and if a group $\mathcal{G}$ is a direct product of subgroups, each of the direct factors may be considered to be *imbedded* in $\mathcal{G}$. The following theorem is an important "imbedding theorem" for rings.

Theorem 5.22. *If a ring $\mathcal{B}$ is isomorphic to a subring $\mathcal{B}'$ of a ring $\mathcal{A}'$, then $\mathcal{B}$ can be imbedded in a ring $\mathcal{A}$ which is isomorphic to $\mathcal{A}'$, provided $\mathcal{A}' \cap \mathcal{B} = \phi$.*

Proof. For let S be the subset of those elements in $\mathcal{A}'$ which are not in $\mathcal{B}'$ and designate by $\mathcal{A}$ the set consisting of the set-theoretic union of $\mathcal{B}$ and S, i.e., $\mathcal{A} = \mathcal{B} \cup S$. In any equations $a' + b' = c'$ or $a'b' = c'$ in $\mathcal{A}'$, we replace the elements a', b', c' which are in $\mathcal{B}'$ by their correspondents in $\mathcal{B}$, and leave the other elements of $\mathcal{A}'$ (i.e., the elements of S) unaltered. This defines the operations of addition and multiplication in $\mathcal{A}$, and it is clear that $\mathcal{A}$ is isomorphic to $\mathcal{A}'$. ∎

It is a simple matter to extend to rings some of the other ideas and terminology, originally introduced for groups or other more general systems. For example, it is easy to verify [Problem 12] that the *intersection* of any collection of subrings of a ring $\mathcal{R}$ is also a subring of $\mathcal{R}$. In particular, the intersection of all subrings of $\mathcal{R}$ which contain a subset S is the subring of $\mathcal{R}$ *generated by* S. It is not difficult to see what the structure of such a "generated" subring must be [Problem 13], and we shall use $[S]$ to designate this subring— extending the usage of a symbolism introduced earlier for groups. If $f: \mathcal{A} \to \mathcal{B}$ is a homomorphism of a ring $\mathcal{A}$ into a ring $\mathcal{B}$, it is a simple matter to verify [Problem 1] that the "image" $f(\mathcal{A})$ of $\mathcal{A}$ is a subring of $\mathcal{B}$. If we understand that the *kernel* of such a homomorphism f is $f^{-1}(0)$, i.e., the subset of $\mathcal{A}$ which is mapped onto the *additive* identity of $\mathcal{B}$, it is not difficult to prove that the kernel of f is a subring of $\mathcal{A}$ [Problem 2].

In the ring $\mathbf{Z}$ of integers, the additive order of any nonzero $b \in \mathbf{Z}$ is infinite: for $nb = 0$ if and only if $n = 0$. However, in the ring $\mathbf{Z}_n$ [see Example 4 of § 5.1] of integers modulo n, we know that $nb = 0$, for any $b \in \mathbf{Z}_n$, and so the order of b is a divisor of n. This idea leads us to the following concept which is of importance in the study of any ring.

Definition. If $\mathcal{R}$ is a ring such that $mx = 0$, for every $x \in \mathcal{R}$ and some positive integer m, the *least positive* integer with this property is called the *characteristic* of $\mathcal{R}$; and $\mathcal{R}$ is said to have *positive characteristic n* if n is this least integer. If no such n exists, then $\mathcal{R}$ is said to have characteristic 0 (or ∞, as some prefer).

It may be in order to caution the student here again that nx means $x + x + \cdots + x$, with n summands, and—except in special cases—cannot be considered the product of n and x. The notion of "characteristic" is so important in the theory of rings and fields that this theory usually splits into two separate cases: characteristic n; chatacteristic 0. This will be clarified somewhat in the next section. For the most part in this book, however, we shall be concerned with the more common "characteristic 0" case.

PROBLEMS 5–2

*1. If $f: \mathcal{A} \to \mathcal{B}$ is a homomorphism of a ring $\mathcal{A}$ into a ring $\mathcal{B}$, prove that $f(\mathcal{A})$ is a subring of $\mathcal{B}$.

**2. Prove that the kernel of f, in Problem 1, is a subring of $\mathcal{A}$.

3. If n is an integer and a is an element of a ring, why must na not be considered the ring product of n and a unless a is an integer?

**4. Show that $(a + b)(c + d) = ac + ad + bc + bd$, where a, b, c, d are arbitrary elements of a ring.

*5. If a, b, c are arbitrary elements of a ring, prove that $a(b - c) = ab - ac$.

*6. If a and b are arbitrary ring elements and n is an integer, prove that $n(ab) = (na)b = a(nb)$.

7. Prove that the postulate that the additive group of a ring is abelian can be replaced by the condition that there exists an element c in the system, such that $ca = cb$ implies that $a = b$ for arbitrary elements a, b of the ring. That is, show that the existence of an element that can be left-cancelled will imply that the additive group of the ring is abelian.

8. Make a complete multiplication table for the ring of integers modulo 5.

9. Let $\mathcal{A} \times \mathcal{B}$ be the ring described in Problem 17 of § 5.1. Then prove that the mappings ϕ and ψ of this ring, defined by $(a, b)\phi = (a, 0)$ and $(a, b)\psi = (0, b)$, are homomorphisms.

10. If $\mathcal{A}$ is an arbitrary ring, prove that the mapping $\begin{bmatrix} a & c \\ d & b \end{bmatrix} \to a$ of $M_2(\mathcal{A})$ onto $\mathcal{A}$ is not a ring homomorphism, but is a homomorphism of the underlying additive group of $M_2(\mathcal{A})$.

11. Prove that the only endomorphisms of the ring $\mathbf{Z}$ of integers are the identity mapping and the mapping that sends each integer into 0. (Hint: recall that $n = 1 + 1 + 1 + \cdots + 1$ (n summands), for any positive integer n.)

*12. Prove that the intersection of any collection of subrings of a ring $\mathcal{R}$ is a subring of $\mathcal{R}$.

13. Describe the subring $[S]$ generated by a subset S of a ring $\mathcal{R}$.

14. Describe the subring $[2, 3]$, generated in $\mathbf{Z}$ by the integers 2 and 3.

15. Try to generalize the result in Problem 14 to describe the subring $[a, b]$ generated by any two elements a, b of a ring $\mathcal{R}$.

16. Determine the characteristic of each of the following rings: (a) $\mathbf{Z}$; (b) $\mathbf{Z}_5$; (c) $M_n(\mathcal{A})$, where $\mathcal{A}$ is a ring of characteristic 7.

17. If a ring $\mathcal{R}$ has a prime characteristic p, prove that $(a + b)^p = a^p + b^p$ and $(a - b)^p = a^p - b^p$, for arbitrary a, $b \in \mathcal{R}$.

18. Review the meanings of the words "epimorphism" and "monomorphism" as they apply to rings. Give an example of each.

19. If f is the "defining" homomorphism of $\mathbf{Z}$ onto $\mathbf{Z}_n$, so that $f(b) = b'$, where b' is the class of integers having the same remainder as b when divided by n, determine the kernel of f.

20. If $xy = yx$, for elements x, y of a ring $\mathcal{R}$, prove that $f(x) \cdot f(y) = f(y) \cdot f(x)$ for any homomorphism f of $\mathcal{R}$.

21. If g is any endomorphism of a ring $\mathcal{R}$, prove that $\{x \in \mathcal{R} \mid g(x) = x\}$ is a subring of $\mathcal{R}$. This is known as the *subring of fixed elements* of g.

22. Determine all idempotent elements [see Problem 14 of § 5.1] of the rings Z_6 and Z_{12}.

23. Let h be a mapping of Z into Z, defined by $h(x) = 2x$, for any $x \in Z$. Then show that, while h is an endomorphism of the additive group of Z, it is not a ring endomorphism.

24. Prove that the set of all matrices of the form $\begin{bmatrix} a & b \\ 0 & 0 \end{bmatrix}$, with $a, b \in Z$, forms a subring of the ring $M_2(Z)$ of all 2×2 matrices over Z.

25. Find as many subrings as you can of the ring $M_2(\mathcal{R})$ of all 2×2 matrices over $\mathcal{R}$ [see Problem 24].

5.3. Types of Rings

We obtain rings of different types by imposing various conditions on the multiplicative semigroup of a ring. Thus a ring $\mathcal{R}$ is *commutative* if its multiplicative semigroup is commutative: $xy = yx$, for arbitrary x, $y \in \mathcal{R}$ [see Problems 14 and 20 of § 5.2]. A ring is said to *have an identity* if its multiplicative semigroup has an identity element and so is a multiplicative monoid. Since every ring has an *additive* identity, this usage of the word "identity" will always refer to the multiplicative system. In the event of any possible confusion, however, the words "additive" or "multiplicative" should be included. We shall designate the identity by 1, except when confusion may result—in which case e will be used. The ring Z of integers, as well as most of the other rings previously mentioned, is a commutative ring with an identity. The set of even integers, with the usual operations, is a simple example of a ring without an identity element. The ring $M_n(Z)$ of all $n \times n$ square matrices with elements in Z is an especially important example of a non-commutative ring, as we have already noted. This ring does have an identity element, however, and it is easily seen to be the matrix 1_n defined by

$$1_n = \begin{bmatrix} 1 & 0 & 0 \dots 0 \\ 0 & 1 & 0 \dots 0 \\ 0 & 0 & 1 \dots 0 \\ \dots\dots\dots\dots \\ 0 & 0 & 0 \dots 1 \end{bmatrix}, \text{ a matrix in which the diagonal element 1 occurs } n \text{ times,}$$

while all other elements are 0. If there is no danger of confusion, it will often be convenient to use the familiar 1 instead of 1_n. We note in passing that if $1 = 0$, in any ring $\mathcal{R}$, then $a = a1 = a0 = 0$, for an arbitrary element $a \in \mathcal{R}$, and so the ring $\mathcal{R}$ must be the trivial zero ring 0. Hence, the exclusion of this trivial ring is equivalent to the assumption that $1 \neq 0$.

An element $a(\neq 0)$ in a ring $\mathcal{R}$ is said to be a *divisor of zero* if there exists a nonzero element $b \in \mathcal{R}$ such that either $ab = 0$ or $ba = 0$. A ring $\mathcal{R}$ has no divisors of zero if and only if its nonzero elements form a multiplicative semigroup: for, if a and b are nonzero elements of $\mathcal{R}$, it follows that $ab \neq 0$ and $ba \neq 0$. A commutative ring with a unity element, but with no divisors of zero, is frequently called an *integral domain* while a subring with the same properties is called an *integral subdomain*. It is immediate that the ring $\mathbf{Z}$ of rational integers is an integral domain, and this important special system may be regarded as the model from which the general system derives its name. The student should be cautioned at this point, however, that the exact definition of an integral domain varies somewhat in the literature: several well-known authors merely require the absence of divisors of zero for a ring to be so identified.

The ring $M_n(\mathcal{A})$ of matrices is not an integral domain except when $n = 1$ and $\mathcal{A}$ itself is an integral domain. For example, in the ring $M_2(\mathbf{Z})$ we have $\begin{bmatrix} 0 & 1 \\ 0 & 1 \end{bmatrix} \begin{bmatrix} 2 & 3 \\ 0 & 0 \end{bmatrix} = \begin{bmatrix} 0 & 0 \\ 0 & 0 \end{bmatrix}$, so that the product of two nonzero matrices can be the zero matrix. As another example of a ring which is not an integral domain, we offer the ring of real-valued functions described in Example 3 of § 5.1. For consider the functions f and g defined on $\mathbf{R}$ as follows:

$$f(x) = 0, \text{ for } x \leq \tfrac{1}{4},$$
$$= x^2 - \tfrac{1}{16}, \text{ for } \tfrac{1}{4} < x;$$
$$g(x) = -x^2 + \tfrac{1}{16}, \text{ for } x \leq \tfrac{1}{4},$$
$$= 0, \text{ for } \tfrac{1}{4} < x.$$

Then $f \neq 0$ (the constant function 0) and $g \neq 0$, but $fg = 0$. However, probably the most familiar example of a ring which is not an integral domain—by *our* definition—is the ring of even integers: for this ring had no identity element, as we have noted earlier. It is the content of the following theorem that the absence of divisors of zero in a ring is equivalent to the multiplicative cancellation laws.

Theorem 5.31. *A ring $\mathcal{R}$ has no divisors of zero if and only if the following cancellation law holds: if $a(\neq 0) \in \mathcal{R}$, each of $ab = ac$ and $ba = ca$ implies that $b = c$, for arbitrary elements $b, c \in \mathcal{R}$.*

Proof. Let a, b, c be elements of a ring $\mathcal{R}$ with no divisors of zero and such that $ab = ac$, where $a \neq 0$. Then, $a(b - c) = 0$, and the assumed property of $\mathcal{R}$ requires that $b - c = 0$ so that $b = c$, as desired. The "right" cancellation law is proved similarly. Conversely, if the "left" cancellation law holds and $ab = 0$, with $a \neq 0$, we have $ab = a0$ and so $b = 0$. Similarly, if the "right" cancellation law holds and $ba = 0$, where $a \neq 0$, it follows that $b = 0$. Hence the presence of either cancellation law in $\mathcal{R}$ precludes the existence of divisors of zero. ∎

Corollary. *A commutative ring with an identity is an integral domain if and only if the (left and right) cancellation law holds.*

While there are many rings without identity elements, the next result shows that there is no theoretical loss in generality if we always assume the existence of an identity in a ring under study.

Theorem 5.32. *Any ring $\mathcal{R}$ can be imbedded in a ring with an identity element.*

Proof. If the ring $\mathcal{R}$ has an identity element, there is nothing to do. If not, we construct the desired ring from the product set $\mathcal{R} \times \mathbf{Z}$, by making the following definitions for addition and multiplication: $(x, m) + (y, n) = (x + y, m + n)$; $(x, m)(y, n) = (xy + nx + my, mn)$, for arbitrary $x, y \in \mathcal{R}$ and $m, n \in \mathbf{Z}$ [see Problem 21]. It is easy to verify [Problem 20] that $\mathcal{R} \times \mathbf{Z}$ has now the structure of a ring with an identity element, the identity element being $(0, 1)$. It is also a simple exercise to show that the subset of elements of $\mathcal{R} \times \mathbf{Z}$ of the form $(x, 0)$ constitute a subring [Problem 22]; and this subring is isomorphic to $\mathcal{R}$ under the natural mapping α, where $(x, 0)\alpha = x$ for each $(x, 0) \in \mathcal{R} \times \mathbf{Z}$ [Problem 22]. We may now either use Theorem 5.22 to construct a ring isomorphic to $\mathcal{R} \times \mathbf{Z}$ which contains $\mathcal{R}$ or, more simply, consider $\mathcal{R}$ as being imbedded in $\mathcal{R} \times \mathbf{Z}$ in the sense of isomorphism. ∎

It may be well to inject a word of caution at this point: for while we have imbedded an arbitrary ring in a ring with an identity, it should not be assumed that the imbedding ring will necessarily inherit all the properties originally possessed by the imbedded ring. However, *it can be shown* [see [4], page 86] that the imbedding can be accomplished so that the most important properties of the ring are preserved [cf. Problem 24]. The case of most interest to us will be described in § 5.7.

A ring is called a *division ring, skew field,* or *sfield* if its nonzero members comprise a subgroup of the multiplicative semigroup of the ring. Thus a division ring contains an identity element and also the multiplicative inverse a^{-1} of each element $a \neq 0$ of the ring. The rings of rational numbers, real numbers, and complex numbers are familiar examples of division rings. However, these important number rings are also commutative under multiplication, and as *commutative division rings* they are generally known as *fields*. It is somewhat more difficult to find an example of a division ring that is not also a field. They do exist, however, and we include a brief discussion of one in the following section.

Theorem 5.33. *A finite integral domain $\mathcal{E}$ is a field.*

Proof. Apply the result in Problem 13 of § 4.5, if this problem was worked. If not consider the set $a\mathcal{E}$, for any $a(\neq 0) \in \mathcal{E}$, and show that $a\mathcal{E} = \mathcal{E}$. Conclude from this that $\mathcal{E}$ is a field [Problem 18]. ∎

Corollary. *The ring* $\mathbf{Z}_p$, *p any prime, is a field.*

The basic concept of "characteristic," as defined for a completely general ring $\mathcal{R}$ in § 5.2, is not very useful, since the information it supplies is little more than whether or not the additive group of the ring is periodic. If it is known that $\mathcal{R}$ has an identity, however, the characteristic of $\mathcal{R}$ acquires a more important meaning. For, if we designate this identity by e—in order to avoid notational confusion with the natural number 1—we see that $nx = n(ex) = (ne)x$, for any $x \in \mathcal{R}$. Since $ne = 0$ will now imply that $nx = 0$, it is clear that *the least n such that $ne = 0$* is also *the least n such that $nx = 0$ for all $x \in \mathcal{R}$,* provided such an n exists; and so *the additive order of e is the characteristic of* $\mathcal{R}$. Of course, there may well be specific elements $y \in \mathcal{R}$ such that $my = 0$, with $m < n$ [see Problem 8], but *if $\mathcal{R}$ has no divisors of zero* this cannot happen. For, in this case, suppose $na = 0$ for some $a(\neq 0) \in \mathcal{R}$. Then, if $b(\neq 0) \in \mathcal{R}$, $a(nb) = n(ab) = (na)b = 0b = 0$ and, since $\mathcal{R}$ has no divisors of zero, $nb = 0$. Hence, all nonzero elements of $\mathcal{R}$ must have the same additive order, and this—when combined with the preceding result—gives us: *The characteristic of an integral domain is the additive order of the identity element.* If the characteristic of a ring $\mathcal{R}$ is positive, and there are no divisors of zero, we can obtain an even better description of the characteristic, for we have the following theorem.

Theorem 5.34. *If there are no divisors of zero in a ring* $\mathcal{R}(\neq 0)$ *of positive characteristic, this characteristic is a prime number p.*

Proof. For suppose, to the contrary, that the characteristic of $\mathcal{R}$ is $n = pq$, where $p > 1$ and $q > 1$. Since $\mathcal{R} \neq 0$, there exists a nonzero $x \in \mathcal{R}$ with additive order n. Then $0 = nx^2 = (pq)x^2 = (px)(qx)$, so that $px = 0$ or $qx = 0$. But this contradicts our assumption that the additive order of x is n, and so n must be prime. It is customary to designate this prime characteristic as p. ∎

Corollary 1. *The characteristic of an integral domain is either 0 or a prime p.*

The following theorem is a very important one, but in view of the simplicity of its proof, we merely state the result and suggest that the student construct the proof for himself.

Theorem 5.35. *Any ring $\mathcal{R}$ with an identity contains a subring which is isomor-*

phic to either **Z** *or* **Z**$_p$, *for some prime p, according as the characteristic of* $\mathcal{R}$ *is* 0 *or* p.

Proof. See Problem 13.

PROBLEMS 5–3

1. If $A = \begin{bmatrix} 0 & 1 \\ 0 & 0 \end{bmatrix}$ and $B = \begin{bmatrix} 1 & 2 \\ 0 & 0 \end{bmatrix}$, show that A and B are divisors of zero in the ring $M_2(\mathbf{Z})$. Note that $AB = 0$, while $BA \neq 0$.

2. If addition and multiplication modulo 10 is defined on the set of integers $\{0, 2, 4, 6, 8\}$, prove that the resulting system is a ring *with identity*.

**3. Verify without recourse to Theorem 5.33 or its Corollary, that the ring $\mathbf{Z}_3$ of integers modulo 3 is a field.

4. Discover a divisor of zero to verify that the ring of integers modulo 6 is not an integral domain, and so cannot be a field.

**5. Prove that if $e \neq 0$ is an idempotent element of an integral domain, then e is the identity of the system. (See Problem 14 of § 5.1, and cf. Problem 17 of § 4.1.)

6. An element z of a ring is said to be *nilpotent* if $z^n = 0$, for some positive integer n. Prove that $z = 0$ is the only nilpotent element of an integral domain.

7. Verify that $\begin{bmatrix} 0 & 1 & 0 \\ 0 & 0 & 1 \\ 0 & 0 & 0 \end{bmatrix}$ is a nilpotent [see Problem 6] element of the matrix ring $M_3(\mathbf{Z})$.

8. The characteristic of the ring $\mathbf{Z}_6$ is 6, but find an element in this ring whose additive order is less than 6. Explain why this does not violate Theorem 5.34.

9. Prove that the ring $\mathbf{Z}[\sqrt{2}]$, discussed in Example 2 of § 5.1, is an integral domain. Show that the system remains an integral domain if $\sqrt{2}$ is replaced by $\sqrt{m}$ for any positive integer m without square factors.

10. Prove that the binomial expansion of $(a + b)^n$, which is familiar from elementary algebra, is valid for arbitrary a, b in any integral domain and for any nonnegative integer n [cf. Problem 16 of § 5.1].

11. If a and b are nilpotent elements of a commutative ring, prove that $a + b$ is also nilpotent [see Problems 6 and 10].

12. Prove that any matrix ring $M_n(\mathcal{A})$ will have divisors of zero even if the ring $\mathcal{A}$ does not, provided $n > 1$.

*13. Prove Theorem 5.35. (Hint: consider the system generated by the identity element e in the ring, and examine the mapping $n \to ne$, $n \in \mathbf{Z}$, for both characteristics.)

14. If $\mathcal{E}$ is an integral domain with characteristic p, prove that the mapping $a \to a^p$, for all $a \in \mathcal{E}$, is an isomorphism of $\mathcal{E}$ onto the subdomain of all pth powers of elements of $\mathcal{E}$.

15. If a ring $\mathcal{R}$ has no nonzero nilpotent elements [see Problem 6], prove that any idempotent element [see Problem 14, § 5.1] of $\mathcal{R}$ lies in the center of the ring [see Problem 19, § 5.1].

16. Let $\mathcal{A}$ be a ring with identity in which the operations are designated as usual in the additive and multiplicative symbolisms. Then, if we define two new operations in the set $\mathcal{A}$ by $a \oplus b = a + b - 1$ and $a \odot b = a + b - ab$, show that the elements of $\mathcal{A}$ also comprise a ring with respect to these operations. Moreover, prove that the two rings are isomorphic. [Hint: consider $a \to 1 - a$, $a \in \mathcal{A}$]

17. Let $\mathcal{R} = \{a + b\sqrt{p}\}$, with a, $b \in \mathbf{Q}$ and p any prime integer. Then verify that $\mathcal{R}$ is a field with the usual operations of addition and multiplication in $\mathbf{R}$.

18. Fill in the details of the proof of Theorem 5.33.

19. Explain why the Corollary to Theorem 5.33 follows.

Problems 20–26 refer to Theorem 5.32 and its proof.

*20. Verify that the system $\mathcal{R} \times \mathbf{Z}$ is a ring with identity $(0, 1)$.

21. Identify three distinct meanings which we have attached to the symbol $+$ in the definition of addition in $\mathcal{R} \times \mathbf{Z}$!

22. Verify that the subsystem of elements of the form $(x, 0)$, $x \in \mathcal{R}$, constitutes a subring of $\mathcal{R} \times \mathbf{Z}$.

23. Prove that the subring in Problem 22 is isomorphic to $\mathcal{R}$, using the mapping indicated in the proof of the theorem.

24. Prove that the ring $\mathcal{R} \times \mathbf{Z}$ is commutative if $\mathcal{R}$ is commutative.

25. If the ring $\mathcal{R}$ already has an identity element e, show that $(e, -1)(a, 0) = (a, 0)(e, -1) = (0, 0)$, for any $a \in \mathcal{R}$. Hence, $\mathcal{R} \times \mathbf{Z}$ has divisors of zero regardless of whether $\mathcal{R}$ has any elements of this kind.

26. Try to extend the illustration in Problem 25 to include a case where $\mathcal{R}$ does not have an identity element.

5.4. Two Important Rings

In this section we are first going to present the example, promised in the preceding section, of a division ring which is not a field. In order to introduce this ring, as is usual we let $\mathbf{C}$ designate the complex numbers—which we shall consider here to be structured simply as a ring. The ring $M_2(\mathbf{C})$ is then the ring of all 2×2 matrices of complex numbers, and we recall that the identity element of any such matrix ring is $\begin{bmatrix} 1 & 0 \\ 0 & 1 \end{bmatrix}$. It follows that the multiplicative inverse A^{-1} of any matrix $A \in M_2(\mathbf{C})$, if it exists, must be such that $AA^{-1} = A^{-1}A = \begin{bmatrix} 1 & 0 \\ 0 & 1 \end{bmatrix}$. If we consider the subset of $M_2(\mathbf{C})$ of all matrices of the form $\begin{bmatrix} a + bi & c + di \\ -c + di & a - bi \end{bmatrix}$, where a, b, c, d are arbitrary real numbers, it can be verified directly that this subset is closed under both subtraction and multiplication. An application of Theorem 5.11 then shows that this subset, which we may call Q, is a subring of $M_2(\mathbf{C})$ [Problem 1]. It is clear, of course, that the zero matrix occurs as the member of Q in which $a = b = c = d = 0$, and only for these values is a matrix of Q equal to 0. Since $\Delta \equiv a^2 + b^2 + c^2 + d^2 = 0$ is a necessary and sufficient condition that $a = b = c = d = 0$, it follows that the condition $\Delta \neq 0$ is equivalent to asserting that the corresponding matrix in Q is not the zero matrix. It can be verified by direct multiplication [Problem 2] that each matrix of Q, such that $\Delta \neq 0$, has an inverse in the form $\begin{bmatrix} \dfrac{a - bi}{\Delta} & -\dfrac{c + di}{\Delta} \\ \dfrac{c - di}{\Delta} & \dfrac{a + bi}{\Delta} \end{bmatrix}$, and that the product of two

nonzero matrices of Q is a nonzero matrix of Q [Problem 4]. Hence the non-zero members of Q form a multiplicative subgroup. Since we have shown previously that Q is a subring, the proof that Q is a division ring is complete. An almost random product will verify the assertion that Q is not commutative, and so we have produced a division ring which is not a field. This ring is known as the *ring of Hamilton's quaternions*, named after the Irish mathematician W. R. Hamilton (1805–1865), and the elements of this ring are known as *quaternions*. It should be remarked that quaternions are frequently defined without any reference to matrices, but nevertheless comprise a system which is isomorphic to our ring of matrix quaternions. The student will recall that a brief discussion was given in § 4.13 on what was called the *quaternion group*, and Problem 19 of that section was included for further clarification of this group. For the relationship between our *ring of quaternions* and the *quaternion group*, we refer the student to Problem 5 below. Since there should be no danger of confusing the two systems, we are using Q to designate either of them—but it is noteworthy that this double usage of Q is somewhat different from our current multiple usage of $\mathbf{Z}$ to designate several distinct systems structured from the rational integers.

The other important type of ring to be discussed briefly in this section is the so-called *ring of polynomials* with coefficients in an integral domain $\mathcal{E}$. There are several ways to approach a study of polynomial rings, but probably the simplest is to consider $\mathcal{E}$ properly imbedded in an integral domain $\mathcal{U}$, and examine the structure of the subring generated by $\mathcal{E}$ and a single element $u \in \mathcal{U}$ with $u \notin \mathcal{E}$. This subring $\mathcal{E}[u]$ is the subring of $\mathcal{U}$, containing $\mathcal{E}$ and u, which is "smallest" in the sense of set inclusion. The properties of a ring imply that $\mathcal{E}[u]$ contains every element of $\mathcal{U}$ of the form $a_0 + a_1 u + a_2 u^2 + \cdots + a_n u^n$, for arbitrary elements $a_0, a_1, a_2, \ldots, a_n \in \mathcal{E}$. An element such as this is called a *polynomial in u* with *coefficients* a_i in $\mathcal{E}$. Inasmuch as these polynomials are elements of $\mathcal{U}$, the addition and multiplication of polynomials of this kind is already prescribed by the rules for these operations in $\mathcal{U}$. As a matter of fact, without going into details, we are able to state that the rules of operation for these polynomials turn out to be precisely the rules learned for polynomials in college algebra. The set of all polynomials in u with coefficients in $\mathcal{E}$ is a subset of $\mathcal{U}$, and it is clear from the preceding remark that this subset is closed under both subtraction and multiplication. An application of Theorem 5.11 then shows that this subset is a ring, and so $\mathcal{E}[u]$ is precisely this subset of polynomials in u with coefficients in $\mathcal{E}$.

A general study of polynomial rings falls into two categories, according to the nature of the element u. If u is a solution of a polynomial equation with coefficients in $\mathcal{E}$, so that $d_0 + d_1 u + d_2 u^2 + \cdots + d_m u^m = 0$ for certain elements $d_0, d_1, d_2, \ldots, d_m \in \mathcal{E}$, the element u is said to be *algebraic* over $\mathcal{E}$. If u is not algebraic, it is *transcendental* over $\mathcal{E}$. The *degree* of a nonzero polynomial in u, or of the polynomial equation resulting from equating the polynomial to 0, is the largest exponent of u whose coefficient is not 0 in the polynomial. For example, the degree of u in $a + bu + cu^2$ or of $a + bu + cu^2 = 0$ is 2, provided $c \neq 0$. It is easy to see that, if u is algebraic and is a solution of an equation of degree m, any polynomial in $\mathcal{E}[u]$ can be reduced to one of degree $m - 1$ or less. On the other hand, if u is transcendental over $\mathcal{E}$, polynomials of every finite degree will occur in $\mathcal{E}[u]$, and no reduction in degree can take place.

A somewhat more sophisticated—but also more familiar—approach to polynomials may be considered a generalization of the place-value system of notation in ordinary arithmetic. To illustrate, we remind ourselves that the number 256 may be expressed in the form $6(10^0) + 5(10^1) + 2(10^2)$, the latter expression being "a polynomial in 10 with coefficients in Z_{10}" with Z_{10} considered a "remainder" system. But we note that the ordered triple $(2, 5, 6)$ or simply 256 gives us the same information as the "polynomial"—if we understand that "base 10" is being assumed. It is then easy to make the generalization from arithmetic by identifying a *polynomial over an integral domain* $\mathcal{E}$ with an n-tuple $(a_0, a_1, \ldots, a_{n-1})$, where $a_0, a_1, \ldots, a_{n-1} \in \mathcal{E}$. It is convenient—and customary—however, to introduce a symbol x to play the role of "place-finding" like 10 in the arithmetic situation, so that the "n-tuple" polynomial above would be expressed in the form $a_0 x^0 + a_1 x^1 + \cdots + a_{n-1} x^{n-1}$. We reemphasize that x is nothing but a symbol or *indeterminate* in this polynomial construction and may even be omitted—if the "n-tuple" form for a polynomial is desired. We shall use $\mathcal{E}[x]$ to designate the set of all these polynomials in x, for arbitrary $a_0, a_1, \ldots, a_{n-1} \in \mathcal{E}$ and any $n \in \mathbf{N}$. It is now easy to make $\mathcal{E}[x]$ into a ring by using the definitions of *equality*, *addition*, and *multiplication* which are familiar from college algebra [see Problems 15–17]. The correspondence $a_0 \to a_0 x^0$ makes it clear [Problem 18] that $\mathcal{E}[x]$ contains a subring which is isomorphic to $\mathcal{E}$. We could then use Theorem 5.22 and construct a ring isomorphic to $\mathcal{E}[x]$ which contains $\mathcal{E}$; but we prefer simply to identify $\mathcal{E}$ with the subring of elements $\{a_0 x^0\}$, so that $a_0 x^0$ may be replaced by a_0. We also follow the usual custom and replace

$a_1 x^1$ by $a_1 x$, so that a typical polynomial in $\mathcal{E}[x]$ has the form $a_0 + a_1 x + \cdots + a_{n-1} x^{n-1}$. As a further help toward simplification, we shall also agree to replace $1 x^m$ by x^m, for any m, where 1 is, of course, the identity of $\mathcal{E}$ [see Problem 23].

If $f(x) \in \mathcal{E}[x]$, where $f(x) = a_0 + a_1 x + \cdots + a_n x^n$ and $a_n \neq 0$, we say that $f(x)$ has *degree n, leading coefficient* a_n, and *leading term* $a_n x^n$. If $a_n = 1$, the polynomial $f(x)$ is said to be *monic*. We note that this assigns degree 0 to every nonzero "constant" polynomial—which is an element of $\mathcal{E}$—but leaves the polynomial 0 without a degree. (Some people assign this trivial polynomial the degree $-\infty$.) We are now able to give a satisfactory algebraic description of the ring $\mathcal{E}[x]$.

Theorem 5.41. *The ring* $\mathcal{E}[x]$ *is an integral domain.*

Proof. It is immediate that the ring $\mathcal{E}[x]$ is commutative [see Problem 19], while our identification of $\mathcal{E}$ with the subring of elements $a_0 x^0$ allows us to assert that the identity element of $\mathcal{E}$ is also the identity of $\mathcal{E}[x]$. In order to establish the absence of divisors of zero, let $f(x)$ and $g(x)$ be polynomials in $\mathcal{E}[x]$ of degrees n and m, respectively, so that the leading coefficient of $f(x)$ is a_n and the leading coefficient of $g(x)$ is b_m. The "nominal" leading coefficient of the product is $a_n b_m$ and, since $\mathcal{E}$ is an integral domain, $a_n b_m \neq 0$. The degree of $f(x) \cdot g(x)$ is then $n + m$, and so the product of two nonzero polynomials can never be the zero polynomial, i.e., $\mathcal{E}[x]$ contains no divisors of zero. Hence $\mathcal{E}[x]$ is an integral domain. ∎

It is possible to use a recursive definition to define polynomial rings in more than one indeterminate. For example, we can define $\mathcal{E}[x_1, x_2] = \mathcal{E}[x_1][x_2]$ and, more generally, $\mathcal{E}[x_1, x_2, \ldots, x_n] = \mathcal{E}[x_1, x_2, \ldots, x_{n-1}][x_n]$. The following result is now an immediate consequence of the preceding theorem.

Corollary. *The ring* $\mathcal{E}[x_1, x_2, \ldots, x_n]$ *is an integral domain, where* $x_1, x_2, \ldots, x_n$ *are indeterminates over* $\mathcal{E}$.

Proof. The inductive proof is left to the student [Problem 20].

We have already noted that a polynomial ring $\mathcal{E}[x]$ inherits many of the properties of the integral domain $\mathcal{E}$ of coefficients, and these in turn are very much like the properties of the "basic" integral domain $\mathbf{Z}$. The resemblance between $\mathcal{E}[x]$ and $\mathbf{Z}$ is especially pronounced when $\mathcal{E} = \mathcal{F}$ is a field, and we shall explore some of these similarities in the following section.

PROBLEMS 5–4

*1. Prove that the operations of addition and multiplication are adequately defined in the system of quaternions, as described in this section—i.e., show that Q is "closed" under both operations. Then complete the verification that Q is a subring of $M_2(\mathbf{C})$.

*2. Verify that the inverse of a quaternion, as given in this section, does satisfy the requirements of a multiplicative inverse.

3. The number Δ, used in describing the multiplicative inverse of a quaternion, is called the *norm* of the quaternion. Prove that the norm of the product of two quaternions—in either order—is equal to the product of their norms.

4. Show that the product of two nonzero quaternions is nonzero.

**5. Verify that the quaternions $\pm\mathbf{1}$, $\pm\mathbf{i}$, $\pm\mathbf{j}$, $\pm\mathbf{k}$, where

$$\mathbf{1} = \begin{bmatrix} 1 & 0 \\ 0 & 1 \end{bmatrix}, \quad \mathbf{i} = \begin{bmatrix} i & 0 \\ 0 & -i \end{bmatrix}, \quad \mathbf{j} = \begin{bmatrix} 0 & 1 \\ -1 & 0 \end{bmatrix}, \quad \mathbf{k} = \begin{bmatrix} 0 & i \\ i & 0 \end{bmatrix}$$

form a multiplicative system which is isomorphic to the quaternion group in Problem 19 of § 4.13.

6. Show that the mapping $a \to a' = \begin{bmatrix} a & 0 \\ 0 & a \end{bmatrix}$ defines an isomorphism of $\mathbf{R}$ into the quaternion ring Q, with a' in the center of Q.

7. With $\mathbf{1}$, $\mathbf{i}$, $\mathbf{j}$, $\mathbf{k}$ defined in Problem 5, and a' defined in Problem 6 for any $a \in \mathbf{R}$, prove that any quaternion has a *unique* representation in the form $a_0'\mathbf{1} + a_1'\mathbf{i} + a_2'\mathbf{j} + a_3'\mathbf{k}$—i.e., the "coefficients" a_0', a_1', a_2', a_3' are uniquely determined by the quaternion.

8. Find the indicated quaternion product, using the notation and form described in Problems 5 and 7: $(\mathbf{1} - 2\mathbf{i} + 3\mathbf{j} + \mathbf{k})(\mathbf{1} + 4\mathbf{i} - \mathbf{j} + \mathbf{k})$. (Hint: use the isomorphism established in Problem 5, and check your result by matrices.)

9. Find the inverse of each of the following quaternions, written in the notation of Problem 7, both as an element of $M_2(\mathbf{C})$ and also in the notation of Problem 5:

(a) $\mathbf{2} - \mathbf{j} + 2\mathbf{k}$, where $\mathbf{2} = 2\mathbf{1}$;   (b) $\mathbf{1} + 2\mathbf{i} + 2\mathbf{j}$.

10. Write the number 57 in *binary* form, i.e., as a polynomial in 2 with coefficients in the "remainder" system $\mathbf{Z}_2$.

11. Write the number 57 in *ternary* form, i.e., as a polynomial in 3 with coefficients in the "remainder" system $\mathbf{Z}_3$.

**12. If u is a solution of the equation $3 - 2x + 4x^2 + x^3 = 0$, express the product $(2u^2 + 1)(3u^2 - 2u - 1)$ as a polynomial of degree 2. Write this product if u is transcendental over $\mathbf{Z}$.

13. Use the directions in Problem 12 with u a solution of the equation $2 - 3x + x^2 - x^3 = 0$.

14. If u is a solution of the equation $3 - 5x + x^2 - 2x^3 - x^4 = 0$, express the product $(x^3 - x^2 + 1)(3x^2 + 1)$ as a polynomial of degree 3. Find the product if u is transcendental over $\mathbf{Z}$.

*15. Let $f(x) = a_0 + a_1x + \cdots + a_nx^n$ and $g(x) = b_0 + b_1x + \cdots + b_mx^m$, be polynomials in $\mathcal{E}[x]$, where the "college algebra" definition of *equality* requires that $f(x) = g(x)$ if and only if $m = n$ and $a_i = b_i$, $i = 1, 2, \ldots, m = n$. Explain why it is *this definition* that allows us to include any desired number of additional terms with coefficients 0 in a polynomial.

16. Explain why the result in Problem 15 is of importance in the "college algebra" definition of the sum of two polynomials.

17. With $f(x)$ and $g(x)$ defined as in Problem 15, verify that the definition
$$f(x) \cdot g(x) = \sum_{i=0}^{m+n} c_i x^i, \text{ where } c_k = \sum_{i+j=k} a_i b_j = \sum_{i=0}^{k} a_i b_{k-i}, \text{ gives us the familiar}$$
    "college algebra" rule for the multiplication of two polynomials.
*18. Verify that the subring of $\mathcal{E}[x]$, consisting of all elements $a_0 x^0$, with $a_0 \in \mathcal{E}$, is isomorphic to $\mathcal{E}$.
19. Verify that $\mathcal{E}[x]$, as defined in the text, is a commutative ring.
*20. Use induction on n, the number of indeterminates, to prove the Corollary to Theorem 5.41.
21. Explain why our definition of $\mathcal{E}[x_1, x_2]$ will imply that a typical term of a polynomial in this ring will have the form $a x_1^i x_2^j$ rather than $a x_2^j x_1^i$. Generalize this "notational" result to $\mathcal{E}[x_1, x_2, \ldots, x_n]$.
22. Explain why $\mathcal{E}[x] \cong \mathcal{E}[u]$, where x is an indeterminate and u is a real number which is transcendental over $\mathcal{E}$.
23. Explain the difference in reasons for the decision to replace x^1 by x and $1x^m$ by x^m, in the representation of a polynomial, from the decision to replace $a_0 x^0$ by a_0.
24. Show that the ring $\mathcal{E}[x]$, with x an indeterminate, is isomorphic to a subring of the "infinite Cartesian product of $\mathcal{E}$ with itself" consisting of all elements $(a_0, a_1, \ldots, a_n, 0, 0, \ldots)$—after giving [see Problems 15–17] the definitions for *equality*, *addition*, and *multiplication* in the subring by analogy with those in $\mathcal{E}[x]$.
25. Represent each of the following polynomials of $\mathcal{E}[x]$ as an element of the "infinite Cartesian product of $\mathcal{E}$ with itself" [see Problem 24]. Then use the rule for multiplication given in Problem 24 to find their product; and finally express this product as an element of $\mathcal{E}[x]$. Check your answer by "college algebra" multiplication.
$$f(x) = 2 - 3x + x^2 - x^3, \qquad g(x) = 1 + 4x - 2x^2$$
*26. For the purposes of *this and the following* problem, let C, I, and D designate, respectively, the ring properties of *commutativity*, *possessing an identity*, and having *no divisors of zero*, while $\sim C$, $\sim I$, and $\sim D$ designate the respective denials of these properties. Find at least one example of a ring having the properties:
    (a) C, I, D; (b) $C, \sim I, D$; (c) $C, \sim I, \sim D$; (d) $C, I, \sim D$.
*27. Use the directions in Problem 26 for each of the following:
    (a) $\sim C, I, D$; (b) $\sim C, I, \sim D$; (c) $\sim C, \sim I, \sim D$.

5.5. The Division Algorithm in $\mathcal{F}[x]$

It is a fact that if $\mathcal{E} = \mathcal{F}$ is a field, the ring $\mathcal{F}[x]$ has many properties which have important analogous counterparts in the ring $\mathbf{Z}$ of integers. In particular, we have in mind the properties of $\mathbf{Z}$ which we have rather loosely referred to as the Division Algorithm, the Euclidean Algorithm, and the Fundamental Theorem of Arithmetic. It is our objective in this and the following two sections to derive results in $\mathcal{F}[x]$ which are very similar to these, and then show how some of the basic ideas can be generalized to obtain new classifications of rings.

If we examine the proofs of the theorems referred to above in § 2.4, it will be found that the Well-Ordering Principle occupies a very crucial spot in the derivations of the results. Hence, it would seem reasonable to look for some analogous principle applicable to $\mathcal{F}[x]$, if we are to entertain any hopes of obtaining similar theorems concerning polynomials. The key idea is the observation that every polynomial (except 0) has a *degree*, and this degree is a nonnegative integer. It will then be found that we can make the *degree* of a polynomial play a role very similar to that played by *absolute* value in the theory of rational integers; and it will be the common properties of this "degree" function and "absolute value" function which we shall use later for our generalization. But first we obtain the analogue to the "Division Algorithm" theorem.

We recall from § 5.3 that, if every nonzero element of an integral domain has an inverse or is *invertible*, the algebraic system is called a *field*. An invertible element of a ring is often called a *unit*, and so a field may be alternatively described as an integral domain in which every nonzero element is a unit. It is well to repeat the caution given in § 3.2, but applicable to rings as well as monoids, not to confuse the *identity element* with the *units* of the system. The identity element is indeed a unit—if it exists—but there may be other units in a ring: for example, even in the familiar ring $\mathbf{Z}$, there are two—for both 1 and -1 are units.) While our primary interest is in rings $\mathcal{F}[x]$, with $\mathcal{F}$ a field, whenever a comparable result can be stated for a ring $\mathcal{E}[x]$, with $\mathcal{E}$ an integral domain, we shall use this more general context—with the case for $\mathcal{F}[x]$ appearing as a corollary. In this chapter, we shall always use $\mathcal{R}$, $\mathcal{E}$, and $\mathcal{F}$ to designate a ring, an integral domain and a field, respectively, without further comment, and we shall use $\deg f(x)$ to designate the degree of the polynomial $f(x)$ in a ring $\mathcal{F}[x]$.

If one polynomial can be divided by another, the Division Algorithm is a process for determining the quotient and remainder resulting from such a division. The basic idea of the algorithm in $\mathcal{E}[x]$ can perhaps best be explained with an example in $\mathbf{Z}[x]$. Suppose, then, that we wish to divide $a(x) = 2x^3 - x^2 + 3x - 1$ by $b(x) = x^2 + x - 2$. It is probably true that the student is familiar with the "long division" process for doing this, and this is in fact the final "polished" form of the algorithm: *eliminate the successively highest terms of $a(x)$ by subtracting from it appropriate products of $b(x)$ by monomials cx^k.* Thus $a(x) - 2xb(x) = 2x^3 - x^2 + 3x - 1 - 2x(x^2 + x - 2) = 2x^3 - x^2 + 3x - 1 - 2x^3 - 2x^2 + 4x = -3x^2 + 7x - 1$, and we label this polynomial $a_1(x)$. Similarly, $a_1(x) - (-3)b(x) = -3x^2 + 7x - 1 + 3x^2 +$

$3x - 6 = 10x - 7$, a polynomial which we label $r(x)$; and $\deg r(x) < \deg b(x)$ signifies that the division process is complete. But then $a(x) = 2xb(x) + a_1(x) = 2xb(x) + (-3)b(x) + r(x) = (2x - 3)b(x) + r(x) = q(x)b(x) + r(x)$, where $q(x) = 2x - 3$ is the *quotient* and $r(x) = 10x - 7$ is the *remainder*. This example is somewhat oversimplified, because we would have had trouble if the leading coefficient of $b(x)$ had been an integer different from 1 or -1 (the units of **Z**). In such a case, we could have proceeded as before by regarding our polynomials as elements of **Q**$[x]$, so that our coefficients need no longer be integers. The formal *proof that the above process does provide an algorithm*, with results guaranteed, is the purpose of the following theorem—the polynomial equivalent of Theorem 2.41. It would be possible to pattern our "polynomial" proof on this earlier proof—and we suggest this to the student in Problem 21—but it is easier to obtain the result more directly by using the language of polynomials.

Theorem 5.51 (Division Algorithm). *Let* $a(x)$ *and* $b(x)$ *be polynomials in* $\mathcal{E}[x]$ *of degrees n and m, respectively. If the leading coefficient* b_m *of* $b(x)$ *is a unit of* $\mathcal{E}$, *then* $a(x) = b(x)q(x) + r(x)$, *for unique polynomials* $q(x)$ *and* $r(x)$ *in* $\mathcal{E}[x]$, *where either* $r(x) = 0$ *or* $\deg r(x) < \deg b(x)$.

Proof. We first note that the result is trivial if $n < m$: for we can then let $q(x) = 0$ and $r(x) = a(x)$. Hence we may assume that $n \geq m$, and we apply the Second Principle of Induction to the degree n of $a(x)$. If $n = 1$, the proof follows very easily and we leave it to the student [Problem 5]. Our induction hypothesis is that the theorem is true for any dividend polynomial $a(x)$ of degree $k < n$. But, since b_m is a unit, b_m^{-1} exists and, if a_n is the leading coefficient of $a(x)$, $a(x) - a_n b_m^{-1} x^{n-m} b(x) = a_1(x)$, where $\deg a_1(x)$ is at most $n - 1$. Hence, the induction hypothesis may be applied to $a_1(x)$, so that $a_1(x) = b(x)q_1(x) + r(x)$, with $q_1(x), r(x) \in \mathcal{E}[x]$ and $r(x)$ is 0 or $\deg r(x) < \deg b(x)$. We then have $a(x) = a_1(x) + a_n b_m^{-1} x^{n-m} b(x) = b(x)q_1(x) + r(x) + a_n b_m^{-1} x^{n-m} b(x) = [q_1(x) + a_n b_m^{-1} x^{n-m}]b(x) + r(x) = q(x)b(x) + r(x)$, where $q(x) = q_1(x) + a_n b_m^{-1} x^{n-m}$; and this is a decomposition of $a(x)$ in the form desired. In order to establish uniqueness, let us assume that $a(x) = q'(x)b(x) + r'(x)$, for polynomials $q'(x), r'(x) \in \mathcal{E}[x]$, with $r'(x) = 0$ or $\deg r'(x) < \deg b(x)$, But then $[q(x) - q'(x)]b(x) = r'(x) - r(x)$, and we note that the right member of this equality is either 0 or has degree *less than m*, while the left member is either 0 or has degree *not less* than m. It is clear that the common value of both members must be 0, and this implies that $q'(x) = q(x)$ and $r'(x) = r(x)$. Hence, the representation of $a(x)$ in the desired form is unique. ∎

Corollary 1. *If* $a(x)$, $b(x) \neq 0$ *are polynomials in* $\mathcal{F}[x]$, *there exist unique polynomials* $q(x)$, $r(x) \in \mathcal{F}[x]$ *such that* $a(x) = b(x)q(x) + r(x)$, *where either* $r(x) = 0$ *or* $\deg r(x) < \deg b(x)$.

Note that the condition on b_m is missing when the polonymials are in $\mathcal{F}[x]$. A special case of Theorem 5.51 occurs when $b(x) = x - c$, $c \in \mathcal{E}$, is both monic and linear, and we state this as Corollary 2.

Corollary 2 (Remainder Theorem). *The remainder, when a polynomial $a(x) \in \mathcal{E}[x]$ is divided by $x - c$, for $c \in \mathcal{E}$, is $a(c)$, where $a(c)$ is the result of replacing x in $a(x)$ by c.*

Proof. An application of the theorem shows that $r(x)$ is a constant r, and $r = a(x) - (x - c)q(x)$. If we let $x = c$, we obtain $r = a(c)$. ∎

If $a(x) = b(x)c(x)$, for polynomials $a(x)$, $b(x)$, $c(x) \in \mathcal{E}[x]$, we say that $a(x)$ is *divisible* by $b(x)$ and $c(x)$, and that $b(x)$ and $c(x)$ are *factors* of $a(x)$. Our next corollary is then an immediate consequence of Corollary 2.

Corollary 3 (Factor Theorem). *A polynomial $a(x) \in \mathcal{E}[x]$ has $x - c$ for a factor, with $c \in \mathcal{E}$, if and only if $a(c) = 0$, with $a(c)$ defined as in Corollary 2.*

By a *zero* of a polynomial $f(x) \in \mathcal{E}[x]$ we mean, of course, an element $c \in \mathcal{E}$ such that $f(c) = 0$, with $f(c)$ defined analogous to $a(c)$ in Corollary 2. Corollary 3 then leads us to our final important corollary to Theorem 5.51.

Corollary 4. *A polynomial $f(x)$ of degree n in $\mathcal{E}[x]$ has at most n distinct zeros in $\mathcal{E}$.*

Proof. The case where $n = 1$ is simply an application of Corollary 3 above. We then proceed by induction on n, and assume the theorem true for polynomials of degree $n - 1$. If c is any zero of $f(x)$, Corollary 3 allows us to write $f(x) = (x - c)g(x)$, where $g(x) \in \mathcal{E}[x]$ has degree $n - 1$. By our induction assumption, $g(x)$ has at most $n - 1$ distinct zeros and, since $\mathcal{E}[x]$ is an integral domain [Theorem 5.41], $f(x) = 0$ if and only if $x = c$ or $g(x) = 0$. Hence, $f(x)$ has at most n distinct zeros, as desired. ∎

It has been the most important result in this section to show that a division algorithm exists in any ring $\mathcal{F}[x]$—and to a limited extent in $\mathcal{E}[x]$—so that $\mathcal{F}[x]$ and $\mathbf{Z}$ have the common property that any element of either system can be divided by any nonzero element of the same system, with a remainder which —in a certain sense—is " less " than the divisor. In the case of $\mathbf{Z}$, the remainder is " less " in the sense of absolute value, while in the polynomial rings the remainder is " less " in the sense of degree or is zero. We now use the property of *existence* of a decomposition by division—*but with no actual algorithm described*—to obtain a general classification of rings which will include $\mathbf{Z}$ and $\mathcal{F}[x]$ as special cases. As was suggested earlier, we shall do this by defining on a commutative ring a function with properties much like the "absolute value" function on $\mathbf{Z}$ and the "degree" function on the nonzero members of $\mathcal{F}[x]$.

Definition. A *Euclidean* ring is a commutative ring $\mathcal{R}$, on the nonzero elements of which is defined a (valuation) function δ whose values are nonnegative integers, such that:

(i) $\delta(ab) \geq \delta(a) \cdot \delta(b)$, if $ab \neq 0$;

(ii) For any $a, b(\neq 0) \in \mathcal{R}$, there exist elements $q, r \in \mathcal{R}$ such that $a = bq + r$, and either $r = 0$ or $\delta(r) < \delta(b)$.

If $\mathcal{R} = \mathcal{E}$ is an integral domain, in addition to being a Euclidean ring, it is called a *Euclidean domain*. We have implied, of course, that both $\mathbf{Z}$ and $\mathcal{F}[x]$ are Euclidean domains: if $0 \neq a \in \mathbf{Z}$, $\delta(a) = |a|$; if $0 \neq a(x) \in \mathcal{F}[x]$, $\delta[a(x)] = \deg a(x)$. It may be well to point out that while we had to *prove* that the rings $\mathbf{Z}$ and $\mathcal{F}[x]$ have the "decomposition by division" property, Euclidean rings have this property *by definition*. The most elementary example of a Euclidean ring, apart from the basic rings $\mathbf{Z}$ and $\mathcal{F}[x]$, is provided by the ring of Gaussian integers [see Problem 13, § 5.1]. If we define $\delta(a + bi) = a^2 + b^2$, for any Gaussian integer $a + bi$, we leave it to the student to verify [Problem 24] that this ring is a Euclidean domain.

PROBLEMS 5–5

*1. Explain why the units of $\mathcal{E}[x]$ are merely the units of $\mathcal{E}$.

2. Determine the quotient $q(x)$ and remainder $r(x)$ if $a(x) = x^5 - 2x^3 + x^2 - 2x + 1$ is divided by $b(x) = x^2 - 3$.

3. Perform the division required in Problem 2, but consider the coefficients to be in $\mathbf{Z}_5$.

4. Use the term-by-term "elimination" process to determine the quotient and remainder after division of $3x^4 - 2x^2 + x - 1$ by $x^2 - x + 3$.

*5. Give the proof for the case $n = 1$ of Theorem 5.51.

6. In an integral domain, prove that
   (a) the relation "$x \mid y$" is reflexive and transitive;
   (b) $x \mid y$ if and only if $ax \mid ay$, for $a(\neq 0)$ in the domain.

7. Prove that any field $\mathcal{F}$ is a Euclidean domain by showing that the trivial function δ, with $\delta(a) = 0$, for every $a(\neq 0) \in \mathcal{F}$, satisfies the requirements of a valuation function.

8. If $\Delta = ad - bc$, verify that $\begin{bmatrix} d/\Delta & -b/\Delta \\ -c/\Delta & a/\Delta \end{bmatrix}$ is the inverse of $\begin{bmatrix} a & b \\ c & d \end{bmatrix}$ in $M_2(\mathcal{E})$ provided a, b, c, d are divisible by Δ.

9. Use the result in Problem 8 to determine four units of $M_2(\mathbf{Z})$.

10. Prove that the ring $\mathbf{Z}[\sqrt{3}]$ is Euclidean. (Hint: let $\delta(m + n\sqrt{3}) = m^2 - 3n^2$.)

**11. If a is a unit of a Euclidean domain, with valuation function δ, prove that $\delta(ab) = \delta(b)$, for any b in the domain, and $\delta(a) = \delta(1)$.

12. If $f(x) = (x - a)(x - b)$, we know that $f(c) = c^2 - (a + b)c + ab$, for a, b, c

in an integral domain. Explain why this is not necessarily true with a, b, c in an arbitrary ring with identity.

13. Verify that the polynomial $x^2 + 1$ has $\mathbf{i}, -\mathbf{i}, \mathbf{j}, -\mathbf{j}, \mathbf{k}, -\mathbf{k}$ as zeros in the ring Q of quaternions [see Problem 5, § 5.4]. Explain why this does not violate Corollary 4 of Theorem 5.51.

14. Find the four zeros of $x^2 - 1$ in $\mathbf{Z}_{15}$ [cf. Problem 13].

**15. Prove that the set of units of a ring $\mathcal{R}$ is either empty or comprises a multiplicative subgroup—called the *subgroup of units*—of $\mathcal{R}$. Give an example where this set is empty.

16. The number of positive integers less than and prime to a positive rational integer m is known as the "totient" or "Euler ϕ-function" of m, usually written $\phi(m)$. Prove that the order of the subgroup of units of $\mathbf{Z}_m$ is $\phi(m)$ [see Problem 15].

*17. Refer to Example 2 of § 5.1 and Problem 9 of § 5.3 and show that $a + b\sqrt{m}$ is a unit of $\mathbf{Z}[\sqrt{m}]$ if and only if $a^2 - b^2 m$ is 1 or -1. (Hint: consider the g.c.d. of a and b.)

18. Use Problem 17 to determine four units (distinct from ± 1) of (a) $\mathbf{Z}[\sqrt{2}]$; (b) $\mathbf{Z}[\sqrt{5}]$.

19. Determine all units of $\mathbf{Z}_{10}$.

20. If $a(x) = \begin{bmatrix} 1 & 0 \\ 0 & 1 \end{bmatrix} + \begin{bmatrix} 2 & 1 \\ 0 & 1 \end{bmatrix} x^2$ and $b(x) = \begin{bmatrix} 1 & 1 \\ 2 & 1 \end{bmatrix} - \begin{bmatrix} 1 & 0 \\ 0 & 1 \end{bmatrix} x$, determine the quotient and remainder when $a(x)$ is divided by $b(x)$ in $M_2(\mathbf{Z})[x]$ [see Problem 8].

21. Use the proof of Theorem 2.41 as a pattern to prove Theorem 5.51. (Hint: replace a, b, x in the symbolism of Theorem 2.41 by polynomials $a(x)$, $b(x)$, $p(x) \in \mathcal{E}[x]$, and let S be a set of *degrees* rather than a set of polynomials—recalling that a polynomial is either 0 or its degree is nonnegative.)

22. If $a = bc$, where a, b, c are in a Euclidean ring with valuation function δ, and b, c are not units, prove that $\delta(b) < \delta(a)$.

23. An element p of a ring $\mathcal{R}$ is *prime* if a decomposition $p = ab$, with a, $b \in \mathcal{R}$, is possible only with either a or b a unit. If δ is a valuation function on a Euclidean ring, use induction on $\delta(a)$ to prove that any element a in the ring can be expressed as a product of primes:

$$a = p_1 p_2 \cdots p_r.$$

24. Prove that the ring of Gaussian integers is Euclidean. (Hint: with x, $y \in \mathbf{Z}[i]$, consider $x/y = \alpha + \beta i$, for α, $\beta \in \mathbf{Q}$. There exist a, $b \in \mathbf{Z}$ such that $|a - \alpha| \leq 1/2$ and $|b - \beta| \leq 1/2$. Then prove that $x/y = (a + b)i + r$, where $\delta(r) < \delta(y)$].

25. Prove that $\delta(ab) = \delta(a) \cdot \delta(b)$, for any two Gaussian integers a, b.

26. Use Problem 25 to show that $1 + 2i$ and $1 - 2i$ are prime Gaussian integers [see Problem 23].

27. Determine all units of the subring of $M_2(\mathbf{Z})$, consisting of all matrices of the form

(a) $\begin{bmatrix} a & 0 \\ 0 & a \end{bmatrix}$, $a \in \mathbf{Z}$;   (b) $\begin{bmatrix} a & 0 \\ 0 & b \end{bmatrix}$, with a, $b \in \mathbf{Z}$.

5.6. The Euclidean Algorithm in $\mathcal{F}[x]$

We now turn to a consideration of the analogue, in a polynomial ring $\mathcal{F}[x]$, of the familiar Euclidean Algorithm (Theorem 2.42) in **Z**. As was the case with the Division Algorithm, the proof of this "polynomial" theorem may be patterned after the earlier proof in Chapter 2—with the Well-Ordering Principle being applied to corresponding sets of *degrees* of polynomials [Problem 8]. However, it is convenient in the context of rings to introduce the important concept of an "ideal," and to use these "ideals" in our proof. While our interest will be centered on commutative rings and—for the most part—on integral domains, we shall phrase the definitions for an arbitrary ring. However, for the polynomial rings $\mathcal{F}[x]$, under discussion in this section, it will be important that we have available the Division Algorithm developed in the preceding section.

Definition. A nonempty subset A of a ring $\mathcal{R}$ is called an *ideal* of $\mathcal{R}$ if A is a subring which is closed under left and right multiplication by ring elements. The requirements that A be an ideal may be alternatively stated in the following form:

(i) $a - b \in A$, for arbitrary a, $b \in A$; i.e., A is a subgroup of the additive group of $\mathcal{R}$.

(ii) $ra \in A$ and $ar \in A$, for arbitrary $a \in A$ and $r \in \mathcal{R}$.

It will turn out that ideals play a role in ring theory somewhat analogous to that played by normal subgroups in group theory. Every ring $\mathcal{R}$ contains the "trivial" ideals $\mathcal{R}$ and the subring 0, and we shall see later that some types of rings contain no others.

If the ring $\mathcal{R}$ has an identity element (for example, if $\mathcal{R} = \mathcal{E}$ is an integral domain) and $a \in \mathcal{R}$, it is clear that the set of all ring multiples ra, $r \in \mathcal{R}$, is an ideal: for $r_1 a - r_2 a = (r_1 - r_2)a$ and $r_1(r_2 a) = (r_1 r_2)a$, for any r_1, $r_2 \in \mathcal{R}$. It follows immediately from the definition [Problem 7] that the intersection of any collection of ideals of a ring is also an ideal. In particular, the intersection of all ideals which contain a given set of elements of the ring is an ideal— the ideal *generated by* the elements or with the given elements as its *generators*. The ideal of ring multiples of an element a in a ring with identity is a special case of this, this ideal being generated by a. If $a \in \mathcal{R}$ and $\mathcal{R}$ has no identity, the ideal generated by a will consist of all ring elements of the form $ra + na$, for arbitrary $r \in \mathcal{R}$ and $n \in \mathbf{Z}$. (Why does the presence or absence of an identity

in $\mathcal{R}$ make a difference?) In any case, an ideal with one generator a is called
a *principal* ideal and is designated (a). It might be more in harmony with
earlier symbolism for "generated" systems to designate such an ideal $[a]$, but
the one we have suggested and will use is the one most widely adopted. We
shall, of course, use $(a_1, a_2, \ldots, a_n)$ to designate the ideal generated by the
n elements $a_1, a_2, \ldots, a_n$ in a ring, and the context should eliminate any confusion with an n-tuple of elements. A *minimal* set of generators of an ideal is
called a *basis* for the ideal.

One of the very important properties which the rings $\mathbf{Z}$ and $\mathcal{F}[x]$ have in
common is that all ideals in either domain are principal. Such rings (domains)
in general, *if they also have an identity element*, are called *principal ideal
rings* (*domains*) and are often designated PIR(PID). We now give the proof
that $\mathcal{F}[x]$ is a PID, and we suggest that the student formulate a similar proof
for the case of the ring $\mathbf{Z}$ [Problem 9]. It should be noted that $\mathcal{F}[x]$ is commutative so that the distinction between left and right multiplication dis-
appears.

Theorem 5.61. $\mathcal{F}[x]$ *is a principal ideal domain.*

Proof. If A is an ideal of $\mathcal{F}[x]$, either $A = 0 = (0)$ or A contains a polynomial $p(x)$ of minimal degree. We then assume that $A \neq (0)$, and note that A
contains all polynomial multiples of $p(x)$, by definition of an ideal. If $a(x)$
is an arbitrary polynomial in A, an application of Theorem 5.51 shows
that polynomials $q(x)$ and $r(x)$ exist in $\mathcal{F}[x]$ such that $a(x) - q(x)p(x) =
r(x)$, where $\deg r(x) < \deg p(x)$ or $r(x) = 0$. But $r(x) \in A$, by (i) of the above
definition, and a contradiction with the choice of $p(x)$ would result if $r(x)
\neq 0$. Hence, $r(x) = 0$, $a(x) = q(x)p(x)$ and $A = (p(x))$, as asserted. ∎

In § 5.5 we reviewed the usual meaning of a "divisor" of a polynomial,
but the precise meaning of a "greatest common divisor" is clarified by the
following definition.

Definition. If $a(x)$ and $b(x)$ are two polynomials in $\mathcal{F}[x]$, *a greatest common
divisor* $d(x)$ of $a(x)$ and $b(x)$ is a polynomial with the properties:

   (i) $d(x) \,|\, a(x)$ and $d(x) \,|\, b(x)$;
   (ii) If $c(x) \,|\, a(x)$ and $c(x) \,|\, b(x)$, then $c(x) \,|\, d(x)$.

This is, of course, the extension to polynomial rings of the usual meaning
of g.c.d. for two rational integers. A greatest common divisor is unique except
for unit factors [Problem 11], and a slight further condition on a g.c.d. will
make it unique: in the case of $\mathbf{Z}$, the only units are ± 1, and we select the
g.c.d. which is positive; in the case of $\mathcal{F}[x]$, any nonzero element of $\mathcal{F}$ is a

unit, and we select the polynomial g.c.d. which is *monic*. By *the* g.c.d. of elements in **Z** or $\mathcal{F}[x]$, we will always mean *this unique* one. We are now ready to obtain the analogue in $\mathcal{F}[x]$ of Theorem 2.42.

Theorem 5.62 (Euclidean Algorithm). *Any two polynomials* $a(x)$, $b(x) \in \mathcal{F}[x]$ *have a unique monic greatest common divisor* $d(x)$, *and there exist polynomials* $s(x)$, $t(x) \in \mathcal{F}[x]$ *such that* $d(x) = s(x)a(x) + t(x)b(x)$.

Proof. The proof is a direct application of the fact that $\mathcal{F}[x]$ is a PID. Let us then consider the set A of all polynomial "linear combinations" $p(x)a(x) + q(x)b(x)$, for $p(x)$, $q(x) \in \mathcal{F}[x]$. This set is certainly nonempty, and a simple check shows [Problem 18] that it is an ideal. By Theorem 5.61 we then know that $A = (\bar{d}(x))$, for some polynomial $\bar{d}(x)$ in $\mathcal{F}[x]$. But $\bar{d}(x)$ divides $a(x) = 1 \cdot a(x) + 0 \cdot b(x)$ and $b(x) = 0 \cdot a(x) + 1 \cdot b(x)$. Moreover, since $\bar{d}(x) = \bar{s}(x)a(x) + \bar{t}(x)b(x)$, for certain $\bar{s}(x)$, $\bar{t}(x) \in \mathcal{F}[x]$, it follows that $\bar{d}(x)$ is divisible by any common divisor of $a(x)$ and $b(x)$. Hence $\bar{d}(x)$ is a g.c.d. of $a(x)$ and $b(x)$, while $d(x) = s(x)a(x) + t(x)b(x)$ is the unique monic g.c.d., where $d(x)$, $s(x)$, and $t(x)$ differ from $\bar{d}(x)$, $\bar{s}(x)$, and $\bar{t}(x)$, respectively, by at most a unit of $\mathcal{F}[x]$—i.e., a nonzero element of $\mathcal{F}$. ∎

We use the same terminology as for integers, and assert that two polynomials are *relatively prime* if their g.c.d. is 1. We then have the following result as an immediate corollary to the theorem.

Corollary. *If* $a(x)$ *and* $b(x)$ *are relatively prime polynomials in* $\mathcal{F}[x]$, *there exist polynomials* $p(x)$ *and* $q(x)$ *in* $\mathcal{F}[x]$ *such that* $p(x)a(x) + q(x)b(x) = 1$.

The above theorem—like Theorem 2.42—is actually an "existence" theorem rather than an "algorithm" for the determination of the g.c.d. of two ring elements. However, it is possible to use the Division Algorithm for the determination of the unique greatest common divisor. The procedure is the same in **Z** and $\mathcal{F}[x]$—except for the details of division—and we shall indicate the process in $\mathcal{F}[x]$. Let us assume, then, that $a(x)$ and $b(x)$ are polynomials in $\mathcal{F}[x]$, where $\deg a(x) \geq \deg b(x)$, and we use the Division Algorithm successively to obtain the following equations, with $q_1(x)$, $q_2(x)$, $\ldots$, $q_{k+1}(x)$ designating quotients and $r_1(x)$, $r_2(x)$, $\ldots$, $r_k(x)$, r_{k+1} designating remainders:

$$a(x) = q_1(x)b(x) + r_1(x)$$
$$b(x) = q_2(x)r_1(x) + r_2(x)$$
$$r_1(x) = q_3(x)r_2(x) + r_3(x)$$
$$\cdots\cdots\cdots\cdots\cdots\cdots\cdots\cdots$$
$$r_{k-2}(x) = q_k(x)r_{k-1}(x) + r_k(x)$$
$$r_{k-1}(x) = q_{k+1}(x)r_k(x) + r_{k+1}, \text{ where } r_{k+1} = 0.$$

In other words, after the first division of $a(x)$ by $b(x)$, we divide the remainders, successively, into the preceding divisors until a remainder $r_{k+1}(x)$ is 0. Since $\deg r_1(x) > \deg r_2(x) > \cdots > \deg r_k(x)$, it is necessarily the case that $r_{k+1}(x) = 0$ for some k, and we assert that $r_k(x)$—*the last nonzero remainder*—is a g.c.d. We leave the verification of this to the student [Problem 17]. The representation of the g.c.d. in the form $s(x)a(x) + t(x)b(x)$ may be accomplished by successive substitution, as indicated in the following example. It should be understood, of course, that a strict application of the algorithm above will not necessarily yield the unique *monic* g.c.d., but this can be obtained easily from any g.c.d. In the example below, the computation is facilitated at various stages by the multiplication or division of certain polynomials by units of $\mathbf{Q}[x]$—i.e., by rational numbers. If only the g.c.d. is desired, we may ignore these units. However, if we wish to express the g.c.d. in the characteristic form given in the theorem, it is necessary to "account for" all the units that have been introduced.

Example. Find the g.c.d. $d(x)$ of $a(x) = 2x^4 - 3x^3 + 3x^2 - 3x + 1$ and $b(x) = x^3 - 2x^2 - 5x + 6$, and express $d(x)$ in the form $s(x)a(x) + t(x)b(x)$.

Solution. In this example, the division process terminates after three stages which can be designated as follows—it being understood that the symbolism for a polynomial may differ from that in the earlier theoretical outline by a rational-number factor:

$a(x) = q_1(x)b(x) + 5r_1(x)$, where $q_1(x) = 2x + 1$, $r_1(x) = 3x^2 - 2x - 1$.
$9b(x) = q_2(x)r_1(x) - 50r_2(x)$, where $q_2(x) = 3x - 4$, $r_2(x) = x - 1$.
$r_1(x) = q_3(x)r_2(x)$, where $q_3(x) = 3x + 1$.

The complete process may be shown in the following table in "algorithmic" form:

	$3x + 1$	$x - 4/3$	$2x + 1$
$x - 1$ $= d(x)$	$3x^2 - 2x - 1$ $3x^2 - 3x$	$x^3 - 2x^2 - 5x + 6 = b(x)$ $3x^3 - 6x^2 - 15x + 18$	$2x^4 - 3x^3 + 3x^2 - 3x + 1 = a(x)$ $2x^4 - 4x^3 - 10x^2 + 12x$
	$\overline{x - 1}$ $x - 1$	$\overline{3x^3 - 6x^2 - 15x + 18}$ $3x^3 - 2x^2 - x$	$\overline{x^3 + 13x^2 - 15x + 1}$ $x^3 - 2x^2 - 5x + 6$
	$\overline{0}$	$\overline{- 4x^2 - 14x + 18}$ $- 4x^2 + \dfrac{8x}{3} + \dfrac{4}{3}$	$\overline{15x^2 - 10x - 5}$ $5(3x^2 - 2x - 1)$
		$\overline{-\dfrac{50}{3}(x - 1)}$	

It is clear from the above computation that $d(x) = r_2(x) = x - 1$. Moreover,

$$50d(x) = 50r_2(x) = q_2(x)r_1(x) - 9b(x) = \left[\frac{a(x) - q_1(x)b(x)}{5}\right]q_2(x) - 9b(x)$$

$$= \frac{q_2(x)a(x)}{5} - \left[\frac{q_1(x)q_2(x)}{5} + 9\right]b(x)$$

$$= \left[\frac{(3x - 4)}{5}\right]a(x) + \left[\frac{(-6x^2 + 5x - 41)}{5}\right]b(x). \quad \text{Hence} \quad d(x) = s(x)a(x) +$$

$t(x)b(x)$, where $s(x) = (3x - 4)/250$ and $t(x) = (-6x^2 + 5x - 41)/250$.

We now show that the common property of $\mathbf{Z}$ and $\mathcal{F}[x]$, as discussed in this section, is, in fact, possessed by any Euclidean ring. If we remind ourselves that this type of ring is essentially an abstraction of rings with a "decomposition by division"—and that the Division Algorithm was the all-important tool in the developments just completed—this assertion should really come as no surprise. We combine the important results in one statement, leaving most of the verification to the reader.

Theorem 5.63. *Any Euclidean ring $\mathcal{R}$ is a PIR. Any two elements a, b of this or any principal ideal ring $\mathcal{R}$ have a greatest common divisor d which is expressible in the form $d = sa + tb$, with s, $t \in \mathcal{R}$.*

Proof. The proof that a Euclidean ring $\mathcal{R}$ is a PIR follows much like that of Theorem 5.61, except that an element d, with minimal $\delta(a)$, replaces the polynomial $p(x)$ of minimal degree. We leave the details of the proof that every ideal in $\mathcal{R}$ is principal to the student [Problem 14]. It is rather curious that the only part of the present proof that is really different from the earlier one is the verification that $\mathcal{R}$ has an identity element! Since every ideal in $\mathcal{R}$—including the trivial ideal $\mathcal{R}$—is principal, it follows that $\mathcal{R} = (b)$, for some $b \in \mathcal{R}$. Every element of $\mathcal{R}$ is then a ring multiple of b and, in particular, $b = eb = be$, for some $e \in \mathcal{R}$. If we now take an arbitrary $a \in \mathcal{R}$, it follows that $a = bq$, for $q \in \mathcal{R}$ whence $a = (eb)q = e(bq) = ea = ae$. Hence, e is the identity element of $\mathcal{R}$, and so $\mathcal{R}$ is a PIR. The proof that each pair of elements a, b in *any* PIR $\mathcal{R}$ has a g.c.d., expressible in the characteristic form stated in the theorem, also follows very closely the pattern of the proof of Theorem 5.62: we consider the ideal (a, b), and use the fact that $\mathcal{R}$ is a PIR. We again leave the details to the student [Problem 15]. It may be worthwhile to note, in passing, that for the general case we are *not* able to include a further condition to assure that a *unique* g.c.d. may be identified. ∎

Our final result in this section is an immediate consequence of the proof of Theorem 5.63.

Corollary. *In any Euclidean ring, d is the g.c.d. of elements a, b if and only if d generates the same ideal as that generated by a and b.*

Hence, $d = (a, b)$ and also $(d) = (a, b)$, the former being an equality of ring elements with (a, b) the g.c.d. of a and b, while the latter is an equality of ideals. This is the justification for the "ambiguous" symbolism (a, b) for both a g.c.d. and an ideal. There is, of course, an obvious extension of this result to the g.c.d. of any finite number of elements of the ring [Problem 16]. In general, as a result of this extension, we may assert that in a Euclidean ring (actually any PIR) any ideal has a *basis* of one element.

PROBLEMS 5–6

1. Prove that any nonzero element of a field $\mathcal{F}$ is a g.c.d. of any two elements in $\mathcal{F}$.
2. Review the Division Algorithm in § 2.4, and determine the g.c.d. of
   (a) 396 and 840;   (b) 7920 and 41160.
3. Find the g.c.d. in $\mathbf{Q}[x]$ of
   (a) $x^5 - 2x^4 + 6x^3 - 12x^2 + 8x - 16$ and $x^4 - 2x^3 - 3x + 6$;
   (b) $x^6 + x^5 - x^4 - x^3 + x + 1$ and $2x^4 + 3x^3 + x^2 + 2x + 2$.
4. Find the single positive integral generator of each of the following ideals in $\mathbf{Z}$:
   (a) $(2, 3)$; (b) $(3, 5)$; (c) $(2, 4)$.
5. Find the single positive integral generator of each of the following ideals in $\mathbf{Z}$:
   (a) $(2, 3, 5)$; (b) $(2, 5, 10)$; (c) $(2, 4, 8)$.
6. Verify that $(2) \cup (3)$ is not an ideal in $\mathbf{Z}$.
*7. Prove that the intersection of any collection of ideals in a ring is also an ideal.
8. Give a proof of Theorem 5.62, patterned after the proof of Theorem 2.42— and with no mention of ideals.
**9. Prove that the ring $\mathbf{Z}$ is a PID.
10. Use the result in Problem 9 to prove Theorem 2.42.
*11. Prove that the g.c.d. of ring elements must be unique except for unit factors.
12. Express 1 as a sum of integral multiples of (a) 2 and 3; (b) 5 and 7; (c) 3, 5, and 7.
**13. Express 1 as a sum of $\mathbf{Q}[x]$-multiples of (a) $x - 1$ and $x^2 - x - 6$; (b) $x^2 + 1$ and $2x^2 - x - 1$; (c) $x + 1$, $x^2 + 1$, and $2x^2 - x - 1$.
*14. Give the details of the proof that every ideal in a Euclidean ring is principal.
*15. Give the details of the proof of the existence of a g.c.d. of any two elements of a Euclidean ring.
16. Establish the extension of the corollary to Theorem 5.63 for the case of three ring elements.
*17. Verify, in the Euclidean algorithm for two polynomials in $\mathcal{F}[x]$, that the last nonzero remainder is a g.c.d.
18. Prove that the set of ring "linear combinations" of $a(x)$ and $b(x)$ in $\mathcal{F}[x]$ is an ideal.
*19. A *left* (*right*) ideal in a noncommutative ring is a subring which is closed under *left* (*right*) multiplication by ring elements. Verify that the set of matrices of the form $\begin{bmatrix} a & b \\ 0 & 0 \end{bmatrix}$, with a, b in a ring $\mathcal{R}$, comprises a *right* but not a *left* ideal of $M_2(\mathcal{R})$.

20. Refer to Problem 19 and verify that the set of matrices of the form $\begin{bmatrix} a & 0 \\ b & 0 \end{bmatrix}$ comprises a *left* but not a *right* ideal of $M_2(\mathcal{R})$.

21. Refer to Problem 19 and verify that the matrices of the form $\begin{bmatrix} a & 0 \\ 0 & 0 \end{bmatrix}$ comprise a subring but *neither* a left nor a right ideal of $M_2(\mathcal{R})$.

22. Refer to Problem 19 and verify that the matrices of the form $\begin{bmatrix} x-2y & y \\ 2x-4y & 2y \end{bmatrix}$ comprise a right ideal of $M_2[\mathbf{Z}]$, with $x, y \in \mathbf{Z}$.

23. Prove that the nilpotent elements of a commutative ring $\mathcal{R}$ make up an ideal of $\mathcal{R}$ [see Problem 11, § 5.3].

24. For any ring $\mathcal{R}$, prove that the set of positive integers n such that $na = 0$, for all $a \in \mathcal{R}$, is either empty or an ideal of $\mathbf{Z}$. Also prove that the generator of the ideal—if it exists—is the characteristic of $\mathcal{R}$.

25. Prove that if $\mathcal{R} \neq 0$, and $x\mathcal{R} = \mathcal{R}$ for any $x(\neq 0) \in \mathcal{R}$, then $\mathcal{R}$ is a division ring.

26. Prove that the set of polynomials $f(x) \in \mathbf{Q}[x]$, such that $f(3) = f(5) = 0$, is an ideal of $\mathbf{Q}[x]$. Find the unique monic generator of least degree.

27. Show that the set of polynomials $f(x) \in \mathbf{Q}[x]$, such that $f(3) \neq 0$ and $f(5) = 0$, is not an ideal of $\mathbf{Q}[x]$ [cf. Problem 26].

5.7. Unique Factorization in $\mathcal{F}[x]$

We now come to the polynomial analogue of the Fundamental Theorem of Arithmetic [Theorem 2.43], otherwise known as the *Unique Factorization Theorem*. As has been the plan in the preceding two sections, we shall first derive this generalization in $\mathcal{F}[x]$, and then briefly use the property to characterize a whole class of abstract rings. In Problem 23 of § 5.5, it has already been suggested that the student prove that each element of a Euclidean ring has a "prime decomposition," but we shall not assume this result in the present section.

Matters pertaining to divisibility in integral domains are complicated somewhat by the presence of units. For, if u is a unit, any element a of the domain can be expressed in the form $a = auu^{-1}$, so that both u and au are "divisors" of a, and it is clear that we would want to eliminate this type of divisor as "improper." Two domain elements which differ by a unit factor are said to be *associates*: i.e., a and b are associates if $a = bu$ (or, equivalently, $b = au$) for some unit u in the integral domain. All units and associates of a ring element are then referred to as "improper" divisors of the element, while all other divisors are called "proper." A nonzero element of an *integral domain*, which is *not a unit* and has *no proper divisors*, is said to be *prime* or *irreducible*, with the word "prime" preferred for **Z** and "irreducible" preferred for $\mathcal{F}[x]$. The student should be cautioned that the two words have distinct meanings in more general rings, but they coincide for integral domains. Two ring elements whose g.c.d. is a unit are said to be "relatively prime," and in an integral domain their "unique" g.c.d. is 1. In the domain **Z**, the only units are ± 1, and the prime integers are well known to the student. In the domain of polynomials in $\mathcal{F}[x]$, all nonzero elements of $\mathcal{F}$ are units. Hence linear polynomials $ax + b$, $a \neq 0$, are irreducible in $\mathcal{F}[x]$, because their only factors are elements of $\mathcal{F}$ (i.e., units) and nonzero $\mathcal{F}$-multiples of $ax + b$ (i.e., associates). As we have already implied, integers are relatively prime if their g.c.d. is 1, while polynomials are relatively prime if their only common factors are nonzero elements of $\mathcal{F}$—which again means that their g.c.d. is 1. [Why?] Of course, some nonlinear polynomials are irreducible while some are reducible, and a very important problem in polynomial algebra consists in finding suitable tests for the irreducibility of polynomials over certain fields. It should be clear that the field of "constants" does play a very important part in whether a given polynomial is or is not reducible. For example, it is well known that $x^2 + 1$ is irreducible over both **Q** and **R**, while over **C** we can write $x^2 + 1 = (x + i)(x - i)$, with i the familiar characteristic complex number. It is probably well known to the student that the only irreducible polynomials in **C**[x] are, in fact, the linear ones. However, in spite of its great "practical" importance, we prefer merely to accept the *meaning* of "irreducibility," and forgo any polynomial tests at this time. In Chapter 7, where the idea comes to the foreground in connection with field extensions, we shall introduce the very useful "Eisenstein Criterion" for irreducibility.

At the root of all questions on irreducibility in an integral domain is a result similar to the following—which we state in the context of the domain $\mathcal{F}[x]$.

Theorem 5.71. *Let* $p(x)$, $a(x)$, $b(x) \in \mathcal{F}[x]$. *If* $p(x)$ *is irreducible and* $p(x) \,|\, a(x)b(x)$, *then* $p(x) \,|\, a(x)$ *or* $p(x) \,|\, b(x)$.

Proof. The irreducibility of $p(x)$ requires that the g.c.d. of $p(x)$ and $a(x)$ is $p(x)$ or 1. If it is $p(x)$, $p(x) \,|\, a(x)$ and the theorem is true. If the g.c.d. is 1, then $1 = s(x)p(x) + t(x)a(x)$, for some $s(x)$ and $t(x)$ in $\mathcal{F}[x]$, so that $b(x) = b(x) \cdot 1 = s(x)p(x)b(x) + t(x)a(x)b(x)$. We are assuming that $p(x) \,|\, a(x)b(x)$ and so $p(x)$ divides the right member of this equality. Hence, $p(x)$ divides the left member $b(x)$, as required by the theorem. Stated otherwise, the theorem asserts that if an irreducible polynomial divides a product of two polynomials, it must divide one or the other of the polynomials. ∎

It is now easy to use an induction proof to obtain the principal theorem of this section.

Theorem 5.72 (Unique Factorization Theorem). *If $a(x)$ is a polynomial of $\mathscr{F}[x]$, then $a(x) = cp_1(x)p_2(x) \cdots p_n(x)$, where $c \in \mathscr{F}$ and $p_1(x)$, $p_2(x)$, ..., $p_n(x)$ are monic irreducible polynomials in $\mathscr{F}[x]$. Moreover, this representation of $a(x)$ is unique except for the order of the factors.*

Proof. If $a(x)$ has degree 1, we have already noted that it is irreducible; and an elementary argument shows that the representation of $a(x)$ in the form $cp(x)$, with $c \in \mathscr{F}$ and $p(x)$ monic, is unique [Problem 12]. Let us now use the Second Principle of Induction and assume the theorem true for polynomials of degree less than deg $a(x)$. If $a(x)$ is irreducible, an argument similar to the "elementary" argument above establishes the result. On the other hand, if $a(x)$ is not irreducible, then $a(x) = b(x) \cdot c(x)$, with $b(x)$, $c(x) \in \mathscr{F}[x]$, and deg $b(x) <$ deg $a(x)$ and deg $c(x) <$ deg $a(x)$. Our induction hypothesis now implies that $b(x) = c'p_1'(x) \cdots p_r'(x)$ and $c(x) = c''p_1''(x) \cdots p_s''(x)$, for elements c', $c'' \in \mathscr{F}$ and monic irreducible polynomials $p_1'(x), \ldots, p_r'(x), p_1''(x), \ldots, p_s''(s) \in \mathscr{F}[x]$. But then $a(x) = cp_1'(x) \cdots p_r'(x)$ $p_1''(x) \cdots p_s''(x)$, where $c = c'c''$, and we have obtained a decomposition of $a(x)$ of the form asserted in the theorem.

To establish uniqueness, let us assume that $a(x) = cp_1(x)p_2(x) \cdots p_n(x)$ $= dq_1(x)q_2(x) \cdots q_m(x)$, with both of the representations of $a(x)$ having the form asserted in the theorem. Inasmuch as all the irreducible polynomials are monic, the leading coefficient of $a(x)$ must be $c = d$. Since $p_1(x)$ divides the left decomposition, it follows from Theorem 5.71 that $p_1(x)$ must divide a nonconstant factor of the right decomposition, which we may designate as $q_i(x)$ for some i between 1 and m. (An iteration of Theorem 5.71 will lead us to $q_i(x)$, since there are only a finite number of factors in the right decomposition of $a(x)$.) The fact that $p_1(x)$ and $q_i(x)$ are monic and irreducible then requires that $p_1(x) = q_i(x)$, and this common factor can be cancelled from the asserted equality. The resulting equality has the form $p_2(x)p_3(x) \cdots p_n(x) = q_1(x)q_2(x) \cdots q_{i-1}(x)q_{i+1}(x) \cdots q_m(x)$, where both members have degrees less than deg $a(x)$. Another application of the Second Principle of Induction which, this time, we leave to the student [Problem 13], shows us that the "p-factors" and "q-factors" must be equal in pairs. Hence, the representation of $a(x)$, in the form asserted in the theorem, is unique. ∎

Now that we have obtained our principal result on the factorization of polynomials in $\mathscr{F}[x]$, we use this general property to characterize a whole class of abstract rings.

Definition. An integral domain $\mathscr{E}$, in which every nonzero element is uniquely expressible—apart from unit factors and the order of the factors—as a product of prime elements, is called a *unique factorization domain* or *UFD*, and sometimes a *Gaussian domain*.

We now know, as a result of the Fundamental Theorem of Arithmetic and the theorem just established, that both $\mathbf{Z}$ and $\mathcal{F}[x]$ are unique factorization domains. The following theorem shows that this property can be extended [see also Problem 25 below].

Theorem 5.73. *Any Euclidean domain is a UFD.*

Proof. The proof of this theorem follows the lines of the proof of Theorem 5.72, with the valuation function δ replacing the "degree" function. Accordingly, we leave the details of this proof to the student [Problem 15]. ∎

While any Euclidean domain is a UFD, the unique factorization domains are of much more general occurrence and need not be Euclidean, nor even principal ideal domains. For example, in the domain $\mathcal{F}[x, y]$, with two indeterminates x and y, the important Theorem 5.63—which applies in any Euclidean domain—is not valid. All we need do is take $a(x, y) = x$ and $b(x, y) = x + y$ in $\mathcal{F}[x, y]$, and it is clear that the only common divisors of $a(x, y)$ and $b(x, y)$ are 1 and its associates; but certainly no polynomials $s(x, y)$ and $t(x, y)$ exist in $\mathcal{F}[x, y]$ such that $s(x, y)a(x, y) + t(x, y)b(x, y) = 1$. [Why?] Likewise, in the polynomial domain $\mathbf{Z}[x]$, the g.c.d. of the polynomials 3 and x is 1, but no polynomials $s(x)$ and $t(x)$ exist in $\mathbf{Z}[x]$ such that $1 = s(x) \cdot 3 + t(x) \cdot x$. It is well known from "high school" algebra, however, that factorization into primes is both possible and unique in both cases—although we shall not give a proof of this fact here. A very pertinent result on factorization, but also one which we shall not prove, is the more general result that $\mathcal{E}[x]$ is a UFD if $\mathcal{E}$ is of this type. Of course, in considering such polynomial domains, it must be recalled that—unlike the case where $\mathcal{E} = \mathcal{F}$ is a field—not all nonzero elements of $\mathcal{E}$ are units. Hence the notion of what is prime or irreducible must be altered, and the role of monic polynomials in $\mathcal{E}[x]$ is played by "primitive" polynomials: a polynomial $a(x) \in \mathcal{E}[x]$ is said to be *primitive* if the only common divisors of its coefficients are units. For example, $3x^2 + 4x + 21$ is a primitive polynomial of $\mathbf{Z}[x]$, while $3x^2 + 12x + 21$ is not. We shall not consider this more general situation further however.

While the property of unique factorization is inherited in $\mathcal{E}[x]$ from $\mathcal{E}$ when x is an indeterminate, this is not always true for other types of "extension" domains. For example, if we let $\mathbf{Z}[\sqrt{-5}]$ designate the collection of all complex numbers of the form $a + b\sqrt{-5}$, with $a, b \in \mathbf{Z}$, it can be easily verified that this is an integral domain which includes $\mathbf{Z}$ as a subdomain. However, we note that $6 = 2 \cdot 3 = (1 + \sqrt{-5})(1 - \sqrt{-5})$, so that this extended domain has no unique factorization theorem. We shall return to this situation briefly in a later section and see how the unique factorization theorem can be "rescued" by turning our attention to ideals rather than to elements.

PROBLEMS 5–7

1. Express each of the following integers in the unique form asserted by the Fundamental Theorem of Arithmetic: (a) 135; (b) 3465; (c) 8100.

2. Express each of the following polynomials in the unique form asserted by the Unique Factorization Theorem of this section:
   (a) $2x^3 - 3x^2 - 3x - 2$; (b) $x^5 + x^4 - 2x^3 - x^2 - x + 2$.

3. Examine both proofs, and decide whether there are any *essential* differences in our proofs of the Fundamental Theorem of Arithmetic [Theorem 2.43] and the Unique Factorization Theorem in $\mathcal{F}[x]$ [Theorem 5.72].

4. Prove that "is an associate of" is an equivalence relation in any ring with an identity element.

5. Express each of the following as the product of an integer and a primitive polynomial in $\mathbf{Z}[x]$:
   (a) $3x^2 - 3x - 6$;   (b) $2x^2 + 2x + 4$;   (c) $10x^4 - 5x^3 + 5x^2 - 5x - 5$.

6. List the integral associates of (a) 5; (b) 6; (c) -2.

**7. List the associates in $\mathbf{Z}[x]$ of (a) $2x + 1$; (b) $4x^2 + 2$; (c) $x^2 + 1$.

8. Describe the associates in $\mathbf{Q}[x]$ of the polynomials in Problem 7.

9. Explain why there are no irreducible polynomials of degree greater than 1 in $\mathbf{C}[x]$.

10. List two *proper* and two *improper* integral divisors of 6 in $\mathbf{Z}$.

11. List two *proper* and two *improper* divisors of $x^2 - 1$ in $\mathbf{Q}[x]$.

*12. Supply the "elementary argument" suggested in the first sentence of the proof of Theorem 5.72.

*13. Supply the "iteration" argument needed in the proof of uniqueness of the decomposition obtained in Theorem 5.72.

14. Give the details of the induction argument that the p-factors and q-factors are equal, in the latter part of the proof of Theorem 5.72.

*15. Prove Theorem 5.73.

16. In $\mathbf{Z}[x]$, with x an indeterminate, explain why no polynomials $s(x)$ and $t(x)$ can exist such that $1 = 2s(x) + x^2 t(x)$, even though the g.c.d. of 2 and x^2 is 1.

17. Factor 4 in two nontrivial ways in the domain $\mathbf{Z}[\sqrt{-3}]$ of all complex numbers of the form $a + b\sqrt{-3}$, with a and b rational integers.

18. Decompose the numbers 2 and 3 in the ring of Gaussian integers into products of prime factors. Explain why these factorizations are or are not unique.

**19. Prove that if $f(x)$ is irreducible as a polynomial in $\mathbf{Z}[x]$, then $f(x)$ is also irreducible as a polynomial in $\mathbf{Q}[x]$.

20. Determine the units and primes in the matrix ring $M_2(\mathbf{Z})$.

21. Show that every linear polynomial in $\mathbf{Z}[x, y]$ is prime.

22. Find all irreducible polynomials of degree 3 or less in $\mathbf{Z}_2[x]$.

23. Show that $x^4 - 2$ is an irreducible polynomial in $\mathcal{R}[x]$, where $\mathcal{R}$ is the ring of Gaussian integers.

24. Decide on the reducibility or irreducibility of each of the following polynomials in $\mathbf{Z}_2[x]$: (a) $x^2 + 1$; (b) $x^2 - 1$; (c) $x^2 + x + 1$; (d) $x^2 - x + 1$.

25. Try to extend Theorem 5.73 to an arbitrary PID.

5.8. From Integral Domains to Fields: Imbedding

Now that we have completed our discussion of some of the most important properties of polynomial domains $\mathcal{F}[x]$ we return to a discussion of more general integral domains. To be precise, it is the purpose of the present section to show that any integral domain (actually a commutative ring without divisors of zero will do!) can be imbedded in a field. That is, given an integral domain $\mathcal{E}$, there exists a field $\mathcal{Q}$ which contains a subdomain isomorphic to $\mathcal{E}$. The procedure will be to imitate the method used in § 2.5 to imbed $\mathbf{Z}$ in $\mathbf{Q}$, i.e., to "construct" the field of rational numbers from the integers. This will tend to reemphasize, what is doubtless already quite apparent, the great intuitive importance of the familiar systems of arithmetic on the development of abstract algebraic systems. The rational field $\mathbf{Q}$ is "minimal" in the sense that any other field containing an isomorphic copy of $\mathbf{Z}$ will also contain an isomorphic copy of $\mathbf{Q}$. The field to be constructed here, in which we imbed an arbitrary domain, will also be minimal in the analogous sense.

We have defined a field as a commutative division ring, and so an algebraic system $\mathcal{F}$ is a field if it satisfies the following equivalent requirements:

1. $\mathcal{F}$ is an additive abelian group.
2. The set of nonzero elements of $\mathcal{F}$ is nonempty and comprises a multiplicative abelian group.
3. The distributive laws hold.

Since **3** is automatically satisfied in any subsystem of $\mathcal{F}$, it is an immediate consequence of these conditions and Theorem 4.51 that any subsystem $\mathcal{K}$ of $\mathcal{F}$, with at least two elements, is a subfield if the following conditions are met:

1'. If $a, b \in \mathcal{K}$, then $a - b \in \mathcal{K}$.
2'. If $a, b (\neq 0) \in \mathcal{K}$, then $ab^{-1} \in \mathcal{K}$.

It is now easy to obtain the "field" version of Theorem 4.52.

Theorem 5.81. *The intersection of any collection of subfields of a field is also a field.*

Proof. If a and b are arbitrary elements of the intersection, condition **1'** implies that $a - b$ is in each subfield of the collection, and so is in the intersection. The same argument shows that ab^{-1} is in the intersection provided *a* and *b*($\neq 0$) are elements of the intersection. It then follows from **1'** and **2'** that this intersection is a field, as asserted. ∎

It may be of help in understanding the construction of the field in which the integral domain $\mathcal{E}$ is to be imbedded, if we first consider the integral domain as *already imbedded* in a field. Thus let $\mathcal{F}$ be a field which contains the integral domain $\mathcal{E}$. By analogy with similar " generated " systems in earlier chapters, we define the field *generated* by $\mathcal{E}$ to be the intersection of all subfields of $\mathcal{F}$ which contain $\mathcal{E}$. This intersection is a field, as a result of Theorem 5.81. It is now possible to give the following important characterization of this field: *The subfield* $\mathcal{Q}$, *generated by the integral domain* $\mathcal{E}$, *is the set* $\{xy^{-1}\}$ *of all elements of the form* xy^{-1}, *where* $x, y(\neq 0) \in \mathcal{E}$. [Note that $0 \in \{xy^{-1}\}$.]

In order to prove this assertion, we note first that inverses of nonzero elements of $\mathcal{E}$ must be in $\mathcal{Q}$, and $\mathcal{Q}$ is closed under multiplication. Hence $\mathcal{Q} \supset \{xy^{-1}\}$. We make use of Theorem 5.81 to prove the reversed inclusion. Thus, if ab^{-1} and cd^{-1} are arbitrary elements of $\{xy^{-1}\}$, we have $ab^{-1} - cd^{-1} = add^{-1}b^{-1} - cbb^{-1}d^{-1} = (ad - cb)(bd)^{-1}$, which is clearly an element of $\{xy^{-1}\}$. Moreover, $(ab^{-1})(cd^{-1})^{-1} = (ab^{-1})(dc^{-1}) = (ad)(bc)^{-1} \in \{xy^{-1}\}$, and an application of **1'** and **2'** shows that $\{xy^{-1}\}$ is a subfield of $\mathcal{F}$. Since each $a \in \mathcal{E}$ can be expressed in the form $(ab)b^{-1}$, for any $b(\neq 0) \in \mathcal{E}$, we must have $\mathcal{E} \subset \{xy^{-1}\}$. But $\mathcal{Q}$ is the intersection of all subfields of F which contain $\mathcal{E}$, so that $\mathcal{Q} \subset \{xy^{-1}\}$. It follows from the two inclusions that $\mathcal{Q} = \{xy^{-1}\}$, as asserted. In the special case where $\mathcal{E} = \mathbf{Z}$ is the ring of integers, and $\mathcal{F} = \mathbf{R}$ is the field of real numbers, the field $\mathcal{Q}$ generated by $\mathbf{Z}$ is the field $\mathbf{Q}$ of rational numbers. Each element in this field has the form xy^{-1} or x/y, where x and $y(\neq 0)$ are integers.

We are now ready to obtain the principal result of this section.

Theorem 5.82. *Any integral domain can be imbedded in a field.*

Proof. As we are no longer assuming that the integral domain is contained in a field, it is now necessary for us actually *to construct* the elements of the imbedding field. However, it was the purpose of the preceding discussion to indicate that the elements of a minimal field containing an integral domain $\mathcal{E}$ will probably be derived from pairs (a, b), with $a, b(\neq 0) \in \mathcal{E}$. Accordingly, we let S be the set of all such pairs, where *intuitively* we may identify the pair (a, b) with ab^{-1} or a/b. We first define an equivalence relation in S by stating that $(a, b) \sim (c, d)$ if $ad = bc$. It can be easily verified [Problem 1] that this does define an equivalence relation, and so S is partitioned into disjoint classes of equivalent elements [Theorem 1.31]. We now think of each equivalence class as defining a unique number, *which for convenience may be identified with the class itself*, and use the analogy of the field in the preceding discussion to define addition and multiplication in this set $\mathcal{Q}$ of equivalence classes. (For example, if $\mathcal{E} = \mathbf{Z}$, we identify the set of distinct "fractions" $\{\frac{1}{2}, \frac{2}{4}, \frac{3}{6}, \ldots\}$ with a unique rational number.) Thus, if $\overline{(a, b)}$ is the equivalence class which contains (a, b) and $\overline{(c, d)}$ is the equivalence class which contains (c, d), we make the following definitions:

1. $\overline{(a, b)} + \overline{(c, d)} = \overline{(ad + bc, bd)}$.
2. $\overline{(a, b)}\overline{(c, d)} = \overline{(ac, bd)}$.

We note that since $b \neq 0$ and $d \neq 0$, also $bd \neq 0$, so that the pairs defined as sums and products by these definitions are actually in $\mathcal{Q}$. Moreover, if $(a', b') \sim (a, b)$ and $(c', d') \sim (c, d)$, it is easy to verify [Problems 2 and 3] that $(a'd' + b'c', b'd') \sim (ad + bc, bd)$ and $(a'c', b'd') \sim (ac, bd)$, and this shows that the operations have been adequately defined by **1** and **2**. It is now a straightforward matter to check the postulates and so verify that $\mathcal{Q}$ is a *field* [cf. Problems 4 and 5].

Finally, we assert that the mapping $a \rightarrow (a, 1)$, where 1 is the identity element of $\mathcal{E}$, is an isomorphism of $\mathcal{E}$ into $\mathcal{Q}$. The verification of this is illustrated schematically below with $a, c \in \mathcal{E}$.

$$
\begin{array}{ll}
\mathcal{E} & \mathcal{Q} \\
\hline
a & \longrightarrow \overline{(a, 1)} \\
c & \longrightarrow \overline{(c, 1)} \\
a + c & \longrightarrow \overline{(a + c, 1)} = \overline{(a, 1)} + \overline{(c, 1)} \\
ac & \longrightarrow \overline{(ac, 1)} = \overline{(a, 1)}\,\overline{(c, 1)}
\end{array}
$$

This completes the proof of the theorem, for we have imbedded an isomorphic image of $\mathcal{E}$ in a field $\mathcal{Q}$. ∎

The field $\mathcal{Q}$, in which the integral domain $\mathcal{E}$ has been imbedded by the above process, is known as the *field of quotients* or *quotient field* of $\mathcal{E}$. If $\mathcal{E}$ happens to be already imbedded in a field, it is easy to see from the discussion prior to Theorem 5.82 that the "internal" subfield of elements of the form ab^{-1}, with $a, b(\neq 0) \in \mathcal{E}$, is isomorphic to the "external" quotient field of the theorem. We leave the details of this verification to the student in Problem 10. Since this "internal" quotient field is a subfield of *any* field in which $\mathcal{E}$ is imbedded, it is clear that the quotient field is the smallest subfield of any imbedding field of $\mathcal{E}$. In fact, we may go even further and assert the following result, with the especially pertinent corollary.

Theorem 5.83. *Any two isomorphic integral domains have isomorphic fields of quotients.*

Proof. We leave the proof to the student in Problem 15. (If $x \to x'$ is the isomorphic map of the integral domains, examine the map $(a, b) \to (a', b')$, with $b \neq 0$, of their fields of quotients.)

Corollary. *An integral domain has an* isomorphically unique *field of quotients.*

As a result of this corollary, we are then justified in speaking of *the* field of quotients of an integral domain. In view of possible confusion with other "quotient" or "factor" systems which we have discussed in the past, we prefer the name "field of quotients" to "quotient field"—although both are in common usage.

We have already emphasized that the prime motivation for the imbedding procedure in this section has been the well-known process of imbedding the integers in the field of rational numbers. The field **Q** is then the field Q of quotients of **Z**! We continue the parallelism between the properties of **Z** and those of the polynomial ring $\mathcal{F}[x]$, and note that this latter ring has a field of quotients which we designate as $\mathcal{F}(x)$. The elements of the abstract field $\mathcal{F}(x)$ will be equivalence classes of pairs $(f(x), g(x))$, with $f(x), g(x) \neq 0$ in $\mathcal{F}[x]$. However, it is customary to follow the same practice as with rational numbers and write such a pair as a "quotient" in the form $f(x)/g(x)$: the field of quotients $\mathcal{F}(x)$ of $\mathcal{F}[x]$ then consists of all possible "quotients" of polynomials in $\mathcal{F}[x]$. To illustrate, if $\mathcal{F} = \mathbf{Q}$, $\mathbf{Q}(x)$ is the field of all "rational functions of x," and an example of an element of this field is $(x^3 - 2x^2/3 + 1)/(x^2 - 1/2)$ or $(6x^3 - 4x^2 + 6)/(6x^2 - 3)$. This example illustrates something else which we have not formally proved but which is not difficult to establish: if Q is the field of quotients of an integral domain $\mathcal{E}$, the fields of quotients of $\mathcal{E}[x]$ and Q$[x]$ are isomorphic [Problem 16]. As a final remark, it *might* be conjectured that it would be possible to imbed an arbitrary (noncommutative) ring in a division ring, just as we have done for an integral domain in a field. However, it can be shown that this is not the case.

PROBLEMS 5–8

**1. Prove that the relation, defined in the set S of the proof of Theorem 5.82, is an equivalence relation.

*2. Prove that addition has been adequately defined in the set Q of equivalence classes in the proof of Theorem 5.82.

*3. As in Problem 2, verify that the definition of multiplication is satisfactory.

*4. Verify that the system Q, in the proof of Theorem 5.82, is an additive abelian group.

*5. Verify that the nonzero elements of Q in Problem 4 comprise a multiplicative group.

6. List some of the members of the equivalence class of fractions m/n, with $m, n \in \mathbf{Z}$, which is identified with the rational number (a) $2/3$; (b) $-1/2$; (c) $1/4$.

*7. Identify the zero and identity element of the abstract field of quotients of an integral domain $\mathcal{E}$.

8. Use the model of Theorem 5.82 to prove that a commutative ring $\mathcal{R}$ *without* an identity element, but with no divisors of zero, can be imbedded in a field. (Consider the mapping $a \rightarrow (ab, b)$ of $\mathcal{R}$, for any $b(\neq 0) \in \mathcal{R}$.)

9. Use the analogous isomorphism of $\mathbf{Z}$ into $\mathbf{Q}$ in order to clarify the isomorphism of $\mathcal{E}$ into $\mathcal{Q}$, in the proof of Theorem 5.82.

10. Prove that the "internal" field of quotients of an integral domain $\mathcal{E}$, imbedded in a field $\mathcal{F}$, is isomorphic to the "external" field of quotients of $\mathcal{E}$.

11. Prove that the quotient field of a field $\mathcal{F}$ is isomorphic to $\mathcal{F}$.

12. Prove that any field of characteristic 0 contains a subfield isomorphic to $\mathbf{Q}$.

13. Prove that any field of characteristic p, p prime, contains a subfield isomorphic to $\mathbf{Z}_p$ [cf. Corollary to Theorem 5.33].

14. Prove that any commutative semigroup, in which the cancellation law holds, can be imbedded in an abelian group.

*15. Prove Theorem 5.83.

*16. If $\mathcal{Q}$ is the field of quotients of an integral domain $\mathcal{E}$, prove that the fields of quotients of $\mathcal{E}[x]$ and $\mathcal{Q}[x]$ are isomorphic.

17. Describe the field of quotients of the ring of even integers [see Problem 8].

18. Describe the field of quotients of the ring of Gaussian integers.

19. Verify that the subset of rational numbers, expressible in the form m/n, with m and n integers, n odd, is an integral subdomain of $\mathbf{Q}$. Determine its field of quotients.

**20. Explain why the ring $\mathbf{Z}_6$ can not be imbedded in a field.

21. Describe the field of quotients of $\mathbf{Z}_5$ [see Problem 11].

22. Show that the field of quotients of $\mathbf{Z}[\sqrt{5}]$ consists of all real numbers of the form $r + s\sqrt{5}$, with $r, s \in \mathbf{Q}$.

23. Explain why the mapping $a + b\sqrt{5} \rightarrow a + b\sqrt{7}$, with $a, b \in \mathbf{Q}$, is not an isomorphism of the fields of quotients of $\mathbf{Z}[\sqrt{5}]$ and $\mathbf{Z}[\sqrt{7}]$.

5.9. Basic Homomorphism Theory for Rings

The homomorphism theory of a general ring is the composite of the homomorphism theories of abelian groups and semigroups as applied, respectively, to the additive group and multiplicative semigroup of the ring. Inasmuch as these theories have been studied in Chapters 3 and 4, any detailed study of the homomorphisms of rings would involve a great deal of duplication of what has been done earlier. We feel that such a duplication of effort is neither desirable nor necessary on our part, and so we shall be satisfied with merely stating a number of important "ring" results in the first portion of this section, leaving their verification to the reader. (A few duplications of proofs will do the *reader* no harm!) In this section, unless the contrary is stated, we do not assume that our rings are commutative, although we shall draw heavily on the very familiar commutative rings of integers and polynomials for illustrations and problems. In addition, we repeat the passing comment made in § 5.2, that, along with the basic notion of *homomorphism*, we have the associated notions of *isomorphism, endomorphism, epimorphism, monomorphism,* and *automorphism*, the meanings of which are analogous to those given them in the context of groups.

In the first place, a homomorphism of a ring is a mapping which preserves both operations of the ring, and our first theorem is essentially a re-statement of Problem 1 of § 5.2.

Theorem 5.91. *Any homomorphic image of a ring is a ring.*

Our study of the homomorphisms of a group showed us that the normal or invariant subgroups were uniquely associated with these homomorphisms as their kernels. In the context of rings, the groups which appear are the additive structures of the rings, and so the kernels of the homomorphisms are the ring elements which are mapped onto the *additive* identity 0. It is a consequence of Theorem 4.102 that the kernel of a ring homomorphism must be a subgroup of the additive group of the ring and, in Problem 2 of § 5.2, we have already asked the student to verify that this kernel is a subring. But the following result is even more satisfactory.

Theorem 5.92. *The kernel of a homomorphism of a ring is an ideal of the ring.*

> **Proof.** We leave the proof to the student as Problem 1, and merely remark that a critical point in the proof is the familiar fact that any ring multiple of 0 is 0.

In the theory of groups, a normal subgroup gives rise to a *regular partition* (also called a *congruence*) of the elements of the group into cosets, so that a "group" product could be defined on these cosets to form a *factor group*. In the case of rings, in view of the additive nature of their group structure, we designate the cosets additively and speak of their *sum*. For example, if $\mathcal{N}$ is a subgroup of the additive group of a ring $\mathcal{R}$, a coset determined by $\mathcal{N}$ might be designated $x + \mathcal{N}$, for some $x \in \mathcal{R}$; and the *sum* of the cosets $x + \mathcal{N}$ and $y + \mathcal{N}$ would be defined by $(x + \mathcal{N}) + (y + \mathcal{N}) = x + y + \mathcal{N}$. Of course, two cosets $x + \mathcal{N}$ and $y + \mathcal{N}$ are *equal* provided $x - y \in \mathcal{N}$, and we sometimes indicate this by the statement $x \equiv y(\mathrm{mod}\ \mathcal{N})$. *If the subgroup $\mathcal{N} = A$ is also an ideal of the ring $\mathcal{R}$* [see Problem 2], it is possible to define the *product* of two cosets as follows:

$$(x + A)(y + A) = xy + A.$$

The student should not only notice the important role played by the *ideal* properties of A in this definition, but he should check that this is a satisfactory definition and in no sense dependent on the coset representatives [Problem 3]. Our next result then follows easily.

Theorem 5.93. *If A is an ideal of a ring $\Re$, the system of cosets or "residue classes" $\{x + A\}$, with $x \in \Re$, forms a ring under the operations and equality relation designated above.*

Proof. See Problem 4.

The ring of cosets in Theorem 5.93 is called the *factor* or *quotient ring* of $\Re$ relative to A, and is designated $\Re/A$. (Some prefer the terminology of "difference ring" here, and designate it as $\Re - A$. However, while this has merit, we feel that the context will distinguish a quotient *ring* from a quotient *group*—for which we are using a similar notation.) As for the analogous group situation in § 4.10, the mapping $x \to x + A$, for any $x \in \Re$, is called the *natural homomorphism* of $\Re$ onto $\Re/A$ [Problem 5], the kernel of this homomorphism being A. A familiar example of this type of homomorphism occurs when we map the ring $\mathbf{Z}$ onto the residue class ring $\mathbf{Z}_n$ or $\mathbf{Z}/(n)$, for any positive integer n.

We now have the "ring" equivalent of Theorem 4.103.

Theorem 5.94. *If the kernel of a homomorphism of a ring $\Re$ is A, the homomorphic image of $\Re$ is isomorphic to $\Re/A$.*

Proof. See Problem 32.

This theorem asserts then that, just as all homomorphic images of a group are determined by its normal subgroups, so are all homomorphic images of a ring determined by its ideals. There are several "isomorphism theorems" for rings, which are analogous to those given in § 4.10 for groups, but we list them as Problems 33–34. We invite the student to fill in the details of their proofs for himself.

Since all homomorphic images of a ring are determined by its ideals, the nature of any particular image must depend on the nature of the particular ideal involved. This is the matter which is of most interest to us in this and the following sections, now that we have surveyed the preliminary matters of importance. Hence, we proceed with a discussion leading to two particularly important types of ideals.

It was due at least in part to the lack of "universal" divisibility in the ring of integers that an arithmetic of ideals was attempted. In fact the word "ideal," in the sense of an "ideal number," owes its origin to this notion. The addition or *sum* of two ideals A and B in a ring $\mathcal{R}$ is defined in the "obvious" way: $A + B = \{a + b \mid a \in A, b \in B\}$. For multiplication or the *product* of A and B, the collection of simple products is not enough (Why?), so we make the definition as follows: $AB = \left\{\sum\limits_{i=1}^{n} a_i b_i\right\}$, for all positive integers n, with $a_i \in A$ and $b_i \in B$. It is easily checked that both $A + B$ and AB are ideals of $\mathcal{R}$ [Problem 7]. It may be noted that, in general, the sum of two ideals is a "larger" ideal which contains both of the summand ideals, while the product is a "smaller" ideal which lies within the intersection of the component ideal factors. In fact it is useful to keep in mind that in any product of ideals, each factor of the product contains the whole ideal of which it is a factor. The "difference" $A - B$ of two ideals A and B is of no interest, since any reasonable definition of this would make it indistinguishable from the sum $A + B$, but the *quotient* $A : B$ is defined such that $A : B = \{c \in \mathcal{R} \mid bc \in A$ for *some* $b \in B\}$. It is a simple matter to verify that this quotient *of any two ideals* is an ideal of $\mathcal{R}$ [Problem 8]. The fact that the quotient always exists is the most interesting point, because this shows that "universal" division is possible in the context of ideals, and we are well on our way to verifying that we have obtained an arithmetic of ideals which is, at least in some respects, even more satisfactory than the arithmetic of commutative rings. It is again intuitively helpful to notice that, in the language of ideals, to "divide" means to "contain": that is, an ideal A divides an ideal B if and only if $B \subset A$. In the ring $\mathbf{Z}$, we know that the integers 12 and 21 are not divisible by each other. However, all the usual arithmetic operations can be performed with the principal ideals $A = (12)$ and $B = (21)$: for $A + B = (3)$, $AB = (252)$, $A : B = (4)$, $B : A = (7)$ and, we also note, incidentally, that $A \cap B = (84)$. The student is asked to verify these assertions in Problems 9–10.

The great success with the arithmetic of ideals leads one to speculate hopefully that perhaps we can "recapture" some sort of unique factorization theorem for ideals—a property which we noted in the preceding section was missing even in some commutative rings. We shall look into this matter in more detail in the final section of this chapter, but it is clear that any attempt at a unique decomposition must first involve the concept of "prime" as applied to an ideal. In the case of integers, we have available two approaches to the concept of "prime": an integer p is prime if it has no proper divisors—i.e., none except p and 1; an integer p is prime if, whenever $p \mid ab$ for two integers a, b, then either $p \mid a$ or $p \mid b$. When we identify the notion of "divides" with "contains," in the case of ideals, we are led to the corresponding notions for ideals: an ideal P in $\mathcal{R}$ would be "prime," according to the first approach, if an inclusion $P \subset Q \subset \mathcal{R}$, for an ideal Q, must imply that $Q = P$ or $Q = \mathcal{R}$; the second approach would lead us to the notion that P is "prime" if $AB \subset P$, for ideals A and B, must imply that either $A \subset P$ or $B \subset P$. While the two viewpoints lead us to the same concept in the ring of integers, we shall see shortly that this is not the case for rings in general. However, the concepts introduced by both approaches are of importance, and we are led by them to the following definitions.

Definition. An ideal M in a ring $\mathcal{R}$ is *maximal* if $M \subset Q \subset \mathcal{R}$, for an ideal Q, implies that $Q = M$ or $Q = \mathcal{R}$.

Definition. An ideal P in a *commutative* ring $\mathcal{R}$ is *prime* if $ab \in P$, for elements $a, b \in \mathcal{R}$, implies that $a \in P$ or $b \in P$.

In the ring $\mathbf{Z}$, we know that all ideals are principal, and it is clear [Problem 25] that an ideal is maximal if and only if it is generated by a prime. Moreover, it is easy to verify [Problem 25] that $(a)(b) = (ab)$, for integers a, b, and so we see that an ideal in $\mathbf{Z}$ is prime if and only if it also is generated by a prime. Hence in $\mathbf{Z}$ the notions of prime and maximal ideals coincide. The same sort of argument can be applied to the ring $\mathcal{F}[x]$, so that in this type of polynomial ring, too, there is no distinction between prime and maximal ideals [Problem 27]. However, while we shall extend this result in § 5.10 to any PID, one does not need to go far to find rings which are even commutative but for which the two notions do *not* coincide. For example, in the ring $\mathbf{Z}[x, y]$, with two indeterminates x and y, the ideals (x) and (x, y) are both prime, but neither is maximal. We can see that (x) is prime by observing that if a product of polynomials in x is a polynomial multiple of x, then so must be one of the factors. Likewise, the ideal (x, y) consists of all polynomials in $\mathbf{Z}[x, y]$ with zero constant terms; and if a product of two polynomials in $\mathbf{Z}[x, y]$ has this property, the fact that $\mathbf{Z}[x, y]$ is an integral domain requires that at least one of the polynomials also has this property. However, since $(x) \subset (x, y) \subset (x, y, 3) \subset \mathbf{Z}[x, y]$, it is clear that neither of the prime ideals (x) or (x, y) is maximal. A similar argument will show that the ideal $(x, y, 3)$ is prime, but suppose that $(x, y, 3) \subset Q \subset \mathbf{Z}[x, y]$ for an ideal Q. Then Q must contain a polynomial $b + h(x, y)$, where $h(x, y) \in (x, y)$ and $b \in \mathbf{Z}$ is not divisible by 3. But it would then follow that Q must contain the g.c.d. of 3 and b, which is 1, and so $Q = \mathbf{Z}[x, y]$. Hence $(x, y, 3)$ is both prime and maximal in $\mathbf{Z}[x, y]$. In the next section, as we resume our study of homomorphic images of a ring, we shall discover some of the important consequences of our making the kernel of a homomorphism either a prime or a maximal ideal.

PROBLEMS 5–9

   *1. Prove Theorem 5.92.
   *2. Check that the definition, which we have given for the product of two cosets of an ideal A, is consistent with our earlier definition of a product of sets, and point out how the "ideal" properties of A are important here.

*3. If A is an ideal of $\mathcal{R}$, explain why our definition of the product of two cosets is satisfactory—and not dependent on the coset representatives.

*4. Prove Theorem 5.93.

*5. If A is an ideal of the ring $\mathcal{R}$, verify that the mapping $r \to r + A$, for $r \in \mathcal{R}$, is a homomorphism.

6. Describe each of the following ideals of $\mathbf{Z}$: (a) $(2, 3)$; (b) $(5, 6, 10)$; (c) (1).

*7. If A and B are ideals of $\mathcal{R}$, verify that $A + B$ and AB are also ideals.

*8. If A and B are ideals of $\mathcal{R}$, verify that $A : B$ is also an ideal of $\mathcal{R}$.

9. If $A = (12)$ and $B = (21)$ are ideals of $\mathbf{Z}$, verify that (a) $A + B = (3)$; (b) $AB = (252)$; (c) $A \cap B = (84)$.

10. With A and B as in Problem 9, verify that (a) $A : B = (4)$; (b) $B : A = (7)$.

11. Determine $A : B$ and $B : A$ if A and B are ideals of $\mathbf{Z}$ defined as $A = (8)$ and $B = (12)$.

12. If $A = (x^2 + 1)$ and $B = (x + 2)$ are ideals of $\mathbf{Z}[x]$, describe the ideal (a) $A + B$; (b) AB.

13. Do Problem 12 with $A = (x - 1)$ and $B = (x)$.

14. Describe $A : B$ and $B : A$, with A and B defined in (a) Problem 12; (b) Problem 13.

15. Describe the quotient ring $\mathbf{Z}/A$, where (a) $A = (2, 5)$; (b) $A = (3, 4, 5)$.

**16. Describe the quotient ring $\mathbf{Q}[x]/A$, where (a) $A = (x + 1)$; (b) $A = (a, b)$ with $a = x + 1$ and $b = x^2 - 1$.

17. Describe the quotient ring $\mathbf{Z}[x]/A$, where (a) $A = (x^2 + 1)$; (b) $A = (x + 1)$.

18. Describe the quotient ring $\mathbf{Z}[x]/A$, where (a) $A = (2)$; (b) $A = (1)$.

19. Verify that the mapping $a + bi \to a - bi$, with $a, b \in \mathbf{R}$, defines an automorphism of the field $\mathbf{C}$ of complex numbers.

*20. Prove that a field, considered as a ring, can have no proper ideals. What about a division ring?

21. Find the ideals—and hence all homomorphic images—of the subring of matrices in $M_2(\mathbf{Z})$ of the form $\begin{bmatrix} a & b \\ 0 & c \end{bmatrix}$. (Note that $M_2(\mathbf{Z})$ is not commutative.)

22. If $a \equiv b$ (mod A) and $c \equiv d$ (mod A), for an ideal A in a ring, prove that (a) $a + c \equiv b + d$ (mod A); (b) $ac \equiv bd$ (mod A); (c) $na \equiv nb$ (mod A), for any positive integer n.

23. Verify that the quotient ring $\mathbf{Z}/(n)$ is merely another way of describing the familiar ring $\mathbf{Z}_n$ of residue classes [see Example 4 of § 5.1], and so it is appropriate not to distinguish between these rings.

24. If the ring $\mathbf{Z}_n$ is considered a homomorphic image [see Problem 23] of $\mathbf{Z}$, what is the kernel of the homomorphism when (a) $n = 2$; (b) $n = 3$; (c) $n = 5$?

*25. Verify that $(a)(b) = (ab)$, for arbitrary integers $a, b \in \mathbf{Z}$; and that (a) is maximal in $\mathbf{Z}$ if and only if a is prime.

26. Decide whether the ideal $(x, y, 4)$ is prime and/or maximal in $\mathbf{Z}[x, y]$.

*27. Prove that the notions of "prime" and "maximal" are equivalent as applied to ideals in $\mathcal{F}[x]$.

28. Decide whether the principal ideal (xy) in the ring $\mathbf{Z}[x, y]$ is either prime or maximal.

29. Prove that any ring with identity is isomorphic to a ring of endomorphisms

of its additive group. (Hint: let r_a designate "right multiplication by a," so that $xr_a = xa$, for any x and fixed a in the ring. Then show that $a \to r_a$ is the desired isomorphism.)

30. If α is a homomorphism of an arbitrary ring $\mathcal{R}$, prove that

    (a) $\mathcal{R}\alpha$ is commutative if $\mathcal{R}$ is commutative;

    (b) the identity of $\mathcal{R}\alpha$ is $e\alpha$ if e is the identity of $\mathcal{R}$;

    (c) $x\alpha$ is a unit of $\mathcal{R}\alpha$ if x is a unit of $\mathcal{R}$, and $(x\alpha)^{-1} = (x^{-1})\alpha$.

31. Refer to Problem 30 and verify that $\mathbf{Z}$ can not be mapped homomorphically onto the ring of even integers.

32. Prove Theorem 5.94.

33. Let $\alpha : \mathcal{R} \to \mathcal{R}'$ be a homomorphism with kernel C. Then prove that A' is an ideal of $\mathcal{R}'$ if and only if $A'\alpha^{-1} = A$ is an ideal of $\mathcal{R}$ such that $A \supset C$, and that $(\mathcal{R}/C)/(A/C) \cong \mathcal{R}/A$. (Hint: refer to Theorem 4.105 and verify the necessary multiplicative properties.)

34. If A and B are ideals of a ring $\mathcal{R}$, prove that $(A + B)/B \cong A/(A \cap B)$. (Hint: see Theorem 4.104. Show that the natural homomorphism of $\mathcal{R}$ onto $\mathcal{R}/B$ induces a homomorphism of A onto $(A + B)/B$; then take note of the kernel of the induced homomorphism, and apply Theorem 5.94.)

**35. Verify the isomorphism asserted in Problem 34, for the case where $\mathcal{R} = \mathbf{Z}$, $A = (9)$, and $B = (15)$.

5.10. From Rings to Integral Domains and Fields: Homomorphisms

In § 5.8, we saw how it is possible to obtain a field from an integral domain by a process of "imbedding." We now discuss another method for obtaining fields from integral domains or even commutative rings with identity. Our present method will be by way of homomorphisms.

We have made the observation several times in the past that many properties of an algebraic system are regularly preserved by homomorphisms of the system: in the case of rings, we may refer to Theorem 5.91 and Problem 30 of § 5.9. At the same time, it is possible for certain properties of a system to be lost under homomorphism, and one of these somewhat "tenuous" properties is *the absence of divisors of zero*. For example, the ring $\mathbf{Z}$ of integers has no divisors of zero, but it is a familiar fact that the homomorphic image $\mathbf{Z}_n$ or $\mathbf{Z}/(n)$ *has* divisors of zero if n is a composite (i.e., nonprime) integer. It has been noted before that the homomorphic images of a ring are determined by the kernels of these mappings, and so the ideals of a ring come naturally to the foreground in the study of this section. It turns out that the prime ideals and maximal ideals are the kinds of particular interest. Our first result is indicative of this.

Theorem 5.101. *If $\mathcal{R}$ is a commutative ring, the quotient ring $\mathcal{R}/P$ has no divisors of zero if and only if P is a prime ideal of $\mathcal{R}$.*

Proof. The elements of $\mathcal{R}/P$ are cosets of P, and it should be recalled that the zero coset in the quotient ring is P. Let us designate two arbitrary cosets $a + P$ and $b + P$ in $\mathcal{R}/P$ by $\bar{a}$ and $\bar{b}$, respectively. Then $\mathcal{R}/P$ has no divisors of zero if and only if $\bar{a} \cdot \bar{b} = 0 = P$ implies that either $\bar{a} = 0 = P$ or $\bar{b} = 0 = P$. Now, a coset $\bar{x} \in \mathcal{R}/P$ is equal to P if and only if $x \in P$, and our definition of multiplication in $\mathcal{R}/P$ requires that $\bar{a} \cdot \bar{b} = \overline{ab}$. Hence, we have asserted that $\mathcal{R}/P$ has no divisors of zero if and only if $ab \in P$ implies that either $a \in P$ or $b \in P$. Since this latter condition is precisely the defining property of a prime ideal of $\mathcal{R}$, our proof is complete. ∎

Since the presence of an identity element is a property which is passed on to any homomorphic image of a ring, we have the following corollary.

Corollary. *If $\mathcal{E}$ is an integral domain, a homomorphic image $\mathcal{E}/P$ is also an integral domain if and only if P is a prime ideal of $\mathcal{R}$.*

Since the prime ideals of $\mathbf{Z}$ are the principal ideals (p), where p is a prime integer, we again have the well-known result that the quotient rings $\mathbf{Z}/(p)$ or $\mathbf{Z}_p$ are integral domains. For example, the rings $\mathbf{Z}_5$, $\mathbf{Z}_7$, and $\mathbf{Z}_{17}$ are integral domains, while a ring such as $\mathbf{Z}_6$ is not. In these cases, of course, the original ring $\mathbf{Z}$ has no divisors of zero, and the theorem tells us how to preserve this property in a homomorphic image. It is also easy to start with a ring which *does* have divisors of zero and obtain a quotient ring which is free of divisors of zero. For example, we can make the Cartesian product $\mathbf{R} \times \mathbf{R}$ of all ordered pairs of real numbers into a ring $\mathcal{R}$ by defining addition and multiplication of these pairs as follows:

$$(x_1, y_1) + (x_2, y_2) = (x_1 + x_2, y_1 + y_2);$$

$$(x_1, y_1)(x_2, y_2) = (x_1 x_2, y_1 y_2).$$

We leave to the student [Problem 4] the verification that $\mathcal{R}$ is a ring, with zero element $(0, 0) = 0$ and identity element $(1, 1)$. It is easy to see that $\mathcal{R}$ has divisors of zero: $(x, 0) \neq 0$ and $(0, y) \neq 0$, but $(x, 0)(0, y) = (0, 0) = 0$. The subset of elements of the form $(x, 0)$ constitute an ideal P of $\mathcal{R}$, and it is not difficult to see that P is prime. For, if $(x_1, y_1)(x_2, y_2) = (x_1 x_2, y_1 y_2) \in P$, then $y_1 y_2 = 0$. But, since y_1 and y_2 are real numbers, $y_1 y_2 = 0$ if and only if either $y_1 = 0$ or $y_2 = 0$, i.e., if and only if either $(x_1, y_1) \in P$ or $(x_2, y_2) \in P$. Hence, the ideal P is prime. The above theorem then assures us that, even though the ring $\mathcal{R}$ has divisors of zero, the quotient ring $\mathcal{R}/P$ has none; and, since an identity is present, the quotient ring is an integral domain.

If we know that the kernel of a homomorphism is a maximal ideal of the ring, we are able to obtain a much stronger result.

Theorem 5.102. *If $\mathcal{R}$ is a commutative ring* with identity, *the quotient ring $\mathcal{R}/M$ is a field if and only if M is a maximal ideal of $\mathcal{R}$.*

Proof. For suppose M is a maximal ideal of $\mathcal{R}$, with a an element which is in $\mathcal{R}$ but not in M. It can be easily seen that the set of all elements of the form $m + xa$, with $m \in M$ and $x \in \mathcal{R}$, is an ideal in $\mathcal{R}$ [Problem 1]. Since this ideal contains an element a, which is not in the maximal ideal M, it follows that this constructed ideal is the whole ring $\mathcal{R}$. In particular, the identity element 1 is in this ideal, so that $1 = m_1 + ba$, where $m_1 \in M$ and $b \in \mathcal{R}$. In the quotient ring $\mathcal{R}/M$, this means that $(b + M)(a + M) = 1 + M$ or, in the usual symbolism for cosets, $\bar{b} \cdot \bar{a} = \bar{1}$. Since a was an arbitrary element of $\mathcal{R}$ that was not in M, we may regard $\bar{a}$ as an arbitrary nonzero element of $\mathcal{R}/M$, and we have shown that $\bar{a}$ has a multiplicative inverse, Hence [Problem 2] $\mathcal{R}/M$ is a field.

Conversely, let us suppose that $\mathcal{R}/M$ is a field. If M is not maximal, there must exist an ideal Q in $\mathcal{R}$ such that $M \subset Q \subset \mathcal{R}$. Let a be an arbitrary element of $\mathcal{R}$, with b an arbitrary element of Q which is not in M. In the quotient ring $\mathcal{R}/M$, we let $a + M$ and $b + M$ be $\bar{a}$ and $\bar{b}$, respectively, and since $\mathcal{R}/M$ is a field we know that there exists an element $\bar{c} \in \mathcal{R}/M$ such that $\bar{b} \cdot \bar{c} = \bar{a}$ [Problem 3]. But this equation can be written as $(b + M)(c + M) = a + M$, from which we see that $bc - a \in M$. Since $M \subset Q$ we must have $bc - a \in Q$ and, since $b \in Q$, this implies that $a \in Q$. We have shown that an arbitrary element of $\mathcal{R}$ is in Q and so $\mathcal{R} = Q$. Hence M is a maximal ideal. ∎

An application of Theorem 5.102 to Theorem 5.101 gives us the following result.

Corollary. *Any maximal ideal of a commutative ring with an identity is prime.*

The converse of this corollary is not true, for in § 5.9 we noted examples of prime ideals of the ring $Z[x, y]$ which are not maximal. However, in the familiar ring Z [see Problems 25 of § 5.9], it is the case that any prime ideal is maximal: for, let us suppose that $(p) \subset (n) \subset Z$, for integers n, p, with p prime. Then $p = mn$, for some integer m, and, since p is a prime, $m = \pm 1$. Hence $n = \pm p$ and $(n) = (p)$, contrary to our supposition, and we conclude that (p) must be maximal. It follows—and we have already observed this, independent of the present result, in the corollary to Theorem 5.33—that the rings Z_5, Z_7, and Z_{17}, previously recognized as integral domains, are in reality fields. In fact, if (p) is a prime ideal of Z, with $\bar{a}$ any nonzero element of

Z_p, Theorem 2.42 asserts the existence of integers s and t such that $1 = sa + tp$. Hence, $\bar{1} = \bar{s} \cdot \bar{a}$, so that $\bar{s}$ is the multiplicative inverse of $\bar{a}$ in Z_p or $Z/(p)$. In particular, if $p = 7$ and $a = 3$, we know that $1 = (-2) \cdot 3 + (1) \cdot 7$. Hence, the multiplicative inverse of $\bar{3}$ in Z_7 is $\overline{-2}$ or, in the more usual form, $\bar{5}$. In the isomorphic ring of "remainders" this states that the multiplicative inverse of 3 is 5.

We have noted before [see § 5.9 and Problem 27 of § 5.9] that in Z and $\mathcal{F}[x]$, for any field $\mathcal{F}$, the concepts of "prime" and "maximal", as applied to ideals, coincide. However, we can obtain a stronger result which includes these as important special cases.

Theorem 5.103. *Any nonzero ideal of a PID is prime if and only if it is maximal.*

Proof. Let us assume that P is a nonzero prime ideal of the principal ideal domain $\mathcal{R}$. Then $P = (p)$, for some prime element $p \in \mathcal{R}$, and if a is any element of $\mathcal{R}$ not in P, the g.c.d. of a and p must be the identity element 1 of $\mathcal{R}$. (We recall that we have always required a PID to have an identity element!) By Theorem 5.63, it follows that $1 = ra + sp$, for some r, $s \in \mathcal{R}$, so that $(1) = \mathcal{R} \subset (a, P) \subset \mathcal{R}$. But then $(a, P) = \mathcal{R}$, and P is a maximal ideal of $\mathcal{R}$. In view of the Corollary to Theorem 5.102, our proof is complete. ∎

As was implied above, the polynomial ring $Q[x]$ falls into the domain of applicability of this theorem, For example, it is easy to see that the ideal $(x + 1)$ is prime in $Q[x]$, and hence also maximal. The theorem then assures us that the quotient ring $Q[x]/(x + 1)$ is not only an integral domain but a field. On the other hand, it may be seen that the quotient ring $Q[x]/(x^2 + 2x)$ is not even an integral domain, for it has divisors of zero [see Problem 12].

PROBLEMS 5–10

*1. Explain why the set $\{m + xa\}$, in the proof of Theorem 5.102, is an ideal of $\mathcal{R}$.

*2. With reference to the first part of the proof of Theorem 5.102, explain why the existence of inverses is sufficient to establish the fact that $\mathcal{R}/M$ is a field.

*3. In the "converse" portion of the proof of Theorem 5.102, explain how we know that the element $\bar{c}$ exists.

4. Prove that the algebraic system constructed in this section from the set $R \times R$ is a ring.

5. Solve the following congruences for $x \in Z$: (a) $2x \equiv 1 \pmod 5$; (b) $x^2 \equiv -1 \pmod 7$; (c) $x^2 \equiv -1 \pmod 6$.

**6. Determine the multiplicative inverse of each of the following elements of $Z/(7)$: (a) $\bar{2}$; (b) $\bar{4}$; (c) $\bar{5}$.

7. Determine the multiplicative inverse of each of the following elements of $Z/(5)$: (a) $\bar{2}$; (b) $\bar{3}$; (c) $\bar{4}$.

8. Use the results in Problem 7 to write down the complete addition and multiplication table for the elements of $Z/(5)$.

9. Give a proof, independent of Theorem 5.103, that any prime ideal of $Q[x]$ is maximal.

10. Consider Problem 9, and decide whether any prime ideal in $Z[x]$ is also maximal. If your decision is negative, a counterexample will suffice.

11. Prove that every prime ideal of $Z[x]$ is generated by a monic, irreducible polynomial.

12. Exhibit a divisor of zero in the quotient ring $Q[x]/(x^2 + 2x)$.

13. Determine the multiplicative inverse of each of the following elements of $Q[x]/(x + 1)$: (a) $\overline{3x}$; (b) $\overline{x^2}$; (c) $\overline{2x^2 - 1}$.

14. Determine the multiplicative inverse of each of the following elements of $Q[x]/(x^3 + 3)$: (a) $\bar{x}$; (b) $\overline{x + 5}$; (c) $\overline{x^2 + 5}$.

15. If $p(x)$ is a monic polynomial of $Z[x]$, decide whether there is any difference between the quotient rings $Z[x]/(p(x))$ and $Q[x]/(p(x))$.

16. Is (2) a prime ideal in either $Z[x]$ or $Q[x]$? Describe both $Z[x]/(2)$ and $Q[x]/(2)$.

17. Find a prime ideal which is not maximal in the ring $\mathcal{R}[x]$, where $\mathcal{R}$ is the ring of even integers.

18. Describe each of the following quotient rings: (a) $Q[x]/(x - 3)$; (b) $Q[x]/(x^2 + 1)$.

**19. Prove that the quotient ring in Problem 18(b) is isomorphic to the familiar field of complex numbers.

20. With reference to Problem 19, identify the correspondent of i in the quotient ring and verify that its square is the correspondent of -1.

21. Examine the quotient ring $Z[x, y]/(x)$ and conclude that it is an integral domain but not a field. Explain why (x) is not maximal in $Z[x, y]$.

22. In the ring $Q[x, y]$, decide which of the following ideals are prime and which are maximal: (a) $(x^2 + 1)$; (b) (x^2); (c) $(x - 2)$.

23. Use the directions of Problem 22 for the following ideals: (a) $(x^2 - 1)$; (b) $(x - 1, y + 1)$; (c) $(x^2 + 1, y - 1)$.

24. Describe each of the following quotient rings: (a) $Z[x, y]/(x, y + 1)$; (b) $Z[x]/(x, 2)$.

25. Determine the inverse of $\overline{x + y + 1}$ in the ring $Z[x, y]/(x, y, 3)$.

26. Discover a nonzero element of $Z[x, y]/(x, y)$ which does not have an inverse.

27. If P is an ideal of a commutative ring $\mathcal{R}$, prove that P is prime if and only if the set-theoretic complement of P in $\mathcal{R}$ is closed under the operation of multiplication.

28. Let M be an ideal of a commutative ring $\mathcal{R}$. Then prove that $\mathcal{R}/M$ is a field if M is a maximal ideal of $\mathcal{R}$ and $x \in M$ whenever $x^2 \in M$.

29. Prove the converse of the assertion in Problem 28.

30. Use results in this section to prove "Fermat's Little Theorem": $a^{p-1} \equiv 1 \pmod{p}$, for any prime integer p and $a \not\equiv 0 \pmod{p}$.

31. Show that the field $Z/(p)$, for any prime p, contains exactly two distinct elements whose square is congruent to 1 (mod p).

32. Use results in this section, including Problem 31, to prove "Wilson's Theorem": For any prime integer p, $(p - 1)! \equiv -1 \pmod{p}$.
33. If $\mathscr{R}$ is a commutative ring without identity and M is a maximal ideal of $\mathscr{R}$, prove that either $\mathscr{R}/M$ is a field or $\mathscr{R}/M$ is a zero ring.

5.11. Noetherian Rings

We now return to the matter of unique factorization which was discussed in § 5.7 and again in § 5.9. We have noted before that all Euclidean rings, including the familiar rings $\mathbf{Z}$ and $\mathscr{F}[x]$, for any field $\mathscr{F}$, possess the three basic properties which we may list in abbreviated form as: universal divisibility (except by 0) with remainder; the existence of a g.c.d. of any two elements and its representation as a "linear combination" of the elements—the latter being a characteristic property of any PIR; unique factorization. If we attempt to preserve these properties in more general rings, we usually encounter difficulties. In the ring $\mathbf{Z}[x]$, for example, we lose "universal divisibility" and the characteristic PIR property of the g.c.d. due to the presence of non-units in $\mathbf{Z}$. We suffer the same losses if we extend $\mathbf{Q}[x]$ to $\mathbf{Q}[x, y]$, for there are nonunits in $\mathbf{Q}[x]$—which we can regard as the "coefficient" ring—and it is well known that $\mathbf{Q}[x, y]$ is not a PID [see Problem 14]. It may be observed, however, that both $\mathbf{Z}[x]$ and $\mathbf{Q}[x, y]$ are unique factorization domains. In fact, in any UFD it is possible to give a suitable definition of "prime" or "irreducible" (such as "primitive" in the case of $\mathbf{Z}[x]$), so that any two elements will certainly have a g.c.d. But a representation of the g.c.d. as a "linear combination" will not be guaranteed unless we know that the UFD is also a PID. When we turn from polynomial rings to subrings of real numbers of the form $\mathbf{Z}[\sqrt{m}]$, where m is a positive integer possessing no square factors, the situation does not improve! It is easy to see that we have unique factorization [Problem 15] but not universal divisibility in such a ring, while a characterization of its ideals would require more study than we care to give at this time. If we consider subrings of the *ring* of complex numbers, of the same form but with $m < 0$, we encounter an entirely different situation. A special ring of this type is the ring of Gaussian integers, and it *can* be shown that all three of the properties listed at the beginning of this section are possessed by this ring. (For the g.c.d. property, see pp. 385–386 of [3]). On the other hand, we have noted already in § 5.7, in the case of the ring $\mathbf{Z}[\sqrt{-5}]$ or $\mathbf{Z}[i\sqrt{5}]$, that the number 6 has two distinct factorizations: $6 = 2 \cdot 3 = (1 + i\sqrt{5})(1 - i\sqrt{5})$. A very useful technique, in connection with "factorization" problems in rings of the type $\mathbf{Z}[\sqrt{m}]$, involves the "norm" and we refer the student to Problem 17.

We remarked in § 5.9 that "ideal numbers" or ideals were introduced, at least in part, in an attempt to salvage some sort of unique factorization theorem in rings without losing universal divisibility and the existence of a g.c.d. Moreover, we have already seen that ideals *are* always divisible by each other; and the g.c.d. of any number of ideals *does* exist—where we must interpret "divisor" in the sense of "container." It is also easy to see that, in the particular "adverse" case of $\mathbf{Z}[i\sqrt{5}]$ above, we *do* have unique factorization —at least for the element 6. For, in $\mathbf{Z}[i\sqrt{5}]$, the ideals (2), (3), $(1 + i\sqrt{5})$, $(1 - i\sqrt{5})$ are principal but not prime: we can show, in fact, that the ideals $P = (2, 1 + i\sqrt{5})$ and $Q = (3, 1 + i\sqrt{5})$ are prime and that $P^2 = (2)$ and $Q^2 = (3)$. To see that P is prime in $\mathbf{Z}[i\sqrt{5}]$, we observe that $m + ni\sqrt{5} \in P$ if and only if $m + n \equiv 0 \pmod 2$. Thus, $\mathbf{Z}[i\sqrt{5}]/P$ has only two elements, and so is a field, whence P is a prime by Theorems 5.102 and 5.103. A similar argument shows that Q is prime. Thus, while 6 has two distinct factorizations in the ring $\mathbf{Z}[i\sqrt{5}]$, the prime ideal (6) has only one as a product [see Problem 2] of powers of prime ideals: $(6) = P^2 Q^2$. Actually any ideal in $\mathbf{Z}[i\sqrt{5}]$ has such a unique decomposition, and it is possible to generalize this result to include all ideals in the so-called "domain of algebraic integers"; but we do not wish to pursue the "factorization" problem further in this direction.

Unfortunately, our hopes in ideals are soon shattered by a consideration of the situation in the simple polynomial domain $\mathbf{Z}[x]$—a domain, incidentally, which does have unique factorization of its *elements* in terms of primitive polynomials. To support this remark, let us consider the ideal $(x^2, 3)$ in $\mathbf{Z}[x]$. It is easy to see that this ideal is not prime: for example, x^2 is in the ideal, but x is not. However, it is not possible to express $(x^2, 3)$ as a product of primes, for suppose that P is a prime ideal such that $(x^2, 3) \subset P$. The assumption that P is prime now assures us that x is in P, and so $(x, 3) \subset P$. The ideal $(x, 3)$ consists of all polynomials of $\mathbf{Z}[x]$ whose constants are multiples of 3, and it is clear that $(x, 3)$ is maximal: for if $f(x) \notin (x, 3)$, the constant term of $f(x)$ must be prime to 3, so that $(x, 3, f(x))$ must contain 1 and be the ring $\mathbf{Z}[x]$. In view of Theorem 5.103, it follows that $P = (x, 3)$ is the *only* proper prime ideal which contains $(x^2, 3)$. Since the constant term of any polynomial in P^2 must be a multiple of 9, $(x^2, 3) \not\subset P^2$, and so we must conclude that $(x^2, 3)$ has no representation as a product of prime ideals.

There is one rather large class of rings, however, in which we do have a factorization theorem which is at least somewhat satisfactory—although it is far from comparable to the pleasant situation which prevails in $\mathbf{Z}$ and $\mathcal{F}[x]$. These rings are called "Noetherian," after Emmy Noether (1882– 1935) who initiated the abstract development of their structure theory, and their definition will be given shortly.

A ring $\mathcal{R}$ is said to satisfy the *ascending chain condition* (a.c.c.) for ideals if every sequence of ideals A_1, A_2, A_3, ... in $\mathcal{R}$, such that $A_1 \subset A_2 \subset A_3 \subset ...$, has only a finite number of terms without repetitions. That is, there can not exist any *infinite, properly ascending* chain of ideals in this kind of ring. Since a field has no proper ideals [Problem 20, § 5.9], this condition is trivially satisfied in any field. In the ring $\mathbf{Z}$, since $(n) \subset (m)$ implies that m divides n, whereas n can have only a finite number of distinct divisors, it is immediate that the a.c.c. is also satisfied here. We shall formally state later (Hilbert's Basis Theorem) that the a.c.c. is also inherited by any polynomial domain in a finite number of indeterminates which has coefficients in a domain which satisfies the condition. However, if we consider the ring of polynomials in an infinite number of indeterminates x_1, x_2, x_3, ..., with coefficients in any field, it is easy to see that the a.c.c. does not hold: for the properly ascending chain $(x_1) \subset (x_1, x_2) \subset (x_1, x_2, x_3) \subset \cdots$ does not terminate.

We recall that a *basis* of an ideal is a *minimal* set of generators for the ideal, and we now define a *Noetherian ring* to be a *commutative ring with identity* which satisfies any (and so all) of the conditions which are asserted in the following theorem to be equivalent.

Theorem 5.111. *In any commutative ring $\mathcal{R}$ the following conditions are equivalent:*

   (i) *$\mathcal{R}$ satisfies the ascending chain condition.*
  (ii) *Every ideal in $\mathcal{R}$ has a finite basis, i.e., a finite number of basis elements.*
 (iii) *Every nonempty set of ideals in $\mathcal{R}$ contains at least one which is not contained in any other of the set. Such an ideal may be said to be maximal in the set.*

Proof. We shall show that (i) implies (ii), (ii) implies (iii), and (iii) implies (i) in this order. First, let A be an ideal in $\mathcal{R}$, which we assume now to satisfy the a.c.c., and pick an element $a_1 \in A$. If $(a_1) = A$, the ideal A has a basis of one element and there is nothing to prove. Otherwise, pick another element $a_2 \in A$ so that $a_2 \notin (a_1)$, and it is clear that $(a_1) \subset (a_1, a_2) \subset A$. If $(a_1, a_2) = A$, the ideal A has a basis of two elements and again there is nothing more to prove. Otherwise, we can select another element $a_3 \in A$ and repeat the above reasoning. In view of the a.c.c., the chain of ideals $(a_1) \subset (a_1, a_2) \subset (a_1, a_2, a_3) \subset \cdots$ must properly terminate, and so for some integer k, $(a_1, a_2, a_3, \cdots, a_k) = A$, thus establishing (ii).

In order to prove (iii) from (ii), we assume that every ideal in $\mathcal{R}$ has a finite basis, and let us consider any set S of ideals in $\mathcal{R}$. Any particular ideal A_1 in S is either maximal or is properly contained in some other ideal $A_2 \in S$. Likewise, either A_2 is maximal or is properly contained in some other ideal $A_3 \in S$. A continuation of this reasoning leads either to a maximal ideal A_k after k selections, or to an infinite proper chain of ideals:

$A_1 \subset A_2 \subset A_3 \subset \cdots$. It can be seen [Problem 1] that the set theoretic union A of all ideals in this chain is an ideal in $\mathcal{R}$, and so has a basis by our assumption in (ii). Hence $A = (a_1, a_2, a_3, \ldots, a_r)$, for some integer r, and each element a_i is an element of some ideal A_{k_i} of the chain. If k is chosen as the largest of the k_i occurring, it follows that $A \subset A_k$. But $A_k \subset A$, and so $A = A_k$, which requires that each A_i lies in A_k. Hence no infinite, properly ascending chain of ideals is possible, and S must contain a maximal ideal, as required in (iii).

In order to prove that (iii) implies (i), let $A_1, A_2, A_3, \ldots$ be a collection of ideals such that $A_1 \subset A_2 \subset A_3 \subset \cdots$. By our assumption of (iii), this collection contains a maximal ideal—say A_m—so that $A_m = A_{m+1} = \cdots$, and so the properly ascending chain must have finite length m. This is the statement of (i), and completes the proof of the theorem. ∎

We have seen before that many properties of a ring $\mathcal{R}$ are inherited by the polynomial ring $\mathcal{R}[x]$. For example, we showed that if $\mathcal{E}$ is an integral domain, then so is $\mathcal{E}[x]$; we pointed out—although we did not prove it—that if $\mathcal{R}$ is a UFD, then so is $\mathcal{R}[x]$, this result being one (of many) whose proof goes back to Gauss; any field $\mathcal{F}$ is a trivial PID, and we have seen that $\mathcal{F}[x]$ is a nontrivial PID—but, unfortunately, this particular result does not carry over from any principal ideal domain $\mathcal{R}$ to $\mathcal{R}[x]$. We now come to another case, previously alluded to, where a property does carry over to the extension by an indeterminate, and we state this result in the following theorem.

Theorem 5.112 (Hilbert Basis Theorem). *If $\mathcal{R}$ is any Noetherian ring, then so is $\mathcal{R}[x]$.*

By induction, of course, we are then able to assert that $\mathcal{R}[x_1, x_2, \ldots, x_n]$ is also Noetherian, for a finite number of indeterminates $x_1, x_2, \ldots, x_n$. For a proof of this theorem, we refer the student to pp. 171–172 of [4].

PROBLEMS 5–11

**1. If $A_1 \subset A_2 \subset A_3 \subset \cdots$ is an infinite, ascending chain of ideals in a ring, prove that the set-theoretic union of all ideals in the chain is an ideal.

*2. Make the reasonable extension of the definition of the product of two ideals in a commutative ring to include arbitrary products and powers of ideals. In particular, what is the definition of A^n, for an ideal A and arbitrary positive integer n?

*3. If $m = rs$ is a factorization of the integer m as a product of integers r and s, prove that $(m) = (r)(s)$.

4. If $m = pq$, where p and q are distinct prime integers, use Problem 3 to prove that $(m) = (p) \cap (q)$.

5. Describe each of the following ideals in $\mathbf{Z}$: (a) (2); (b) (2, 3); (c) (3, 5, 7, ...).

6. Find a one-element basis for each of the following ideals in $\mathbf{Z}$: (a) (2, 5); (b) (2, 4); (c) (2, 4, 6).

7. Describe each of the following ideals in $\mathbf{Z}[x]$: (a) (2); (b) (2, 3); (c) (3, 5, 7, ...)
   [cf. Problem 5].

8. Find a one-element basis for each of the following ideals in $\mathbf{Q}[x]$: (a) $(2, x)$;
   (b) $(2, 3, x)$; (c) $(x^2, x^4, x^6, ...)$.

9. Describe the ideals, generated as in Problem 7, but considered ideals of $\mathbf{Q}[x]$.

10. Explain why no ideal in $\mathbf{Z}[\sqrt{2}]$ can contain two relatively prime rational
    integers.

11. Describe the ideal $(\sqrt{2})$ in $\mathbf{Z}[\sqrt{2}]$.

12. Describe the following ideals in the ring $\mathbf{Z}[\sqrt{3}]$: (a) $(2, \sqrt{3})$; (b) $(3, \sqrt{3})$.

13. Explain why $(2, x) = (1)$ in $\mathbf{Q}[x]$, but $(2, x) \neq (1)$ in $\mathbf{Z}[x]$.

14. The g.c.d. of the polynomials $a(x, y) = x$ and $b(x, y) = y$ in $\mathbf{Z}[x, y]$ is clearly 1.
    Show, however, that polynomials $s(x, y)$ and $t(x, y)$ do *not* exist such that
    $s(x, y)a(x, y) + t(x, y)b(x, y) = 1$.

15. If $m > 1$ is a square-free positive integer, explain why unique factorization
    is a property of the ring $\mathbf{Z}[\sqrt{m}]$.

16. With m as in Problem 15, and $u = a + b\sqrt{m}$, show that the mapping $u \to \bar{u} = a - b\sqrt{m}$ is an automorphism of the ring $\mathbf{Z}[\sqrt{m}]$.

17. With u as in Problem 16, we define the *norm* $N(u)$ as $u\bar{u} = a^2 - b^2 m$. Then
    show that $u = vw$, for elements $v, w \in \mathbf{Z}[\sqrt{m}]$, if and only if $N(u) = N(v)N(w)$;
    and conclude that an element of $\mathbf{Z}[\sqrt{m}]$ has a nontrivial factorization if and
    only if its norm has a nontrivial factorization in $\mathbf{Z}$.

18. With m as in Problem 15 and $u = a + bi\sqrt{m} \in \mathbf{Z}[i\sqrt{m}]$, we define $N(u) = a^2 + b^2 m$. Prove that *this* norm has the same multiplicative property as the
    one defined and described in Problem 17.

19. Use the norm, defined in Problem 18, to obtain two distinct factorizations of 4
    in $\mathbf{Z}[i\sqrt{3}]$.

20. Try to discover a ring, different from $\mathcal{F}[x_1, x_2, ...]$, which is not Noetherian.

21. Let $\mathcal{G}$ be an infinite abelian group, with $\mathcal{R}$ the set of all *formal* expressions
    of the form $a_1 g_1 + a_2 g_2 + \cdots + a_n g_n$, for any $n \in \mathbf{N}$, with $a_i \in \mathbf{Z}$ and $g_i \in \mathcal{G}$,
    $i = 1, 2, ..., n$. If these expressions are added and multiplied like polynomials
    in college algebra, taking into account the correct products of the group
    elements, show that $\mathcal{R}$ is a ring—called an *integral group ring*. Decide whether
    such a ring must or may be Noetherian.

24. Let A be an ideal in the ring $\mathcal{R}[x]$, where $\mathcal{R}$ is an arbitrary commutative ring
    with identity. If $J_i(A)$ is the set of leading coefficients of the polynomials
    of degree i in A, show that this set is an ideal of $\mathcal{R}$ for any $i = 0, 1, 2, ...,$ and
    that $J_0(A) \subset J_1(A) \subset \cdots$. What conclusion can be drawn if $\mathcal{R}$ is a Noetherian
    ring?

**25. Establish the following *Principle of Divisor Induction* for any Noetherian ring
    $\mathcal{R}$: if it is known that a property is valid for any ideal of $\mathcal{R}$, provided its
    validity is known for all proper divisors of the ideal, then the property is valid
    for all ideals of $\mathcal{R}$. (Hint: use (iii) of Theorem 5.111, along with an indirect
    argument.)

26. Prove that any ideal of a Noetherian ring is a Noetherian subring.

27. If A is an ideal of a Noetherian ring $\mathcal{R}$, prove that $\mathcal{R}/A$ is also a Noetherian
    ring [see Problem 26].

28. For the purposes of *this* problem, let P, U, N represent, respectively, the ring properties of "principal ideal," "unique factorization," and "Noetherian," while $\sim P$, $\sim U$, and $\sim N$ designate their negation. Out of the 8 "theoretical" possibilities for the presence or negation of these properties, find one ring to illustrate each of as many of these possibilities as you can.

5.12. Decomposition of Ideals in Noetherian Rings

We now come to the final topic of this chapter—an investigation of what sort of "unique" factorization theorem we can obtain for ideals in a Noetherian ring. In any attempt at a unique decomposition, there are three very relevant and basic matters: (1) the operation to be used in the decomposition; (2) a concept of "irreducibility" which is meaningful for the operation being used; (3) the sense in which our decomposition is "unique." Another very important and useful observation is that, since the familiar ring $\mathbf{Z}$ is Noetherian, the result we obtain must be valid here. Hence, our first thoughts should be directed toward the various possibilities which are available to us in $\mathbf{Z}$. Of course, we already know that any ideal in $\mathbf{Z}$ is expressible as a product of prime powers, and this representation is unique except for order: if $m = p_1^{e_1} p_2^{e_2} \cdots p_r^{e_r}$ is a prime power decomposition of the integer m, then $(m) = (p_1)^{e_1}(p_2)^{e_2} \cdots (p_r)^{e_r}$. However, the fact that we do have a satisfactory solution to the decomposition problem in $\mathbf{Z}$ should not deter us from investigating *other* possibilities in this familiar ring.

If we first consider the matter of the operation, as suggested above in (1), we note that we have used several operations in the past in sets of ideals. If A and B are arbitrary ideals of a ring, we have given definitions for their *sum* $A + B$, their *product* AB, their *intersection* $A \cap B$, and the two *quotients* $A : B$ and $B : A$. It is only natural that our initial hope would be that the decomposition result already established in $\mathbf{Z}$, with each ideal expressible as a *product* of *prime* powers, would carry over to Noetherian rings. However, this hope is short-lived, for we have already seen in § 5.11 that the ideal $(x^2, 3)$ in the Noetherian ring $\mathbf{Z}[x]$ is neither prime itself nor expressible as a product of primes. We now take another look at $\mathbf{Z}$ and note that the decomposition $(m) = (p_1^{e_1})(p_2^{e_2}) \cdots (p_r^{e_r})$ is also valid there. The component ideals in this case are not prime, but are "primary" as described in the following definition.

Definition. An ideal Q in a Noetherian ring is said to be *primary* if $ab \in Q$, with $a \notin Q$, implies that $b^n \in Q$ for some positive integer n. An alternative symbolic way to state this condition is as follows: $ab \equiv 0 \pmod{Q}$ and $a \not\equiv 0 \pmod{Q}$ implies that $b^n \equiv 0 \pmod{Q}$, for some positive integer n.

It is quite clear, of course, that the ideals in the decomposition given immediately prior to the definition are all primary ideals of $\mathbf{Z}$ [Problem 8]. But again our hope that this type of decomposition might be valid in any Noetherian ring is demolished when we consider the ideal $A = (x^2, xy, 3)$ in the Noetherian ring $\mathbf{Z}[x, y]$. Since $xy \in A$, while neither x nor any power of y is in A, we see that A is not primary. On the other hand, if B is any ideal which properly contains A, $3 \in B$ and B cannot contain any nonzero constants except powers of 3 [Why?] But every nonzero constant in any product of such ideals would necessarily be divisible by 9, and so 3 would not be in the product. Hence, it is not possible to express A even as a product of *primary* ideals, so that this type of decompositon has been effectively eliminated from consideration.

We again return to $\mathbf{Z}$, and we note that not only is $(m) = (p_1)^{e_1}(p_2)^{e_2} \cdots (p_r)^{e_r}$ and $(m) = (p_1^{e_1})(p_2^{e_2}) \cdots (p_r^{e_r})$, but also $(m) = (p_1^{e_1}) \cap (p_2^{e_2}) \cap \cdots \cap (p_r^{e_r})$ [Problem 7]. This representation describes (m) as an *intersection* of primary ideals; i.e., (m) is represented as the largest ideal contained within *all* of the component ideals. In the "paradoxical" language borrowed from $\mathbf{Z}$, we have expressed (m) as the *least common multiple* of the component primary ideals. For the case $m = 24$, this representation gives $(24) = (2^3) \cap (3)$. While we do not claim to have exhausted all the possibilities for $\mathbf{Z}$, it turns out that the decomposition just suggested is the "correct" one for Noetherian rings. It will be deemed beyond the scope of this book to justify this remark completely, but it is easy to see that the decomposition is satisfactory for the ideal $A = (x^2, xy, 3)$ discussed above [Problem 14]. The expression of an ideal in a Noetherian ring as the intersection of primary ideals is, however, not always unique. For we can show, in the ring $\mathbf{Z}[x, y]$, that $(x^2, xy) = (x^2, y) \cap (x) = (x^2, xy, y^2) \cap (x)$, with each component ideal primary (or, as a special case, prime). If $Q = (x^2, y)$ in $\mathbf{Z}[x, y]$, and $f(x, y)$ is any element of $\mathbf{Z}[x, y]$ we may write $f(x, y) \equiv a + bx \pmod{Q}$, for integers a, b; and $f(x, y) \equiv 0 \pmod{Q}$ if and only if $a = b = 0$. If we now assume that $f(x, y)g(x, y) \equiv 0 \pmod{Q}$, with $g(x, y) \in \mathbf{Z}[x, y]$ such that $g(x, y) \equiv c + dx \pmod{Q} \equiv 0 \pmod{Q}$, then $f(x,y)g(x, y) \equiv ac + (bc + ad)x \pmod{Q}$, whence $ac = bc + ad = 0$. But not both c and d are 0; hence $a = 0$, $[f(x, y)]^2 \equiv 0 \pmod{Q}$ and so Q is primary. A similar analysis will show that (x^2, xy, y^2) is also primary [Problem 15]. However, while we do not have unique factorization for this type of decomposition, we shall point out later—without proof —a sense in which we do have a weak substitute for "uniqueness."

As was suggested in (2) at the beginning of this section, any satisfactory decomposition theory for ideals must involve a concept of "irreducible" which is appropriate to the case under study. In the present context, it is clear that the following is a reasonable definition: an ideal A in a Noetherian ring $\mathcal{R}$ is *reducible* if it can be expressed as a finite intersection of ideals properly containing it; otherwise, A is said to be *irreducible*. Some primary ideals are reducible and some are not: for example, the primary ideal (9) in $\mathbf{Z}$ is clearly [Problem 1] irreducible; on the other hand, the ideal (x^2, xy, y^2) is known to be primary [Problem 15], and it can be expressed as an intersection of proper divisors [Problem 16]. However, if an ideal in a Noetherian ring is known to be irreducible, the following theorem asserts that it must be primary.

Theorem 5.121. *Every irreducible ideal in a Noetherian ring is primary.*

Proof. Our method of proof is to show that any nonprimary ideal A in a Noetherian ring $\mathcal{R}$ is reducible. By our assumption on A, there exist elements $b, c \in \mathcal{R}$ such that $bc \in A$, $c \notin A$ and $b^k \notin A$, for all positive integers k. If it is known that $rb^k \in A$, for $r \in \mathcal{R}$, then certainly $rb^{k+1} \in A$, and so $A : (b^k) \subset A : (b^{k+1})$ for all k. By the a.c.c. [(i) of Theorem 5.111], $A : (b^n) = A : (b^{n+1})$, for some positive integer n. The ideals $A + (b^n)$ and $A + (c)$ are both proper divisors of A, and $A \subset (A + (b^n)) \cap (A + (c))$. To establish the reverse inclusion, we note that an arbitrary element x in the right member can be expressed as $x = \alpha + \beta b^n = \alpha' + \beta'c$, where $\alpha, \alpha' \in A$ and $\beta, \beta' \in \mathcal{R}$. But then $\beta b^{n+1} = (\alpha' - \alpha)b + \beta'cb$ is in A, and so β must be in $A : (b^{n+1})$ and so also in $A : (b^n)$. It follows that $\beta b^n \in A$, $x = \alpha + \beta b^n \in A$, and hence $A \subset (A + (b^n)) \cap (A + (c))$. From the two inclusions, we conclude that $A = (A + (b^n)) \cap (A + (c))$, and so A is reducible. ∎

The next result follows easily as an application of the Principle of Divisor Induction [Problem 25 of § 5.11].

Theorem 5.122. *Every ideal A in a Noetherian ring $\mathcal{R}$ can be represented as a finite intersection of primary ideals.*

Proof. If A is irreducible, A is also primary by Theorems 5.121, and we are through. If not, we assume that the property stated in the theorem is valid for all ideals in $\mathcal{R}$ which properly contain A. The reducibility of A now implies that $A = A_1 \cap A_2$, for ideals A_1, A_2 properly containing A; and the property in the theorem is possessed by A_1 and A_2, by our induction assumption. But if A_1 and A_2 both have a representation as a finite intersection of primary ideals, it follows immediately that the combined intersection is a representation of A. The proof is then complete. ∎

Now that we have our decomposition result established, there remains the matter of " uniqueness "—and we have already shown by example that there may be distinct decompositions of the type being discussed for the same ideal.

However, while the decompositions are distinct, there is *something* which is "unique" about them—and this brings us to the definition of the "radical" of an ideal of a commutative ring.

Definition. If A is a proper ideal of a commutative ring, the *radical* of A, sometimes written $\sqrt{A}$ is the set of all $r \in \mathcal{R}$ such that $r^n \in A$ for some positive integer n, where n is allowed to vary with r. The radical of $\mathcal{R}$ is defined to be $\sqrt{0}$ i.e., the set of all nilpotent elements of $\mathcal{R}$.

In the ring $\mathbf{Z}$, it is clear that $\sqrt{(4)} = (2)$; and in the ring $\mathbf{Z}[x, y]$, $\sqrt{(x^2, y^3)}$ is (x, y). It is not difficult to show quite generally that the radical of any ideal A in a commutative ring is an ideal [Problem 9] and that if A is primary, its radical is a prime ideal [Problem 10]. It is possible to rephrase our earlier definition of a primary ideal in terms of the radical as follows: an ideal Q in a commutative ring is *primary* if $ab \in Q$, where $a \notin Q$, implies that $b \in \sqrt{Q}$. A representation of an ideal A as an intersection of ideals is said to be *irredundant* if none of the component ideals may be omitted without destroying its equality with A. It is not difficult to show [Problem 22] that the intersection of two primary ideals with a common radical is also primary and with the same radical. In this way, it is then possible to combine the components of a primary representation of an ideal so that the radicals of the primary components which remain are all distinct. It is the *number of these primary components* in an irredundant representation of an ideal and the *set of associated radicals* which is unique for a Noetherian ring. We do not attempt to prove this final remark, but will merely include it in the complete statement of the fundamental decomposition theorem. For further details, the student is referred to [2], [4], [5], [7] below.

Theorem 5.123. *Any ideal in a Noetherian ring can be represented as an irredundant intersection of a finite number of primary ideals with distinct radicals. The number of primary ideals and the set of their radicals are unique for the given ideal, while the primary ideals themselves may vary from one representation to another.*

PROBLEMS 5–12

1. Explain why (9) is an irreducible ideal of $\mathbf{Z}$.
**2. Verify that $\sqrt{(12)} = \sqrt{(72)} = (6)$ in the ring $\mathbf{Z}$.
3. If $m = p_1^{e_1} p_2^{e_2} \cdots p_r^{e_r}$ is a factorization of the integer m into distinct primes, show that $\sqrt{(m)} = (p_1 p_2 \cdots p_r)$ in $\mathbf{Z}$.
4. Represent $(2, x^2) \cap (x, 4) \cap (x, 2)$ as an irredundant intersection of ideals in $\mathbf{Z}[x]$.

5. Represent $(2x^2, 2xy) \cap (2) \cap (x) \cap (x^2)$ as an irredundant intersection of ideals of $\mathbf{Z}[x, y]$.

6. If A and B are ideals of a commutative ring, verify that

$$AB \subset A \cap B \subset A \text{ (or } B) \subset A + B.$$

7. If $m = p^r q^s$, for distinct primes p and q, prove that $(m) = (p)^r (q)^s = (p^r)(q^s) = (p^r) \cap (q^s)$. Generalize this result to include an arbitrary integer m.

*8. Prove that (q) is a primary ideal of $\mathbf{Z}$, with $(q) \neq (0), (1)$, if and only if $q = p^e$, for some prime p and positive integer e.

9. Prove that the radical of any ideal of a commutative ring is an ideal.

10. Prove that the radical of a primary ideal of a commutative ring is a prime ideal [see Problem 9].

11. If A and B are ideals of a commutative ring, prove that

$$\sqrt{A \cap B} = \sqrt{A} \cap \sqrt{B} = \sqrt{AB}.$$

12. In the ring $\mathcal{F}[x, y]$, show that $(xy, y^2) = (x^k, xy, y^2) \cap (y)$, for any integer $k > 1$.

13. Verify that the ideal (x^k, xy, y^2) in Problem 12 is primary with radical (x, y), regardless of the magnitude of k.

14. Express $(x^2, xy, 3)$ as an intersection of primary ideals of $\mathbf{Z}[x, y]$.

**15. Verify that (x^2, xy, y^2) is a primary ideal of $\mathbf{Z}[x, y]$.

16. Express the ideal in Problem 15 as an intersection of proper divisor ideals.

17. Determine $\sqrt{(x, y^3)}$ in $\mathcal{F}[x, y]$.

18. Express (y^2, xy) as a finite irredundant intersection of primary ideals of $\mathbf{Z}[x, y]$ in two ways. Use the two representations to check the truth of Theorem 5.123.

19. Verify that $(x^2, 2x, 4)$ is a primary ideal of $\mathbf{Z}[x]$, but is expressible in the form $(x^2, 2) \cap (x, 4)$.

20. Represent the ideal $(9, 3x + 3)$ as an intersection of primary ideals of $\mathbf{Z}[x]$.

21. If A and B are arbitrary ideals of a commutative ring, prove the following Dedekind Modular law: If $B \subset A$, then $A \cap (B + C) = B + (A \cap C)$.

22. Prove that the intersection of two primary ideals with common radical is a primary ideal with the same radical.

23. An ideal A is said to be a *radical ideal* if some power of an element of the ring is in A if and only if the element is in A. Prove that a prime ideal is a radical ideal.

24. If Q is a primary ideal of a Noetherian ring, prove that $(\sqrt{Q})^n \subset Q$, for some integer $n \geq 1$.

25. A ring is said to be *local* if it has a unique maximal ideal. If M is the maximal ideal of a Noetherian local ring, prove that $\bigcap_{i=1}^{\infty} M^i = 0$.

References

[1] ALBERT, A.: *Fundamental Concepts of Higher Algebra*, Chapter 2 (Chicago, University of Chicago Press, 1956).

[2] BARNES, W.: *Introduction to Abstract Algebra*, Chapter 3 (Boston, Heath, 1963).

[3] BIRKHOFF, G. and MACLANE, S.: *A Survey of Modern Algebra*, Third Edition, Chapter 13 (New York, Macmillan, 1965).

[4] JACOBSON, N.: *Lectures in Abstract Algebra*, Vol. 1, Chapters 2, 3, 6 (Princeton, N. J.,, Van Nostrand, 1951).

[5] McCOY, N.: *Rings and Ideals* (Carus Mathematical Monograph No. 8, Buffalo, N. Y., The Mathematical Association of America, 1948).

[6] McCOY, N.: *The Theory of Rings* (New York, Macmillan, 1964).

[7] VAN DER WAERDEN, B.: *Modern Algebra*, Vol. 1, Chapter 3; Vol. 2, Chapters 12–13 (New York, Ungar, 1949 and 1950).

Selected Readings from The American Mathematical Monthly

AYOUB, R. and AYOUB, C.: *On the Commutativity of Rings*, **71** (1964), 267–271.

BEAUMONT R. A.: *Equivalent Properties of a Ring*, **57** (1950), 183.

BITZER C. W.: *Inverses in Rings with Unity*, **70** (1963), 315.

ERICKSON, D. B.: *Orders for Finite Noncommutative Rings*, **73** (1966), 376–377.

GEMIGNANI, M.: *A Note on Embedding Commutative Rings in Rings with Unity*, **73** (1966), 395–396.

KHAN, N. A.: *The Characteristic of a Ring*, **70** (1963), 736.

KOH, K.: *Integral Domains Embedded in Primitive Rings*, **72** (1965), 197–198.

KOH, K.: *A Note on a Certain Class of Prime Rings*, **72** (1965), 46–48.

KOHLS, C. W.: *Primary Ideals in Rings of Continuous Functions*, **71** (1964), 980–984.

McCOY, H.: *Annihilators in Polynomial Rings*, **64** (1957), 28–29.

TOSKEY, B. R.: *A Class of Nonisomorphic Rings, Each Isomorphic to a Proper Subring of Every Other*, **73** (1966) 186–187.

WAHAB, J. H.: *Irreducibility of Polynomials*, **68** (1961), 366–367.

WARNER, S.: *Rings with Cyclic Additive Group*, **71** (1964), 449–450.

6 *Operator Systems*

6.1. Introduction

Everything to be done in this chapter can be regarded as a generalization of earlier notions or, alternatively, we may regard everything that has gone before as a special case of what we are about to do in this chapter. However, inasmuch as we are going to limit the coverage of the present chapter, it will be best to take the former viewpoint. There are many advantages in obtaining general theories, apart from the mathematical satisfaction derived from such: for example, a generalization will often suggest new points of view which may be taken to advantage with respect to the earlier theories; and one can often obtain a unification of theories which had previously been considered as quite distinct. In particular, in this chapter we are going to direct our attention briefly to algebraic systems which will include the familiar semigroups, groups, rings, and fields, as well as the previously unmentioned "vector spaces" and "modules" as special cases. The central idea which unifies all these systems is that of an "operator," so we give a definition of this concept, first as it applies to a system with one operation.

Definition. An *operator* on a groupoid (semigroup or group) is something which is associated with or induces an endomorphism of the system.

In other words, with every operator on such a system we have an associated endomorphism of the system—although we do not require that "distinct" operators be necessarily associated with distinct endomorphisms. It is very often the case that a set of operators *is* actually a set of endomorphisms, and there is usually no harm in making this identification anyway. The important point is that any operator on a system is associated with a mapping of the system and this mapping is an endomorphism. For example, if a and b are elements of one of these systems on which m is an operator, we shall designate the elements onto which a and b are mapped by m as am and bm, respectively. The mapping rule for the operator could then be expressed as $(ab)m = (am)(bm)$ (or $(a + b)m = am + bm$, if additive notation is used). We remark that we are following the most usual practice in this book in writing the operator (or mapping) symbol to the right of the elements on which it operates—and so treating it as a *right* operator. We shall discuss the matter of symbolism at greater length when we consider modules later in the chapter.

While the theory of operator systems can be made quite general, our interest will be centered on operator *groups* and *rings*; and, even in the case of rings, our operators will be on the additive groups of the rings rather than on the systems *as rings*. Our first concern will be with *operator groups* or *groups with operators*, and a somewhat more formal definition of such a system could be given as follows: a *group with operators* is a group $\mathfrak{G}$, together with a set M and a mapping $\mathfrak{G} \times M \longrightarrow \mathfrak{G}$ such that $(ab)m = (am)(bm)$ for every a, $b \in \mathfrak{G}$ and every $m \in M$. It may be well to emphasize two points at this time: (1) the "image" elements belong to the same system as the original; (2) nothing "really new" has been introduced, for we are essentially dealing merely with a group and a set of its endomorphisms. In this formal definition we have expressed the endomorphism property in multiplicative notation, as is customary for groups in general. However, most of our discussions will be directed to abelian groups and for such we shall use the more usual additive notation. A group with operator set M is often called an *M-group*, and it should be clear than an M-group is simply a group whenever M is an empty set. A similar remark would apply to any operator system, and so any algebraic system *without operators* can be regarded as an operator system whose set M of operators is empty. Hence the remark about generalizations!

We shall return to abstract systems later, but at this time we wish to review the essential ingredients of a very familiar system, which, while it does have some special properties, is in fact a *group with operators*. This is the system of *plane vectors*, and for a major portion of this chapter we shall be concerned with abstractions motivated by this elementary system. At this time there arises the pedagogical question, whether it is better to consider first a familiar example and later use this as a basis for abstraction; or first to present an abstract system and follow it with familiar examples. In the former course of action, there is the risk that students will carry over to the abstract system additional properties of the special system which we have not assumed, while the latter course lacks the initial motivating impetus. There are admittedly dangers either way, but we have decided to run the risks of the former procedure—which is usually the one that is historically correct—and review the familiar system first. If the other approach is preferred, one has merely to postpone or omit this and the connecting portions of the following section, and begin the discussion with the definition of an abstract vector space.

We recall that a vector quantity is one which possesses both a magnitude and a direction and is usually represented by a *directed line segment* known roughly as a *vector*. In this representation, the length of the segment measures the magnitude of the quantity, while its direction corresponds to the actual direction of the vector quantity. Familiar examples of vector quantities are forces, displacements, velocities, and accelerations.

There is a simple arithmetic of plane vectors which we now describe very briefly. Two vectors are *equal* if they have the same length and direction. The *sum* **A** + **B** of two vectors **A** and **B** is obtained with the use of the *parallelogram* or *triangle* law, as indicated in Figure 2 below. Thus, to obtain the sum of the vectors **A** and **B**, we place the tail of **B** on the head of **A**, and draw the directed segment from the tail of **A** to the head of **B**. This vector, a diagonal of the associated parallelogram, is the sum—or resultant—of **A** and **B** in both magnitude and direction; and we note that this direction is ordinarily different from that of either **A** or **B**.

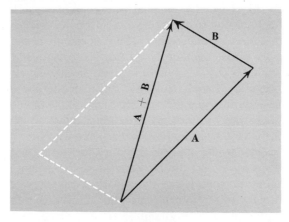

Figure 2

Another arithmetic "operation" of elementary vector analysis is usually known as *scalar multiplication* or *multiplication by a scalar*. We indicate this type of multiplication by writing a real number (i.e., a *scalar*) in juxtaposition with a vector. The resulting vector is one which is in the same or opposite direction as the original, but with a magnitude that is ordinarily different. For example, if **A** is a vector, the vectors 2**A**, 3**A**, and $\sqrt{3}$ **A** are vectors in the same direction as **A**, but whose magnitudes are, respectively, twice, three times, and the square root of three times as great as that of **A**. These vectors are shown in Figure 3 below. The product of a scalar and a vector is sometimes referred to as a "scalar product," but this usage is to be discouraged in deference to another "product" of two vectors which is a scalar—to be mentioned later.

We have recalled that the representation of a vector quantity as a directed line segment depends only on its magnitude and direction, so that the actual location of the segment is quite arbitrary. This suggests that it should be permissible to consider that all plane vectors emanate from the origin of a Cartesian coordinate system. But then each vector is completely determined by the coordinate pair of its end point, and so it is permissible to consider this coordinate pair as the algebraic equivalent of the vector. If, in fact, we agree to identify in this way any vector with its associated coordinate pair, it can ʰe seen that the relation of equality and the operations of addition and scalar

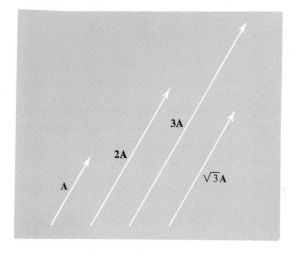

Figure 3

multiplication in the set of plane vectors are equivalent to the equality relation and operations defined in the set of ordered pairs of real numbers as follows:

$$(a_1, b_1) = (a_2, b_2) \text{ if and only if } a_1 = a_2 \text{ and } b_1 = b_2;$$
$$(a_1, b_1) + (a_2, b_2) = (a_1 + a_2, b_1 + b_2);$$
$$c(a, b) = (ca, cb) \text{ for any } c \in \mathbf{R}.$$

The definition of equality states, in effect, that two vectors are equal if their end points have the same coordinates. The rule for addition requires that the coordinates of the end point of the sum of two vectors be the respective sums of the coordinates of the end points of the vectors; this is in accordance with the parallelogram law. Finally, the rule for multiplication of a vector by a

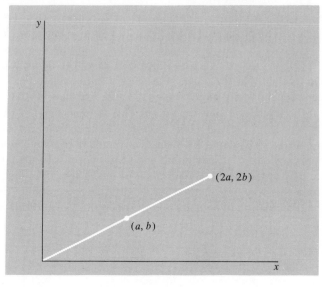

Figure 4

scalar states that this multiplication effects a multiplication of each of the coordinates of the end point of the vector by this scalar; and so this results in a stretching or compression of the vector, with a possible reversal in direction. In Figures 4 and 5 we have illustrated the two vector operations, with vectors considered as coordinate pairs.

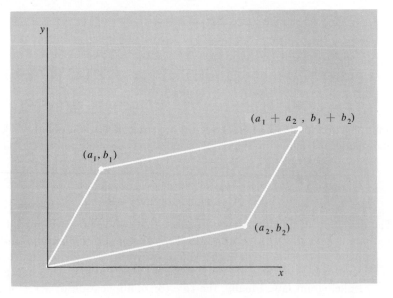

Figure 5

If we consider $-\mathbf{A}$ to be the vector with the same magnitude as $\mathbf{A}$ but sensed in the opposite direction, it is clear that $\mathbf{A}$ and $-\mathbf{A}$ will annihilate each other on addition. Hence, if we designate the vector with zero magnitude by $\mathbf{0}$, we have $\mathbf{A} + (-\mathbf{A}) = \mathbf{0}$. Moreover, if $\mathbf{A} = (a_1, b_1)$ then $-\mathbf{A} = (-a_1, -b_1)$. It follows easily from either the physical concept or the arithmetic of vectors as coordinate pairs that $\mathbf{A} + (\mathbf{B} + \mathbf{D}) = (\mathbf{A} + \mathbf{B}) + \mathbf{D}$, and $\mathbf{A} + \mathbf{B} = \mathbf{B} + \mathbf{A}$, for arbitrary plane vectors $\mathbf{A}$, $\mathbf{B}$, $\mathbf{D}$. Hence we have the following result:

(1)   The set of all plane vectors comprises an
           abelian group under vector addition.

The properties of scalar multiplication which are listed in (2) below can be verified either with reference to the meaning of the physical concept or directly from the arithmetic of coordinate pairs:

$$a(\mathbf{A} + \mathbf{B}) = a\mathbf{A} + a\mathbf{B}$$
(2)
$$(a + b)\mathbf{A} = a\mathbf{A} + b\mathbf{A}$$
$$(ab)\mathbf{A} = a(b\mathbf{A})$$
$$1\mathbf{A} = \mathbf{A}.$$

In the above equations, $\mathbf{A}$ and $\mathbf{B}$ are arbitrary plane vectors, while a and b are arbitrary real numbers. We have used 1, as usual, to designate the multiplicative identity of the real number system.

Along with vector addition and scalar multiplication, most studies of elementary vector analysis include another operation on any two vectors known as their *inner* or *scalar product*. This is a metric concept, and it happens that a large part of the theory of analytic geometry depends only on the other two operations. In particular, the theory of linear transformations—which is to be one of the principal vector topics of this chapter—does not involve any metric notions. Thus we shall not be concerned with inner products.

The basic example that we have given of a vector, as either a plane directed line segment or as an ordered pair of real numbers, is an illustration of an element of a *two-dimensional vector space over the field of real numbers*. The vector space is said to be " over the field of real numbers " because the scalars are real numbers. The idea of dimension will be made precise later, but for our example we may say tentatively that the *dimension* is two because it requires an ordered *pair* of real numbers to determine each vector.

Finally, how does this example of the system of plane vectors fit into the context of groups with operators? The group $\mathcal{G}$ is clearly the additive system of vectors, because we have already demonstrated that they do form an abelian group under addition. The apparently new concept of multiplication by a scalar, which was not present in the case of any of the algebraic systems studied heretofore can be considered to have arisen from a set M of operators: each element $m_r \in M$ " operates " on the vectors of $\mathcal{G}$ by effectively multiplying each of them by the real number r. In the symbolism used earlier, we are stating that $Am_r = rA$, for any vector A. One may well ask why we have written rA instead of Ar to designate scalar multiplication, and the answer is that it makes no real difference which notation we use, but it is *customary* to put the scalars on the left of a vector. We leave it to the student to verify [Problem 7] that m_r does induce an endomorphism of the additive group $\mathcal{G}$ of plane vectors. Hence $\mathcal{G}$, with operator set M of scalar multiplications, is a group with operators as described in our definition. In this case, the cardinality of the set M is the same as that of $\mathbf{R}$.

PROBLEMS 6–1

**1. Use the arithmetic of ordered pairs to prove that the additive set of two-dimensional plane vectors is abelian and associative.

2. Use a diagram to illustrate the "distributive" law: $a(A + B) = aA + aB$, for vectors, A, B and a real number a.

3. Show that every plane vector—considered as a directed line segment—can be represented as the sum of two vectors, one parallel to each of the coordinate axes of the Cartesian plane.

4. If $(1, 1)$ and $(3, 2)$ represent the vectors A and B, respectively, give the ordered pair representation of (a) $-A$; (b) $-B$; (c) $A + B$; (d) $A + 2B$.

5. With A and B as in Problem 4, and D represented by $(2, -3)$, determine the ordered pair representation of (a) $A - B + D$; (b) $2A - 3B + 4D$; (c) $(2A + 3B) + (4A - 6D) + 5B$.

6. Use a diagram to show that the sum of three vectors, considered as directed line segments, can be accomplished by "stringing" them together in a broken line with the head of one on the tail of the next and then joining the tail of the first with the head of the third. Generalize this to obtain the sum of any number of plane vectors.

7. Prove that m_r, as defined in the text, does induce an endomorphism on the system of plane vectors.

8. Our concept of scalar multiplication implies that $nA = A + A + \cdots + A$, for any plane vector A, and n summands, whenever n is a positive integer. If m is any operator on this space of plane vectors, verify that $n(Am) = (nA)m$.

9. If $\pi_h : A \to X$ is a mapping which maps every plane vector A onto its horizontal projection X, prove that π_h is an endomorphism. Note that this establishes the existence of endomorphisms distinct from "scalar multiplications" in the space of plane vectors.

10. Verify that the mapping m_r, as defined in the text on the space of plane vectors, is an automorphism while the mapping π_h of Problem 9 is not.

11. For any positive integer n, let $\mathbf{n}$ designate a vector n units in length. Then explain why $2 + 2$ is not necessarily equal to 4!

12. Decide whether the mapping $A \to A + 2$ [see Problem 11] is an endomorphism of the space of plane vectors.

13. Determine all possible (endomorphism-distinct) operator sets for the cyclic group C_3 of order 3.

14. Determine all possible (endomorphism-distinct) operator sets for the four-group $C_2 \times C_2$.

15. Discover a nontrivial operator on the group S_4. (By "nontrivial" we mean that the elements are mapped neither all onto themselves nor all onto the identity element.)

16. If $b \in \mathcal{G}$, for any group $\mathcal{G}$, verify that m_b is an operator of $\mathcal{G}$ where we define $gm_b = gb$, for all $g \in \mathcal{G}$. Describe m_e, where e is the identity element of $\mathcal{G}$.

17. Use the definition of m_b in Problem 16 as a guide and define another operator on $\mathcal{G}$ which is very similar in form. Are the two operators ever identical on $\mathcal{G}$?

18. With $a \in \mathcal{G}$, for any group $\mathcal{G}$, recheck that the mapping $g \to a^{-1}ga$ defines an endomorphism of $\mathcal{G}$. Use this example as a hint to discover two "distinct" operators which induce the same mappings on a subgroup of a group $\mathcal{G}$.

**19. Verify that the set of *all* endomorphisms of an abelian group forms a ring under the usual operations of the sum and product of mappings. Point out where the "proof" would fail if the group were not abelian.

20. Identify by name the most complex algebraic system formed by the set of all endomorphisms of (a) S_3 ; (b) S_4?

21. Use the notation of operators m_r, as defined in the text, to express the properties (2) of the system of plane vectors.

6.2. Abstract Vector Spaces

The basic example of the vector space of ordered pairs of real numbers can be readily generalized in two ways. In the first place, the "dimension"—which was two in the example—can be made arbitrary. That is, instead of ordered *pairs* of real numbers we can consider ordered sets or *n-tuples* $(a_1, a_2, \ldots, a_n)$ of n real numbers $a_1, a_2, \ldots, a_n$, where these numbers are called the *components* of the n-tuple. The definition of equality and the rules for addition and scalar multiplication for n-tuples will be strictly analogous to those in the case of ordered pairs. It is commonplace in physics to use *space* vectors for displacements, velocities, and accelerations, with components in three mutually perpendicular directions. In a study of relativity the fourth dimension of time is included so that, in the four-dimensional world of relativity, each vector has four components. Even in Newtonian physics a force acting on a rigid body is often considered to have six components, three of a translational and three of a rotational nature. So there are many occasions when a physicist uses vectors with more than two components. To the mathematician it is more satisfying to make the number of components or the "dimension" of a vector quite arbitrary and to work with the vectors as n-tuples.

The other way in which the vectors of the introductory example can be

generalized is in the choice of the number system from which the components
are selected. In most physical applications the components of a vector are
real numbers, though vectors with complex components are used regularly in
the theory of electric circuits. It would appear to be a reasonable generalization to allow the field of real numbers to be replaced by an arbitrary field $\mathcal{F}$,
and we shall do this in our subsequent discussions. It is possible to go a step
further and allow these scalars to be elements of a more general algebraic
system; but this brings us to the subject of "modules," which we shall discuss
later in the chapter.

To recapitulate, we have generalized the primitive example of the preceding section to the vector space of n-tuples, with components in an arbitrary
field $\mathcal{F}$. We shall regularly use $\mathcal{V}_n(\mathcal{F})$ to designate this vector space. As
indicated earlier, the definitions of equality and the two operations of vector
addition and scalar multiplication are as follows:

$$(a_1, a_2, \ldots, a_n) = (b_1, b_2, \ldots, b_n) \text{ if and only if } a_i = b_i, i = 1, 2, \ldots, n;$$
$$(a_1, a_2, \ldots, a_n) + (b_1, b_2, \ldots, b_n) = (a_1 + b_1, a_2 + b_2, \ldots, a_n + b_n);$$
$$c(a_1, a_2, \ldots, a_n) = (ca_1, ca_2, \ldots, ca_n), \text{ for arbitrary } c \in \mathcal{F}.$$

It is a simple matter to check that properties (1) and (2) of our primitive
vector space of § 6.1 continue to hold in $\mathcal{V}_n(\mathcal{F})$ [see Problem 1].

We now direct our attention away from the *elements* of the vector spaces
which we have considered, and use properties (1) and (2) to give a characterization of an *abstract vector space*.

Definition. Let $\mathcal{V} = \{\xi, \eta, \ldots\}$ be a set of elements in which is defined an
additive binary operation. Moreover, let us define a multiplication of
the elements of $\mathcal{V}$ by the elements $\{a, b, \ldots\}$ of a field $\mathcal{F}$, so that $a\xi \in \mathcal{V}$,
for arbitrary $a \in \mathcal{F}$ and arbitrary $\xi \in \mathcal{V}$. Then $\mathcal{V}$ is an *abstract vector space
over* $\mathcal{F}$, with the elements of $\mathcal{V}$ called *vectors* and the elements of $\mathcal{F}$ called
scalars, provided the following conditions are satisfied, for arbitrary ξ,
$\eta \in \mathcal{V}$ and arbitrary $a, b \in \mathcal{F}$:

   1. $\mathcal{V}$ is an additive abelian group;
   2. $a(\xi + \eta) = a\xi + a\eta; (a + b)\xi = a\xi + b\xi; (ab)\xi = a(b\xi); 1\xi = \xi.$

The abstract operations are called *vector addition* and *scalar multiplication*.
We draw attention to the fact that properties **1** and **2** are the same as properties (1) and (2) of our basic example of § 6.1. In addition it probably
should be emphasized that the elements of $\mathcal{V}$ are no longer necessarily
n-tuples, but are merely elements of a set in which our two operations have
been appropriately defined. As an operator system, a vector space is an
abelian group with a *field* of operators [see Problem 21 of § 6.1 and Problem 11 below]. The operator set *as a system* will be discussed more fully later.

It is easy to think of examples of the vector space concept. Of course the space $\mathcal{U}_n(\mathcal{F})$ of n-tuples is fundamental, and will, at a later date, prove to be of even more importance than is now evident. The field of complex numbers is a vector space over the field of real numbers. In this case, the "vectors" are the complex numbers, and the real numbers play the role of scalars, while the vector space operations are identified with the familiar operations in the complex number system. It is immediate that conditions **1** and **2** are satisfied. Another elementary example is provided by the ring $\mathcal{F}[x]$ of polynomials in an indeterminate x, with coefficients in a field $\mathcal{F}$. In this example, the "vectors" are the polynomials, while the scalars are the elements of $\mathcal{F}$. The ordinary operations of polynomial additior and multiplication by field elements are the operations of this vector space, and it is elementary to check that conditions **1** and **2** are satisfied [Problem 2]. The preceding example can be modified to include 0 and polynomials of, at most, some finite degree—say polynomials of degree three or less. Our illustration with $\mathcal{U}_n(\mathcal{F})$ can also be modified so that the "vectors" are infinite sequences $(a_1, a_2, a_3, \ldots)$, with operations analogous to those of $\mathcal{U}_n(\mathcal{F})$; or we can consider the "vectors" to be infinite sequences, each with a finite number of nonzero components. In either of these cases, the validity of properties **1** and **2** can be easily established.

As a final, and not quite so simple, example of a vector space, consider the set of all continuous real-valued functions on **R**. The functions are the "vectors," and two functions f and g are *equal* if $f(x) = g(x)$, for each $x \in$ **R**. We define vector addition in the familiar way: $(f + g)(x) = f(x) + g(x)$, for any $x \in$ **R**. The scalars are the real numbers, and scalar multiplication is defined as follows: $(cf)(x) = cf(x)$, for each $x \in$ **R** and arbitrary scalar $c \in$ **R**. It is easy to verify that conditions **1** and **2** are satisfied, so that the set of functions under consideration forms a vector space over **R**. If we wish, we may regard any function f of the space as having a "component" $f(x)$ at each point $x \in$ **R**. The number of components of each vector is then infinite.

Problems 6–2

*   ***1.** Verify that the space of 3-tuples of real numbers does satisfy requirements **1** and **2** of a vector space.
*   ***2.** Verify that the space of polynomials in x with real coefficients does satisfy requirements **1** and **2** of a vector space.
*   ***3.** Verify that the space of real functions described above does satisfy requirements **1** and **2** of a vector space.
*   ****4.** Let $\xi = (1, -2, 3)$, $\eta = (-3, -2, 5)$, and $\zeta = (2, -5, 6)$ be in $\mathcal{U}_3(\mathbf{R})$.
    *   (a) Determine $\xi + 2\eta - 3\zeta$.
    *   (b) Solve the equation $4\xi + 2x - 3\zeta = 0$ for x.
*   **5.** Let $\xi = (0, i, -2)$, $\eta = (1 + i, -i, 4)$, and $\zeta = (1 - i, -3, 1)$ be in $\mathcal{U}_3(\mathbf{C})$.
    *   (a) Determine $4\xi - 2\eta + \zeta$.
    *   (b) Solve the equation $3y - 6\xi = 2\eta$ for y.

6. Prove that the set of all ordered triples (a_1, a_2, a_3) of real numbers, such that $2a_1 + 3a_2 - 5a_3 = 0$, is a vector space over the field $\mathbf{R}$.

7. Decide whether the set of all real-valued functions on $\mathbf{R}$ such that $f(x) = f(x + 1)$ for each function f of the set is a vector space over $\mathbf{R}$.

8. Consider the set of all polynomials in an indeterminate x with real coefficients and zero constant term, and decide whether it constitutes a vector space over the field $\mathbf{R}$, assuming the usual polynomial operations.

9. Show that the polynomials of the set $\{0, 1, 2, x + 1, x + 2, 2x + 1, 2x + 2, x, 2x\}$ constitute the elements of a vector space over the field $\mathbf{Z}/(3)$, assuming the usual operations for polynomials.

10. If we regard a vector space $\mathcal{U}$ as a group with operators, describe the operator set when $\mathcal{U}$ is the space of
    (a) complex numbers over $\mathbf{R}$;
    (b) polynomials $f(x)$ over $\mathcal{F}$;
    (c) real-valued continuous functions over $\mathbf{R}$.

11. Explain why an abstract vector space is an abelian group with a "field of operators." In particular, the identity $a(\xi + \eta) = a\xi + a\eta$ in **2** is the basic "operator" property, but what is the function of the other identities?

12. If $\mathcal{F}$ is a field and $\mathcal{U}$ is a vector space over $\mathcal{F}$, let $\mathcal{FU}$ be described as the set of all finite sums $\sum_{i=1}^{n} a_i\xi_i$, with $a_i \in \mathcal{F}$ and $\xi_i \in \mathcal{U}$. Then verify that the condition $\mathcal{FU} = \mathcal{U}$ is equivalent to the condition $1\xi = \xi$ in **2** of the definition of a vector space [cf. Problem 11].

13. Prove that every field is a vector space over any of its subfields, including the field itself.

14. Make "appropriate" definitions for the isomorphism of two vector spaces over the same field, and their direct sum. Then decide whether $\mathcal{U}_2(\mathcal{F})$ is isomorphic to the direct sum of two isomorphic copies of $\mathcal{F}$, each regarded as a vector space over itself [see Problem 13].

15. Decide whether $\mathcal{W}$ can be regarded as a vector space over $\mathcal{K}$, where (a) $\mathcal{W} = \mathbf{C}$, $\mathcal{K} = \mathbf{Q}$; (b) $\mathcal{W} = \mathbf{Z}$, $\mathcal{K} = \mathbf{N}$; (c) $\mathcal{W} =$ set of Gaussian integers, $\mathcal{K} = \mathbf{R}$.

16. Verify that the set of all real functions f on the interval $[0, 1]$, with the property that $2f(0) = f(1)$, is a vector space over $\mathbf{R}$.

17. Verify that the set of all real functions f on the interval $[0, 1]$, with the property that $f(0) = f(1) + 1$, is not a vector space over $\mathbf{R}$ [cf. Problem 16].

18. Show that the abelian nature of vector addition is actually redundant with the properties of scalar multiplication.

**19. Let m be an operator on the additive group of a ring $\mathcal{R}$ such that $(ab)m = (am)b = a(bm)$ for all $a, b \in \mathcal{R}$. Then prove that if $\mathcal{R}$ has an identity element, the effect of m on any ring element is to multiply it by a fixed element from the center of the ring.

20. Give at least one illustration of the type of operator described in Problem 19.

6.3. Simple Properties of a Vector Space

Before proceeding further with our brief discussion of vector spaces, there are two matters on which a comment may be in order at this time: symbolism, and the set of operators. A vector space has been our first major example of a group with operators, this example being an additive abelian group $\mathcal{V}$ with its operators (left multiplications) drawn from a field $\mathcal{F}$ associated with the vector space. We pointed out earlier that if m_r is to designate that operator on $\mathcal{V}$ which multiplies each vector $\xi \in \mathcal{V}$ by the real number r, we are following the common practice of writing $\xi m_r = r\xi$ rather than $\xi m_r = \xi r$. It makes no great difference which symbolism is adopted—and so we adopted the one in common usage—but there is one important point to observe: there should never be any question of the possible "equality" of $r\xi$ with ξr, because *only one* has been defined. In our case, $r\xi$ has been defined while the symbolism ξr does not occur with any meaning in our discussions. The other comment concerns the operator set M which, in our general definition of a group with operators, had no announced structure in itself. It may be, of course, that M does have an algebraic structure, and we have already observed in the case of a vector space that the set of operators is actually a field. We shall return to the matter of the structure of the operator set when we consider modules in a later section but, for the present elementary discussion of vector spaces, the only field properties of $\mathcal{F}$ which we are using are those implied by conditions **2** in the definition of an abstract vector space: the existence of two operations and an identity element 1. In the present context we have motivated these conditions from our familiar example of plane vectors; in the discussion of modules, to which we have referred, we shall provide a more "abstract" justification for them.

To resume our study of vector spaces, one of the most important notions in the study of any algebraic system is the matter of isomorphism. We asked the student in Problem 14 of § 6.2 to formulate his own "appropriate" definition of this concept for vector spaces, and he may now check his definition with the one we present here.

Definition. Two vector spaces $\mathcal{V}$ and $\mathcal{V}'$ over the same field $\mathcal{F}$ are *isomorphic* if

(a) $\mathcal{V}$ and $\mathcal{V}'$ are isomorphic as additive abelian groups;
(b) the mapping in (a) "preserves" scalar multiplication. That is, if $\xi \to \xi'$ designates the mapping of $\mathcal{V}$ onto $\mathcal{V}'$, then $c\xi \to c\xi'$, for any $c \in \mathcal{F}$.

Again we remark that our definition leans heavily on the intuitive example of plane vectors for its motivation. (Explain!) As always with isomorphic systems, we shall regard isomorphic vector spaces as algebraically indistinguishable. If vector spaces are regarded as groups with operators, the above definition describes what is called an "*operator isomorphism*" of these groups.

Our definition of a vector space implies the existence of a vector $-\xi$, associated with each vector ξ, such that $\xi + (-\xi) = 0$. The symbol 0 in this equation designates the zero vector—i.e., the additive identity of the group of the vector space—but in other contexts the same symbol will designate the zero element of the coefficient field. (By this time the student should be used to the multiple usage of the symbols 0 and 1!) A few of the elementary properties of a vector space are described in the following theorem.

Theorem 6.31. *Let $\mho$ be a vector space over the field $\mathcal{F}$. Then, for any $a \in \mathcal{F}$ and $\xi \in \mho$, the following are true:*

1. $a0 = 0$;
2. $0\xi = 0$;
3. $a(-\xi) = (-a)\xi = -a\xi$;
4. *if $a\xi = 0$, then either $a = 0$ or $\xi = 0$.*

Proof. Since $a\xi = a(\xi + 0) = a\xi + a0$, it follows that $a0 = 0$, which is **1**. To prove **2**, we note that $0\xi = (0 + 0)\xi = 0\xi + 0\xi$, so that $0\xi = 0$. Since $a\xi + a(-\xi) = a(\xi - \xi) = a0 = 0$, it follows that $a(-\xi)$ is the additive inverse of $a\xi$, and so $a(-\xi) = -a\xi$. Also, $a\xi + (-a)\xi = (a - a)\xi = 0\xi = 0$, so that $(-a)\xi = -a\xi$, completing the proof of **3**. Finally, if $a \neq 0$, then a^{-1} exists. Hence if $a\xi = 0$, $0 = a^{-1}(a\xi) = (a^{-1}a)\xi = 1\xi = \xi$, so that $\xi = 0$ and **4** is established. ∎

Whenever an algebraic system is discussed, the notion of a subsystem arises. In the case of a vector space $\mho$, the subsystem is usually referred to as a *subspace* and is merely a subset of $\mho$, which is itself a vector space with respect to the operations of $\mho$. The subspace 0, consisting of the vector 0 alone, is a subspace of every space as is the whole space itself. These are the two "trivial" subspaces of any space. In the language of operator groups, a subspace is an *admissible* subgroup, i.e., one which is mapped into itself by each operator. The proof of the following important result is almost immediate.

Theorem 6.32. *A nonempty subset S of a vector space is a subspace if S is closed under the operations of addition and scalar multiplication of the vector space.*

Proof. Since $-x = (-1)x$, for any vector $x \in S$, it follows that $-x \in S$. Hence the supposition of closure confirms that $y - x = y + (-x) \in S$, for arbitrary x, $y \in S$, while an application of Theorem 4.51 shows that S is an additive abelian subgroup. The other requirements for a subspace are evidently satisfied by S [Problem 2]. ∎

As an illustration of the preceding theorem, consider the elements of $\mathcal{V}_3(\mathcal{F})$ of the form $(x_1, 0, x_3)$, where x_1, $x_3 \in \mathcal{F}$. It is clear that the sum of two elements of this form is another element of the same form, and an almost immediate application of Theorem 6.32 shows that these elements form a subspace [Problem 3]. Similarly, one can show that 0 and the set of all polynomials in an indeterminate x, with real coefficients and degree at most 5, is a subspace of the vector space $\mathbf{R}[x]$. In like manner we can show that the set of all continuous real-valued functions on $\mathbf{R}$ comprises a subspace of the vector space of all functions on $\mathbf{R}$, with the usual operations for functions.

By a "linear combination" of vectors $\xi_1, \xi_2, \ldots, \xi_n$ from a vector space over a field $\mathcal{F}$ we mean an element of the form $c_1\xi_1 + c_2\xi_2 + \cdots + c_n\xi_n$, where $c_1, c_2, \ldots, c_n \in \mathcal{F}$. It is sometimes convenient to designate the set of all such elements as $\mathcal{L}\{\xi_1, \xi_2, \ldots, \xi_n\}$. For a particularly interesting application of Theorem 6.32 let us consider the set $\mathcal{L}\{\xi_1, \xi_2, \ldots, \xi_n\}$ and derive the following important result.

Theorem 6.33. *The set $\mathcal{W}$ of all linear combinations of an arbitrary set of vectors from a vector space $\mathcal{V}$ is a subspace of $\mathcal{V}$.*

Proof. In the symbolism of the paragraph preceding the theorem, let us suppose that $c_1\xi_1 + c_2\xi_2 + \cdots + c_n\xi_n = \xi \in \mathcal{W}$ and also

$$c_1'\xi_1 + c_2'\xi_2 + \cdots + c_n'\xi_n = \xi' \in \mathcal{W}.$$

Then

$$\xi + \xi' = (c_1 + c_1')\xi_1 + (c_2 + c_2')\xi_2 + \cdots + (c_n + c_n')\xi_n \in \mathcal{W};$$

and likewise,

$$c\xi = c(c_1\xi_1) + c(c_2\xi_2) + \cdots + c(c_n\xi_n)$$
$$= (cc_1)\xi_1 + (cc_2)\xi_2 + \cdots + (cc_n)\xi_n \in \mathcal{W},$$

for arbitrary $c \in \mathcal{F}$. Hence, by Theorem 6.32, $\mathcal{W}$ is a subspace of $\mathcal{V}$. ∎

The subspace $\mathcal{W}$ of Theorem 6.33 is evidently the smallest subspace that contains the given set of vectors, and so it may be called the subspace *generated* or *spanned* by them. These vectors may be called *generators* of the subspace, a word with a similar meaning in both the theory of groups and the theory of rings. We say that a vector space is *finitely generated* if it can be generated by a finite number of vectors.

PROBLEMS 6–3

1. List the properties of a vector space that are not required in the definition of a group with operators.

*2. Complete the proof of Theorem 6.32.

3. Prove that the system of vectors $(x_1, 0, x_3)$, with $x_1, x_3 \in \mathcal{F}$, is a subspace of $\mathcal{V}_3(\mathcal{F})$.

*4. Prove that the set-theoretic intersection of any two subspaces of a vector space $\mathcal{V}$ is a subspace of $\mathcal{V}$.

*5. If $\mathcal{U}$ and $\mathcal{W}$ are subspaces of a vector space $\mathcal{V}$, we can define $\mathcal{U} + \mathcal{W}$ to be the set of all sums $\xi + \eta$, with $\xi \in \mathcal{U}$ and $\eta \in \mathcal{W}$. Prove that $\mathcal{U} + \mathcal{W}$ is a subspace of $\mathcal{V}$.

*6. Prove the following "cancellation" laws for elements ξ, η of any vector space over a field $\mathcal{F}$.
   (a) If $\xi \neq 0$, then $a\xi = b\xi$ implies that $a = b$, where $a, b \in \mathcal{F}$.
   (b) If ξ and η are nonzero elements of $\mathcal{V}$, prove that $a\xi = a\eta$ implies that $\xi = \eta$, where $a(\neq 0) \in \mathcal{F}$.

**7. Which of the following subsets of $\mathcal{V}_4(\mathbf{R})$ constitute subspaces where $X = (x_1, x_2, x_3, x_4)$?
   (a) All X where x_1, x_2, x_3, x_4 are integers.
   (b) All X where $x_2 = 2x_1$ and $x_3 = x_1 + x_2$.
   (c) All X where $x_2 = x_3 = 0$.
   (d) All X where $3x_1 - 2x_2 = 0$.

8. Determine all subspaces of $\mathcal{V}_2(\mathbf{Z}/(3))$.

9. Which of the following subsets of real-valued functions on $\mathbf{R}$ are subspaces of the vector space of all such functions?
   (a) All polynomial functions of degree 5.
   (b) All functions f such that $f(x) = f(x - 1)$.
   (c) All polynomial functions of degree 5 or less—including the zero function.
   (d) All functions f such that $3f(0) = 2f(1)$.

10. The additive group of $\mathcal{V}_2(\mathbf{Z}/(2))$ has four elements. List them and decide whether the group is isomorphic to $\mathbf{Z}/(4)$.

11. The additive group of $\mathcal{V}_2(\mathbf{Z}/(3))$ has nine elements. List them and decide whether the group is isomorphic to $\mathbf{Z}/(9)$.

12. In $\mathcal{V}_3(\mathbf{R})$ let $\mathcal{U}$ be the subspace spanned by $(1, 2, -1)$, $(1, 0, 2)$, and $(-1, 4, -8)$, while $\mathcal{W}$ is the subspace spanned by all vectors of the form $(x_1, 0, x_3)$. Refer to Problems 4 and 5 and describe the intersection of $\mathcal{U}$ and $\mathcal{W}$ and also the space $\mathcal{U} + \mathcal{W}$.

13. Show that every vector in $\mathcal{V}_3(\mathbf{R})$ can be expressed as a linear combination of $(1, 1, 1)$, $(1, 0, 1)$, and $(1, -1, -1)$.

14. Prove that the subset of $\mathcal{V}_3(\mathbf{R})$, consisting of triples (x_1, x_2, x_3) where $x_3 = 0$, is a subspace which is isomorphic to $\mathcal{V}_2(\mathbf{R})$.

15. Prove that all vector spaces over $\mathcal{F}$, generated by a single nonzero vector, are isomorphic to each other and to $\mathcal{F}$ (considered as a vector space over itself).

16. Prove that the vector space over $\mathbf{R}$, consisting of 0 and all polynomials in $\mathbf{R}[x]$ of degree 3 or less, is isomorphic to $\mathcal{V}_4(\mathbf{R})$.

17. If $\mathcal{U}$ and $\mathcal{W}$ are subspaces of $\mathcal{V}$, which are spanned, respectively, by $\{\xi_1, \xi_2\}$, and $\{\lambda_1, \lambda_2\}$, prove that $\mathcal{U} + \mathcal{W}$ is spanned by $\{\xi_1, \xi_2, \lambda_1, \lambda_2\}$.

18. Let $\mathcal{U}$ and $\mathcal{W}$ in Problem 17 be subspaces of $\mathcal{V}_3(\mathbf{R})$, and illustrate a case where $\mathcal{U}$ and $\mathcal{W}$ have two generators each but where $\mathcal{U} + \mathcal{W}$ may be spanned by three vectors.

19. If $\mathcal{U}$ and $\mathcal{W}$ are subspaces of $\mathcal{V}$, prove that $\mathcal{U} \cup \mathcal{W} = \mathcal{U} + \mathcal{W}$ if and only if $\mathcal{U} \subset \mathcal{W}$ or $\mathcal{W} \subset \mathcal{U}$.

20. If $\mathcal{U}$ and $\mathcal{W}$ are subspaces of $\mathcal{V}$, prove that the representation of vectors of $\mathcal{U} + \mathcal{W}$ in the form $\xi + \eta$, with $\xi \in \mathcal{U}$ and $\eta \in \mathcal{W}$, is unique if and only if $\mathcal{U} \cap \mathcal{W} = 0$.

**21. Let $\mathcal{W}$ be a subspace of $\mathcal{V}$ over $\mathcal{F}$, and define scalar multiplication on the factor group $\mathcal{V}/\mathcal{W}$ so that it becomes a vector space over $\mathcal{F}$ (called the *factor* or *quotient space* $\mathcal{V}/\mathcal{W}$). Verify that the requirements of a vector space over $\mathcal{F}$ are satisfied by $\mathcal{V}/\mathcal{W}$.

22. Use the familiar comparison between homomorphisms and isomorphisms to define a homomorphism of a vector space $\mathcal{V}$ over $\mathcal{F}$. Then prove that the *kernel* (the elements mapped onto the vector 0) of any homomorphism of $\mathcal{V}$ is a subspace of $\mathcal{V}$.

23. Let Hom $(\mathcal{V}, \mathcal{W})$ be the set of all homomorphisms [see Problem 22] of the vector space $\mathcal{V}$ into the vector space $\mathcal{W}$. Then make suitable definitions of the operations to make Hom $(\mathcal{V}, \mathcal{W})$ into a vector space, all vector spaces being over the same field $\mathcal{F}$. As a special case, Hom $(\mathcal{V}, \mathcal{F})$ is called the *dual space* $\hat{\mathcal{V}}$ of $\mathcal{V}$ and its elements are called *linear functionals* on $\mathcal{V}$ into $\mathcal{F}$.

24. If a vector space $\mathcal{V}$ is regarded as a group with operators, explain why a subspace of $\mathcal{V}$ is "admissible" under the field of operators of the group.

6.4. Linear Dependence

The notion of *dimension* of a vector space of n-tuples was introduced intuitively in the early sections of this chapter, but up to this point we have not defined it precisely for an abstract vector space. In this section we define the concept of *linear dependence*, an idea which plays a central role in the theory of vector spaces and in particular in connection with any definition of dimension.

Definition. A set of vectors $\{\xi_1, \xi_2, \ldots, \xi_n\}$ is said to be *linearly dependent* over the field $\mathcal{F}$ of scalars, if and only if there exist scalars $c_1, c_2, \ldots, c_n$, *not all zero*, such that $c_1\xi_1 + c_2\xi_2 + \cdots + c_n\xi_n = 0$. Otherwise, the vectors $\xi_1, \xi_2, \ldots, \xi_n$ are *linearly independent*. That is, the vectors $\xi_1, \xi_2, \ldots, \xi_n$ are linearly independent if $c_1 = c_2 = \cdots = c_n = 0$ whenever $c_1\xi_1 + c_2\xi_2 + \cdots + c_n\xi_n = 0$.

For example, in $\mathcal{V}_3(\mathbf{Q})$ the vectors $(1, 0, 1)$, $(0, 1, 1)$, $(1, 3/2, 5/2)$ are linearly dependent over the field $\mathbf{Q}$ of rational numbers, for it is easy to check that $2(1, 0, 1) + 3(0, 1, 1) - 2(1, 3/2, 5/2) = (0, 0, 0) = 0$. On the other hand it is clear that the vectors $(1, 0, 0)$, $(0, 1, 0)$, $(0, 0, 1)$ constitute a linearly independent set over the rational numbers: for if

$$c_1(1, 0, 0) + c_2(0, 1, 0) + c_3(0, 0, 1) = (c_1, c_2, c_3) = (0, 0, 0),$$

it follows that $c_1 = c_2 = c_3 = 0$. In any study of a vector space of n-tuples, questions of the solvability of systems of equations are tied up with questions of linear independence of vectors. For example, if we wish to determine whether the vectors $(1, 1, 1)$, $(2, 0, 1)$, $(1, 2, -1)$ are linearly independent over $\mathbf{Q}$, we must ask whether there exist rational numbers c_1, c_2, c_3, not all zero, such that $c_1(1, 1, 1) + c_2(2, 0, 1) + c_3(1, 2, -1) = (0, 0, 0)$. The question now is whether the equations below have any nontrivial (i.e., not all zero) solutions:

$$c_1 + 2c_2 + \ c_3 = 0;$$
$$c_1 + 0c_2 + 2c_3 = 0;$$
$$c_1 + \ c_2 - \ c_3 = 0.$$

The theory of equations tells us that such a homogeneous system of equations has a nontrivial solution if and only if the determinant of the coefficients is 0. On expansion of this determinant, we find that

$$\begin{vmatrix} 1 & 2 & 1 \\ 1 & 0 & 2 \\ 1 & 1 & -1 \end{vmatrix} = 5 \neq 0.$$

Hence the only possible solution of the system is the trivial one, and the given vectors are linearly independent.

The following theorem expresses the essential property of linear dependence as applied to a set of vectors.

Theorem 6.41. *The set $\{\xi_1, \xi_2, \ldots, \xi_n\}$ of nonzero vectors from a vector space $\mathcal{V}$ over $\mathcal{F}$ comprises a linearly dependent set if and only if some member of the set can be expressed as a linear combination of the members which precede it in the listing.*

Proof. If ξ_k is a linear combination of $\xi_1, \xi_2, \ldots, \xi_{k-1}$, then

$$\xi_k = c_1\xi_1 + c_2\xi_2 + \cdots + c_{k-1}\xi_{k-1},$$

for scalars $c_1, c_2, \ldots, c_{k-1}$, and this equation can be written in the form:

$$c_1\xi_1 + c_2\xi_2 + \cdots + c_{k-1}\xi_{k-1} + (-1)\xi_k + 0\xi_{k+1} + \cdots + 0\xi_n = 0.$$

Inasmuch as not all the coefficients in this equation are zero, our definition implies that the set $\{\xi_1, \xi_2, \ldots, \xi_n\}$ is linearly dependent. Conversely, suppose that $\{\xi_1, \xi_2, \ldots, \xi_n\}$ is a linearly dependent set of vectors, so that some linear combination of $\xi_1, \xi_2, \ldots, \xi_n$ is equal to zero, while not all the coefficients are zero. If we select the vector with the largest subscript whose coefficient is not zero, say ξ_k, we can solve for ξ_k as a linear combination of $\xi_1, \xi_2, \ldots, \xi_{k-1}$, unless $k = 1$. But it is not possible that $k = 1$, since $c_1 \xi_1 = 0$, with $c_1 \neq 0$, would imply that $\xi_1 = 0$ [Theorem 6.31], contrary to assumption. Hence the theorem is established. ∎

Corollary. *Any finite set of vectors, not all zero, contains a linearly independent subset which generates or " spans" the same space.*

Proof. In the first place, we may discard any zero vector of the set. Then, if $\{\xi_1, \xi_2, \ldots, \xi_n\}$ is the remaining set of nonzero vectors, we can examine each of these vectors as listed, in order from left to right, and discard it if and only if it can be expressed as a linear combination of the preceding vectors. The remaining subset of vectors will generate the same space as the original set, and since no vector is a linear combination of those which precede it in the array, Theorem 6.41 implies that the subset is linearly independent. ∎

PROBLEMS 6–4

1. Why is it reasonable to require in the definition of linear dependence that not all the scalar coefficients be zero?
*2. If one vector of a set of vectors is zero, could the set be linearly independent?
*3. Show that a single vector ξ comprises a linearly independent set if $\xi \neq 0$.
*4. Prove that any nonempty subset of a linearly independent set of vectors is linearly independent.
5. Let $\xi_1, \xi_2, \ldots, \xi_m$ be a linearly independent set of vectors over the field $\mathcal{F}$. Then prove that if $a_1 \xi_1 + a_2 \xi_2 + \cdots + a_m \xi_m = b_1 \xi_1 + b_2 \xi_2 + \cdots + b_m \xi_m$, with $a_1, a_2, \ldots, a_m, b_1, b_2, \ldots, b_m \in \mathcal{F}$, it follows that $a_1 = b_1, a_2 = b_2, \ldots, a_m = b_m$.
6. Let us suppose that of the five vectors $\xi_1, \xi_2, \xi_3, \xi_4, \xi_5$, vectors ξ_4 and ξ_5 can be expressed as linear combinations of the vectors which respectively precede them. Then show that ξ_1, ξ_2, ξ_3 will generate the same space as the given set of five vectors.
**7. Prove that the vectors (a_1, b_1) and (a_2, b_2) are linearly dependent over any field containing a_1, b_1, a_2, b_2, if and only if $a_1 b_2 - a_2 b_1 = 0$.
8. Determine whether the following sets of vectors in $\mathcal{V}_3(\mathbf{Q})$ are linearly dependent or independent over $\mathbf{Q}$:
   (a) $\{(0, 1, 2), (1, 1, 1), (1, -2, 1)\}$;
   (b) $\{(1, 0, 2), (2, 0, 1), (1, 1, 1)\}$;
   (c) $\{(2, 0, 1), (0, 1, 4), (2, 1, 5)\}$;
   (d) $\{(1, 1, 1), (0, 3, 2), (1, 0, 0), (2, 1, -1)\}$.
9. Prove that two vectors comprise a linearly dependent set if and only if one is a scalar multiple of the other.

10. Determine whether the following sets of vectors from $\mathcal{V}_3(\mathbf{Z}/(3))$ are linearly dependent or independent:
    (a) $\{(1, 2, 1), (0, 1, 1)\}$;
    (b) $\{(0, 1, 1), (0, 2, 2)\}$;
    (c) $\{(1, 0, 2), (1, 1, 1), (2, 2, 1)\}$.

11. If $c_1\xi_1 + c_2\xi_2 + c_3\xi_3 = 0$, where ξ_1, ξ_2, ξ_3 are vectors and c_1, c_2, c_3 are scalars such that $c_1 c_3 \neq 0$, show that ξ_1 and ξ_2 generate the same subspace as do ξ_2 and ξ_3.

12. In the space $\mathbf{Q}[x]$ over $\mathbf{Q}$, decide whether the vectors $1 + 2x$, $1/2 - x$, $2 + x - 3x^2$ comprise a linearly independent set.

13. Prove that three vectors with rational components are linearly independent in $\mathcal{V}_3(\mathbf{R})$, if and only if they are linearly independent in $\mathcal{V}_3(\mathbf{Q})$.

14. For what values of x and y are vectors $(x, y, 3)$, $(2, x - y, 1)$ linearly independent in $\mathcal{V}_3(\mathbf{R})$?

15. Show that the vectors $(1, -1, 1)$, $(8, 4, 2)$, $(2, 2, 0)$, $(2, 6, -2)$ comprise a linearly dependent set of vectors in $\mathcal{V}_3(\mathbf{R})$ and determine a linearly independent subset which generates the same subspace of $\mathcal{V}_3(\mathbf{R})$.

16. Determine maximal subsets of linearly independent vectors of each of the following sets of vectors:
    (a) $\{(1, 0, 1), (2, 0, 1), (3, 0, 0), (3, 0, 1)\}$ in $\mathcal{V}_3(\mathbf{R})$;
    (b) $\{(6, 3, -9), (3, -2, 1), (2, 1, -3), (3, 1, -8), (5, 2, -11)\}$ in $\mathcal{V}_3(\mathbf{Q})$;
    (c) $\{(2, 0, 1), (1, 2, 1), (0, 0, 2), (1, 2, 2)\}$ in $\mathcal{V}_3(\mathbf{Z}/(3))$;
    (d) $\{1, x, 2x^2 + 1, x^3 - 2x, x - 1\}$ in $\mathbf{Q}[x]$ over $\mathbf{Q}$.

**17. If $\mathcal{V}$ is a finitely generated vector space over $\mathcal{F}$ and $x(\neq 0) \in \mathcal{V}$, prove that there exists f in the dual space $\hat{\mathcal{V}}$ [see Problem 23 of § 6.3] such that $f(x) \neq 0$.

18. If $\xi_1 \neq \xi_2$ in a vector space $\mathcal{V}$, prove that $f(\xi_1) \neq f(\xi_2)$ for some linear functional f in the dual space $\hat{\mathcal{V}}$ of $\mathcal{V}$ [see Problem 17].

19. If $\hat{\mathcal{V}}$ is the dual space of $\mathcal{V}$ over $\mathcal{F}$, and $f, g \in \hat{\mathcal{V}}$ such that $g(x) = 0$ whenever $f(x) = 0$ for any $x \in \mathcal{V}$, prove that $g = cf$ for some $c \in \mathcal{F}$ [see Problem 17].

20. Determine whether the following sets of vectors are linearly dependent or independent over $\mathcal{F}$:
    (a) $\{2, 1 + i\}$ with $\mathcal{F} = \mathbf{R}$;
    (b) $\{i, i + 1\}$ with $\mathcal{F} = \mathbf{R}$;
    (c) $\{1, \sqrt{2}, \sqrt{3}\}$ with $\mathcal{F} = \mathbf{Q}$;
    (d) $\{2, 1 + x^2, 2 + 3x^2\}$ with $\mathcal{F} = \mathbf{Q}$.

6.5. Bases for a Vector Space

A set of vectors $\{\xi_1, \xi_2, \ldots, \xi_n\}$ has been called a set of *generators* for a vector space $\mathcal{V}$ over $\mathcal{F}$ if each $\xi \in \mathcal{V}$ can be expressed in the form $\xi = c_1\xi_1 + c_2\xi_2 + \cdots + c_n\xi_n$, for suitable $c_1, c_2, \ldots, c_n \in \mathcal{F}$. The notion of a "basis" is closely associated with that of a set of generators, and this association is made clear by the following definition.

Definition. A *basis* for a vector space is a set of generators with the property that each vector of the space can be expressed in a *unique* way as a linear combination, with scalar coefficients, of the generating elements.

In the symbolism introduced above this means that the set $\{\xi_1, \xi_2, \ldots, \xi_n\}$ is a basis if $c_1, c_2, \ldots, c_n$ are *unique* elements of $\mathcal{F}$, dependent only on the vector ξ.

Theorem 6.51. *A set of vectors forms a basis for a vector space if and only if the vectors of the set are linearly independent and generate the space.*

Proof. If $\{\xi_1, \xi_2, \ldots, \xi_n\}$ is a basis for a vector space $\mathcal{V}$, these vectors certainly generate $\mathcal{V}$. Moreover, if there exist scalars $c_1, c_2, \ldots, c_n$ such that $c_1\xi_1 + c_2\xi_2 + \cdots + c_n\xi_n = 0 = 0\xi_1 + 0\xi_2 + \cdots + 0\xi_n$, the uniqueness of representation of the vector 0 requires that $c_1 = c_2 = \cdots = c_n = 0$. Hence a basis is a linearly independent set of generators. Conversely, suppose that $\{\xi_1, \xi_2, \ldots, \xi_n\}$ is a linearly independent set of generators and that some vector ξ has two representations in terms of this basis as follows: $\xi = c_1\xi_1 + c_2\xi_2 + \cdots + c_n\xi_n = d_1\xi_1 + d_2\xi_2 + \cdots + d_n\xi_n$, for certain scalars, $c_1, c_2, \ldots, c_n, d_1, d_2, \ldots, d_n$. But then $(c_1 - d_1)\xi_1 + (c_2 - d_2)\xi_2 + \cdots + (c_n - d_n)\xi_n = 0$, and the linear independence of the generators requires that $c_1 = d_1, c_2 = d_2, \ldots, c_n = d_n$. Hence each vector of $\mathcal{V}$ has a unique representation, and $\{\xi_1, \xi_2, \ldots, \xi_n\}$ is a basis. ∎

As a prelude to Theorem 6.52, the proof of which is relatively difficult, let us consider a proof of the following simple proposition: *If a vector space $\mathcal{V}$ has a basis of two elements η_1, η_2, any three vectors ξ_1, ξ_2, ξ_3 of $\mathcal{V}$ are linearly dependent.* If one of ξ_1, ξ_2, ξ_3 is 0, the set is clearly dependent [Problem 2 of §6.4], and so we may assume that each of these vectors is nonzero. Then there exist scalars $c_{11}, c_{12}, c_{21}, c_{22}, c_{31}, c_{32}$, where no two with the same first subscript are 0, such that

$$\xi_1 = c_{11}\eta_1 + c_{12}\eta_2$$
$$\xi_2 = c_{21}\eta_1 + c_{22}\eta_2$$
$$\xi_3 = c_{31}\eta_1 + c_{32}\eta_2.$$

If perchance $c_{12} = c_{22} = c_{32} = 0$, the vectors ξ_1, ξ_2, ξ_3 are in the subspace $\mathcal{V}_0$ of scalar multiples of η_1. In this case $c_{21}\xi_1 + (-c_{11})\xi_2 + 0\xi_3 = 0$, where neither c_{21} nor c_{11} is 0, so that the set $\{\xi_1, \xi_2, \xi_3\}$ is linearly dependent as asserted. If, on the other hand, at least one of ξ_1, ξ_2, ξ_3, say ξ_3, is not in $\mathcal{V}_0$, so that $c_{32} \neq 0$, we can define two vectors ζ_1 and ζ_2 which *are* in $\mathcal{V}_0$ as follows:

$$\zeta_1 = \xi_1 - c_{12}(c_{32}^{-1})\xi_3; \quad \zeta_2 = \xi_2 - c_{22}(c_{32}^{-1})\xi_3.$$

But since each vector in $\mathcal{V}_0$ is a scalar multiple of η_1, there exist scalars d_1, d_2 such that $\zeta_1 = d_1\eta_1$ and $\zeta_2 = d_2\eta_1$, so that

$$d_2\zeta_1 + (-d_1)\zeta_2 = d_1d_2\eta_1 - d_1d_2\eta_2 = 0.$$

If we replace ζ_1 and ζ_2 by their equivalent representations in terms of ξ_1, ξ_2, ξ_3, this equation becomes

$$d_2\zeta_1 + (-d_1)\zeta_2 = 0 = d_2\xi_1 + (-d_1)\xi_2 + (-c_{32}^{-1})(d_2c_{12} - d_1c_{22})\xi_3,$$

which shows, if d_1 and d_2 are not both zero, that $\{\xi_1, \xi_2, \xi_3\}$ is a linearly dependent set. If $d_1 = d_2 = 0$, then $\zeta_1 = \zeta_2$ and so

$$\xi_1 - \xi_2 + c_{32}^{-1}(c_{22} - c_{12})\xi_3 = 0,$$

and again $\{\xi_1, \xi_2, \xi_3\}$ is a linearly dependent set. Our simple proposition has thus been established.

The following result is the one from which the important property is derived.

Theorem 6.52. *If a vector space $\mathcal{V}$ has a basis of n vectors, any $n + 1$ vectors from $\mathcal{V}$ are linearly dependent.*

Proof. We shall prove this theorem by induction on n. First let us suppose that $n = 1$. Since a set of vectors is necessarily dependent if one of its vectors is the zero vector, we may assume that ξ_1 and ξ_2 are nonzero vectors of a vector space with one basis vector η. But then $\xi_1 = c_1\eta$ and $\xi_2 = c_2\eta$, for certain scalars c_1, c_2, and so $c_2\xi_1 + (-c_1)\xi_2 = c_1c_2\eta - c_1c_2\eta = 0$. Hence $\{\xi_1, \xi_2\}$ is a dependent set, and the theorem is proven for $n = 1$. Now let us assume that the theorem is true for $n = k$, i.e., if a vector space has a basis of k vectors, any $k + 1$ of its vectors are linearly dependent. We must show that, if a space has a basis of $k + 1$ vectors, any $k + 2$ of its vectors are linearly dependent. Thus let us consider a space with a basis $\{\eta_1, \eta_2, \ldots, \eta_{k+1}\}$. If $\xi_1, \xi_2, \ldots, \xi_{k+2}$ are $k + 2$ vectors of this space, they can be expressed in the form $\xi_1 = c_{i1}\eta_1 + c_{i2}\eta_2 + \cdots + c_{i,k+1}\eta_{k+1}$, for $i = 1, 2, \ldots, k + 2$. If each ξ_i is in the subspace $\mathcal{V}_0$ generated by $\eta_1, \eta_2, \ldots, \eta_k$, our inductive assumption implies that any $k + 1$ of the vectors $\xi_1, \xi_2, \ldots, \xi_{k+2}$, are linearly dependent, and so $\{\xi_1, \xi_2, \ldots, \xi_{k+2}\}$ is a linearly dependent set. There remains the case where at least one of the vectors $\xi_1, \xi_2, \ldots, \xi_{k+2}$ is not in $\mathcal{V}_0$; let us relabel them if necessary so that $\xi_{k+2} \notin \mathcal{V}_0$, which in turn implies that $c_{k+2,k+1} \neq 0$. But then the $k + 1$ elements $\zeta_i = \xi_i - c_{i,k+1}(c_{k+2,k+1})^{-1}\xi_{k+2}$ are in $\mathcal{V}_0$, for $i = 1, 2, \ldots, k + 1$; and by our inductive assumption there exist scalars $d_1, d_2, \ldots, d_{k+1}$, not all zero, such that $d_1\zeta_1 + d_2\zeta_2 + \cdots + d_{k+1}\zeta_{k+1} = d_1\xi_1 + d_2\xi_2 + \cdots + d_{k+1}\xi_{k+1} + (-c_{k+2,k+1})^{-1}[d_1c_{1,k+1} + \cdots + d_{k+1}c_{k+1,k+1}]\xi_{k+2} = 0$. Hence $\{\xi_1, \xi_2, \ldots, \xi_{k+2}\}$ is a linearly dependent set, and our theorem is established for $n = k + 1$. An application of the Principle of Mathematical Induction then completes the proof of the theorem for arbitrary n. ∎

The important result in the next theorem now follows easily.

Theorem 6.53. *The number of elements in a basis of a vector space $\mho$ is unique. This number is known as the* dimension *of $\mho$ and may be designated " dim $\mho$."*

Proof. For suppose $\mho$ has two bases B_1 and B_2, with n_1 and n_2 elements, respectively. If $n_1 < n_2$ and we consider B_1 as a basis and B_2 as a set of elements, it follows from Theorem 6.52 that B_2 is a linearly dependent set. But this is contrary to Theorem 6.51. A similar untenable conclusion is reached if we assume that $n_2 < n_1$, so we are forced to conclude that $n_1 = n_2$. ∎

In the case of $\mho_n(\mathcal{F})$ the vectors $\varepsilon_1 = (1, 0, 0, \ldots, 0)$, $\varepsilon_2 = (0, 1, 0, 0, \ldots, 0)$, $\ldots, \varepsilon_n = (0, 0, 0, \ldots, 0, 1)$ certainly generate the space. For if $\xi = (a_1, a_2, \ldots, a_n)$ is an arbitrary element of $\mho_n(\mathcal{F})$, $\xi = a_1\varepsilon_1 + a_2\varepsilon_2 + \cdots + a_n\varepsilon_n$. Moreover, if there exist scalars $c_1, c_2, \ldots, c_n$, such that

$$c_1\varepsilon_1 + c_2\varepsilon_2 + \cdots + c_n\varepsilon_n = (c_1, c_2, \ldots, c_n) = (0, 0, \ldots, 0),$$

it follows that $c_1 = c_2 = \cdots = c_n = 0$. Since any set of generators must contain a basis as a subset [Problem 2], the set $\{\varepsilon_1, \varepsilon_2, \ldots, \varepsilon_n\}$ must be a basis for $\mho_n(\mathcal{F})$. This is sometimes referred to as the "ε-basis" of the space. In the next section, we define an algorithm for obtaining a basis for any finitely-generated vector space.

PROBLEMS 6–5

*1. If $\{\eta_1, \eta_2, \ldots, \eta_n\}$ is a basis and $\{\xi_1, \xi_2, \ldots, \xi_r\}$ is a linearly independent subset of vectors of a vector space $\mho$, why is it clear that $\{\xi_1, \xi_2, \ldots, \xi_r, \eta_1, \eta_2, \ldots, \eta_n\}$ is a generating set?

*2. Explain why any set of generators of a vector space must contain a subset of basis elements.

3. In the vector space of real-valued functions on **R decide whether the following vectors are linearly independent:
   (a) $1, x, x^2$;
   (b) $2, \sin x, \cos x$;
   (c) $1, \sin^2 x, \cos^2 x$;
   (d) $x, x + x^2, x^2 + 4x, 3 - x^2$.

4. Explain why $(1, 1, 0)$ and $(0, 1, 1)$ could not comprise a basis for the space $\mho_3(\mathbf{R})$. Generalize this result to $\mho_n(\mathcal{F})$.

5. Show that the vector space of all real polynomial functions on **R** does not have a finite dimension.

6. Decide whether the following constitute a basis for the space of zero and all polynomials of degree 3 or less over **R**: $\{3, x^2 - x, 3x^3 + 2, x + 1\}$.

7. Prove that the set $\{a + bi, c + di\}$ is a basis for the vector space of complex numbers over the field of real numbers, if and only if $ad - bc \neq 0$

8. If $\xi_1, \xi_2, \ldots, \xi_m$ are linearly independent vectors of a vector space of dimension n, prove that $m \leq n$.

9. If $\mathcal{W}$ is a subspace of $\mathcal{V}$, such that dim $\mathcal{W} =$ dim $\mathcal{V}$, prove that $\mathcal{W} = \mathcal{V}$.

10. Decide whether (a) $\{1, 2x - 1, x^2 + 1\}$ or (b) $\{1, x^2 + x\}$ constitutes a basis for the space of zero and all polynomials of degree 2 or less over $\mathbf{R}$.

11. Prove that any isomorphism $\mathcal{V} \rightarrow \mathcal{W}$ of vector spaces must map any basis of $\mathcal{V}$ onto a basis of $\mathcal{W}$.

12. Use Problem 11 to show that $\mathcal{V}_n(\mathcal{F})$ is isomorphic to $\mathcal{V}_m(\mathcal{F})$ if and only if $n = m$.

13. With $\{\varepsilon_1, \varepsilon_2, \varepsilon_3, \varepsilon_4\}$ constituting the " ε-basis " of $\mathcal{V}_4(\mathcal{F})$, decide whether the following vectors are linearly independent over $\mathcal{F}$:
   (a) $\varepsilon_1 + \varepsilon_2, \varepsilon_1 + \varepsilon_3, \varepsilon_2 + \varepsilon_4$;
   (b) $\varepsilon_1, \varepsilon_2 - \varepsilon_1, \varepsilon_1 + 2\varepsilon_2$;
   (c) $\varepsilon_2, \varepsilon_2 + 2\varepsilon_4, \varepsilon_4 - \varepsilon_2$.

14. Show that the vectors $(1, 1, 1), (0, -1, 1), (3, 0, 1)$ are linearly independent as elements of $\mathcal{V}_3(\mathbf{R})$. Find a field $\mathcal{F}$ such that these vectors are linearly dependent as elements of $\mathcal{V}_3(\mathcal{F})$.

15. Verify that $\mathbf{Q}[\sqrt{2}]$, as a vector space over $\mathbf{Q}$, is isomorphic to the space of linear polynomials over $\mathbf{Q}$ in an indeterminate x.

16. Review the reason why the *rings* $\mathbf{Q}[\sqrt{2}]$ and $\mathbf{Q}[x]$ are not isomorphic, and reconcile this result with that of Problem 15.

**17. Show why $\mathbf{Q}[\sqrt{2}]$ and $\mathbf{Q}[\sqrt{3}]$ are not isomorphic as rings but are isomorphic as vector spaces over $\mathbf{Q}$.

18. If we define scalar multiplication in the system $M_n(\mathcal{F})$ of matrices so that $rA = r[a_{ij}] = [ra_{ij}]$, for any $A \in M_n(\mathcal{F})$ and $r \in \mathcal{F}$, prove that $M_n(\mathcal{F})$ is a vector space over $\mathcal{F}$.

19. Refer to Problem 18 and determine the dimension of the vector space of $n \times n$ matrices over $\mathcal{F}$, by finding a basis for the space.

20. Prove that the subset of matrices $\begin{bmatrix} a & 0 \\ 0 & 0 \end{bmatrix}$ in $M_2(\mathcal{F})$ is a vector space which is isomorphic to the field $\mathcal{F}$.

21. Prove that the vector space of all real-valued linear functions on $\mathbf{R}$ is one-dimensional: i.e., if $\mathcal{V}$ is a one-dimensional vector space over $\mathbf{R}$, so is its dual $\hat{\mathcal{V}}$. Conjecture a generalization of this!

6.6. An Important Dimension Theorem

In this section we consider the problem of actually determining a basis for a vector space and conclude with an important theorem concerning any finite-dimensional vector space.

For the basis-construction problem we note that any set of r linearly independent vectors of an n-dimensional vector space can be supplemented with $n - r$ other vectors to form a basis. For suppose $\{\xi_1, \xi_2, \ldots, \xi_r\}$ is a linearly independent set of vectors from a space with $\{\eta_1, \eta_2, \ldots, \eta_n\}$ as a basis. The set $\{\xi_1, \xi_2, \ldots, \xi_r, \eta_1, \eta_2, \ldots, \eta_n\}$ generates the space, as we saw in Problem 1 of §6.5. We now examine each of these $r + n$ elements in order from left to right, as in the proof of the corollary to Theorem 6.41, and discard it if it is a linear combination of the preceding elements. Since the first r are linearly independent, none of these will be discarded, and the resulting basis of linearly independent vectors will include the original r vectors. In particular we note that *any maximal subset of linearly independent vectors is a basis for a vector space.* In other words any subset of linearly independent vectors, with the property that the inclusion of any additional nonzero vector will make the set dependent, is a basis set.

It is the characterization of a basis as a maximal linearly independent subset, along with the invariance of the number of elements in any basis [Theorem 6.53], which allows us to determine a basis for a vector space from a given set of generators. All that is necessary is to be able to tell whether a set of vectors is linearly independent or dependent. In the case of elements of any $\mathcal{V}_n(\mathcal{F})$, the method discussed in § 6.4 for $n = 3$ and $\mathcal{F} = \mathbf{Q}$ could be easily generalized. For a vector space of real-valued functions on $\mathbf{R}$, it is known† that a set of functions $f_1, f_2, \ldots, f_r$ is linearly independent if their Wronskian $W(f_1, f_2, \ldots, f_r)$ is not identically 0 on $\mathbf{R}$, where $W(f_1, f_2, \ldots, f_r)$ may be described in the following determinantal form:

$$W(f_1, f_2, \ldots, f_r) = \begin{vmatrix} f_1 & f_2 & \cdots f_r \\ f_1' & f_2' & \cdots f_r' \\ f_1'' & f_2'' & \cdots f_r'' \\ \cdots\cdots\cdots\cdots \\ f_1^{(r-1)} & f_2^{(r-1)} & \cdots f_r^{(r-1)} \end{vmatrix}$$

We do not give a method for determining the linear independence of vectors from an arbitrary vector space. For the most part, however, our examples will be drawn from the above two types of spaces—the function spaces including, of course, the very important spaces of real polynomials.

Our one theorem in this section is a most important result, and one which makes apparent the importance of the vector spaces $\mathcal{V}_n(\mathcal{F})$.

Theorem 6.61. *Any n-dimensional vector space $\mathcal{V}$ over a field $\mathcal{F}$ is isomorphic to the vector space $\mathcal{V}_n(\mathcal{F})$.*

† For example, see Earl D. Rainville, *Elementary Differential Equations*, 2nd ed., p. 100 (New York, Macmillan, 1958).

Proof. Let $\{\eta_1, \eta_2, \ldots, \eta_n\}$ be a basis for $\mathcal{V}$. We shall show that the mapping $\xi_1 = c_1\eta_1 + c_2\eta_2 + \cdots + c_n\eta_n \to (c_1, c_2, \ldots, c_n)$, where ξ_1 is an arbitrary element of $\mathcal{V}$, is the desired isomorphism. Since the representation of a vector in terms of a basis of the space is unique, it is clear that this mapping is bijective. Now let $\xi_2 = d_1\eta_1 + d_2\eta_2 + \cdots + d_n\eta_n$ be another arbitrary element of $\mathcal{V}$. But then

$$\xi_1 + \xi_2 = (c_1 + d_1)\eta_1 + (c_2 + d_2)\eta_2 + \cdots + (c_n + d_n)\eta_n,$$

so that

$$\xi_1 + \xi_2 \to (c_1 + d_1, c_2 + d_2, \ldots, c_n + d_n)$$
$$= (c_1, c_2, \ldots, c_n) + (d_1, d_2, \ldots, d_n),$$

thereby verifying that addition is preserved by the correspondence. Finally, if

$$c \in \mathcal{F}, \ c\xi_1 = cc_1\eta_1 + cc_2\eta_2 + \cdots + cc_n\eta_n \to (cc_1, cc_2, \ldots, cc_n)$$
$$= c(c_1, c_2, \ldots, c_n),$$

so that scalar multiplication is also preserved by the correspondence. It follows that the mapping is an isomorphism, as desired. ∎

The above theorem suggests that a study of finite-dimensional vector spaces might well be restricted to spaces of n-tuples of field elements. While this is true, it is sometimes simpler not to do this but rather to work with vector spaces in their original formulation. The theorem is an important one, however, for it gives a complete characterization of finite dimensional vector spaces.

PROBLEMS 6–6

1. In the indicated vector space, determine a basis which includes the given vectors:
   (a) $(1, 1, 0)$, $(0, 1, 1)$ in $\mathcal{V}_3(\mathbf{Q})$;
   (b) $(-3, 1, -2, 0)$, $(1, 1, 1, 0)$, $(0, 0, 1, 1)$ in $\mathcal{V}_4(\mathbf{Q})$;
   (c) $3x$, $x^2 - 1$, $x^3 + x$ in the space of zero and all polynomial functions on $\mathbf{R}$ of degree 4 or less;
   (d) $2 + i$ in $\mathbf{C}$, with $\mathbf{C}$ considered a vector space over $\mathbf{R}$.
   (e) $(1, 0, 2, 1)$, $(1, 1, 0, 0)$ in $\mathcal{V}_4(\mathbf{Z}/(3))$.

2. Show that the set $\{(1, 2 + i, 3), (2 - i, i, 1), (i, 2 + 3i, 2)\}$ is a basis for $\mathcal{V}_3(\mathbf{C})$ and express each member of the ε-basis for $\mathcal{V}_3(\mathbf{C})$ in terms of these vectors.

**3. In $\mathcal{V}_3(\mathbf{Q})$, determine a basis as a subset of $\{(-1, 2, 2), (2, 2, -1), (3, 0, -3), (2, -1, 2)\}$ and express the dependent member as a linear combination of these basis elements.

4. Determine a basis for the subspace of $\mathcal{V}_4(\mathbf{Q})$ consisting of all vectors (a_1, a_2, a_3, a_4) for which $a_1 = a_2 - a_3$, and $a_3 = a_4$.

5. In $\mathcal{V}_4(\mathbf{R})$ let $\mathcal{U}$ be the subspace generated by $\{(1, -2, 1, -1), (2, 0, 0, 6), (-4, -4, 2, -14)\}$ and $\mathcal{W}$ be the subspace generated by $\{(0, 1, 1, 3), (3, -3, 0, 0), (9, -11, -2, -6)\}$. Determine the dimensions of $\mathcal{U}, \mathcal{W}, \mathcal{U} + \mathcal{W}$, and $\mathcal{U} \cap \mathcal{W}$. [See Problem 5 of § 6.3.]

6. Supplement the vectors $(1, -1, 2, 3), (3, 0, 4, -2)$ to form a basis for $\mathcal{V}_4(\mathbf{Q})$.

7. Prove that two finite-dimensional vector spaces over the same field are isomorphic if and only if they have the same dimension.

8. Show that $\{1, 2^{1/3}, 2^{2/3}\}$ is a basis for the vector space of all polynomials, with rational coefficients, in the irrational number $2^{1/3}$. If $\mathcal{V}_3(\mathbf{Q})$ is mapped isomorphically onto this space so that $(1, 0, 1) \to 1$ and $(2, 3, -1) \to 2^{1/3}$ describe the possible choices for the inverse image of $2^{2/3}$.

9. Prove that an isomorphic mapping between two vector spaces is completely determined by the correspondence between their basis elements.

10. Show that the subspace of $\mathcal{V}_3(\mathbf{Q})$, consisting of triples of rational numbers with first component 0, has dimension 2 and is isomorphic to $\mathcal{V}_2(\mathbf{Q})$.

11. Prove that the vector space of polynomials of degree at most 3 in an indeterminate x, with coefficients in $\mathcal{F}$, and including 0, is isomorphic to $\mathcal{V}_4(\mathcal{F})$.

12. Let α and β be vectors and $\mathcal{W}$ a subspace of a vector space $\mathcal{V}$, with $\mathcal{L}\{\mathcal{W}, \alpha\}$ and $\mathcal{L}\{\mathcal{W}, \beta\}$ the subspaces spanned by the elements of $\mathcal{W}$ and the vectors α and β, respectively. Then, if $\beta \notin \mathcal{W}$, but $\beta \in \mathcal{L}\{\mathcal{W}, \alpha\}$, prove that $\alpha \in \mathcal{L}\{W, \beta\}$.

13. The sum of two subspaces $\mathcal{F}$ and $\mathcal{W}$ is said to be *direct*, and we then write $\mathcal{U} \oplus \mathcal{W}$, if the representation of any vector of $\mathcal{U} + \mathcal{W}$ in the form $\alpha + \beta$, with $\alpha \in \mathcal{U}$ and $\beta \in \mathcal{W}$, is unique. Then use Theorem 6.61 to prove that $\mathcal{V}_n(\mathcal{F})$ is isomorphic to $\mathcal{V}_1 \oplus \mathcal{V}_2 + \cdots \oplus \mathcal{V}_n$, where $\mathcal{V}_i$ is isomorphic to $\mathcal{F}$, $i = 1, 2, \ldots, n$.

14. If ξ_1 and ξ_2 are arbitrary vectors of a vector space $\mathcal{V}$, prove that $\mathcal{L}\{\xi_1, \xi_1 + \xi_2\} + \mathcal{L}\{\xi_2\}$ is not a direct sum.

15. Let $\mathcal{V}$ be the vector space over $\mathcal{F}$ consisting of 0 and all polynomials of degree less than n in an indeterminate x. Then verify that the mapping $f(x) = a_0 + a_1 x + \cdots + a_{n-1} x^{n-1} \to f(x + 1) = a_0 + a_1(x + 1) + \cdots + a_{n-1}(x + 1)^{n-1}$ is an automorphism of $\mathcal{V}$.

16. Refer to Problem 13 and verify that a sum $\mathcal{V}_1 + \mathcal{V}_2 + \cdots + \mathcal{V}_n$ of vector subspaces is direct if and only if $\mathcal{V}_i \cap (\mathcal{V}_1 + \mathcal{V}_2 + \cdots + \mathcal{V}_{i-1} + \mathcal{V}_{i+1} + \cdots + \mathcal{V}_n) = 0$, $i = 1, 2, \ldots, n$.

17. If $\mathcal{U}$ and $\mathcal{W}$ are subspaces of a vector space, prove that $(\mathcal{U} + \mathcal{W})/\mathcal{W}$ is isomorphic to $\mathcal{U}/(\mathcal{U} \cap \mathcal{W})$ [see Problem 21 of § 6.3].

**18. Refer to Problem 23 of § 6.3 and prove that the dual $\hat{\mathcal{V}}$ of a vector space $\mathcal{V}$ of dimension n is also of dimension n. (Hint: if $\{\eta_1, \eta_2, \ldots, \eta_n\}$ is a basis of $\mathcal{V}$, show that $\{\hat{\eta}_1, \hat{\eta}_2, \ldots, \hat{\eta}_n\}$ is a basis of $\hat{\mathcal{V}}$, where $\hat{\eta}_i(a_1\eta_1 + a_2\eta_2 + \cdots + a_n\eta_n) = a_i$, $i = 1, 2, \ldots, n$. This basis of $\hat{\mathcal{V}}$ is called the *dual* of the given basis of $\mathcal{V}$.)

19. Let $\sum_{j=1}^{n} a_{ij}x_j = 0$, $i = 1, 2, \ldots, m$, be a system of m linear homogeneous equations in n unknowns. If we regard $X = (c_1, c_2, \ldots, c_n)$ as a *solution* of the system provided $\sum_{j=1}^{n} a_{ij}c_j = 0$, for each $i = 1, 2, \ldots, m$, prove that the system

of all solutions X is a vector space over $\mathcal{F}$—assuming the same operations as for $\mathcal{V}_n(\mathcal{F})$.

20. If $\mathcal{W}$ is a subspace of a vector space $\mathcal{V}$, the *annihilator* of $\mathcal{W}$ is the subset of functions $f \in \hat{\mathcal{V}}$ [see Problem 23 of § 6.3], such that $f(w) = 0$ for all $w \in \mathcal{W}$. Prove that the annihilator of $\mathcal{W}$ is a subspace of $\hat{\mathcal{V}}$.

21. Refer to Problems 19 and 20 and verify that the functions f_i, $i = 1, 2, \ldots, m$, where $f_i(x_1, x_2, \ldots, x_n) = \sum_{j=1}^{n} a_{ij}x_j$, are elements of the annihilator of the solution space of the equations $\sum_{j=1}^{n} a_{ij}x_j = 0$, $i = 1, 2, \ldots, m$.

22. Give a geometric interpretation of the result in Problem 21, using the following system of equations:
$$2x + y + z = 0,$$
$$x - y + 2z = 0.$$

23. Let $f(x, y, z) = 0$ be the defining equation of a surface in 3-dimensional geometric space $\mathcal{V}_3(\mathcal{R})$. Then verify that the points of the surface constitute a subspace of $\mathcal{V}_3(\mathcal{R})$, and that f is an element of the annihilator of the subspace.

24. Let $f_1, f_2 \in \hat{\mathcal{V}}_3(\mathcal{R})$ [see Problem 23 of § 6.3]. Then refer to Problem 20, and determine the subspace of $\mathcal{V}_3(\mathcal{R})$ annihilated by f_1 and f_2 where $f_1(x, y, z) = 2x - y + z$ and $f_2(x, y, z) = x + y - z$.

6.7. Linear Transformations

The theory of matrices is closely associated with the study of vector spaces through what are known as *linear transformations* of these spaces. In fact, vector spaces may almost be considered the *raison d'être* of matrices! But first let us clarify the notion of a linear transformation.

If f and g are real-valued polynomial functions which are differentiable at the point x, and c is an arbitrary real number, it is well known from a study of differential calculus that
$$[f(x) + g(x)]' = f'(x) + g'(x)$$
and
$$[cf(x)]' = cf'(x),$$
where we have used the customary symbolism of calculus. If we consider the mapping $f \to f'$ of a polynomial function onto its derived function (or derivative), this provides us with an example of a *linear transformation* of the vector space of all such polynomial functions onto itself. For the derivative of the sum of two functions is the sum of their derivatives, and the derivative of a scalar multiple of any function is the same scalar multiple of its derivative. To be precise we have the following definition.

Definition. A *linear transformation* $T: \mathcal{V}_1 \to \mathcal{V}_2$ of a vector space $\mathcal{V}_1$ into a vector space $\mathcal{V}_2$ over the same field $\mathcal{F}$ is a mapping of $\mathcal{V}_1$ into $\mathcal{V}_2$ such that

$$(\xi_1 + \xi_2)T = \xi_1 T + \xi_2 T \text{ and}$$
$$(c\xi_1)T = c(\xi_1 T),$$

for arbitrary vectors ξ_1, $\xi_2 \in \mathcal{V}_1$ and an arbitrary scalar $c \in \mathcal{F}$. In many instances the spaces $\mathcal{V}_1$ and $\mathcal{V}_2$ are the same space $\mathcal{V}$, and then we speak simply of a *linear transformation of* $\mathcal{V}$.

The reader will observe that a "linear transformation" is just a new name for the familiar concept of homomorphism, for this was the definition requested in Problem 22 of § 6.3. If the vector space is considered a group with operators, we usually call this mapping an "operator homomorphism" (or "operator endomorphism" if the elements are mapped into the original space), but the name used in the definition above is well established in the language of vector spaces.

It may be readily verified that the mapping defined on the polynomial function space above is in fact a linear transformation according to this definition. As another example we might consider the mapping of $\mathcal{V}_3(\mathcal{F})$ onto $\mathcal{F}$, defined by $(c_1, c_2, c_3) \to c_1 \lambda + c_2 \mu + c_3 \nu$, where λ, μ, ν are arbitrary but fixed elements of $\mathcal{F}$. The student should verify that this is a linear transformation [Problem 1]. This type of linear transformation is more frequently called a *linear functional* on $\mathcal{V}_3(\mathcal{F})$, for it maps the elements of the vector space onto the field $\mathcal{F}$ of scalars which is, of course, a vector space of dimension 1 over itself. In Problem 23 of § 6.3, the student was asked to consider the set of all homomorphisms of a vector space $\mathcal{V}$ into a vector space $\mathcal{W}$ over $\mathcal{F}$ and show that it, too, can be made into a vector space over $\mathcal{F}$ in a very natural way. The special case of the vector space of linear functionals is known variously as the *dual* space $\hat{\mathcal{V}}$ of $\mathcal{V}$ or the space *Hom* $(\mathcal{V}, \mathcal{F})$, the latter designation being more suggestive of the membership of the space [see Problem 18 of § 6.6].

There are many illustrations of a linear transformation in plane geometry. For plane geometry can be considered a study of the vector space $\mathcal{V}_2(\mathbf{R})$ of ordered pairs (x, y) of real numbers, just as solid geometry can be considered a study of $\mathcal{V}_3(\mathbf{R})$. As a simple example, let us suppose that the plane has been coordinatized with a rectangular coordinate system and that there has been effected a rotation R_θ of all points of the plane about the origin through an angle of $\theta°$. The situation "before and after" is shown in Figure 6 below. It is clear that, if ξ_1 and ξ_2 are the original vectors under observation, $(\xi_1 + \xi_2)R_\theta = \xi_1 R_\theta + \xi_2 R_\theta$: for the figure shows that the diagonal $\xi_1 + \xi_2$ of the original parallelogram is rotated onto the diagonal $\xi_1 R_\theta + \xi_2 R_\theta$ of the rotated parallelogram. Moreover, $(c\xi_1)R_\theta = c(\xi_1 R_\theta)$: for any scalar multiple

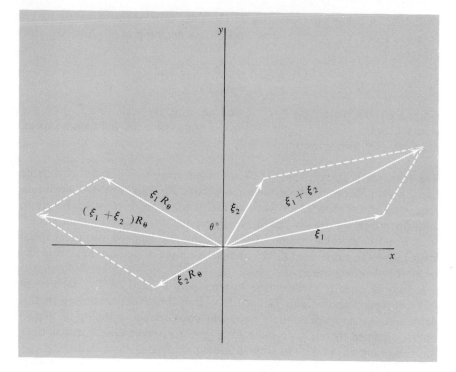

Figure 6

of the vector ξ_1 is clearly rotated onto the same scalar multiple of $\xi_1 R_\theta$. The rotation R_θ is then a linear transformation of $\mathcal{V}_2(\mathbf{R})$ onto itself [see Problem 4]. The following theorem is of great interest in this connection.

Theorem 6.71. *Any mapping T of $\mathcal{V}_2(\mathbf{R})$ into itself defined by $(x, y)T = (x', y')$ is a linear transformation if and only if there exist real numbers a_1, a_2, b_1, b_2 such that $x' = a_1 x + a_2 y$ and $y' = b_1 x + b_2 y$.*

Proof. First, let us suppose that the mapping T is defined as above so that $x' = a_1 x + a_2 y$, $y' = b_1 x + b_2 y$. It then follows easily that $[(x_1, y_1) + (x_2, y_2)]T = (x_1 + x_2, y_1 + y_2)T = (a_1(x_1 + x_2) + a_2(y_1 + y_2), b_1(x_1 + x_2) + b_2(y_1 + y_2)) = (a_1 x_1 + a_2 y_1 + a_1 x_2 + a_2 y_2, b_1 x_1 + b_2 y_1 + b_1 x_2 + b_2 y_2) = (a_1 x_1 + a_2 y_1, b_1 x_1 + b_2 y_1) + (a_1 x_2 + a_2 y_2, b_1 x_2 + b_2 y_2) = (x_1, y_1)T + (x_2, y_2)T$, so that T satisfies the first requirement of a linear transformation. Also, if c is an arbitrary real number, $[c(x, y)]T = (cx, cy)T = (a_1(cx) + a_2(cy), b_1(cx) + b_2(cy)) = (c(a_1 x + a_2 y), c(b_1 x + b_2 y)) = c(a_1 x + a_2 y, b_1 x + b_2 y) = c[(x, y)T]$, completing the proof that T is linear. Conversely, let T be an arbitrary linear transformation on $\mathcal{V}_2(\mathbf{R})$. Then, using the

ε-basis for the space, with $\varepsilon_1 = (1, 0)$ and $\varepsilon_2 = (0, 1)$, let us suppose that $\varepsilon_1 T = (a_1, b_1)$ and $\varepsilon_2 T = (a_2, b_2)$, where a_1, b_1, a_2, b_2 are certain real numbers. If (x, y) is an arbitrary vector of $\mathcal{V}_2(\mathbf{R})$, we can write $(x, y) = x\varepsilon_1 + y\varepsilon_2$, and the linearity condition on T implies that $(x, y)T = (x\varepsilon_1 + y\varepsilon_2)T = (x\varepsilon_1)T + (y\varepsilon_2)T = x(a_1, b_1) + y(a_2, b_2) = (xa_1 + ya_2, xb_1 + yb_2)$. Hence, if $(x, y)T = (x', y')$, we have shown that $x' = a_1 x + a_2 y$ and $y' = b_1 x + b_2 y$, as desired. ∎

The converse portion of this theorem points out the important fact that, if the transforms of the "unit" vectors ε_1 and ε_2 are known, the linear transformation is completely determined. A more general form of this result will be established in the following section.

PROBLEMS 6–7

**1. Prove that the mapping $T : \mathcal{V}_3(\mathcal{F}) \to \mathcal{F}$, defined by $(c_1, c_2, c_3) \to c_1\lambda + c_2\mu + c_3\nu$ for fixed elements λ, μ, ν in $\mathcal{F}$, is a linear transformation.

2. Prove that an "expansion" of the real plane, in which each point is moved radially out to a position k times as far from the origin as originally, is a linear transformation of $\mathcal{V}_2(\mathbf{R})$.

3. Why is a rotation of $\mathcal{V}_2(\mathbf{R})$ about the origin of the plane *onto* itself; i.e., why is it surjective?

4. Show that a rotation of the Cartesian plane about the origin through an angle of θ radians is defined by $(x, y) \to (x', y')$, where $x' = x \cos \theta - y \sin \theta$ and $y' = x \sin \theta + y \cos \theta$. (Hint: consider the transforms of ε_1 and ε_2.)

5. Use the result of Problem 4 to define a rotation of the Cartesian plane about the origin through an angle of $135°$.

6. A mapping T of $\mathcal{V}_2(\mathbf{R})$ into $\mathcal{V}_3(\mathbf{R})$ is defined by $(x, y) \to (x', y', z')$, where $x' = x - y$, $y' = x + y$, $z' = 2x + y$. Verify that T is a linear transformation, and determine the transforms of ε_1 and ε_2 in $\mathcal{V}_3(\mathbf{R})$.

7. Describe the geometric effect of each of the following linear transformations of $\mathcal{V}_2(\mathbf{R})$: $(x, y) \to (x', y')$.
   (a) $x' = 0$, $y' = x$;
   (b) $x' = cx$, $y' = cy$;
   (c) $x' = y$, $y' = x$;
   (d) $x' = -y$, $y' = -x$;
   (e) $x' = 3x$, $y' = y$.

8. Generalize Theorem 6.71 to apply to $\mathcal{V}_3(\mathbf{R})$.

9. Use the result of Problem 8 to describe the mapping of $\mathcal{V}_3(\mathbf{R})$, that is defined by $x' = 3x$, $y' = 3y$, $z' = z$.

10. Use the result of Problem 8 to describe the mapping of $\mathcal{V}_3(\mathbf{R})$, that is defined by $x' = y$, $y' = y$, $z' = x + y - 2z$.

11. Which of the following mappings of $\mathcal{V}_2(\mathbf{R})$ are linear transformations?
   (a) $(x, y) \to (0, 0)$;
   (b) $(x, y) \to (2x + y, x - y)$;
   (c) $(x, y) \to (x + 1, y - x)$;
   (d) $(x, y) \to (x, y)$.

12. A linear transformation T of $\mho_3(\mathbf{R})$ is defined by the following:

$$\varepsilon_1 T = \varepsilon_1 + \varepsilon_2 \; ; \; \varepsilon_2 T = \varepsilon_1 + \varepsilon_3 \; ; \; \varepsilon_3 T = \varepsilon_2 + \varepsilon_3 .$$

   (a) Determine the transform of the vector $\varepsilon_1 - \varepsilon_2 + \varepsilon_3$.
   (b) Verify that the transforms of the ε-basis comprise another basis for $\mho_3(\mathbf{R})$, and represent the vector in (a) in terms of this new basis.

13. If $\xi = (1, 1)$ and $\eta = (-1, 3)$ are vectors in $\mho_2(\mathbf{R})$, verify that $(1 - t)\xi + t\eta$ generates a straight line through the given points of the space, as t varies throughout $\mathbf{R}$. Sketch the line.

**14. Prove that the linear transform of any straight line [see Problem 13] in $\mho_2(\mathbf{R})$ is either a straight line or a point.

15. Refer to Problem 14 and obtain the expression that generates the transform of the line in Problem 13 under the transformation T, where
   (a) $(x_1, x_2)T = (x_2, x_1)$;
   (b) $(x_1, x_2)T = (3x_1, 2x_2)$;
   (c) $(x_1, x_2)T = (x_1 + x_2, x_1 - x_2)$.

16. Let $\mho = \mho_1 \oplus \mho_2$, for a vector space $\mho$ and subspaces $\mho_1$, $\mho_2$ [see Problem 13 of § 6.6]. If we define a mapping T of $\mho$ such that, for any $\xi = \xi_1 + \xi_2 \in \mho$, with $\xi_1 \in \mho_1$ and $\xi_2 \in \mho_2$, $\xi T = \xi_1$, prove that T is a linear transformation. This transformation is called the *projection* of $\mho$ on $\mho_1$ along $\mho_2$.

17. Give an illustration of a projection [see Problem 16] in $\mho_3(\mathbf{R})$, from a geometrical point of view.

18. Let $\{\eta_1, \eta_2, \eta_3\}$ be a basis for a 3-dimensional vector space over $\mathcal{F}$. Then if we represent an arbitrary vector η of $\mho$ by $\eta = a_1\eta_1 + a_2\eta_2 + a_3\eta_3$, decide whether the mapping f is a linear functional on $\mho$ where
   (a) $f(\eta) = a_1 + a_2 + a_3$;
   (b) $f(\eta) = (a_1 - a_3)^2$;
   (c) $f(\eta) = a_1 - 2a_3$;
   (d) $f(\eta) = a_2 + 2$.

19. Refer to Problem 18 of § 6.6 and represent each linear functional in Problem 18 as a linear combination of the elements of the dual basis $\{\hat{\eta}_1, \hat{\eta}_2, \hat{\eta}_3\}$.

20. Refer to Problem 18 of § 6.6 and find the dual basis for each of the following bases of $\mho_3(\mathbf{R})$:
   (a) $\{(1, 0, 0), (0, 1, 0), (0, 0, 1)\}$;
   (b) $\{(1, 1, 1), (1, 0, 1), (1, 1, 0)\}$;
   (c) $\{(1, -1, 1), (-1, 1, 0), (0, 1, 1)\}$.

21. Let $\mho$ be the space consisting of 0 and all real polynomials of degree less than n in an indeterminate. For $c \in \mathbf{R}$ and any $p \in \mho$, let $f(p) = p^{(k)}c$, where $p^{(k)}$ designates the kth derivative of p. Prove that f is a linear functional on $\mho$, and determine a basis for the dual space $\hat{\mho}$.

22. Let $\mho$ be the vector space of real continuous functions on the interval $[0, 1]$, with g any fixed vector in $\mho$. If $L_g(f) = \int_0^1 f(x)g(x) \, dx$, for each $f \in \mho$, verify that L_g is a linear functional on $\mho$.

23. Let α and β be linearly independent vectors of a vector space $\mho$. Then verify the existence of a linear functional $f \in \hat{\mho}$, such that $f(\alpha) = 1$ and $f(\beta) = 0$.

6.8. Linear Transformations and Matrices

Before we establish the isomorphism theorem, which shows the important relationship between matrices and linear transformations of vector spaces, we shall derive the generalization referred to at the end of the preceding section. This result is that a linear transformation is completely determined once the transforms of any basis set are known [cf. Problem 11 of § 6.5].

Theorem 6.81. *If $\{\eta_1, \eta_2, \ldots, \eta_n\}$ is a basis for a vector space $\mathcal{V}$, and $\{\xi_1, \xi_2, \ldots, \xi_n\}$ is a set of n arbitrary vectors from a vector space $\mathcal{W}$, both spaces over the same field $\mathcal{F}$, there is one and only one linear transformation $T: \mathcal{V} \to \mathcal{W}$, such that $\eta_1 T = \xi_1$, $\eta_2 T = \xi_2$, $\ldots$, $\eta_n T = \xi_n$. Moreover, this transformation is defined by $\eta T = c_1\xi_1 + c_2\xi_2 + \cdots + c_n\xi_n$, for any vector $\eta = c_1\eta_1 + c_2\eta_2 + \cdots + c_n\eta_n \in \mathcal{V}$.*

Proof. Let us define T so that, if $\eta = \sum\limits_{i=1}^{n} c_i\eta_i$ is an arbitrary element of $\mathcal{V}$, $\eta T = \sum\limits_{i=1}^{n} c_i\xi_i$. If $c_i = 1$ and $c_j = 0$, for $j \neq i$, this definition requires that $\eta_i T = \xi_i$, so that T is consistent with or "an extension of" the given mapping of the basis elements. To prove that T is linear, suppose that $\eta' = \sum\limits_{i=1}^{n} d_i\eta_i$ is another element of $\mathcal{V}$, so that $\eta' T = \sum\limits_{i=1}^{n} d_i\xi_i$. Then

$$(\eta + \eta')T = \left(\sum_{i=1}^{n} c_i\eta_i + \sum_{i=1}^{n} d_i\eta_i\right)T = \left[\sum_{i=1}^{n} (c_i + d_i)\eta_i\right]T = \sum_{i=1}^{n} (c_i + d_i)\xi_i$$

$$= \sum_{i=1}^{n} c_i\xi_i + \sum_{i=1}^{n} d_i\xi_i = \eta T + \eta' T. \text{ Also, for an arbitrary } c \in \mathcal{F},$$

$$(c\eta)T = \left[c\sum_{i=1}^{n} c_i\eta_i\right]T = \left[\sum_{i=1}^{n} (cc_i)\eta_i\right]T = \sum_{i=1}^{n} (cc_i)\xi_i = c\left[\sum_{i=1}^{n} c_i\xi_i\right] = c(\eta T).$$

Hence T is a linear transformation of $\mathcal{V}$. Finally, T is the *unique* extension of the given basis mapping, for suppose T' is another linear transformation of $\mathcal{V}$ such that $\eta_i T' = \xi_i$, $i = 1, 2, \ldots, n$. Then $\eta T' = \left(\sum\limits_{i=1}^{n} c_i\eta_i\right)T' = \sum\limits_{i=1}^{n} c_i(\eta_i T') = \sum\limits_{i=1}^{n} c_i\xi_i = \eta T$. Since η is an arbitrary element of $\mathcal{V}$, it follows that $T' = T$, as stated in the theorem. ∎

As an illustration of this result, a linear transformation of the Cartesian plane can be completely defined by means of the following mappings:

$$\varepsilon_1 = (1, 0) \longrightarrow (1, 0);\ \varepsilon_2 = (0, 1) \longrightarrow (2, 1).$$

Theorem 6.81 then asserts that this transformation can be described in terms of an arbitrary vector $(x, y) \in \mho_2(R)$ by

$$(x, y) = x\varepsilon_1 + y\varepsilon_2 \longrightarrow x(1, 0) + y(2, 1) = (x + 2y, y,).$$

Expressed in this form, it is clear that this particular transformation is a horizontal "shear" of the plane, in which each point is moved parallel to the x-axis a distance proportional to its ordinate. For example, under this transformation a rectangle whose sides are parallel to the coordinate axes is mapped into a parallelogram which is not a rectangle.

Let us now consider an arbitrary n-dimensional vector space $\mho$ over a field $\mathcal{F}$ and which is mapped into itself by a linear transformation T_1. We have just seen that T_1 is completely determined by the images of the elements of any basis set. Thus, if $\{\eta_1, \eta_2, \eta_3, \ldots, \eta_n\}$ is a basis set for $\mho$, let us suppose that these basis elements are mapped by T_1 as follows, where $a_{ij} \in \mathcal{F}$, $i, j = 1, 2, \ldots, n$:

$$\eta_1 T_1 = a_{11}\eta_1 + a_{12}\eta_2 + \cdots + a_{1n}\eta_n$$
$$\eta_2 T_1 = a_{21}\eta_1 + a_{22}\eta_2 + \cdots + a_{2n}\eta_n$$
$$\cdots\cdots\cdots\cdots\cdots\cdots\cdots\cdots\cdots$$
$$\eta_n T_1 = a_{n1}\eta_1 + a_{n2}\eta_2 + \cdots + a_{nn}\eta_n.$$

Then the transformation T_1 is determined and completely described by the matrix

$$\begin{bmatrix} a_{11} & a_{12} & \cdots & a_{1n} \\ a_{21} & a_{22} & \cdots & a_{2n} \\ \cdots\cdots\cdots\cdots\cdots\cdots\cdots\cdots \\ a_{n1} & a_{n2} & \cdots & a_{nn} \end{bmatrix}$$

In fact, if we represent this matrix by $[a_{ij}]$, in the usual designation of a matrix with a_{ij} at the intersection of its ith row and jth column, it is clear that the correspondence $T_1 \leftrightarrow [a_{ij}]$ is one-to-one between the set of linear transformations of $\mho$ and the set of $n \times n$ matrices with elements in $\mathcal{F}$. We recall that the sum and product of mappings of a set were defined in Chapter 1. Hence, since transformations of a vector space are mappings, the sum $T_1 + T_2$ and product $T_1 T_2$ of two linear transformations T_1 and T_2 have already been defined. To review, however, if ξ is an arbitrary element of the vector space $\mho$, these operations are defined as follows:

$$\xi(T_1 + T_2) = \xi T_1 + \xi T_2;\ \xi(T_1 T_2) = (\xi T_1)T_2.$$

We are now in a position to state the important isomorphism theorem for linear transformations.

Theorem 6.82. *The set of linear transformations of an n-dimensional vector space $\mathcal{V}$ over a field $\mathcal{F}$ forms a ring under the operations of addition and multiplication of mappings, and this ring is isomorphic to the ring of all $n \times n$ matrices with elements in $\mathcal{F}$.*

Proof. It is a simple matter of checking the postulates for a ring to verify that the set of all linear transformations of $\mathcal{V}$ is a ring with an identity element [Problems 3 and 4]. We have then merely to show that the correspondence between transformations and matrices is an isomorphism. Inasmuch as we have noted already that this correspondence is one-to-one, there remains only the verification that the correspondence preserves the operations in the two rings.

In addition to $T_1 \leftrightarrow [a_{ij}]$, let $T_2 \leftrightarrow [b_{ij}]$ be the correspondence between another linear transformation T_2 of $\mathcal{V}$ and the matrix $[b_{ij}]$, where we are assuming the same basis $\{\eta_1, \eta_2, \ldots, \eta_n\}$ in both instances, Then, since $\eta_i T_1 = \sum_{j=1}^{n} a_{ij}\eta_j$ and $\eta_i T_2 = \sum_{j=1}^{n} b_{ij}\eta_j$, $i = 1, 2, \ldots, n$, it follows that:

$$\eta_i(T_1 + T_2) = \eta_i T_1 + \eta_i T_2 = \sum_{j=1}^{n} a_{ii}\eta_j + \sum_{j=1}^{n} b_{ij}\eta_j = \sum_{j=1}^{n} (a_{ij} + b_{ij})\eta_j.$$

Hence $T_1 + T_2 \leftrightarrow [a_{ij} + b_{ij}] = [a_{ij}] + [b_{ij}]$, which verifies that addition is preserved by the correspondence. Now let us change index symbols, replacing i and j, respectively, by j and k, in the formula for $\eta_i T_2$, so that $\eta_j T_2 = \sum_{k=1}^{n} b_{jk}\eta_k$, $j = 1, 2, \ldots, n$. Then $\eta_i(T_1 T_2) = (\eta_i T_1)T_2 = \left(\sum_{j=1}^{n} a_{ij}\eta_j\right)T_2$

$$= \sum_{j=1}^{n} a_{ij}\left(\sum_{k=1}^{n} b_{jk}\eta_k\right) = \sum_{k=1}^{n} \left(\sum_{j=1}^{n} a_{ij}b_{jk}\right)\eta_k = \sum_{k=1}^{n} c_{ik}\eta_k,$$

where $c_{ik} = \sum_{j=1}^{n} a_{ij}b_{jk}$, or, equivalently, $c_{ij} = \sum_{j=1}^{n} a_{ik}b_{kj}$. But if we recall the rule for matrix multiplication, we know that the matrix $[c_{ij}]$ is then precisely the product $[a_{ij}][b_{ij}]$ of the matrices $[a_{ij}]$ and $[b_{ij}]$. Hence $T_1 T_2 \leftrightarrow [a_{ij}][b_{ij}]$, so that the correspondence between transformations and matrices also preserves multiplication. This completes the proof of the theorem. ∎

As a result of Theorem 6.82, a study of linear transformations of finite-dimensional vector spaces is equivalent to a study of matrices. That is, any theorem about matrices can be phrased as a theorem about linear transformations, and conversely. Sometimes a study of matrices is made in close relation to associated linear transformations; and at other times matrices are studied without any apparent connection with linear transformations, but as mere arrays of numbers. The approach to matrix theory depends on the viewpoint.

There is another point which we would like to emphasize in connection with Theorem 6.82. While this theorem has established an isomorphism between a ring of linear transformations and a ring of matrices, the actual isomorphic map depends on the basis that is chosen for the vector space. As different bases are chosen for the space, the matrix which corresponds to a *given* linear transformation T will change. One of the important problems in the theory of vector spaces is to choose a basis for a space so that the matrix of a given linear transformation is in some simple form. In matrix theory this is known as the process of reducing a matrix to its various "canonical" forms, but we prefer not to discuss this matter further.

We have now brought the student to the threshold of matrix theory, and have, in fact, made contact with that theory. However, a further discussion of matrices is outside the intended scope of this book, for this topic belongs more properly in a book on linear algebra. The student is invited to consult one of the many books on this subject for a more extensive treatment, and we have listed a few of them in the References at the end of this chapter. For the remainder of the present chapter, we shall return to our proposal, announced earlier, of seeing how groups with operators may be used to unify a study of all the algebraic systems heretofore studied, including vector spaces, and to extend this study to a brief survey of algebras.

PROBLEMS 6–8

*1. Why is the correspondence $T \leftrightarrow [a_{ij}]$ between linear transformations and matrices *unique* with respect to a given basis?

2. Prove the associative and distributive laws for matrix multiplication by using the corresponding properties for linear transformations.

*3. Verify that the set of linear transformations of a vector space forms an abelian group under addition.

*4. Use the result of Problem 3 and complete the proof that these linear transformations form a ring with identity, with the inclusion of the definition of multiplications of transformations.

5. Let $R_n[x]$ be the vector space which includes 0 and all polynomials of degree less than n, in an indeterminate x, with coefficients in R. If D is the derivative operator, show that D is *nilpotent* in the sense that $D^n = 0$ [see Problem 6 of § 5.3]; and determine the matrix of D, regarded as a linear transformation, relative to the basis $\{1, x, x^2, \ldots, x^{n-1}\}$ of $R_n[x]$.

6. Let C be the vector space of complex numbers over the field R of real numbers. Show that the mapping $a + bi \to a - bi$ of each complex number onto its conjugate is a linear transformation and determine its associated matrix with respect to the basis $\{1, i\}$.

7. Write down the matrix of the linear transformation of $\mathcal{U}_2(R)$ defined by:
(a) $(1, 0) \to (3, 0), (0, 1) \to (-2, 1)$;
(b) $(1, 0) \to (-3, 6), (0, 1) \to (3, -2)$.

8. Verify that $\{(1, 1), (-2, 3)\}$ is a basis for $\mathcal{U}_2(R)$ and write down the matrices of the linear transformations given in Problem 7, with respect to this basis.

**9. A linear transformation T of $\mathcal{U}_2(\mathbf{R})$ takes $(0, 1)$ into $(0, 1)$, and $(-1, 1)$ into $(1, -2)$. What is the matrix of T with respect to the ε-basis of the space?

10. The matrix of a linear transformation T of $\mathcal{U}_3(\mathbf{R})$ is $[a_{ij}]$, where $a_{ij} = i^2 - ij$, $i, j = 1, 2, 3$.
   (a) Determine the transform of each element of the ε-basis.
   (b) Determine $(x, y, z)T$, where (x, y, z) is an arbitrary element of the space.

11. The matrix of a linear transformation of $\mathcal{U}_3(\mathbf{R})$ is $\begin{bmatrix} -1 & 0 & 3 \\ 1 & 1 & 1 \\ -2 & 0 & 1 \end{bmatrix}$ with respect to the ε-basis. Determine the images of each of the following vectors under this transformation: (a) $(-2, 3, 1)$; (b) $(1, 1, 1)$; (c) $(0, -3, 2)$.

12. If $\{\xi_1, \xi_2, \ldots, \xi_n\}$ is an " ξ-basis " of a vector space $\mathcal{U}$ over $\mathcal{F}$, it is convenient to refer to the n-tuple of coefficients of an arbitrary $\alpha = x_1\xi_1 + x_2\xi_2 + \cdots + x_n\xi_n \in \mathcal{U}$ as the "coordinate vector" of α, relative to the ξ-basis. This "coordinate vector" is actually the isomorphic image of α, in the isomorphism asserted by Theorem 6.61. Then, if a linear transformation T with matrix A maps the ξ-basis onto the η-basis $\{\eta_1, \eta_2, \ldots, \eta_n\}$, prove that the coordinate vector of α, relative to the η-basis is $(y_1, y_2, \ldots, y_n)$ where $[y_1\ y_2 \cdots y_n] = [x_1\ x_2 \cdots x_n]A$. In this connection, we are to regard $[y_1\ y_2 \cdots y_n]$ and $[x_1\ x_2 \cdots x_n]$ as $1 \times n$ matrices.

**13. Use the technique suggested in Problem 12 to work Problem 11.

14. Verify that the substitution $x = x' + y'$, $y = -x' + y'/2$ reduces the equation of the conic $5x^2 + 4xy + 8y^2 = 9$ to $(x')^2 + (y')^2 = 1$. Use the result in Problem 12 to interpret the substitution as a linear transformation of $\mathcal{U}_2(\mathbf{R})$.

15. Verify that the substitution $x = y'$, $y = x' + 12y'$ simplifies the equation $6x^2 + 24xy - y^2$ of a hyperbola, and use Problem 12 to interpret the substitution as a linear transformation of $\mathcal{U}_2(\mathbf{R})$.

16. Use Theorem 6.82 to see that the *ring* of all $n \times n$ square matrices $M_n(\mathcal{F})$ is isomorphic to the *ring* of linear transformations of any n-dimensional vector space over $\mathcal{F}$.

17. Verify that the isomorphism asserted in Problem 16 is also a vector space isomorphism.

*18. If T is a linear transformation of an n-dimensional vector space $\mathcal{U}$ over $\mathcal{F}$, show that $p(T)$ is also a linear transformation of V for any polynomial $p(x) \in \mathcal{F}[x]$. (By $p(T)$ we mean the result of replacing x in $p(x)$ by T.)

19. Use the result in Problem 18 to see that the polynomials $p(T)$ in a linear transformation T of $\mathcal{U}$ over $\mathcal{F}$ constitute a *ring* but, in general, not a *field*, of operators on $\mathcal{U}$.

20. Let T be a linear transformation of an n-dimensional vector space over $\mathcal{F}$. Then if $\mathcal{F}[T]$ is the ring of polynomials in T with coefficients in $\mathcal{F}$, establish the existence of a (minimal) polynomial $m(T) \in \mathcal{F}[T]$, such that $\xi p(T) = 0$ for all $\xi \in \mathcal{U}$.

21. Determine the relationship between the matrix of a linear transformation of a vector space $\mathcal{U}$, relative to a given basis, and the matrix of the transformation induced in the dual space $\hat{\mathcal{U}}$, relative to the dual basis [see Problem 18 of § 6.6].

6.9. Operator Groups

At the beginning of this chapter, we introduced the idea of a general "operator" system but, for the most part, we have been concerned with an investigation of the very special operator system known as a "vector space." Now that we have pushed that study as far as we wished, we resume our study of more general operator systems—although some of the things we do here have been referred to earlier either in the textual material or in the problems.

An *operator groupoid* or *M-groupoid* is a groupoid S with a set M of operators, with the property that each $m \in M$ is associated with an endomorphism of the groupoid—and we usually do not distinguish between the operators and their associated endomorphisms. The subgroupoids of S, which are mapped into themselves by the operators in M, are said to be " M-admissible" or " M-operator" subgroupoids, the set M being the operator set for these admissible subgroupoids as well as for the original groupoid S [Problem 1]. Of course, any admissible subgroupoid of an operator groupoid is a subgroupoid, but not every subgroupoid is admissible—the admissible subgroupoids comprising generally a more select class of subgroupoids. The nonempty intersection of any set of M-admissible subgroupoids is also an M-admissible subgroupoid [Problem 3], as is also the subgroupoid generated by any system of M-admissible subgroupoids [Problem 4]. The notion of isomorphism, as applied to vector spaces, is a special case of the more general concept: two M-operator groupoids S and S' are said to be *M-operator isomorphic* or *M-isomorphic* if there is an isomorphic mapping ψ of S onto S' such that $(gm)\psi = (g\psi)m$, for any $g \in S$ amd $m \in M$. This characteristic property can then be extended as usual to define an *M-operator homomorphism*, an *M-operator endomorphism* and an *M-operator automorphism* of an M-operator groupoid [Problem 9]. The following characterization of an M-operator endomorphism is very useful: an endomorphism α of an M-operator groupoid is an M-operator endomorphism if and only if α permutes, as a factor of a product of endomorphisms, with the endomorphisms of M [Problem 8].

We have noted before that M may be empty, and in this case an M-operator groupoid is simply a groupoid (without operators). The next most general situation occurs when M is a nonempty set with no algebraic structure. But, there is never any lack of generality in assuming that such an M is a semigroup: for, if $g \in S$ and we regard $m_1, m_2 \in M$ as endomorphisms, $g(m_1 m_2) = (gm_1)m_2$, and this equation defines the associative product of the operators m_1, m_2. Under these circumstances, we may then say that S is a groupoid

with M as its operator semigroup. It is clear [Problem 10] that *M*-admissible
subgroupoids remain admissible and *M*-operator isomorphisms remain operator isomorphisms if we regard *M* as a semigroup in this way.

One of the most interesting and useful cases arises when $S = G$ is an abelian
group and $M = R$ is a ring. An abelian group G with a ring R of operators is
called an R-*operator group* or R-*module*, and, in view of the importance of
this algebraic system in modern mathematics, we shall detail its defining
properties.

Definition. An R-*module* is an additive abelian group M, with a ring R of
operators, such that for arbitrary g, g_1, $g_2 \in M$ and r, r_1, $r_2 \in R$:

1. $(g_1 + g_2)r = g_1 r + g_2 r$;

2. $g(r_1 + r_2) = gr_1 + gr_2$;

3. $g(r_1 r_2) = (gr_1)r_2$.

It should be noted that **1** is the basic "endomorphism" property of all
operators, in the additive notation of M, while **2** and **3** give appropriate
meanings to the sum and product of any two operators in the ring R. We
note further, that **2** and **3** are merely the "semigroup" properties of R as both
an additive and a multiplicative system, as discussed in the preceding paragraph. An R-admissible subgroup of an R-module M is usually called simply
a *submodule* of M.

The connection between modules and abelian groups is made clear if we
observe that every abelian group is an R-module, where R is any subring of
its ring of endomorphisms [Problem 11]. Moreover, since *na* has been defined
for any *a* in an abelian group and integer *n* [Problem 2], an abelian group
can also be regarded as a **Z**-module [Problem 7]. This may be a good time
to point out again that it is unimportant where we place the operator symbol,
but a module is called a *left* or *right* R-module according as the R-operators
are written to the left or right of the group elements. It is then in harmony
with established symbolism to regard as abelian group as a *left* **Z**-module,
while in general we have preferred *right* operators in this book. We shall
include other important examples of groups with operators, and in particular
of modules, in the Problems. If the ring R of operators of a module has an
identity element *e*—as in the two examples just cited—it is clearly desirable
to have the identity operator induce the identity endomorphism: i.e., *ae = a*,
for any *a* in the module. Any R-module with this property is said to be
unitary. It is now clear that our definition of a *vector space* in § 6.3 has described it as a *unitary R-module where the ring R is a field*. The submodules
are then the subspaces while the operator endomorphisms are the linear

transformations; and so we have described vector spaces in the language of groups with operators. In addition to performing a unifying role in algebra, modules are very useful in the study of group representations—another topic beyond the scope of this book.

If $\mathfrak{K}$ is a normal subgroup of an M-group $\mathfrak{G}$, there is a natural way in which to regard $\mathfrak{G}/\mathfrak{K}$ also as an M-group. This is done by defining $(g\mathfrak{K})m = (gm)\mathfrak{K}$, for any coset $g\mathfrak{K} \in \mathfrak{G}/\mathfrak{K}$ and any $m \in M$. We leave it to the student to verify that this definition is independent of the representative of a coset [Problem 12] and that each $m \in M$ is actually an operator on $\mathfrak{G}/\mathfrak{K}$ [Problem 13]. There is also a decomposition theory of M-groups which parallels the decomposition theory of groups without operators; and, of course, in this more general theory, the role of direct factors (or summands) is played by subgroups which have the additional property of being M-subgroups. In fact, while it would take us too far off our desired course and also involve a great deal of repetition from Chapter 4 to prove it, the fact is that most of the theory of groups carries over to M-groups—although a few of the results are more difficult to obtain. For example, in the theory of M-groups we have results analogous to the Fundamental Homomorphism theorem and the related isomorphism theorems, the Jordan–Hölder theorem for composition series, and the Remak–Krull–Schmidt theorem for the direct decomposition of an M-group. The interested student will find the proofs for these results in Chapter 5 of [3].

We have already remarked that one of the most important types of operator systems is the $\mathfrak{R}$-module, its theory encompassing not only that of abelian groups and vector spaces but also—as we shall see in § 6.10—rings and their ideals. In view of the importance of vector spaces in many applications, it is interesting and very useful to observe that a vector space $\mathfrak{V}$ over $\mathfrak{F}$ is a module over a polynomial ring as well as over the field $\mathfrak{F}$. To see this, we first select a linear transformation T of $\mathfrak{V}$ and recall [Problem 18 of § 6.8] that any polynomial $p(T)$, with coefficients in $\mathfrak{F}$, is also a linear transformation of $\mathfrak{V}$. We now make the polynomial ring $\mathfrak{F}[x]$, with x an indeterminate, into a ring of operators by defining $\xi p(x) = \xi p(T)$, for any $\xi \in \mathfrak{V}$ and $p(x) \in \mathfrak{F}[x]$. We note in passing [see Problem 15] that many distinct polynomials of $\mathfrak{F}[x]$ may give rise to the same endomorphism of $\mathfrak{V}$. It is this representation of $\mathfrak{V}$ as an $\mathfrak{R}[x]$-module which makes the study of modules of such great importance in the theory of vector spaces, for the whole decomposition theory of vector spaces—relative to a given linear transformation T—can be based on their representation as modules over these polynomial rings. However, as we already said in § 6.8, this development belongs to a course in linear algebra and we merely mention it here.

In Theorem 5.111 we showed the equivalence of the ascending chain condition (a.c.c) and two other conditions on ideals of a commutative ring; and one can prove a similar theorem for modules, in which submodules play the role of ideals in the earlier result. It is then natural to speculate on any possible connection between the a.c.c. in a ring $\mathcal{R}$ and the corresponding condition in an $\mathcal{R}$-module. The answer is supplied by the following theorem.

Theorem 6.91. *Let $\mathcal{M}$ be a finitely-generated unitary (left) $\mathcal{R}$-module. Then, if $\mathcal{R}$ is commutative and satisfies the a.c.c. for ideals, $\mathcal{M}$ satisfies the a.c.c. for submodules. (The theorem also holds for left ideals in a noncommutative ring $\mathcal{R}$, as defined in Problem 19 of § 5.6.)*

Proof. Let $\{x_1, x_2, \ldots, x_n\}$ be a set of generators for $\mathcal{M}$, with $\mathcal{M}_1$ any submodule of $\mathcal{M}$. Then, if A_j is the set of elements $a_j \in \mathcal{R}$ such that there exists an element $a_j x_j + a_{j+1} x_{j+1} + \cdots + a_n x_n \in \mathcal{M}_1$, it is an easy deduction [Problem 16] that A_j is an ideal of $\mathcal{R}$, for $j = 1, 2, \ldots, n$. That is, with each submodule of $\mathcal{M}$ there is associated n ideals of $\mathcal{R}$, and it is not difficult to prove that two submodules are equal if their respective associated ideals are equal [see Problem 17]. It is now easy to deduce that the presence of the a.c.c. for ideals in $\mathcal{R}$ implies the presence of this condition for submodules in $\mathcal{M}$ [Problem 18]. ∎

PROBLEMS 6–9

*1. Explain why the elements of M may be taken as operators for an M-admissible subgroup of an M-group.

2. Review the definition of na, for any integer n and ring element a.

*3. Prove that the nonempty intersection of any set of M-admissible subgroupoids is an M-admissible subgroupoid.

*4. Prove that the subgroupoid generated by any system of M-admissible subgroupoids is an M-admissible subgroupoid.

5. A subgroup $\mathcal{H}$ of a group $\mathcal{G}$ is said to be *characteristic (fully invariant)* if $\mathcal{H}$ is mapped onto (into) itself by all automorphisms (endomorphisms) of $\mathcal{G}$. If we let M designate the set of all automorphisms (endomorphisms) of $\mathcal{G}$, verify that the characteristic (fully invariant) subgroups are merely those which are M-admissible in $\mathcal{G}$—considered as an M-group.

*6. Let M be the set of all inner automorphisms of a group $\mathcal{G}$: i.e., if $m \in M$, $gm = a^{-1}ga$ for some a and every g in $\mathcal{G}$. Then verify that if we regard $\mathcal{G}$ as an M-group, the normal subgroups are those which are M-admissible.

*7. Explain why any abelian group is a **Z**-module.

8. Justify the characterization given in the text for an M-endomorphism of an M-groupoid.

*9. Give exact definitions for an M-homomorphism, an M-endomorphism, and an M-automorphism of an M-groupoid.

10. Explain why an M-admissible subgroupoid remains M-admissible, and an M-isomorphism remains an M-isomorphism, when the operator set M of a groupoid is structured as a semigroup in the natural way.

11. Explain why any abelian group $\mathcal{G}$ is an $\mathcal{R}$-module, where $\mathcal{R}$ is any subring of the ring of endomorphisms of $\mathcal{G}$.

12. If $\mathcal{K}$ is a normal M-subgroup of the M-group $\mathcal{G}$, verify that the method we used to make $\mathcal{G}/\mathcal{K}$ into an M-group is independent of the coset representatives of the quotient group.

13. Complete the proof that the elements of M, discussed in Problem 12, are indeed operators of $\mathcal{G}/\mathcal{K}$.

**14. Verify that the additive group of a ring $\mathcal{R}$ is an $\mathcal{R}$-module, and that the ideals of $\mathcal{R}$ (assumed commutative) are submodules.

**15. If T is a linear transformation of a vector space $\mathcal{V}$ over $\mathcal{F}$, explain why distinct polynomials $p(x) \in \mathcal{F}[x]$ can give rise to the same linear transformation $p(T)$ of $\mathcal{V}$. Support your explanation with an example.

*16. Prove that A_j, in the proof of Theorem 6.91, is an ideal of $\mathcal{R}$.

*17. With reference to the proof of Theorem 6.91, prove that two submodules are equal if their respective associated ideals are equal.

*18. Complete the final deduction in the proof of Theorem 6.91.

19. Give appropriate definitions of the *descending chain condition* (d.c.c.) for ideals in a ring and for submodules of a module, and supply at least one example of a ring and a module where the condition does (does not) hold.

20. Check that Theorem 6.91 is valid with the d.c.c. replacing the a.c.c. [see Problem 19].

21. Verify that the image of an M-group under an M-endomorphism is an M-invariant subgroup.

22. Let $\mathcal{G}$ be any additive abelian group and $\mathcal{R}$ any ring. Then, if we define $rg = 0$, for all $r \in \mathcal{R}$ and all $g \in \mathcal{G}$, prove that $\mathcal{G}$ is a (trivial) left $\mathcal{R}$-module.

23. If A is an ideal of a ring $\mathcal{R}$, and $\mathcal{M}$ is an $\mathcal{R}$-module, verify that the set of all elements $y \in \mathcal{M}$, such that $ay = 0$ for all $a \in A$, is a submodule of $\mathcal{M}$.

24. Show that the submodule, generated by the elements $x_1, x_2, \ldots, x_n$ of an $\mathcal{R}$-module $\mathcal{M}$, consists of all elements of $\mathcal{M}$ of the form $a_1 x_1 + a_2 x_2 + \cdots + a_n x_n + t_1 x_1 + t_2 x_2 + \cdots + t_n x_n$, with $a_i \in \mathcal{R}$ and $t_i \in \mathbf{Z}$, $i = 1, 2, \ldots, n$. Describe the elements of the submodule if $\mathcal{M}$ is unitary.

25. Use the case of a vector space as a guide and make appropriate definitions for the notions of "linear independence" and "basis" as applied to an arbitrary $\mathcal{R}$-module. Discover at least one "basis" property which is different for even a unitary $\mathcal{R}$-module, with $\mathcal{R}$ not a field, from the case where the module is a vector space.

6.10. Operator Rings

Now that we have completed our brief discussion of operator groups, we turn our attention to rings to see if there is a comparable theory of operators here. We shall discover that there is, but that it is not quite what one might speculate from the operator theory of groups! If we were to define an operator on a ring, in a manner strictly analogous to a group operator, we would require than an operator be associated with an endomorphism of the ring:

i.e., if m is an operator—regarded as an endomorphism of the ring $\mathcal{R}$—then $(a + b)m = am + bm$ and also $(ab)m = (am)(bm)$, for any $a, b \in \mathcal{R}$. However, if we look at the manner in which we perform "scalar multiplication" in the ring $M_n(\mathcal{R})$ of $n \times n$ matrices and in any ring of functions, a slightly different concept of a ring operator is suggested. Before obtaining this operator concept, however, let us look at an operator *group* which is closely associated with any ring: the *additive group of the ring*.

If a is an element of a ring $\mathcal{R}$, which we do not assume to be commutative, the mapping $x \to xa$, for all $x \in \mathcal{R}$, defines an endomorphism of the additive group of $\mathcal{R}$ [Problem 2] known as *right multiplication*. The additive group of $\mathcal{R}$ is then an $\mathcal{R}$-group, with the right ideals of $\mathcal{R}$ as admissible subgroups [see Problem 19 of § 5.6]. The mapping $x \to ax$ shows us that the elements of $\mathcal{R}$ can also induce endomorphisms of $\mathcal{R}$ known as *left multiplications*, and the subgroups that are admissible under these operators are the left ideals of $\mathcal{R}$ [cf. Problem 14 of § 6.9]. In case $\mathcal{R}$ is commutative, there is, of course, no distinction between left and right multiplications and the admissible subgroups under the "multiplication" operators are the ideals of $\mathcal{R}$. The ring properties of $\mathcal{R}$ require, for arbitrary $a, b, x \in \mathcal{R}$, that

$$x(a + b) = xa + xb$$

$$x(ab) = (xa)b$$

Hence, in accordance with our discussions of § 6.9, the elements of $\mathcal{R}$, as *right* multiplications, constitute a *ring of operators* for the additive group of $\mathcal{R}$. Moreover, since $ae = a$, in case $\mathcal{R}$ has the identity element e, the additive group of $\mathcal{R}$ is a unitary (right) $\mathcal{R}$-module. We leave it to the student to verify [Problem 3], however, that if $\mathcal{R}$ is not commutative, the additive group of $\mathcal{R}$ is not a *left* $\mathcal{R}$-module.

The clue to the definition of what we are going to consider an operator for a ring is now provided by our observation of scalar multiplication in matrix and polynomial rings. Any "reasonable" definition of a ring operator would require that it induce an endomorphism of the additive group of the ring, and we now require in addition that the endomorphism permute with left and right multiplications of the ring. We state this in the following formal definition.

Definition. A *ring with a set M of operators*, or an *M-ring*, is a ring $\mathcal{R}$ whose additive group is an *M*-group, and such that $(ab)m = (am)b = a(bm)$, for any $a, b \in \mathcal{R}$.

We are now able to define the notions of admissible subrings, admissible ideals, operator isomorphisms, operator homomorphisms and operator endomorphisms in a manner strictly analogous with the case for groups [Problem 4]. It is interesting to verify that if the ring $\mathcal{R}$ has an identity, *every* endomorphism is a multiplication by an element of $\mathcal{R}$ which actually permutes (as a product) with each element of the ring [Problem 5]. It is an immediate consequence [Problem 6] that all ideals of any such M-ring are admissible.

As in the group case, the operator set M may always be imbedded in a semigroup (additive), and it may be that M is already a group or ring. As a matter of fact, the most interesting operator rings occur when M is a ring, which we also assume to have an identity element, and so we make a new listing of the properties of such an M-ring. A ring $\mathcal{R}$ is an *operator ring, with a ring M of operators with identity e*, provided the following equalities hold for arbitrary $a, b \in \mathcal{R}$ and $m, m_1, m_2 \in M$:

(1) $(a + b)m = am + bm$;

(2) $a(m_1 + m_2) = am_1 + am_2$;

(3) $a(m_1 m_2) = (am_1)m_2$;

(4) $(ab)m = (am)b = a(bm)$;

(5) $ae = a$.

Condition **(1)** is the usual endomorphism property as applied to the additive group of $\mathcal{R}$, conditions **(2)** and **(3)** are based on the ring properties of M, **(4)** is the special "permuting" property required of the elements of M, while **(5)** is due to the presence of the identity e in M. We hasten to add that it may not be entirely obvious that the subset of endomorphisms of the additive group of a ring, possessing the "permuting" property **(4)**, is a ring. However, we leave it to the student to verify [Problem 7] that this subset *is* a subring of the ring of all endomorphisms of the addive group of $\mathcal{R}$. An example of an operator ring of the type just discussed is provided by any ring $\mathcal{R}$, with the mapping $a \to na$, $a \in \mathcal{R}$ and a fixed $n \in Z$. For this mapping is clearly an endomorphism of the additive group of $\mathcal{R}$ (It is customary to write the mapping symbol n on the left here!), and the other properties above—including the special property **(4)**—are easily verified. Hence $\mathcal{R}$ is an operator ring with Z as its ring of operators. All subrings of this Z-ring are admissible and all isomorphisms are Z-isomorphisms [Problem 8].

If the ring of operators of a ring $\mathcal{R}$ is noncommutative, it is not difficult to discover [Problem 9] the presence of "annihilators" of $\mathcal{R}$, i.e., elements $b \in \mathcal{R}$ such that $bx = xb = 0$ for all $x \in \mathcal{R}$. While operator rings of this kind do exist [Problem 10], they are not usually the interesting and useful ones, and so it is customary to regard the ring of operators of a ring as commutative. In fact, the most useful case occurs when this ring is a field, and we then have the very important algebraic system known as an *algebra*.

Definition. An *algebra over a field $\mathcal{F}$* is a ring with a field $\mathcal{F}$ of operators [see Problem 21].

The admissible subsystems, in this case, are called *subalgebras*, while the operator isomorphisms, operator homomorphisms, and operator endomorphisms are usually called simply *isomorphisms, homomorphisms*, and *endomorphisms* of the algebra. Algebras—sometimes called "linear algebras"—play a central role in the theory of operator rings which is comparable to that played by vector spaces in the theory of operator groups.

Of course, the additive structure of an algebra over a field $\mathcal{F}$ is that of a vector space, and so the notions of "linear independence" and "basis" carry over to algebras. Thus, if $\{x_1, x_2, \ldots, x_n\}$ is a basis of an algebra, considered as a vector space over $\mathcal{F}$, each element x of the algebra can be expressed uniquely in the form $x = a_1 x_1 + a_2 x_2 + \cdots + a_n x_n$, with $a_i \in \mathcal{F}$, $i = 1, 2, \ldots, n$. The essential structure of such a "finite-dimensional" algebra is then determined by a knowledge of the field elements ε_{ij}^k, where $x_i x_j = \sum_{k=1}^{n} \varepsilon_{ij}^k x_k$. The field elements ε_{ij}^k make up what is sometimes called the "multiplication table" of the algebra. Special algebras arise when we impose certain restrictions on their multiplicative structures. For example, if we demand that each nonzero element of the algebra have a multiplicative inverse, we obtain what are known as *division algebras*. It is an interesting result—which we shall not prove—that the only finite-dimensional commutative algebras over the field **R** of real numbers are **R** and **C**, of respective dimensions 1 and 2. Another interesting example of an algebra is the *algebra of real quaternions* [see Problem 14], a noncommutative division algebra of dimension 4 over **R**. It can be shown, in fact, that this is the only finite-dimensional noncommutative algebra over **R**.

If we consider the ring $M_n(\mathcal{F})$ of $n \times n$ matrices with elements in a field $\mathcal{F}$, it is easy to check [Problem 18] that each $a \in \mathcal{F}$ can be regarded as an operator on the ring: for $\mathcal{F}$ is isomorphic to the field of $n \times n$ matrices $[a_{ij}]$ where $a_{ij} = 0$, $i \neq j$, $a_{ii} = a \in \mathcal{F}$, for $i = 1, 2, \ldots, n$, so that each a induces a left (or right) multiplication of the members of $M_n(\mathcal{F})$. Since matrix multiplication is noncommutative, this ring provides us with another example of a noncommutative algebra over a field $\mathcal{F}$ but, unlike the quaternion algebra, this matrix algebra does have divisors of zero. It is finite dimensional, however, and has dimension n^2. Another important algebra can be constructed from the ring $\mathcal{F}[x]$ of polynomials, the operators again being provided by the field multiplications. This algebra is commutative, with multiplication being defined essentially by the rule that $x^m x^n = x^{m+n}$, but the basis $\{1, x, x^2, \ldots\}$ shows that it is not finite dimensional.

There are many other interesting and useful algebras, but it would take us too far off our desired course even to mention them all here. While we have required all of our algebras to be associative—being constructed out of (associative) rings—it is also possible to study nonassociative algebras. A very important algebra of this type over **R** is the *Cayley algebra*, which is the only finite-dimensional nonassociative algebra over **R** without divisors of zero. A discussion of this algebra is given in [4], while the interested student can find a brief description of each of several other important associative algebras in [2].

PROBLEMS 6–10

    1. Distinguish between what we have called an "operator ring" and a "ring with operators."

****2.** Verify that left and right multiplications by ring elements produce endomorphisms of the additive group of a ring.

    3. Check that a noncommutative ring $\mathcal{R}$ is not a left $\mathcal{R}$-module.

    4. Define the concepts of "admissible subgroup," "admissible ideal," and "operator homomorphism" for rings with operators.

  ***5.** Prove that any operator on a ring $\mathcal{R}$ with identity element is a multiplication by an element of $\mathcal{R}$ which lies in the center of the ring [cf. Problem 19 of § 6.2].

  ***6.** Use Problem 5 to verify that all ideals of an operator ring are admissible.

  ***7.** Prove that the subset of endomorphisms of the additive group of a ring, which permute with right and left multiplications by ring elements, is a subring of the ring of all endomorphisms of the group.

  ***8.** If a ring is regarded as a **Z**-ring, verify that all subrings are admissible and all isomorphisms are **Z**-isomorphisms.

****9.** If M is a noncommutative ring of operators for a ring $\mathcal{R}$, establish the existence of annihilators of $\mathcal{R}$. (Hint: if $\alpha\beta \neq \beta\alpha$, for α, $\beta \in M$, then $a\alpha\beta \neq a\beta\alpha$, for some $a \in \mathcal{R}$; then show that $a\alpha\beta - a\beta\alpha$ is an annihilator of $\mathcal{R}$.)

 10. Check that every element of a zero ring is an annihilator of the ring.

 11. Prove that the intersection of any collection of subalgebras of an algebra over $\mathcal{F}$ is also a subalgebra—the subalgebra generated by the subalgebras.

 12. Prove that any ring $\mathcal{R}$ with an identity element is an algebra over any field contained within and containing the identity element of the ring $\mathcal{R}$.

 13. Let $\{g_1, g_2, \ldots, g_n\}$ be a basis [see §4.12] of an abelian group $\mathcal{G}$, and consider the collection of all formal expressions $a_1 g_1 + a_2 g_2 + \cdots + a_n g_n$, with $a_1, a_2, \ldots, a_n$ in any field $\mathcal{F}$. Now verify that if these expressions are combined "like polynomials with coefficients in $\mathcal{F}$," with due cognizance being taken of the group products, the result is an algebra over $\mathcal{F}$. This is known as the *group algebra* of $\mathcal{G}$ over $\mathcal{F}$. [cf. Problem 21 of §5.11]

 14. Let $\{1, i, j, k\}$ designate a basis for a vector space over **R**. Then verify that this may be made into an algebra over **R** be defining $i^2 = j^2 = k^2 = -1$, and $ij = k$, $jk = i$, $ki = j$. This is called the *algebra of real quaternions*.

 15. Compare the *algebra* of real quaternions in Problem 14 with the *ring* of quaternions in Chapter 5 and the quaternion *group* in Chapter 4. In particular, compare the number of elements in the three systems.

 16. Write down all the "multiplication table" constants ε_{ij}^k associated with the basis, given in Problem 14, for the algebra of real quaternions.

 17. If $a = 2 + 3i + 4j - 2k$ and $b = 1 + 2i - j - k$ are two quaternions, expressed relative to the basis given in Problem 14, determine the products ab and ba.

18. Complete the verification that each $a \in \mathcal{F}$ can be regarded as an operator on the ring $M_n(\mathcal{F})$ of matrices, for any field $\mathcal{F}$.

19. Write down the "multiplication table" constants ε_{ij}^k for the algebra of $n \times n$ matrices with elements in $\mathcal{F}$, relative to the natural basis consisting of the n^2 matrices with only one nonzero entry of 1. (Hint: recall that $[a_{ik}][b_{kj}] = [c_{ij}]$,

where $c_{ij} = \sum_{k=1}^{n} a_{ik} b_{kj}$.)

20. Describe each of the following as an M-group and/or an M-ring, if possible, identifying the system M in each case:
    (a) any group $\mathcal{G}$;
    (b) a normal subgroup of a group $\mathcal{G}$;
    (c) an ideal of a ring $\mathcal{R}$;
    (d) the polynomial ring $\mathcal{F}[x]$;
    (e) the polynomial ring $\mathbf{Z}[x]$.

21. Our definition of an algebra has required that the operator set be a field. Generalize this definition to include any ring with identity as an operator system of an algebra, and give an example of this type of algebra which is not an algebra according to the earlier definition.

22. Refer to the definition of an algebra over a ring, requested in Problem 21, and decide which of the systems listed in Problem 20 are algebras of this type.

References

[1] BIRKHOFF, G. and MACLANE, S.: *A Survey of Modern Algebra*, Third Edition, Chapters 7–8 (New York, Macmillan, 1965).

[2] HU, S. T.: *Elements of Modern Algebra*, Chapter 6 (San Francisco, Holden-Day, 1965).

[3] JACOBSON, N.: *Lectures in Abstract Algebra*, Vol. 1, Chapters 5–6 (Princeton, N. J., Van Nostrand, 1951).

[4] KUROSH, A. G.: *General Algebra*, Chapter 5 (New York, Chelsea, 1963).

Selected Readings from The American Mathematical Monthly

ACKERSON, R. H.: *A Note on Vector Spaces*, **62** (1955), 721–722.

BING, K.: *A Construction of the Null Space of a Linear Transformation*, **67** (1960), 34–39.

BOURBAKI, N.: *The Architecture of Mathematics,* **57** (1950), 221–232.

MAY, K. O.: *The Impossibility of a Division Algebra of Vectors in Three Dimensional Space,* **73** (1966), 289–291.

MINC, H.: *Left and Right Ideals in the Ring of 2 × 2 Matrices,* **71** (1964), 72–75.

LEAVITT, W. G.: *Mappings of Vector Spaces and the Theory of Matrices,* **59** (1952), 219–222.

TROTTER, H. F.: *A Canonical Basis for Nilpotent Transformations,* **68** (1961), 779–780.

7 *Field Extensions*

7.1. Introduction

In Chapter 5 we have described a field as a special kind of ring—in fact, as an additive abelian group whose nonzero elements form a multiplicative abelian group, with the distributive laws holding. However, we did very little with fields, except to use them as sources for "field elements." The most familiar examples of fields are, of course, the fields of rational, real, and complex numbers, and we have made use of these field elements or "numbers" on many occasions. For example, in Chapter 6, these numbers were often used as the scalars of our vector spaces. The idea of a subsystem is inherent in the definition of any kind of algebraic system, and the system called a "field" is no exception: a *subfield* of a field $\mathcal{K}$ is a system whose elements are a subset of those of $\mathcal{K}$, and whose operations and equality relation are understood to comply with those in $\mathcal{K}$, the subsystem satisfying the requirements of a field in its own right. We shall continue to use the set-theoretic notation $\mathcal{F} \subset \mathcal{K}$ to indicate that the field $\mathcal{F}$ is a subfield of the field $\mathcal{K}$ [see Problem 3]. In the present chapter, the matter of most interest is that of field "extensions," but, before getting into this important topic, there is another matter which is pertinent in any discussion of fields.

Since any field is also an integral domain, it has a *characteristic* which is either 0 or prime integer p. It then follows from Theorem 5.35, that every field contains an isomorphic image of either the ring $\mathbf{Z}$ of integers, or the ring $\mathbf{Z}_p$ of integers modulo p. It is a well-known fact that $\mathbf{Z}_p$ is a field [Corollary to Theorem 5.33], while the quotient field of $\mathbf{Z}$ must also be isomorphically imbedded as a subfield of any field which contains $\mathbf{Z}$. Hence *every* field must contain a subfield isomorphic to either the field **Q** of rational numbers or the field $\mathbf{Z}_p$ of integers modulo p, for some prime p. Neither of these fields can have any proper subfields [Problem 4], and each is called the *prime* subfield of any field that contains it. It is also convenient to define the *prime* subfield of any field as the intersection of all of its subfields, and it is not difficult to see that the two definitions are equivalent [see Problem 6]. The basic fact, which is responsible for the existence of a minimal or prime subfield of any field is, of course, the existence of an identity element. For this element, by itself, along with the field operations, will generate the prime subfield—which is $\mathbf{Z}_p$, if the characteristic of the field is p, and the field **Q**, if the characteristic of the field is 0. A field which contains no proper subfield is sometimes called a *prime field*, and it is clear that such a field must be isomorphic to either $\mathbf{Z}_p$ or **Q** [Problem 12].

Since the prime subfield of a field of characteristic p is always $\mathbf{Z}_p$, the field of integers modulo p, such a field is usually called a *modular* field. Any field of characteristic 0 is then said to be *nonmodular*. The familiar fields of analysis —the rational, real, and complex number fields—are nonmodular, and it might be thought that modular fields are only of theoretical interest. Such is not the case, however, for many applications have recently been found for modular fields in connection with contemporary uses of the binary number system, such as in digital computers and other devices of automation. Any finite field is, of course, modular but a modular field is not necessarily finite. For example, the field of rational functions in an indeterminate x, with coefficients in $\mathbf{Z}_p$, is certainly an infinite field—but with characteristic p [Problem 10].

We now give a brief introduction to the notion of an "extension" field, but will leave most of the developments of this idea to later sections. The notion of an *extension* field is probably intuitively clear, for it is complementary to that of a *subfield*, but we formalize it with a definition.

Definition. The field $\mathcal{K}$ is an *extension* of a field $\mathcal{F}$, if $\mathcal{F}$ is a subfield of $\mathcal{K}$, or, in the notation adopted earlier, if $\mathcal{F} \subset \mathcal{K}$.

Thus, both the fields of real and complex numbers are extension fields of the field of rational numbers, while the complex numbers comprise an extension of the field of real numbers. *In this chapter, the fields $\mathcal{K}$ and $\mathcal{F}$ will always stand in this relation to each other.*

Let $a, a_1, a_2 \in \mathcal{F}$, while $\alpha, \alpha_1, \alpha_2 \in \mathcal{K}$, the common identity element being 1. Then, since $\mathcal{F} \subset \mathcal{K}$ and $\mathcal{K}$ is a field, the identities below follow immediately:

$$a(\alpha_1 + \alpha_2) = a\alpha_1 + a\alpha_2;$$

$$(a_1 + a_2)\alpha = a_1\alpha + a_2\alpha;$$

$$(a_1 a_2)\alpha = a_1(a_2\alpha);$$

$$1 \cdot \alpha = \alpha.$$

Inasmuch as $\mathcal{K}$ is automatically an additive abelian group, it follows from our basic definition in Chapter 6 that $\mathcal{K}$ *is a vector space over* $\mathcal{F}$. This is a very important observation, and it underlies much of what we have to say and do in the remainder of the chapter. Of course, it is to be understood that when we look at $\mathcal{K}$ as a vector space over $\mathcal{F}$, we are not *at such a time* interested in, say, the division properties of $\mathcal{K}$, but rather its properties *as a vector space*. One of these most important "vector space" properties leads us to the following definition.

Definition. The *degree* of a field $\mathcal{K}$ over a subfield $\mathcal{F}$, designated $[\mathcal{K} : \mathcal{F}]$, is the dimension of $\mathcal{K}$ *when regarded as a vector space over* $\mathcal{F}$. If $[\mathcal{K} : \mathcal{F}]$ is a finite number, $\mathcal{K}$ will be called a *finite extension* of $\mathcal{F}$.

If k is an arbitrary nonzero element of $\mathcal{K}$, then $\mathcal{F}[k]$ is the ring of all polynomials in k with coefficients in $\mathcal{F}$, and as such is an integral domain. This follows because $\mathcal{F}[k] \subset \mathcal{K}$, and $\mathcal{K}$ is *a fortiori* an integral domain. The field of quotients of $\mathcal{F}[k]$ then exists, by Theorem 5.82; we designate it as $\mathcal{F}(k)$, and refer to it as a *simple* extension of $\mathcal{F}$—since only *one* new "generating" element has been adjoined to $\mathcal{F}$. This simple extension $\mathcal{F}(k)$ is the minimal extension field of $\mathcal{F}$ which contains k, and its elements are the equivalence classes of quotients $p(k)/q(k)$, with $p(k)$, $q(k) \in \mathcal{F}[k]$, $q(k) \neq 0$. The field $\mathcal{F}(k)$ is imbedded in a natural way [see Problem 2] in $\mathcal{K}$, and, in fact, it is conventional to assume that $\mathcal{F}(k) \subset \mathcal{K}$. If k is a zero of a polynomial with coefficients in $\mathcal{F}$, the element k is said to be *algebraic*—and otherwise *transcendental*—over $\mathcal{F}$. The field $\mathcal{F}(k)$ is then said to be *algebraic* or *transcendental* over $\mathcal{F}$, according as k is algebraic or transcendental over $\mathcal{F}$.

If k is *transcendental* over $\mathcal{F}$, the description of $\mathcal{F}(k)$ is very easy, because no nontrivial polynomial in $\mathcal{F}[k]$ vanishes. The field $\mathcal{F}(k)$ is essentially the collection of all rational functions (that is, quotients of polynomials) in k, with coefficients in $\mathcal{F}$. It is clear that $\mathcal{F}[k]$ and $\mathcal{F}[h]$ are isomorphic rings, for any two elements k, h which are transcendental over $\mathcal{F}$ [Problem 11], and it follows from the assertion near the end of § 5.8 that their quotient fields are likewise isomorphic. The simple transcendental extension field $\mathcal{F}(k)$ is then unique, up to an isomorphism—which is the qualification with which we always endow the word "unique" in algebra. The degree of a transcendental extension is, of course, not finite.

If k is algebraic over $\mathcal{F}$, the situation is more complicated due to the presence of nonzero polynomials $q(x)$, in this case, such that $q(k) = 0$. We shall devote the following section to a discussion of this very important case.

Example. The field $Q(\pi)$ is transcendental over Q, and consists of all quotients of polynomials in π, with rational coefficients and denominators not the zero polynomial. On the other hand, the field $Q(\sqrt{3})$ is algebraic over Q, because $\sqrt{3}$ is a zero of the polynomial $x^2 - 3$. It is far from easy— and beyond the scope of this book—to prove that π is a transcendental number, but a proof may be found in Chapter 9 of [6].

PROBLEMS 7–1

1. List the "field" postulates which are not necessary for a general ring.

*2. If $k \in \mathcal{K}$, explain the "natural" imbedding of $\mathcal{F}(k)$ in $\mathcal{K}$, as discussed in this section.

*3. Explain the inaccuracy present in the symbolism $\mathcal{F} \subset \mathcal{K}$ used to designate that $\mathcal{F}$ is a subfield of $\mathcal{K}$.

*4. Explain why neither Q nor Z_p, for any prime p, can have a proper subfield.

**5. Prove that any intersection of subfields of a given field is also a subfield of the given field.

*6. Explain why the concept of a *prime* subfield, as the intersection of all subfields of a field, is equivalent to the definition given above.

7. What "field" properties are used in the equalities which are listed in this section just prior to the assertion that $\mathcal{K}$ is a vector space over $\mathcal{F}$?

8. What is the conceptual distinction between $\mathcal{F}[k]$ and $\mathcal{F}(k)$, for $k \in \mathcal{K}$?

9. List two irrational numbers which are algebraic over Q, and two which are transcendental over Q.

10. Explain why the field of rational functions in an indeterminate x, with coefficients in Z_p, has characteristic p.

*11. If k and h are elements of $\mathcal{K}$ which are transcendental over $\mathcal{F}$, outline the steps in the proof that $\mathcal{F}[k]$ and $\mathcal{F}[h]$ are isomorphic.

**12. Explain why a prime field must be isomorphic either to Q or to Z_p, for some prime p.

13. If $\mathcal{D}$ is a division ring and x is transcendental over $\mathcal{D}$, prove that $\mathcal{D}$, $\mathcal{D}[x]$ and $\mathcal{D}(x)$ have the same characteristic, using definitions which are analogous to the case when $\mathcal{D}$ is a field. Also prove that if $\mathcal{D}$ is an integral domain, with quotient field $\mathcal{K}$, both $\mathcal{D}[x]$ and $\mathcal{D}(x)$ are integral domains and the quotient field of either is $\mathcal{K}(x)$.

14. Find a basis for the vector space of complex numbers over R. Explain the difficulty in finding a basis for R over Q.

15. An *algebraic integer* is a complex number which is a zero of a monic polynomial with integral coefficients. Prove that if k is an algebraic number (that is, algebraic over Q), then some positive multiple of k is an algebraic integer.

16. Refer to Problem 15 and show why any algebraic integer, which is also a rational number, must be a rational integer.

17. Refer to Problem 15 and show why $\sin k$ and $\cos k$ are algebraic numbers, for any real number k. When, if ever, are they algebraic integers?

18. Explain why a finite field must have a characteristic which is a prime number.

7.2. Simple Algebraic Extensions

In this section we shall take a closer look at simple algebraic extension fields, and obtain a most important result. In fact, amongst other things, we shall discover that if k is algebraic over $\mathcal{F}$, the *ring* $\mathcal{F}[k]$ and its field of quotients $\mathcal{F}(k)$ are identical! As we have pointed out earlier, the essential difference between the algebraic and the transcendental case is the presence, in the algebraic case, of nonzero polynomials $q(x) \in \mathcal{F}[x]$, such that $q(k) = 0$, for some $k \in \mathcal{K}$. The set of all such polynomials as $q(x)$, having $k \in \mathcal{K}$ as a zero, constitute [Problem 1] an ideal in $\mathcal{F}[x]$; and, since $\mathcal{F}[x]$ is a principal ideal domain [Theorem 5.61], this ideal can be described as the ideal $(\phi(x))$, for some polynomial $\phi(x) \in \mathcal{F}[x]$. In other words, the ideal in question consists of all polynomial multiples of $\phi(x)$. The polynomial $\phi(x)$, which generates the ideal of all polynomials in $\mathcal{F}[x]$ possessing k as a zero, is called the *minimum polynomial* of k over $\mathcal{F}$. We may assume [Problem 3] that this polynomial is *monic*, and so is uniquely associated with k and $\mathcal{F}$. It is *minimal*, since it has the smallest degree of all polynomials in the ideal [Problem 4]. It is also quite easy to see that $\phi(x)$ is *irreducible*, because suppose $\phi(x) = \phi_1(x)\phi_2(x)$, for nonconstant polynomials $\phi_1(x), \phi_2(x) \in \mathcal{F}[x]$. Then $\phi(k) = 0 = \phi_1(k)\phi_2(k)$, whereas $\phi_1(k) \neq 0$ and $\phi_2(k) \neq 0$, by definition of $\phi(x)$. Since $\mathcal{F}[x]$ is an integral domain—and so possesses no divisors of zero—the polynomial $\phi(x)$ must be irreducible. The field of quotients or "residue class" field $\mathcal{F}[x]/(\phi(x))$ then exists, [see Theorem 5.102 and pertinent comments on prime or irreducible ideals in § 5.9]. It is part of the result of the following theorem that this field is isomorphic to $\mathcal{F}(k)$. Before stating the theorem, however, it may be worthwhile to reemphasize, in passing, that the minimum polynomial $\phi(x)$ of an element $k \in \mathcal{K}$ depends not only on the element k but also on the field $\mathcal{F}$ from which the coefficients of $\phi(x)$ are taken [see Problem 19]. The degree of the polynomial $\phi(x)$ is also called the *degree* of k over $\mathcal{F}$.

Theorem 7.21. *If $\mathcal{F}(k)$ is an algebraic extension of the field $\mathcal{F}$, such that the minimal polynomial $\phi(x)$ of k has degree n over $\mathcal{F}$, then*

(i) $\mathcal{F}[x]/(\phi(x)) \cong \mathcal{F}[k]$;

(ii) $\mathcal{F}[k] = \mathcal{F}(k)$;

(iii) $[\mathcal{F}(k): \mathcal{F}] = n$

Proof.

(i) Let $\phi(x) = a_0 + a_1 x + \cdots + a_{n-1}x^{n-1} + x^n$, and consider the following mapping from $\mathscr{F}[x]$ into $\mathscr{F}[k]$: $\sum_{i=0}^{t} b_i x^i \to \sum_{i=0}^{t} b_i k^i$, for any integer $t \geq 0$.

This is certainly a mapping of polynomials in x onto polynomials in k, and it is not difficult to see that it is a homomorphism [Problem 9]. Since a polynomial in $\mathscr{F}[x]$ maps onto 0 if and only if k is a zero of the polynomial, the kernel of the homomorphism is the ideal $(\phi(x))$. Since $\mathscr{F}[k]$ is clearly the complete image of $\mathscr{F}[x]$, it follows from the Fundamental Homomorphism theorem for rings, Theorem 5.94, that $\mathscr{F}[x]/(\phi(x)) \cong \mathscr{F}[k]$.

(ii) Since $\mathscr{F}(k)$ is certainly the smallest field containing $\mathscr{F}[k]$ [see § 7.1] while $\mathscr{F}[k]$ is itself a field as a result of (i), it follows that $\mathscr{F}[k] = \mathscr{F}(k)$. This is the rather-surprising result that the *ring* of polynomials $\mathscr{F}[k]$ is the same as the *field* $\mathscr{F}(k)$ of rational functions in k, *whenever k is an element which is algebraic over* $\mathscr{F}$. We shall elaborate on this phenomenon with illustrative examples later in the section [cf. Problems 3, 4 of § 7.3].

(iii) Let $f(x)$ be an arbitrary polynomial of $\mathscr{F}[x]$. Then, by the Division Algorithm for polynomials, $f(x) = g(x)\phi(x) + r(x)$, for certain polynomials $g(x)$ and $r(x)$, where $r(x) = r_0 + r_1 x + \cdots + r_{n-1} x^{n-1}$, $r_i \in \mathscr{F}$, $i = 0, 1, 2, \ldots, n - 1$. Since $\phi(k) = 0$, it follows that $f(k) = r(k)$, and so the elements $1, k, k^2, \ldots, k^{n-1}$ span the vector space $\mathscr{F}[k]$ over $\mathscr{F}$. Inasmuch as $\phi(x)$ is the minimal polynomial of k over $\mathscr{F}$, $r(k) = 0$ if and only if $r_0 = r_1 = \cdots = r_{n-1} = 0$. Hence, $1, k, k^2, \ldots, k^{n-1}$ are linearly independent over $\mathscr{F}$, and so the dimension of the vector space $\mathscr{F}[k]$ over $\mathscr{F}$—that is, $[\mathscr{F}(k):\mathscr{F}]$—is n, the degree of the minimum polynomial of k. ∎

The important fact that $\mathscr{F}[k] = \mathscr{F}(k)$, whenever k is algebraic over $\mathscr{F}$, is the basis for the process of "rationalizing the denominator" found in elementary algebra. For example, a typical element of the field $\mathbf{Q}(\sqrt{2})$ might be $3 - \sqrt{2}$ and its inverse—which must exist since $\mathbf{Q}(\sqrt{2})$ is a field—is $1/(3 - \sqrt{2})$. In order to express this inverse as a *polynomial* element of $\mathbf{Q}(\sqrt{2})$, we multiply numerator and denominator by $3 + \sqrt{2}$, and simplify the result. Thus, $1/(3 - \sqrt{2}) = [1/(3 - \sqrt{2})] \cdot [(3 + \sqrt{2})/(3 + \sqrt{2})] = (3/7) + (1/7)\sqrt{2}$, which is an element of the form $a + b\sqrt{2}$ with $a = 3/7$ and $b = 1/7$. The degree of the minimal polynomial $\phi(x)$ of $\sqrt{2}$ over $\mathbf{Q}$ is 2, since $\phi(x) = x^2 - 2$, while a "vector space" basis for $\mathbf{Q}(\sqrt{2})$ is $\{1, \sqrt{2}\}$.

Of course, the familiar method of "rationalizing the denominator" for finding an inverse is available only for elements of "quadratic" fields, i.e., fields of the form $\mathbf{Q}(\sqrt{b})$, for a positive nonsquare integer b; and we require a more general procedure, if we are to work effectively in more general algebraic fields. A procedure is provided by the Division Algorithm for polynomial elements of $Q[x]$. We shall repeat the above simple illustration by this more general method, before progressing to a more complicated example.

We wish to determine $1/q(\sqrt{2})$, where $q(x) = 3 - x$, knowing that the minimal polynomial $\phi(x)$ of $\sqrt{2}$ is $x^2 - 2$. If we use the Division Algorithm and divide $x^2 - 2$ by $-x + 3$, we obtain the quotient $-x - 3$ with a remainder of 7. Thus, $7 = 1(x^2 - 2) + (x + 3)(3 - x)$ and $1 = (x^2 - 2)/7 + [(x + 3)/7](3 - x)$. We have then expressed 1, the g.c.d. of $q(x)$ and $\phi(x)$, in the form $1 = g(x)\phi(x) + h(x)q(x)$, where $g(x) = 1/7$ and $h(x) = (x + 3)/7$. But $\phi(\sqrt{2}) = 0$, so that $1 = 0 + h(\sqrt{2}) \cdot q(\sqrt{2}) = h(\sqrt{2}) \cdot q(\sqrt{2})$; i.e., $1/q(\sqrt{2}) = h\sqrt{2}) = 3/7 + (1/7)\sqrt{2}$, as before. We now turn to a more complicated illustration.

Example. Find the inverse of $1 - \sqrt[3]{2} + \sqrt[3]{4} \in Q[\sqrt[3]{2}]$.

Solution. In this case, the minimal polynomial of $\sqrt[3]{2}$ is $\phi(x) = x^3 - 2$, while the polynomial $q(\sqrt[3]{2})$—whose inverse is desired—is defined by $q(x) = 1 - x + x^2$. Our problem, then, is to determine polynomials $g(x)$ and $h(x) \in Q[x]$, such that $1 = g(x)\phi(x) + h(x)q(x)$. As in the simpler illustration above, we divide the polynomial of larger degree—in this case $\phi(x)$—by the other polynomial $q(x)$, with the result that $x^3 - 2 = (x + 1)(x^2 - x + 1) - 3$, or, $3 = -1(x^3 - 2) + (x + 1)(x^2 - x + 1)$; and so $1 = (-1/3)(x^3 - 2) + [(x + 1)/3](x^2 - x + 1)$. Since $\sqrt[3]{2}$ is a zero of the polynomial $x^3 - 2$, we have $\phi(\sqrt[3]{2}) = 0$, and we have obtained the desired decomposition of 1, where $g(x) = -1/3$ and $h(x) = (x + 1)/3$. Then $1 = h(\sqrt[3]{2})q(\sqrt[3]{2})$, so that the inverse of $q(\sqrt[3]{2})$ is $h(\sqrt[3]{2})$, i.e., $(\sqrt[3]{2} + 1)/3$. We close this section with a simple result of great importance.

Theorem 7.22. *If k_1 and k_2 are zeros of the same irreducible polynomial $\phi(x) \in \mathcal{F}[x]$, the fields $\mathcal{F}(k_1)$ and $\mathcal{F}(k_2)$ are isomorphic under a mapping which leaves the elements of $\mathcal{F}$ invariant.*

Proof. The proof is almost trivial. That $\mathcal{F}(k_1)$ and $\mathcal{F}(k_2)$ are isomorphic follows from the fact that both these fields are isomorphic to the field $\mathcal{F}[x]/(\phi(x))$, and the transitivity of an isomorphic mapping. The isomorphic mapping of $\mathcal{F}(k_1)$ onto $\mathcal{F}(k_2)$ is clearly that in which a polynomial $\sum_{i=0}^{t} b_i k_1^i$ of $\mathcal{F}(k_1)$ is mapped onto $\sum_{i=0}^{t} b_i k_2^i$ of $\mathcal{F}(k_2)$; and in particular we note that the elements of $\mathcal{F}$ are left invariant under this mapping. The details of the proof are left to the student. ∎

PROBLEMS 7–2

**1. Explain why the set of polynomials $q(x)$ in $\mathcal{F}[x]$, such that $q(k) = 0$, for $k \in \mathcal{K}$, constitutes an ideal in $\mathcal{F}[x]$.

2. Describe the ideal $(p(x))$ in $\mathbf{Q}[x]$, where (a) $p(x) = x^2 + 1$; (b) $p(x) = x^3 - 1$.

*3. Why may we assume, without loss of generality, that the minimum polynomial of an algebraic element $k \in \mathcal{K}$ is monic?

*4. Why is the generator of the ideal of polynomials, which have $k \in \mathcal{K}$ as a zero, necessarily of minimal degree?

5. Describe the product and quotients of the ideals in Problem 2.

6. The complex number i is a zero of the polynomial $\phi(x) = x^2 + 1$. What coset in $\mathbf{R}[x]/(\phi(x))$ corresponds to i in the isomorphism established in Theorem 7.21 between $\mathbf{R}(i)$ (i.e., $\mathbf{C}$) and $\mathbf{R}[x]/(\phi(x))$?

7. Verify that the coset discovered in Problem 6 has the same characteristic property as i: that is, $i^2 = -1$.

8. Exhibit the isomorphic mapping between the field of residue classes in Problem 6, and the field of complex numbers as ordinarily defined. (This is actually a review of Problem 19 of § 5.10.)

*9. Verify that the mapping $\sum_{i=0}^{t} b_i x^i \to \sum_{i=1}^{t} b_i k^i$, in the proof of Theorem 7.21, is a homomorphism.

10. Use the method of "rationalizing the denominator" to express the inverse of $1 - \sqrt{2}$ as a polynomial element of $\mathbf{Q}[\sqrt{2}]$.

11. Use the directions of Problem 10 for $2 + \sqrt{2}$.

12. If k_1 and k_2 are distinct zeros of the same irreducible polynomial in $\mathcal{F}[x]$, give the details of the proof that the mapping $\sum_{i=0}^{t} b_i k_1^i \to \sum_{i=0}^{t} b_i k_2^i$ is an isomorphism of $\mathcal{F}(k_1)$ onto $\mathcal{F}(k_2)$.

13. Express $(2 - \sqrt{2})/(3 + \sqrt{2})$ as a polynomial in $\sqrt{2}$.

14. Express $2/(1 - \sqrt[3]{2} + 3\sqrt[3]{4})$ as a polynomial in $\sqrt[3]{2}$.

15. Express $(1 - 3\sqrt[3]{2})/(2 + 2\sqrt[3]{2} - \sqrt[3]{4})$ as a polynomial in $\sqrt[3]{2}$.

16. If $\mathbf{Q} \subset \mathcal{K}$ and $\mathcal{K}$ contains the number $2 - \sqrt[5]{3}$, describe the ideal $A \subset \mathbf{Q}[x]$ such that $\mathbf{Q}(2 - \sqrt[5]{3}) \cong \mathbf{Q}[x]/A$.

17. If $\mathbf{Q} \subset \mathcal{K}$ and $1 + \sqrt{5} \in \mathcal{K}$, describe the ideal $A \subset \mathbf{Q}[x]$, such that $\mathbf{Q}(1 + \sqrt{5}) \cong \mathbf{Q}[x]/A$.

18. Are the fields $\mathbf{Q}(2 - \sqrt{2})$ and $\mathbf{Q}(\sqrt{2})$ the same? Explain your answer.

19. Show that the complex number $\sqrt{2} - i$ has a minimum polynomial of degree 4 over $\mathbf{Q}$ and one of degree 2 over $\mathbf{R}$, and find the polynomial in each case.

20. Use the directions of Problem 19 for the number $2\sqrt{3} - 2i$.

21. If $p(x)$ is any polynomial of degree n over $\mathcal{F}$, with $(p(x))$ the ideal generated by it, prove that $\mathcal{F}[x]/(p(x))$ is an n-dimensional vector space.

**22. Find the minimum polynomial of $\sqrt{2} - \sqrt{3}$ over $\mathbf{Q}$, and hence the degree of the field $\mathbf{Q}(\sqrt{2} - \sqrt{3})$.

23. Find the minimum polynomial of $\sqrt[3]{2} - \sqrt{5}$ over $\mathbf{Q}$, and hence the degree of $\mathbf{Q}(\sqrt[3]{2} - \sqrt{5})$.

24. Prove that a finite field must have p^n elements, for some prime p and positive integer n.

7.3. Stem Fields of Irreducible Polynomials

In the preceding section, we showed how to obtain a simple algebraic extension of a field $\mathcal{F}$, by adjoining to $\mathcal{F}$ a zero $k \in \mathcal{K}$ of an irreducible polynomial $\phi(x)$, with its coefficients in $\mathcal{F}$. The resulting simple extension field $\mathcal{F}(k)$ was the field of (quotients of) polynomials in $\mathcal{F}[k]$, the degree of the field being equal to the degree of the polynomial. There is a slightly different approach to the matter of simple extensions of $\mathcal{F}$, and it is to this that we first direct our attention in this section: instead of starting with a known zero k of a polynomial—the element k being either given or determinate—we start with an irreducible polynomial $\phi(x) \in \mathcal{F}[x]$, and show that *this polynomial determines an isomorphically-unique extension of $\mathcal{F}$*. This result is a theorem, due originally to Kronecker, and is a very important one, although its *practical* value can be easily overstated. The elements of a simple algebraic extension $\mathcal{F}(k)$ can be taken to be either polynomials or quotients of polynomials in $\mathcal{F}[k]$, as desired, so that a description of such a field is readily supplied. On the other hand, the elements of the field about to be constructed are residue classes and, *at least to the mathematical neophyte*, residue classes probably have a somewhat " shadowy " existence—although they have been encountered many times in the past in this text. Of course, as an alternative to residue classes, it may be useful to think of the equivalence of the members of any one residue class as a " generalized equality," and so essentially " equate " all polynomial members in each class of $\mathcal{F}[x]$. From this viewpoint, we then work with a set of " representatives " as the elements of the new field—and this is really what we do when we consider polynomials to represent distinct elements of $\mathcal{F}(k)$. If this latter point of view is adopted, the elements of the field just constructed are polynomials of $\mathcal{F}[x]$, the only difference between this new field and the ring $\mathcal{F}[x]$ being in the agreement as to what elements are to be considered " equal " in the two systems.

If $\mathcal{F}$ happens to be the field **R** of real numbers, the Fundamental Theorem of Algebra assures us of the existence of a complex (or real) number c, associated as a zero with any given irreducible polynomial $\phi(x) \in \mathbf{R}[x]$. The result of Theorem 7.21, as applied to this case, is then that $\mathcal{F}(c) \cong \mathcal{F}[x]/(\phi(x))$. However, in the general case, $\mathcal{F}$ is a field for which we have no " Fundamental Theorem of Algebra," and so the following theorem is of importance.

Theorem 7.31. *If $\phi(x)$ is a polynomial which is irreducible over a field $\mathcal{F}$, there* *exists a simple algebraic extension field of* $\mathcal{F}$, *which is generated by a zero* k *of* $\phi(x)$. *Such a field* $\mathcal{F}(k)$ *is called a* stem field *of the polynomial* $\phi(x)$.

Proof. It follows from Theorem 7.21 that if such a field $\mathcal{F}(k)$ exists, for some k algebraic over $\mathcal{F}$, this field must be isomorphic to $\mathcal{F}[x]/(\phi(x))$. Since the only element of $\mathcal{F}$ that can [Problem 7] be in the ideal $(\phi(x))$ is 0, the natural mapping of $\mathcal{F}[x]$ onto $\mathcal{F}[x]/(\phi(x))$ must be a homomorphism which leaves the elements of $\mathcal{F}$ invariant. Each polynomial of $\mathcal{F}[x]$ then maps onto a coset of $\mathcal{F}[x]/(\phi(x))$ and, in particular, the "polynomial" x maps onto the coset $x + (\phi(x))$. Then, if we define $k = x + (\phi(x))$, $\phi(k) = \phi(x) + (\phi(x)) = (\phi(x)) = 0$ in $\mathcal{F}[x]/(\phi(x))$ [Problem 7], so that $\mathcal{F}(k)$ is the desired field. We note that k is the coset which contains the element x. ∎

In the alternate intuitive description of $\mathcal{F}[x]/(\phi(x))$, we merely consider as "*equal*" all polynomials in $\mathcal{F}[x]$ which differ by some multiple of $\phi(x)$. For example, if $\phi(x) = x^4 + 1$, we would consider x and $x^4 + x + 1$ as "equal," whereas x would be "unequal" to $x^3 + 1$.

Corollary. *If* $f(x)$ *is any polynomial with coefficients in a field* $\mathcal{F}$, *then* $f(x)$ *has a zero in some extension field of* $\mathcal{F}$.

Proof. The proof consists merely in factoring $f(x)$ into a product of polynomials which are irreducible in $\mathcal{F}$, and then applying the above theorem to any one of the factors. ∎

Example. Construct the complex numbers as a stem field of $x^2 + 1$ [cf. Problem 6, § 7.2].

Solution. Since $x^2 + 1$ is an irreducible polynomial over **R** [Problem 8], the proof of Theorem 7.31 shows that the coset $x + ((x^2 + 1))$ generates the desired field of complex numbers. It may be instructive and of interest to go through the steps of proving that this stem field of residue classes is actually isomorphic to the field more familiarly designated as **R**(i), with $i^2 = -1$. (To the sophisticated mathematician, this demonstration will be unnecessary, since he will be quite willing to identify the coset $x + ((x^2 + 1))$ with i. However, while the student has had some earlier experience with the symbol i, his experience with cosets has likely not been so extensive.) The mapping from **R**$[x]/((x^2 + 1))$ to **R**(i), which we shall show to be an isomorphism is defined as follows:

$$a + bx + ((x^2 + 1)) \rightarrow a + bi, \text{ for real numbers } a, b.$$

It is easily seen that this mapping is one-to-one. If it is also known that $a' + b'x + ((x^2 + 1)) \rightarrow a' + b'i$, for real numbers a', b', then

$$(a + bx) + (a' + b'x) + ((x^2 + 1)) = (a + a') + (b + b')x + ((x^2 + 1))$$
$$\rightarrow (a + a') + (b + b')i = (a + bi) + (a' + b'i)$$

This proves that the given mapping preserves the operations of addition in the two systems. We leave it to the student that a similar situation holds with respect to the operations of multiplication, and the proof that the two systems are isomorphic will then be complete [Problem 10].

The preceding theorem establishes the existence of stem fields, for any irreducible polynomial, while Theorem 7.22 proves that these stem fields —for the same polynomial—are isomorphic. In the next section, we shall investigate extensions in which more than one element are adjoined to the base field $\mathcal{F}$, and obtain our principal result on *finite (or algebraic) extensions*.

PROBLEMS 7–3

*1. What difference, if any, is there in referring to an extension field $\mathcal{F}(a)$, where $a \in \mathcal{K}$, $\mathcal{F} \subset \mathcal{K}$, and in referring merely to "a field $\mathcal{F}(a)$"?

2. What, if any, is the difference between the Fundamental Theorem of Algebra, and the assertion that every polynomial, with real or complex coefficients, has a zero?

3. Let $\mathcal{F} \subset \mathcal{K}$, with $k \in \mathcal{K}$ and x an indeterminate over $\mathcal{F}$. Then prove that the natural mapping of $\mathcal{F}[x]$ onto $\mathcal{F}[k]$ is an isomorphism, provided k is transcendental over $\mathcal{F}$.

**4. With the same notation as in Problem 3, prove that the mapping is not an isomorphism if k is algebraic over $\mathcal{F}$.

5. If $\mathcal{F} \subset \mathcal{K}$ and k is an algebraic element of $\mathcal{K}$, show that $\mathcal{F}(k)$ is isomorphic to $\mathcal{F}[x]/A$, for some ideal A in $\mathcal{F}(x)$.

6. Explain the natural mapping of $\mathcal{F}(x)$ onto $\mathcal{F}(x)/(\phi(x))$, where $\phi(x)$ is an irreducible polynomial over $\mathcal{F}$.

*7. With reference to the proof of Theorem 7.31, explain why no nonzero element of $\mathcal{F}$ can be in $(\phi(x))$. In the same proof, explain why $\phi(k) = 0$.

*8. Prove that $x^2 + 1$ is irreducible over **R**.

9. (a) If $[\mathcal{K} : \mathcal{F}]$ is a prime number, prove that $\mathcal{F} \subset \mathcal{K}' \subset \mathcal{K}$, for any field $\mathcal{K}'$, would require that $\mathcal{K}' = \mathcal{K}$ or $\mathcal{K}' = \mathcal{F}$.
   (b) If $[\mathcal{F}(k) : \mathcal{F}]$ is an odd number, prove that $\mathcal{F}(k) = \mathcal{F}(k^2)$.

*10. Prove that the mapping in the Example in this section preserves the operations of multiplication in the two systems.

11. Prove that the minimal (monic) polynomial of an element k, algebraic over a field $\mathcal{F}$, is unique.

12. Give an illustration of an extension field of **Q** which cannot be expressed as **Q**(k) for either an algebraic or transcendental element k.

13. Does a finite extension of a field $\mathcal{F}$ necessarily contain only a finite number of elements not in $\mathcal{F}$? Is it possible that such is the case?

14. Describe the elements of the field defined as **Q**$[x]/(\phi(x))$, where $\phi(x) = x^2 + x + 1$.

15. Explain why $\mathscr{F}(x)$, with $a \in \mathscr{K}$ and $\mathscr{F} \subset \mathscr{K}$, is the intersection of all subfields of $\mathscr{K}$ which contain a and $\mathscr{F}$.

**16. If $\mathscr{F}$ is a finite field, prove that any simple algebraic extension of $\mathscr{F}$ has only a finite number of elements.

17. Explain why the adjunction of an element k_2 to $\mathscr{F}(k_1)$ would result in the same field as would result from the adjunction of k_1 to $\mathscr{F}(k_2)$, assuming k_1, $k_2 \in \mathscr{K}$ and $\mathscr{F} \subset \mathscr{K}$. Such a field is designated $\mathscr{F}(k_1, k_2)$.

18. Describe the field $\mathbf{Q}(\sqrt{2}, \sqrt{3})$, and find its degree over $\mathbf{Q}$, referring to Problem 17.

19. Refer to Problem 17, and find the degree of the field $\mathbf{Q}(\sqrt{2}, \sqrt{3}, \sqrt{6})$ over $\mathbf{Q}$. Compare this field with the one in Problem 18.

20. Find a real number k such that $\mathbf{Q}(k) = \mathbf{Q}(\sqrt{2}, \sqrt{3})$, referring to Problem 18 for the definition of the latter field.

7.4. Finite Algebraic Extensions

The word "finite" has already been associated with an extension field, and so has the word "algebraic" if the extension is simple. Thus, the field $\mathscr{F}(k)$ is both a *finite* and an *algebraic* extension of $\mathscr{F}$, provided k is an element which is algebraic over $\mathscr{F}$, but this assertion is true *by definition* rather than by any proof. The following definition seems quite natural, as applied to an extension field $\mathscr{K}$ of $\mathscr{F}$.

Definition. A field $\mathscr{K}$ is *algebraic* over a base field $\mathscr{F}$ provided each element of $\mathscr{K}$ is algebraic over $\mathscr{F}$.

The question immediately arises whether this definition of "algebraic" is consistent with the definition of a "finite algebraic" extension field $\mathscr{F}(k)$, just mentioned. That it is, is the content of the following elementary but important lemma. (For an example of an "infinite" algebraic extension field, see Problem 21.)

Lemma. *If $\mathscr{K}$ is a finite extension of $\mathscr{F}$, such that $[\mathscr{K} : \mathscr{F}] = n$, then every element of $\mathscr{K}$ is algebraic over $\mathscr{F}$ of degree not exceeding n.*

Proof. For let k be any element of $\mathscr{K}$. Then $1, k, k^2, \ldots, k^n$ are $n + 1$ elements in an n-dimensional vector space $\mathscr{K}$, and so are linearly dependent over $\mathscr{F}$. Hence, for certain numbers $a_0, a_1, a_2, \ldots, a_n \in \mathscr{F}$, not all zero, it is the case that $a_0 + a_1 k + a_2 k^2 + \cdots + a_n k^n = 0$. But now, since k is a zero of a polynomial of degree n over $\mathscr{F}$, the element k must be algebraic of degree at most n over $\mathcal{F}$. (Why is the degree of k not necessarily n? [Problem 3].) ∎

It was suggested in some of the latter problems of the previous section how one can extend the notion of a *simple* extension to an extension involving the adjunction of more than one element. Thus, if $k_1, k_2, \ldots, k_n$ are elements of some field $\mathcal{K}$ containing the base field $\mathcal{F}$, we obtain the field $\mathcal{F}(k_1, k_2)$ by the adjunction of k_2 to the simple extension $\mathcal{F}(k_1)$. In like manner, we obtain $\mathcal{F}(k_1, k_2, k_3)$ by adjoining k_3 to $\mathcal{F}(k_1, k_2)$, and by continuing this process of the adjunction of elements we ultimately obtain the extension field $\mathcal{F}(k_1, k_2, \ldots, k_n)$. It is an elementary exercise to prove that the order in which the elements are adjoined is of no consequence [Problem 4]. We are now confronted with a question similar to the one above—in fact a generalization of it: is the field $\mathcal{K} = \mathcal{F}(k_1, k_2, \ldots, k_n)$ algebraic over $\mathcal{F}$ if $k_1, k_2, \ldots, k_n$ are algebraic over $\mathcal{F}$? Some authors *define* such a field $\mathcal{K}$ to be algebraic and then *prove* that it has the property of our definition. We do not choose to do this, however, but we make it one of the principal objectives of this section *to prove that $\mathcal{K}$ is algebraic according to our definition*. This result will appear as a corollary of the following important theorem.

Theorem 7.41. *A field $\mathcal{K}$ is a finite extension of $\mathcal{F}$ if and only if $\mathcal{K} = \mathcal{F}(k_1, k_2, \ldots, k_n)$, for certain elements $k_1, k_2 \ldots, k_n$ which are algebraic over $\mathcal{F}$.*

Proof. First, let us assume that $\mathcal{K}$ is a finite extension of $\mathcal{F}$, and that $[\mathcal{K} : \mathcal{F}] = n$. The field $\mathcal{K}$, regarded now as a vector space over $\mathcal{F}$, has n basis elements $k_1, k_2, \ldots, k_n$, so that each element of $\mathcal{K}$ can be expressed as a linear combination, with coefficients in $\mathcal{F}$, of these basis elements. By the lemma above, each element of $\mathcal{K}$, and in particular $k_1, k_2, \ldots, k_n$, are algebraic over $\mathcal{F}$. Since the definition of a basis implies that $\mathcal{K} = \mathcal{F}[k_1, k_2, \ldots, k_n]$, while successive applications of **(ii)** of Theorem 7.21 [Problem 7] assures us that $\mathcal{F}[k_1, k_2, \ldots, k_n] = \mathcal{F}(k_1, k_2, \ldots, k_n)$, we have shown that $\mathcal{K} = \mathcal{F}(k_1, k_2, \ldots, k_n)$, where each k_i is algebraic over $\mathcal{F}$, as asserted.

Conversely, let us assume that $\mathcal{K} = \mathcal{F}(k_1, k_2, \ldots, k_n)$, for certain elements $k_1, k_2, \ldots, k_n$ which are algebraic over $\mathcal{F}$. If we let $\mathcal{F} = \mathcal{F}_0$, and define $\mathcal{F}_1 = \mathcal{F}_0(k_1)$, it follows from **(ii)** of Theorem 7.21 that $\mathcal{F}_1 = \mathcal{F}[k_1] = \mathcal{F}(k_1)$, and $\mathcal{F}_1$ has some finite degree n_1 (the degree of the minimum polynomial of k_1) over $\mathcal{F}$. If we now define $\mathcal{F}_2 = \mathcal{F}_1(k_2)$, a similar argument shows that $\mathcal{F}_2$ has some degree n_2 (the degree of the minimum polynomial of k_2) over $\mathcal{F}_1$. More generally, if $\mathcal{F}_{i-1}$ has degree $r = n_{i-1}$ over $\mathcal{F}$, with a basis $\{u_1, u_2, \ldots, u_r\}$, a similar argument shows us, since k_i is algebraic over $\mathcal{F}$ and hence algebraic over $\mathcal{F}_{i-1}$ [Problem 8], that $\mathcal{F}_i = \mathcal{F}_{i-1}(k_i)$ is a field whose degree over $\mathcal{F}_{i-1}$ is equal to the degree t of the minimum polynomial of k_i over $\mathcal{F}_{i-1}$. A typical element of

$\mathcal{F}_i$ then has the form $b_1 v_1 + b_2 v_2 + \cdots + b_t v_t$, where $\{v_1, v_2, \ldots, v_t\}$ is a basis of the vector space $\mathcal{F}_i$ over $\mathcal{F}_{i-1}$, with the coefficients $b_1, b_2, \ldots, b_t \in \mathcal{F}_{i-1}$. It follows that $\mathcal{F}_i$, as a vector space over $\mathcal{F}$, is spanned by the rt "vectors" $\{u_i v_j\}$, where $i = 1, 2, \ldots, r; j = 1, 2, \ldots, t$. It follows by induction that $\mathcal{K} = \mathcal{F}(k_1, k_2, \ldots, k_n) = \mathcal{F}_{n-1}(k_n)$ has a finite number of generators over $\mathcal{F}$, whence we see that $\mathcal{K}$ is of finite degree over $\mathcal{F}$. ∎

A restatement of the theorem could be that a finite extension can contain no transcendental elements, and that it can be obtained from the base field by the adjunction of a finite number of elements, each of which is algebraic over the base field.

Corollary. *An extension field* $\mathcal{F}(k_1, k_2, \ldots, k_n)$, *where* $k_1, k_2, \ldots, k_n$ *are algebraic over* $\mathcal{F}$, *is algebraic over* $\mathcal{F}$.

Proof. The proof follows from the above theorem and the lemma which precedes it, but we leave the details to the student [Problem 15]. ∎

It was part of the proof of the converse of Theorem 7.41 that, if $\{u_1, u_2, \ldots, u_r\}$ is a basis of $\mathcal{F}_{i-1}$ over $\mathcal{F}$, and $\{v_1, v_2, \ldots, v_t\}$ is a basis of $\mathcal{F}_i$ over $\mathcal{F}_{i-1}$, then the rt "vectors" $\{u_i v_j\}$, with $i = 1, 2, \ldots, r$ and $j = 1, 2, \ldots, t$, form a spanning set for $\mathcal{F}_i$ over $\mathcal{F}$. This result is of importance in its own right, and we restate it in a slightly different and stronger form, and derive a number of important corollaries from it.

Theorem 7.42. *If* $\mathcal{F}, \mathcal{H}, \mathcal{K}$ *are fields such that* $\mathcal{F} \subset \mathcal{H} \subset \mathcal{K}$, *with* $\{u_1, u_2, \ldots, u_n\}$ *a basis for* $\mathcal{H}$ *over* $\mathcal{F}$, *and* $\{v_1, v_2, \ldots, v_m\}$ *a basis for* $\mathcal{K}$ *over* $\mathcal{H}$, *then the* mn *elements* $\{u_i v_j\}$, *where* $i = 1, 2, \ldots, n$ *and* $j = 1, 2, \ldots, m$ *constitute a basis for* $\mathcal{K}$ *over* $\mathcal{F}$.

Proof. It is clear from the proof of Theorem 7.41 (or by mere inspection) that the mn elements $\{u_i v_j\}$ span the "vector space" $\mathcal{K}$ over $\mathcal{F}$ [Problem 10], and so all that remains in the proof is to show the linear independence of these elements. Let us suppose that $\sum_{i,j} a_{ij} u_i v_j = 0$, with $a_{ij} \in \mathcal{F}$, and $i = 1, 2, \ldots, n, j = 1, 2, \ldots, m$. But then, by a rearrangement of terms, $\sum_{i=1}^{n} (\sum_{j=1}^{m} a_{ij} v_j) u_i = 0$, and the linear independence of $u_1, u_2, \ldots, u_n$ over $\mathcal{H}$ implies that $\sum_{j=1}^{m} a_{ij} v_j = 0$, for each $i = 1, 2, \ldots, n$. The linear independence of $v_1, v_2, \ldots, v_m$ over $\mathcal{F}$ then implies that $a_{ij} = 0$, for each j. Hence, $a_{ij} = 0$, for each i and j, and the mn "vectors" $\{u_i v_j\}$ are a basis for $\mathcal{K}$ over $\mathcal{F}$, as asserted. ∎

Corollary 1. *If $\mathcal{H}$ is a finite extension of $\mathcal{F}$, and $\mathcal{K}$ is a finite extension of $\mathcal{H}$, then $\mathcal{K}$ is a finite extension of $\mathcal{F}$. Moreover, $[\mathcal{K} : \mathcal{F}] = [\mathcal{H} : \mathcal{F}][\mathcal{K} : \mathcal{H}]$.*

Corollary 2. *If $\mathcal{K}$ is a finite extension of $\mathcal{F}$, the degree of any element of $\mathcal{K}$ must divide $[\mathcal{K} : \mathcal{F}]$.*

Corollary 3. *An algebraic extension of an algebraic extension of $\mathcal{F}$ is an algebraic extension of $\mathcal{F}$.*

Corollary 4. *If $[\mathcal{K} : \mathcal{F}] = 2^n$ and $p(x)$ is an irreducible polynomial of degree 3 over $\mathcal{F}$, then the polynomial is also irreducible over $\mathcal{K}$.*

We leave the proofs of these corollaries to the student, and will refer to them in the Problems.

Example 1. Let us consider the field $\mathbf{Q}(\sqrt{2}, \sqrt{3}, \sqrt{6})$. The minimum polynomial of $\sqrt{2}$ over $\mathbf{Q}$ is $x^2 - 2$, and so $\mathbf{Q}(\sqrt{2})$ has degree 2 over $\mathbf{Q}$. The polynomial $x^2 - 3$ is irreducible over $\mathbf{Q}$, and remains irreducible over $\mathbf{Q}(\sqrt{2})$ [Problem 16], so that $\mathbf{Q}(\sqrt{2}, \sqrt{3})$ has degree 2 over $\mathbf{Q}(\sqrt{2})$. It then follows from Corollary 1 above that $\mathbf{Q}(\sqrt{2}, \sqrt{3})$ has degree 4 over $\mathbf{Q}$. Since $\sqrt{6} = \sqrt{2} \cdot \sqrt{3} \in \mathbf{Q}(\sqrt{2}, \sqrt{3})$, the given field has degree 4 over $\mathbf{Q}$.

Example 2. Let us consider the field $\mathbf{Q}(\sqrt{2}, \sqrt[3]{3})$. As noted in Example 1, $x^2 - 2$ is the minimum polynomial of $\sqrt{2}$ over $\mathbf{Q}$, and a basis of $\mathbf{Q}(\sqrt{2})$ over $\mathbf{Q}$ is $\{1, \sqrt{2}\}$. The minimum polynomial of $\sqrt[3]{3}$ over $\mathbf{Q}$ is $x^3 - 3$ and this polynomial remains irreducible over $\mathbf{Q}(\sqrt{2})$. A basis of $\mathbf{Q}(\sqrt{2}, \sqrt[3]{3})$ over $\mathbf{Q}(\sqrt{2})$ is then $\{1, \sqrt[3]{3}, \sqrt[3]{9}\}$, and the result of Theorem 7.42 shows that a basis for the given field over $\mathbf{Q}$ is $\{1, \sqrt{2}, \sqrt[3]{3}, \sqrt[3]{9}, \sqrt{2}\sqrt[3]{3}, \sqrt{2}\sqrt[3]{9}\}$. The fact that there are six elements in the basis is in agreement with Corollary 1.

PROBLEMS 7–4

1. If $[\mathcal{K} : \mathcal{F}] = 1$, why does this imply that $\mathcal{K} = \mathcal{F}$?
2. Is a *finite* extension field necessarily finite? Is a finite *algebraic* extension field necessarily finite (algebraic)? Explain.
*3. If $k \in \mathcal{K}$, where $[\mathcal{K} : \mathcal{F}] = n$, why is the degree of the minimum polynomial of k not necessarily n? What *can* be said about this latter degree?
*4. Explain why $\mathcal{F}(a, b) = \mathcal{F}(b, a)$, for any elements a, b in an extension field of $\mathcal{F}$.
5. Using the definition given for an "algebraic extension," explain why it is *necessary to prove* that $\mathcal{F}(k_1, k_2, \ldots, k_n)$ is algebraic, when we are assuming that the adjoined elements are all algebraic over $\mathcal{F}$.

6. Which of our results in this section justifies the equivalence of the notions of "finite extension" and the "adjunction of a finite number of algebraic elements"?

7. With reference to the proof of the first part of Theorem 7.41, explain the "successive applications of (ii) of Theorem 7.21."

**8. With reference to the proof of the converse in Theorem 7.41, explain why the fact that k_i is algebraic over $\mathcal{F}$ implies that k_i is algebraic over $\mathcal{F}_{i-1}$.

9. If k_1 and k_2 have respective degrees m and n over $\mathcal{F}$, explain why the degree of $\mathcal{F}(k_1, k_2)$ is not necessarily mn.

*10. With reference to the proof of Theorem 7.42, explain why it is clear that the elements $\{u_i v_j\}$ span the field $\mathcal{K}$ over $\mathcal{F}$.

*11. Prove Corollary 1 of Theorem 7.42.

*12. Prove Corollary 2 of Theorem 7.42.

*13. Prove Corollary 3 of Theorem 7.42.

*14. Prove Corollary 4 of Theorem 7.42.

*15. Prove the Corollary of Theorem 7.41.

*16. Explain why $x^2 - 3$ is irreducible over $\mathbf{Q}(\sqrt{2})$.

**17. Find a basis for the field $\mathbf{Q}(\sqrt{3}, \sqrt{2})$.

18. Find a basis for the field $\mathbf{Q}(\sqrt{2}, \sqrt[3]{2}, \sqrt{8})$.

19. If we define a number s to be "constructible" if we can construct, with the use of a straight-edge and compass only, a line segment of length s (in some given unit), prove that the numbers $s + t$, $s - t$, st, and s/t $(t \neq 0)$ are constructible whenever s and t have this property.

20. With reference to Problem 19, show that a number is constructible if the number can be imbedded in a field $\mathbf{Q}(k_1, k_2, \ldots, k_n)$, for real numbers $k_1, k_2, \ldots, k_n$, each quadratic over $\mathbf{Q}$.

21. Prove that the system of all algebraic numbers over $\mathbf{Q}$ is a field, but not of finite degree over $\mathbf{Q}$.

22. If $k = 2 + 3r + 4r^2 + 5r^3 \in \mathbf{Q}(r)$, where r is algebraic of degree 4 over $\mathbf{Q}$, show that k^{-1} can be obtained by solving a system of 4 equations in 4 unknowns. (Do not solve them!)

23. If $\mathcal{F} \subset \mathcal{H} \subset \mathcal{K}$, such that $\mathcal{H}$ is algebraic over $\mathcal{F}$ and $\mathcal{K}$ is algebraic over $\mathcal{H}$, prove that $\mathcal{K}$ is algebraic over $\mathcal{F}$. (Hint: if $k \in \mathcal{K}$, k is a zero of some polynomial $a_0 + a_1 x + \cdots + a_n x^n \in \mathcal{H}[x]$, and consider the field $\mathcal{F}(a_0, a_1, \ldots, a_n)$.)

24. It can be shown that the trisection of an angle is equivalent to solving the equation $4x^3 - 3x - c = 0$, where c is the cosine of the angle. Use Corollary 4 of Theorem 7.42 to prove that such a trisection is not always possible, using only a straight-edge and compass.

SPECIAL ASSIGNMENT

1. See if you can verify the assertion made in the first sentence of Problem 24 above.

2. Define e as a "factorial" series, and prove it an irrational number. (If you have trouble, see p. 298 of [4].)
3. Prove that π is an irrational number [see *Bull. of AMS*, **53** (1947), 509].
4. Prove that e is a transcendental number [see p. 176 of [5]].
5. Look up the proof that both e and π are transcendental in Chapter 9 of [6].

7.5. Splitting Fields

A polynomial $f(x)$ in $\mathcal{F}[x]$ is said to *split* in a field $\mathcal{K} \supset \mathcal{F}$, if $f(x)$ can be factored into linear factors with coefficients in $\mathcal{K}$. In such a case, if the degree of $f(x)$ is n, then $f(x) = a_n(x - k_1)(x - k_2) \ldots (x - k_n)$, for certain elements $k_1, k_2, \ldots, k_n \in \mathcal{K}$, and where a_n is, of course, the leading coefficient of $f(x)$. If $f(x)$ can *not* be so factored into linear factors in any *proper* subfield of $\mathcal{K}$, then $\mathcal{K}$ is said to be a *splitting field* of $f(x)$. It possibly should be pointed out that this "minimum" nature of a splitting field is not required by all authors, but our definition is the one usually adopted by Western writers. It is clear that, if $\mathcal{K}$ is a splitting field of $f(x)$, then $\mathcal{K} = \mathcal{F}(k_1, k_2, \ldots, k_n)$ [Problem 1].

Example 1. The polynomial $x^2 - 2$ is irreducible over the field **Q** of rational numbers. However, if we define $\mathcal{K} = \mathbf{Q}(\sqrt{2})$, it is immediate that $x^2 - 2 = (x - \sqrt{2})(x + \sqrt{2})$, and so $\mathcal{K}$ is a splitting field of $x^2 - 2$ [see Problem 2].

Example 2. Since any polynomial with real coefficients factors into linear factors, with coefficients in the field **C** of complex numbers, it follows that **C** "splits" any such polynomial. Does it follow, however, *from our definition* that **C** is then a splitting field of the polynomial [Problem 3]?

The fields $\mathcal{F}(k_1), \mathcal{F}(k_2), \ldots, \mathcal{F}(k_n)$, generated over $\mathcal{F}$ by the respective zeros of the polynomial $f(x)$, are called *stem fields* of $f(x)$, whether $f(x)$ is irreducible or not—thereby extending the usage of this term as defined in Theorem 7.31. It is possible, of course, that these fields may not all be distinct: for instance, in Example 1 above, it is immediate that $\mathbf{Q}(\sqrt{2})$ is the same field as $\mathbf{Q}(-\sqrt{2})$. However, it follows from the proof of Theorem 7.31 that, if $f(x)$ is irreducible, these stem fields are all isomorphic [Problem 7].

The following theorem is actually an immediate consequence of the above mentioned theorem and its corollary, but we emphasize the importance of the result by stating it in the form of a theorem.

Theorem 7.51. *Any polynomial $f(x) \in \mathcal{F}[x]$ of degree n over $\mathcal{F}$ has a splitting field $\mathcal{K}$ of degree at most $n!$ over $\mathcal{F}$.*

Proof. Without loss of generality we may assume that $f(x)$ is irreducible over $\mathcal{F}$, and that $n > 1$ [Problem 8]. An application of the corollary to Theorem 7.31 then asserts the existence of an extension field of $\mathcal{F}$ in which $f(x)$ has a zero k_1. Hence $f(x) = (x - k_1)g(x)$, where the coefficients of the polynomial $g(x)$ are in $\mathcal{F}(k_1)$ [Problem 9]. The degree of $g(x)$ is $n - 1$, and the above argument need be repeated at most $n - 2$ times, until a splitting field of $f(x)$ is obtained. We note that, while we have assumed $f(x)$ to be irreducible, the polynomial $g(x)$ may be reducible, with some of its zeros lying in the field $\mathcal{F}(k_1)$. Hence, while a zero of an *irreducible* polynomial generates over the coefficient field a field of degree equal to that of the polynomial, the degree of the splitting field $\mathcal{K}$ is *at most $n!$* We leave the details of the proof to the student [Problem 10]. ∎

The above theorem has established the *existence* of a splitting field for any polynomial $f(x) \in \mathcal{F}[x]$, but the following question arises: can there be more than one splitting field for a given polynomial? The following results answer this question by showing that all such splitting fields are isomorphic, and that we are then justified in referring to *the* splitting field of a given polynomial.

Theorem 7.52. *An isomorphism between two fields $\mathcal{F}$ and $\mathcal{F}'$ can be extended to any stem fields defined by irreducible polynomials whose coefficients correspond according to the isomorphism.*

Proof. Let the isomorphism of $\mathcal{F}$ onto $\mathcal{F}'$ be designated by $a_i \to a_i'$. It is then immediate that the mapping $\sum_{i=0}^{n} a_i x^i \to \sum_{i=0}^{n} a_i' x^i$ is an isomorphism of $\mathcal{F}[x]$ onto $\mathcal{F}'[x]$ [Problem 11]. Moreover, if the monic polynomial $f(x) = a_0 + a_1 x + a_2 x^2 + \ldots + a_{n-1} x^{n-1} + x^n$ is irreducible over $\mathcal{F}$, the "image" polynomial $f^*(x) = a_0' + a_1' x + a_2' x^2 + \cdots + a_{n-1}' x^{n-1} + x^n$ is also irreducible over $\mathcal{F}'$ [Problem 12]. The quotient rings $\mathcal{F}[x]/(f(x))$ and $\mathcal{F}'[x]/(f^*(x))$ are then both fields, and it is not difficult to prove that they are isomorphic [Problem 13]. The isomorphism between $\mathcal{F}$ and $\mathcal{F}'$ has then been extended to the stem fields of $f(x)$ and $f^*(x)$. ∎

The next result validates the extension of this result to splitting fields of polynomials which correspond as in Theorem 7.52.

Theorem 7.53. *If $f(x)$ and $f^*(x)$ are corresponding polynomials of degree n over isomorphic coefficient fields $\mathcal{F}$ and $\mathcal{F}'$, this isomorphism can be extended to splitting fields of the polynomials.*

Proof. Using the notation in the proof of Theorem 7.52, let $\mathcal{N}$ and $\mathcal{N}'$ be respective splitting fields of $f(x)$ and $f^*(x)$. The proof will be by induction on the degree n of the polynomials. If $n = 1$, the result is apparent: for then $f(x) = x - a$, $f^*(x) = x - a'$, for elements $a \in \mathcal{F}$ and $a' \in \mathcal{F}'$; $\mathcal{N} = \mathcal{F}$ and $\mathcal{N}' = \mathcal{F}'$, whence $\mathcal{N}'$ is isomorphic to $\mathcal{N}$. Let us now suppose the theorem true for all polynomials $f(x)$ and $f^*(x)$ of degree less than n. If $f_1(x)$ is an irreducible factor of $f(x)$, with $\mathcal{F}_1 = \mathcal{F}(a_1)$ a stem field of $f_1(x)$ in $\mathcal{N}$, there is an associated factor $f_1^*(x)$ of $f^*(x)$ with a stem field $\mathcal{F}_1' = \mathcal{F}'(a_1')$ of $f_1^*(x)$ in $\mathcal{N}'$. By Theorem 7.52, the isomorphism between $\mathcal{F}$ and $\mathcal{F}'$ can be extended to one between $\mathcal{F}_1$ and $\mathcal{F}_1'$. Inasmuch as a_1 is a zero of (x) and a_1' is a zero of $f^*(x)$, we may use the Factor theorem to express $f(x)$ and $f^*(x)$ in the following respective forms: $f(x) = (x - a_1)f_2(x)$ and $*(x) = (x - a_1')f_2^*(x)$, where the coefficients of $f_2(x)$ and $f_2^*(x)$ are in the correspondence defined by the isomorphism of $\mathcal{F}_1$ onto $\mathcal{F}_1'$ [Problem 14]. But $\mathcal{N}$ is a splitting field of $f_2(x)$ over $\mathcal{F}_1$ and $\mathcal{N}'$ is a splitting field of $f_2^*(x)$ over $\mathcal{F}_1'$, with the common degree of these polynomials over their respective coefficient fields being $n - 1$. By our inductive assumption, the isomorphism between $\mathcal{F}$ and $\mathcal{F}'$ can then be extended to $\mathcal{N}$ and $\mathcal{N}'$, as asserted. ∎

Corollary. *Any two splitting fields over $\mathcal{F}$ of a polynomial $f(x) \in \mathcal{F}[x]$ are isomorphic.*

Proof. We let $\mathcal{F}' = \mathcal{F}$, assuming the identity isomorphism, and apply the theorem [Problem 15]. ∎

Definition. An isomorphism α is said to be *over a field $\mathcal{F}$*, or α is an *$\mathcal{F}$-isomorphism*, if $\alpha(a) = a$, for every $a \in \mathcal{F}$.

Definition. An $\mathcal{F}$-isomorphism of a field $\mathcal{K}$ onto itself is said to be an *automorphism of $\mathcal{K}$ over $\mathcal{F}$*, or an *$\mathcal{F}$-automorphism*.

Theorem 7.54. *If $\mathcal{N}$ is a splitting field of a polynomial $f(x) \in \mathcal{F}[x]$, any isomorphism between subfields of $\mathcal{N}$ over $\mathcal{F}$ can be extended to an $\mathcal{F}$-automorphism of $\mathcal{N}$.*

Proof. For suppose $\mathcal{F} \subset \mathcal{K} \subset \mathcal{N}$ and $\mathcal{F} \subset \mathcal{K}' \subset \mathcal{N}$, where $\mathcal{K}$ and $\mathcal{K}'$ are subfields of $\mathcal{N}$ which are isomorphic over $\mathcal{F}$. The polynomial $f(x)$ may be considered to have coefficients in either $\mathcal{K}$ or $\mathcal{K}'$ and, for notational purposes, let us designate $f^*(x)$ the polynomial whose coefficients in $\mathcal{K}'$ correspond by the isomorphism to those of $f(x)$ in $\mathcal{K}$. Then $\mathcal{N}$ is a splitting field over $\mathcal{K}$ of $f(x)$ as well as a splitting field over $\mathcal{K}'$ of $f^*(x)$, and Theorem 7.53 assures us that the isomorphism between $\mathcal{K}$ and $\mathcal{K}'$ can be extended to an $\mathcal{F}$-automorphism of $\mathcal{N}$ [Problem 16]. ∎

As indicated earlier, the most important result in this section is the Corollary to Theorem 7.53, for this asserts the "essential uniqueness" of the splitting field of a given polynomial.

Example 3. Probably the simplest example of an automorphism of a field $\mathcal{K}$ over a field $\mathcal{F}$ is provided by the field in Example 1. Here we take $\mathcal{K} = \mathbf{Q}(\sqrt{2}), \mathcal{F} = \mathbf{Q}$, and define the automorphism by: $a + b\sqrt{2} \to a - b\sqrt{2}$, for arbitrary rational numbers a, b. Another simple example is provided by taking $\mathcal{K} = \mathbf{C}$, the field of complex numbers, $\mathcal{F} = \mathbf{R}$, the field of real numbers, and define the automorphism by: $a + bi \to a - bi$, for arbitrary real a, b.

If $f(x)$ is an irreducible polynomial of degree n over $\mathcal{F}$, we have noted that the degree over $\mathcal{F}$ of its splitting field cannot exceed $n!$ Various possibilities for degrees are illustrated in the next example.

Example 4.

(a) If we consider the splitting field of $x^3 - 3$ over $\mathbf{Q}$, we see that the degree of this field must be 6. For $\sqrt[3]{3}$ does not generate it, since $\mathbf{Q}(\sqrt[3]{3})$ must contain only real numbers while our elementary theory of equations tells us that the zeros of the given polynomial are not all real: actually, they are $\sqrt[3]{3}$, $\sqrt[3]{3}\omega$, and $\sqrt[3]{3}\omega^2$, where $\omega = (-1 + \sqrt{3}i)/2$. Since $3!$ (or 6) is an upper bound to the degree of the splitting field of $x^3 - 3$, the degree of this field must be exactly 6.

(b) If we consider the splitting field of $x^4 + x^2 + 1$ over $\mathbf{Q}$, we see that its degree cannot exceed 24 (i.e., $4!$). However, it is easy to see that the actual degree is 2. For, if we define ω as in (a) and use De Moivre's theorem to solve the equation $x^4 + x^2 + 1 = 0$, we find rather easily that the four solutions are ω, $-\omega$, $\omega + 1$, and $-(\omega + 1)$. Hence, if $\mathcal{K}$ is the desired splitting field, we see that $\mathcal{K} = \mathbf{Q}(\omega)$, and note that this field has degree 2 over $\mathbf{Q}$ [Problem 17].

PROBLEMS 7–5

*1. Using our definition for a splitting field $\mathcal{K}$ over $\mathcal{F}$, as given in the first paragraph of this section, explain why $\mathcal{K} = \mathcal{F}(k_1, k_2, \ldots, k_n)$.

*2. With reference to Example 1, why is $\mathcal{K}$ a splitting field over $\mathbf{Q}$ of $x^2 - 2$?

*3. Answer the question raised in Example 2.

**4. Find a generator and the degree of the subfield of complex numbers, which is a splitting field over $\mathbf{Q}$ for $x^3 - 8$.

5. Use the directions, given in Problem 4, for the polynomial $x^3 - 4$. (Hint: note that $\mathbf{Q}(\sqrt[3]{4})$ is not a splitting field.)

6. Use the directions given in Problem 4 for the polynomial $x^4 + 2x^3 - x^2 - 8x - 12$. (Hint: note that $x^2 - 4$ is a factor.)

*7. Explain why the stem fields of an irreducible polynomial are all isomorphic over the field of coefficients.

*8. Why is there no loss of generality in assuming, in the proof of Theorem 7.51, that $f(x)$ is irreducible over $\mathcal{F}$ and that $n > 1$?

*9. With reference to the proof of Theorem 7.51, why are the coefficients of $g(x)$ in $\mathcal{F}(k_1)$?

*10. With reference to the last remark in the proof of Theorem 7.51, why is the degree of the splitting field of $f(x)$ at most $n!$; and under what circumstances is it exactly n or less than n?

*11. Why is the mapping, given in the first part of the proof of Theorem 7.52, an isomorphism?

*12. With reference to the proof of Theorem 7.52, explain why $f^*(x)$ is irreducible over $\mathcal{F}$ whenever $f(x)$ is irreducible.

**13. In the proof of Theorem 7.52, explain why the quotient fields are isomorphic.

*14. In the proof of Theorem 7.53, why do the coefficients of $f_2(x)$ and $f_2^*(x)$ correspond according to the mapping defined by the given isomorphism between $\mathcal{F}_1$ and $\mathcal{F}_1'$?

*15. Complete the proof of the Corollary to Theorem 7.53.

*16. Explain the application of Theorem 7.53 to the proof of Theorem 7.54.

*17. With ω defined as in Example 4, explain why $\mathbf{Q}(\omega)$ has degree 2 over $\mathbf{Q}$.

18. Prove the existence of an automorphism *over* $\mathbf{Q}$ of the fields $\mathbf{Q}(\sqrt{\pi})$ and $\mathbf{Q}(\sqrt[3]{\pi})$. Does such an automorphism exist over $\mathbf{Q}(\pi)$ for these fields?

19. Prove that if $\mathcal{F}(a)$ and $\mathcal{F}(b)$ are simple algebraic extensions of a field $\mathcal{F}$, then no automorphism over $\mathcal{F}$ can exist for these fields unless their degrees over $\mathcal{F}$ are equal.

20. Find the subfield of complex numbers which is the splitting field of each of the following real polynomials:

(a) $x^3 - 2x^2 - x + 2$;   (b) $x^3 - 2x^2 + x - 2$;

(c) $x^3 - x^2 - 2x + 2$;   (d) $x^4 - 5x^2 + 6$.

21. Let $f(x) = x^2 + ax + b$ be a polynomial in $\mathcal{F}[x]$, for some field $\mathcal{F}$, while an extension field $\mathcal{K}$ of $\mathcal{F}$ contains a zero r of $f(x)$. Prove that $-(a + r)$ is also a zero in $\mathcal{K}$ of $f(x)$, so that the second zero lies in the same field as the first one selected.

22. Prove, without recourse to the result of Theorem 7.51, that the field $\mathcal{K}$ of Problem 21 has degree at most 2 over $\mathcal{F}$.

23. Show that the polynomials $f(x) = x^2 + x + 1$ and $g(x) = x^2 + 3x + 3$ have the same splitting field. (Hint: consider $g(r - 1)$, with r in an extension field of $\mathcal{F}$.)

24. If p is a rational prime, prove that the splitting field of $x^p - 1$ has degree $p - 1$ over $\mathbf{Q}$.

25. Prove that the identity is the only automorphism over $\mathbf{Q}$ of the field $\mathbf{Q}(\sqrt[3]{2})$.

TOPIC FOR A SPECIAL STUDY

A field $\mathcal{K}$ is said to be *algebraically closed* (or *complete*) if every polynomial in $\mathcal{K}[x]$ splits in $\mathcal{K}$. Try to prove (and, if unsuccessful, look up a proof in some other book!) that an arbitrary field $\mathcal{F}$ has an algebraically closed extension which is unique up to an automorphism over $\mathcal{F}$. (The proof is not elementary, and uses the so-called "Axiom of Choice" or "Zorn's Lemma.") If $\mathcal{F} = \mathbf{Q}$, is the field $\mathbf{C}$ of complex numbers the algebraically closed extension of $\mathbf{Q}$?

7.6. Separability and the Theorem of the Primitive Element

In Example 1 of § 7.4, we noted that the field $\mathbf{Q}(\sqrt{2}, \sqrt{3}, \sqrt{6})$ has degree 4 over $\mathbf{Q}$, rather than 6—as *might* have been expected from the representation given for the field. In this example, then, three algebraic elements of degree 2 over $\mathbf{Q}$ have been adjoined to $\mathbf{Q}$, and the resulting field generated by these elements has degree 4 over $\mathbf{Q}$. But, even more surprisingly, we can show without much difficulty that this field is actually a *simple* extension of $\mathbf{Q}$, and can be generated by a single element such as $\sqrt{3} - \sqrt{2}$ [see Problem 1]. We first note that $\mathbf{Q}(\sqrt{3} - \sqrt{2}) \subset \mathbf{Q}(\sqrt{2}, \sqrt{3})$, since $\sqrt{3} - \sqrt{2} \in \mathbf{Q}(\sqrt{2}, \sqrt{3})$. To show that $\mathbf{Q}(\sqrt{2}, \sqrt{3}) \subset \mathbf{Q}(\sqrt{3} - \sqrt{2})$, we note by actual multiplication that $(\sqrt{3} - \sqrt{2})^3 = 9\sqrt{3} - 11\sqrt{2}$, so that $(\sqrt{3} - \sqrt{2})^3 - 9(\sqrt{3} - \sqrt{2}) = -2\sqrt{2}$, and $\sqrt{2} \in \mathbf{Q}(\sqrt{3} - \sqrt{2})$. Moreover, $\sqrt{3} = (\sqrt{3} - \sqrt{2}) + \sqrt{2}$, and this shows that $\sqrt{3} \in \mathbf{Q}(\sqrt{3} - \sqrt{2})$. The two inclusions, when taken together, now imply that $\mathbf{Q}(\sqrt{2}, \sqrt{3}) = \mathbf{Q}(\sqrt{3} - \sqrt{2})$ which, by Example 1 of § 4, is the field $\mathbf{Q}(\sqrt{2}, \sqrt{3}, \sqrt{6})$.

We can carry the above illustration even further, and determine the minimum polynomial of $\sqrt{3} - \sqrt{2}$ over $\mathbf{Q}$. To accomplish this, we calculate that $(\sqrt{3} - \sqrt{2})^2 = 5 - 2\sqrt{6}$ and $(\sqrt{3} - \sqrt{2})^4 = 49 - 20\sqrt{6}$. But now $(49 - 20\sqrt{6}) - 10(5 - 2\sqrt{6}) = -1$, so that $\sqrt{3} - \sqrt{2}$ is a solution of the equation $x^4 - 10x^2 + 1 = 0$. Inasmuch as $\sqrt{3} - \sqrt{2}$ does generate the field $\mathbf{Q}(\sqrt{2}, \sqrt{3}, \sqrt{6})$ of degree 4 over $\mathbf{Q}$, $x^4 - 10x^2 + 1$ must be the minimum polynomial of the generating element $\sqrt{3} - \sqrt{2}$. That this result is not special but of a rather general nature is the message conveyed by the "Theorem of the Primitive Element," to be proven shortly. Before giving this proof, however, it is desirable to give a brief discussion of "separable" polynomials and their related extension fields.

Definition. For any field $\mathcal{F}$, a polynomial of degree n in $\mathcal{F}[x]$ is said to be *separable* over $\mathcal{F}$ if it has n distinct zeros in its splitting field. A polynomial which is not separable is said to be *inseparable*. An element, which is algebraic over $\mathcal{F}$, is *separable* if its minimum polynomial is separable, while a *separable extension field* of $\mathcal{F}$ is one which contains only separable elements.

For example, the polynomial whose factored form is $(x - 1)(x + 1)(x - 3)$ is separable over **Q**, while $(x - 1)^2(x + 2)$ is inseparable over **Q**. Of course, the characteristic of a general field $\mathcal{F}$ may be 0 or some prime p, and it is usually necessary to treat these two cases separately. Most of our interest will be in the nonmodular or "characteristic 0" case.

There is a very simple criterion for testing the separability of a polynomial, and we give it as a theorem.

Theorem 7.61. *An irreducible polynomial $f(x)$ in $\mathcal{F}[x]$, for any field $\mathcal{F}$, is separable if and only if $f(x)$ and its derivative $f'(x)$ are relatively prime.*

Proof. Let $d(x)$ be the g.c.d. of $f(x)$ and $f'(x)$.

(a) If $d(x) = 1$, and a is a zero of $f(x)$ in some splitting field, then $f(x) = (x - a)^m g(x)$ and $f'(x) = m(x - a)^{m-1}g(x) + (x - a)^m g'(x)$, where m is the largest power of $x - a$ contained in $f(x)$, and $g(x)$ is defined by the equation in which it occurs. (In what field do the coefficients of $g(x)$ lie? [Problem 4]) It then follows that $(x - a)^{m-1}$ divides both $f(x)$ and $f'(x)$ and hence $d(x)$, which is 1 by our assumption. Hence $m = 1$, and since a was an arbitrary zero of $f(x)$, we have shown that all zeros of $f(x)$ are simple (i.e., each occurs only once) and so $f(x)$ is separable.

(b) For the converse, we assume that $f(x)$ is separable and prove that $d(x)$, the g.c.d. of $f(x)$ and $f'(x)$, is 1. The proof of this simple proposition is left to the student [Problem 5]. ∎

While the above criterion for separability is theoretically simple, it does involve the computation of the g.c.d. of two polynomials. The following consequence of the theorem is much more easily applied.

Corollary 1. *A nonconstant irreducible polynomial $f(x) \in \mathcal{F}[x]$, for any field $\mathcal{F}$, is separable if and only if $f'(x)$ is not identically zero.*

Proof. By our assumption, the only divisors in $\mathcal{F}[x]$ of $f(x)$ are $f(x)$ itself and elements of $\mathcal{F}$. If $f'(x) \not\equiv 0$, the g.c.d. of $f(x)$ and $f'(x)$ must be 1 [Problem 7]. On the other hand, if the g.c.d. of $f(x)$ and $f'(x)$ is 1, it must be the case that $f'(x) \not\equiv 0$ [Problem 8]. The desired conclusion now follows from the theorem. ∎

For the most common case, in which the characteristic of $\mathcal{F}$ is 0, we have the following very simple but very important result.

Corollary 2. *Any nonconstant irreducible polynomial $f(x) \in \mathcal{F}[x]$, where $\mathcal{F}$ has characteristic 0, is separable.*

Proof. Let us suppose that $f(x)$ has degree n, so that we can express $f(x)$ in the form $f(x) = a_0 + a_1 x + a_2 x^2 + \cdots + a_{n-1} x^{n-1} + x^n$. Then $f'(x) = a_1 + 2a_2 x + \cdots + (n-1)a_{n-1} x^{n-2} + nx^{n-1}$. We have assumed, without loss of generality [Problem 9], that the coefficient of x^n in $f(x)$ is 1; and since the characteristic of $\mathcal{F}$ is 0, we know that $n = n(1) \neq 0$, for any $n > 0$. But then $f'(x) \neq 0$, and the conclusion follows from Corollary 1. ∎

Corollary 3. *If k is any element which is algebraic over a field $\mathcal{F}$ of characteristic 0, the minimum polynomial of k is separable.*

Proof. We leave this elementary proof to the student [Problem 10].

Corollary 4. *Any finite extension of a field of characteristic 0 is separable.*

Proof. We leave this proof to the student [Problem 11].

It is also possible to use Corollary 1 to obtain useful criteria for the separability of polynomials in $\mathcal{F}[x]$, where $\mathcal{F}$ has characteristic p. We leave the determination of this result to the student, and refer him to Problem 17.

We are now able to proceed to the principal result of this section which is that all finite extensions of a field of characteristic 0 are simple. Our initial statement, from which the deduction is made, has a somewhat less general form.

Theorem 7.62. *If $\mathcal{F}$ is a field of characteristic 0, with a_1, b_1 elements which are algebraic over $\mathcal{F}$, then $\mathcal{F}(a_1, b_1) = \mathcal{F}(c)$, for some element $c \in \mathcal{F}(a_1, b_1)$.*

Proof. Let $f(x)$ and $g(x)$ be the respective minimum polynomials of a_1 and b_1, where the degree of $f(x)$ is m and that of $g(x)$ is n over $\mathcal{F}$. By the results of the preceding section, we may assume the existence of a field $\mathcal{K}$ in which both polynomials split completely. Moreover, since the characteristic of $\mathcal{F}$ is 0, we may use Corollary 2 above to assert that the zeros of $f(x)$ as well as those of $g(x)$ are distinct. Let us write these zeros as $a_1, a_2, \ldots, a_m$ and $b_1, b_2, \ldots, b_n$, for $f(x)$ and $g(x)$, respectively, and for convenience write $a_1 = a$ and $b_1 = b$. If we consider the equation $a_i + \lambda b_j = a + \lambda b$, for each $i = 2, 3, \ldots, m$, and $j = 2, 3, \ldots, n$ we can solve it uniquely for λ and obtain $\lambda = (a_i - a)/(b - b_j)$, with $b - b_j \neq 0$. (Why? [Problem 12]) Since $\mathcal{F}$ has characteristic 0, it contains infinitely many elements and so we can choose an element $\alpha \in \mathcal{F}$ so that $a_i + \alpha b_j \neq a + \alpha b$, for $i = 2, 3, \ldots, m$ and $j = 2, 3, \ldots, n$. We now let $c = a + \alpha b$ and assert that $\mathcal{F}(a, b) = \mathcal{F}(c)$. It is immediate that $c \in \mathcal{F}(a, b)$, so that $\mathcal{F}(c) \subset \mathcal{F}(a, b)$, and the burden of our proof is to show that a and b are in $\mathcal{F}(c)$.

Since b is a zero of $g(x)$ over $\mathcal{F}$, it is also a zero of $g(x)$ where this polynomial is considered to have coefficients in $\mathcal{F}(c)$ [Problem 13]. We shall designate $\mathcal{F}(c)$ by $\mathcal{K}$ and consider the ring of polynomials $\mathcal{K}[x]$, a ring which contains both $g(x)$ and $h(x) = f(c - \alpha x)$. In addition, we know that $g(b) = 0$ and also $h(b) = f(c - \alpha b) = f(a) = 0$, so that b is a common zero of $g(x)$ and $h(x)$ in some extension field of $\mathcal{K}$. The ring $\mathcal{K}[x]$ is Euclidean, and so the polynomials $g(x)$ and $h(x)$ have a g.c.d. in $\mathcal{K}[x]$: we shall show that this g.c.d. is $x - b$. We know by the Factor theorem that $x - b$ is a common factor, and let us suppose that $x - b_j (j \neq 1)$ is another common factor. But then $h(b_j) = f(c - \alpha b_j) = 0$, which is contradiction to our choice of α [Problem 14], so that b is the only zero which $g(x)$ and $h(x)$ have in common. Since $(x - b)^2$ does not divide $g(x)$, it is not possible for the g.c.d. of $g(x)$ and $h(x)$ to be $(x - b)^2$, and so $x - b$ must be the g.c.d. of these polynomials over some extension field of $\mathcal{K}$. It follows that $g(x)$ and $h(x)$ must have a g.c.d. over $\mathcal{K}$, which must divide $x - b$; and since $x - b$ has degree 1 over $\mathcal{K}$, while $g(x)$ and $h(x)$ are not relatively prime, their g.c.d. is $x - b$, as asserted.

Hence $x - b \in \mathcal{K}[x]$, so that $b \in \mathcal{K} = \mathcal{F}(c)$. Since $a = c - \alpha b$, while $b, c \in \mathcal{F}[c]$ and $\alpha \in \mathcal{F}$, it follows that $a \in \mathcal{F}(c)$, whence $\mathcal{F}(a, b) \subset \mathcal{F}(c)$. If we now combine this set-inclusion with the one in the preceding paragraph, we obtain $\mathcal{F}(a, b) = \mathcal{F}(c)$, as desired. ∎

Corollary (*Theorem of the Primitive Element*). *Any finite extension of a field $\mathcal{F}$ of characteristic 0 is simple.*

Proof. We leave to the student the problem of extending the argument for two algebraic elements adjoined to $\mathcal{F}$ to the case when any finite number of such elements are adjoined [Problem 15].

For a generalization of Theorem 7.62, we refer the student to Problem 16.

PROBLEMS 7–6

*1. Try to find an element, different from $\sqrt{3} - \sqrt{2}$, which will generate $\mathbf{Q}(\sqrt{2}, \sqrt{3}, \sqrt{6})$.

**2. Without using Theorem 7.61 or its corollaries, decide which of the following polynomials are separable over $\mathbf{Q}$: (a) $x^2 - 5x + 6$; (b) $x^2 - 2x + 1$; (c) $x^3 + 3x^2 - x + 3$; (d) $x^3 + 2x^2 - 11x - 12$.

3. Use Theorem 7.61 directly (and not Corollary 2) to decide which of the following polynomials in $\mathbf{Q}[x]$ are separable over $\mathbf{Q}$: (a) $x^2 + x + 1$; (b) $x^3 + x + 1$; (c) $x^4 - x^2 + 2x - 1$; (d) $x^3 + 2x^2 - 3x + 2$.

*4. Answer the question raised in (a) of the proof of Theorem 7.61.

*5. Prove (b) of Theorem 7.61.

6. Explain what is meant by a polynomial being "identically zero" [cf. Corollary 1 of Theorem 7.61].

*7. If $f(x)$ is an irreducible polynomial of $\mathscr{F}[x]$, explain why $f'(x) \not\equiv 0$ implies that the g.c.d. of $f(x)$ and $f'(x)$ is 1.

*8. In the proof of Corollary 1 of Theorem 7.61, why does $f'(x) \not\equiv 0$ follow from the tentative assumption that the g.c.d. of $f(x)$ and $f'(x)$ is 1?

9. If a polynomial in $\mathscr{F}[x]$ is irreducible, why is it permissible in the proof of Corollary 2 of Theorem 7.61, to assume that its leading coefficient is 1?

*10. Give the proof of Corollary 3 of Theorem 7.61.

**11. Prove Corollary 4 of Theorem 7.61.

*12. In the proof of Theorem 7.62, explain why $b - b_j \neq 0$.

*13. If $\mathscr{K}$ is an extension field of $\mathscr{F}$, and b is a zero of some polynomial $f(x) \in \mathscr{F}[x]$, why is b also a zero of $f(x)$ when this polynomial is considered to lie in $\mathscr{K}[x]$? Are there any possible differences in $f(x)$, for the two cases?

*14. In the proof of Theorem 7.62, explain why $h(b_j) = 0$ contradicts our choice of α.

*15. Prove the Corollary to Theorem 7.62.

16. Instead of assuming the characteristic of $\mathscr{F}$ to be 0 in the statement of Theorem 7.62, it is possible to prove that $\mathscr{F}(a_1, b_1)$ is a simple extension of $\mathscr{F}$ by assuming merely that $\mathscr{F}$ is infinite and that one of a_1, b_1 (say b_1) is separable. Give the proof.

17. Use Theorem 7.61 and prove that, if $\mathscr{F}$ has characteristic p, then a polynomial $f(x) \in \mathscr{F}[x]$ is inseparable if and only if $f(x) = g(x^p)$, for some polynomial $g(x) \in \mathscr{F}(x)$.

18. Use Problem 16 to prove that any finite separable extension of a field $\mathscr{F}$ is simple.

19. Use the result of Problem 17 to show that $x^6 - 2ax^3 + a$ is inseparable over $\mathbf{Z}_3(a)$, with a in any extension field of $\mathbf{Z}_3$.

20. Find a single generator over $\mathbf{R}$ for the field $\mathbf{R}(a, b)$, where a is a zero of $x^2 + 1$ and b is a zero of $x^2 + x + 1$.

21. Find a generator over $\mathbf{Q}$ for the field $\mathbf{Q}(\sqrt{2}, \sqrt{8})$, and determine the minimum polynomial for this element.

22. Find a single generator over $\mathbf{Q}$ for the field $\mathbf{Q}(i, \sqrt{2})$, and determine the minimum polynomial of this element.

23. Find a single generator over $\mathbf{Q}$ for the field $\mathbf{Q}(\sqrt{2}, \omega)$, where $\omega = (-1 + \sqrt{3}i)/2$ is a so-called "primitive" cube root of unity.

24. Prove that any (reducible *or* irreducible) polynomial $f(x) \in \mathscr{F}[x]$, for any field $\mathscr{F}$, is separable if the g.c.d. of $f(x)$ and $f'(x)$ is 1.

7.7. Irreducibility in $\mathscr{F}[x]$

One of the notions that has kept recurring from time to time during our discussions in this chapter has been that of the *reducibility* and *irreducibility* of polynomials whose coefficients lie in some given field $\mathscr{F}$. While the *idea* is an elementary one, the problem of deciding whether a given polynomial (x) in $\mathcal{F}[x]$ is reducible or not is, in general, somewhat difficult; and we refer the reader, who is interested in a general treatment, to the first German edition of *Moderne Algebra* by van der Waerden. Since any nonzero element of a field $\mathcal{F}$ is a unit, any reasonable discussion of irreducibility of polynomials in $\mathcal{F}[x]$ must exclude elements of $\mathcal{F}$ as factors [Problem 1]. In the present section, we shall limit our discussion quite drastically, and consider for the most part the case where $\mathcal{F} = \mathbf{Q}$ is the field of rational numbers. For this case, $\mathbf{Q}$ is the field of quotients of the integral domain $\mathbf{Z}$ of rational integers, and it is easy to see that any question of the reducibility of a polynomial in $\mathbf{Q}[x]$ can be reduced [Problem 2] to one where the polynomial is considered to belong to $\mathbf{Z}[x]$. In fact, we can go even further and confine ourselves to primitive polynomials as defined in § 5.7.

The two properties of $\mathbf{Z}$ which are most useful for the present discussion are the presence in $\mathbf{Z}$ of only two units, 1 and -1, and the fact that $\mathbf{Z}$ is a Gaussian domain—so that its elements have an essentially-unique factorization. It will be these two properties which we shall use later to obtain a slight generalization of the early results in this section.

In the familiar case of polynomials in $\mathbf{Z}[x]$, we have available one very simple criterion, which, unfortunately, does not always give results.

Theorem 7.71 (Eisenstein Criterion). *Let* $f(x) = a_0 + a_1 x + a_2 x^2 + \cdots + a_n x^n$ *be a polynomial in* $\mathbf{Z}[x]$. *Then* $f(x)$ *is irreducible in* $\mathbf{Z}$ *if there exists a prime* p *such that* p *divides* a_i, *for* $i < n$, p *does not divide* a_n, *and* p^2 *does not divide* a_0.

Proof. Our proof will be "by contradiction," and so let us assume that $f(x) = g(x)h(x)$ is reducible, where $g(x) = b_0 + b_1 x + \cdots + b_r x^r$ and $h(x) = c_0 + c_1 x + \cdots + c_{n-r} x^{n-r}$, with $0 < r < n$. Since $a_0 = b_0 c_0$, and a_0 is divisible by p, whereas only one of b_0, c_0 is divisible by p, let us assume that p divides b_0. In the notation of congruences, this means that $b_0 \equiv 0$ (mod p), $c_0 \not\equiv 0$ (mod p). Not all coefficients of $g(x)$ can be divisible by p, for otherwise the polynomial $f(x)$—and in particular the coefficient a_n— would be divisible by p, contrary to assumption. So let us assume that b_k is the coefficient of lowest index in $g(x)$ not divisible by p, i.e., $b_k \not\equiv 0$ (mod p), while $b_t \equiv 0$ (mod p) for $0 \le t < k < r$. But then $a_k = b_k c_0 + b_{k-1} c_1 + \cdots + b_0 c_k$ is divisible by p, and since we know that p divides $b_{k-1}, b_{k-2}, \ldots, b_0$, we are forced to conclude that p divides $b_k c_0$. Since p does not divide c_0 [Problem 4], and p does not divide b_k, this conclusion is untenable and we have reached a contradiction. Hence $f(x)$, as a polynomial of $\mathbf{Z}[x]$, is irreducible. ∎

Example 1. The polynomial $x^2 - 8x + 6$ is irreducible in $\mathbf{Z}[x]$. For, if we apply the Eisenstein criterion with $p = 2$, we note that p does divide the coefficients 6 and -8 but not the leading coefficient 1, while p^2 (i.e., 4) does not divide the "constant" term 6.

Example 2. The polynomial $4x^4 - 6x^3 + 3x - 12$ is irreducible in $\mathbf{Z}[x]$. For, if we take $p = 3$ and apply the Eisenstein criterion, we find easily that all the requirements for irreducibility are fulfilled [Problem 5].

We have remarked earlier that the Eisenstein criterion, while always valid, may not always give us a definitive answer on matters of irreducibility. For example, let us consider the "cyclotomic" polynomial $x^{p-1} + x^{p-2} + \cdots + x + 1$, which can be expressed in the rational form $(x^p - 1)/(x - 1)$, where p is an arbitrary prime integer. The Eisenstein criterion gives us no information on this polynomial, because no suitable prime p is available; but it is easy to overcome the difficulty in this case. For any polynomial $f(x) \in Q[x]$ is irreducible if and only if $f(x - c)$ is irreducible, for any $c \in \mathbf{Q}$ [Problem 8]. If we now regard $f(x)$ as the cyclotomic polynomial, defined above, it is easy to apply the Eisenstein criterion to show that $f(x + 1)$ is irreducible over $\mathbf{Q}$ [Problem 9]. Hence $f(x)$, as a polynomial in $\mathbf{Z}[x]$, is also irreducible.

If the coefficients of a polynomial in $\mathbf{Z}[x]$ are considered to lie in $\mathbf{Z}_n$, the polynomial will often assume a simplified form and we say that it has been "reduced modulo n." Moreover, if it happens that the reduced forms of two polynomials $f(x)$ and $g(x)$ in $\mathbf{Z}[x]$ are identical, it is convenient to speak of them as "congruent mod n" and write $f(x) \equiv g(x) \pmod{n}$. The validity of the Eisenstein criterion rests on the fact that any factorization of $f(x)$, when reduced mod p^2, becomes absurd [Problem 11]. This result can be generalized to any Gaussian domain: if $f(x)$ is any reducible polynomial in $\mathfrak{D}[x]$, for any Gaussian domain $\mathfrak{D}$, then $f(x)$ is also reducible mod q, for any $q \in \mathfrak{D}$. An application of this observation sometimes leads to a mere checking of a finite number of possible factors, and a definitive answer may then be given to questions of irreducibility.

Example 3. Let us consider the polynomial $x^5 - x^2 + 1$ in $\mathbf{Z}[x]$ for reducibility, and to do this we examine its reducibility mod 2. If there are any factors of the polynomial, at least one must be linear or quadratic [Problem 13]. The only possible linear factors mod 2 are x and $x + 1$ [Problem 14], while the only irreducible quadratic one is $x^2 + x + 1$ [Problem 15]. We may now check each of these possible factors by actual division, or else note that $x^5 - x^2 + 1 = x^2(x - 1)(x^2 + x + 1) + 1$ and see that none of the above factor candidates can divide the given polynomial. Hence it is irreducible in $\mathbf{Z}_2[x]$, and hence also as a polynomial in $\mathbf{Z}[x]$.

In connection with the discussion immediately preceding, we add one note of caution: it is possible for a polynomial $f(x)$ to be reducible mod q, for some special integer q, while the polynomial remains irreducible if its coefficients are *not* reduced modulo q. For example, if we consider $f(x) = x^2 + x + 2$ in $Z[x]$, we see easily that $f(x) \equiv x(x + 1)$ (mod 2), whereas $f(x)$ is irreducible in $Z[x]$ [Problem 6(d)].

There is another method, due to Kronecker, which can be used for testing the reducibility of a polynomial in $Z[x]$, although the method is a bit clumsy in its application. It depends, basically, on the well-known fact that if two polynomials of degree n in $Z[x]$ assume equal values for n or more real numbers x, they must be identical—except possibly for integral factors. There is no loss in generality in assuming the polynomial to be monic, and if $f(x) = g(x)h(x)$ for polynomials $g(x)$ and $h(x)$, then also $f(c) = g(c)h(c)$, for any real number c. In our search for a polynomial factor of $f(x)$, where $f(x)$ has degree n, it is clear that we may investigate only those "candidate polynomials" whose degrees do not exceed $n/2$: for if $f(x)$ has a factor whose degree exceeds $n/2$, it must also have a factor whose degree is less than $n/2$. If m is the largest integer not exceeding $n/2$, and we pick $m + 1$ distinct numbers c, both $g(c)$ and $h(c)$ must be integral divisors of $f(c)$. Since $f(c)$ has only a finite number of such divisors, the process for determining $g(x)$ and $h(x)$ is finite—though not necessarily short! We illustrate the process with an example.

Example 4. Use the Kronecker method to verify that $x^4 - 3x + 1$ is irreducible in $Z[x]$.

Proof. Let us denote $x^4 - 3x + 1$ by $f(x)$, and suppose that $f(x) = g(x)h(x)$ for polynomials $g(x)$ and $h(x)$ in $Z[x]$. Using the method of Kronecker, with $m = 2$, we can select 3 arbitrary integers for c, and we choose -1, 0, 1. Then $f(-1) = 5$, $f(0) = 1$, and $f(1) = -1$, so that $g(-1)$ must be an integral divisor of 5, $g(0)$ must be an integral divisor of 1, while $g(1)$ must be an integral divisor of -1. If we note that $-g(x)$ is a factor of $f(x)$ whenever $g(x)$ is, we see that the following triplets give, in order, what are essentially the only possibilities for $g(-1)$, $g(0)$, and $g(1)$: $(5, 1, 1)$, $(5, -1, -1)$, $(5, 1, -1)$, $(5, -1, 1)$, $(1, 1, 1)$, $(1, -1, -1)$, $(1, 1, -1)$, $(1, -1, 1)$. Without loss of generality, we may assume that any factor of $f(x)$ is monic, and either linear or quadratic, and so let us suppose that $g(x) = x^2 + bx + c$. If we examine each case separately, for a determination of b and c, we find that the only possibility for $g(x)$ turns out to be $x^2 - 3x + 1$ [Problem 16]. However, a simple check shows that this is not a factor of $f(x)$, and so we conclude that the given polynomial is irreducible. ∎

It is not difficult to extend the Kronecker method to polynomials $f(x)$ in a ring $\mathcal{F}[x]$, provided $\mathcal{F}$ is the field of quotients of an integral domain which is Gaussian and has only a finite number of units. Part of the simplicity of Example 4 was due to the fact that the Gaussian domain Z has only the two units 1 and -1. As a final remark on this Kronecker method, we may add that if a polynomial $g(x)$, under consideration as a factor of $f(x)$, has degree m, it is sometimes convenient to take more than $m + 1$ numbers c in the integral domain, and use them as above to consider the various possible factors $g(c)$ which divide $f(c)$.

PROBLEMS 7–7

*1. Why is it reasonable to exclude elements of $\mathcal{F}$ as factors of a polynomial $f(x) \in \mathcal{F}[x]$, if the reducibility of $f(x)$ is being considered?

*2. Explain why the question of the reducibility of a polynomial in $Q[x]$ can be reduced to a similar question for a polynomial in $Z[x]$. If $\mathcal{F}$ is the quotient field of an integral domain $\mathcal{D}$, does the same situation prevail with respect to polynomials in $\mathcal{F}[x]$ and $\mathcal{D}[x]$?

3. Reduce each of the following to a primitive polynomial, by dividing the given polynomial by a suitable integer:

(a) $2x^3 + 4x + 8$; (b) $12x^2 - 4x + 24$; (c) $4x^3 - 12x^2 + 24x + 12$.

*4. In the proof of Theorem 7.11, explain the remark that p does not divide c_0.

*5. Apply the Eisenstein criterion to the polynomial given in Example 2.

6. Use the Eisenstein criterion to attempt to decide the reducibility of each of the following polynomials in $Z[x]$:

(a) $3x^3 + 4x^2 + 2x + 2$;   (b) $x^4 - 3x^2 + 9x + 9$;

(c) $x^4 - 3x^2 + 9x + 3$;   (d) $x^2 + x + 2$.

7. If p is any prime integer, prove that $x^n - p$ is irreducible in $Z[x]$.

*8. Prove that a polynomial $f(x) \in \mathcal{F}[x]$, for any field $\mathcal{F}$, is irreducible if and only if $f(x - c)$ is irreducible for any $c \in \mathcal{F}$.

*9. If $f(x)$ is the cyclotomic polynomial in $Z[x]$, use the Eisenstein criterion to show that $f(x + 1)$ is irreducible.

10. Use a transformation followed by the Eisenstein criterion to show that $x^2 + 1$ is irreducible in $Z[x]$.

*11. Explain why the congruence $f(x) \equiv g(x)h(x) \pmod{p^2}$ is an absurdity under the conditions cited in the Eisenstein criterion.

12. If $f(x) = x^5 - 4x^4 + 3x^2 - 2x + 1$, determine $f(x)$ reduced modulo 2.

*13. Explain why at least one of the factors of the polynomial in Example 3 must be either linear or quadratic.

14. Why are x and $x + 1$ the only linear polynomials in $Z[x]$ which ensue when the polynomials in this ring are reduced modulo 2?

15. In $Z[x]$, reduced modulo 2, why is $x^2 + x + 1$ the only irreducible quadratic polynomial?

**16. With reference to Example 4, verify that the only possible polynomial $g(x)$ is $x^2 - 3x + 1$.

17. Apply the Kronecker method, with 3 real numbers, to test the reducibility in $Z[x]$ of the polynomials: (a) $x^4 + 2x + 8$; (b) $x^5 - x - 5$.

18. Apply the Kronecker method with 4 real numbers (say, $-1, 0, 1, 2$) to test the reducibility in $Z[x]$ of the polynomials in Problem 17.

19. Show that the polynomial $x^4 + 3x^3 - 2x^2 - x - 3$ reduces, modulo 2, into $(x + 1)^2(x^2 + x + 1)$, and then use the Factor Theorem to show that a linear factor does not exist for the given polynomial as an element of $Z[x]$.

**20. Prove the following "Gauss Lemma": The product of any two primitive polynomials in $Z[x]$ is also primitive.

21. If p is a prime integer, and $a \in \mathcal{F}$, for any field $\mathcal{F}$ of characteristic 0, show that the reducibility of $f(x) = x^p - a$ in $\mathcal{F}[x]$ implies that $f(x)$ has a zero in $\mathcal{F}$, by giving the following sequence of proofs:

    (a) If c is a zero of $f(x)$, the complete set of zeros is $\{\omega_1 c, \omega_2 c, \ldots, \omega_p c\}$, where $\omega_1 = 1$ and $\omega_i^p = 1$, for $i = 1, 2, \ldots, p$.

    (b) Assume $f(x) = g(x)h(x)$, for nontrivial polynomials $g(x)$ and $h(x)$. Then if r is the degree of $g(x)$, show that the constant term in $g(x)$ has the form $(-1)^r b$, for some element $b \in \mathcal{F}$, and that the product of the zeros of $g(x)$ has the form $c^r \omega$, where $\omega^p = 1$.

    (c) Use the fact that r and p are relatively prime (so that $r\lambda + p\mu = 1$, for $\lambda, \mu \in \mathcal{F}$) to show that $c = (a^\mu b^\lambda)^p$, whence $a^\mu b^\lambda \in \mathcal{F}$ is a zero of $f(x)$.

22. Prove the "characteristic p" case of Problem 21, recalling that under these circumstances, $(x - c)^p = x^p - c^p = x^p - a$, for a zero c of $f(x)$.

23. If the field $\mathcal{F}$ has characteristic p, and $a \in \mathcal{F}$, prove that the reducibility of $f(x) = x^p - x - a$ in $\mathcal{F}[x]$ implies the existence of a zero of $f(x)$ in $\mathcal{F}$, using the following plan of proof:

    (a) If c is a zero of $f(x)$ in some field containing $\mathcal{F}$, use Fermat's theorem ($b^p \equiv b \pmod p$, for any integer b and prime p) to show that the complete set of zeros of $f(x)$ in the given field extension is $\{c, c + 1, c + 2, \ldots, c + p - 1\}$.

    (b) Assume that $f(x) = g(x)h(x)$, for nontrivial polynomials $g(x)$ and $h(x)$, with t the degree of $g(x)$. The sum of the zeros of $g(x)$ is an element $b \in \mathcal{F}$, where $b = tc + s$, $s \in Z$. Then, since $t < p$, $t^{-1} \in \mathcal{F}$; and show that $c = (b - s)t^{-1} \in \mathcal{F}$.

24. Use an example to show that the statement in Problem 23 is false if the characteristic of $\mathcal{F}$ is 0.

25. If $a \in \mathcal{F}$, where $\mathcal{F}$ has characteristic p, prove that $x^p - x - a$ is always separable.

7.8. Finite Fields

While the familiar fields of analysis—the fields of rational, real, and complex numbers—all have infinitely many elements, we have also seen examples of finite fields in the fields Z_p of integers modulo any prime integer p. This is not the only type of finite field, however, and it is our intention to make a very brief study of finite fields in general, when we shall see that they are very numerous. The mathematical theory of finite fields is of interest in itself, but the results also have useful applications in the theory of digital computers and other devices of automation in which binary digits are used.

If a field $\mathscr{F}$ is finite, its characteristic must be a prime number p [see Problem 1], and so must contain an isomorphic image of Z_p as its prime subfield. Hence $\mathscr{F}$ can be considered to be a field of some degree n over Z_p [see Problem 2]. We shall use the symbol $\mathscr{F}_q$ to designate a finite field with q elements, and our first theorem gives us information on the relation existing between q and the characteristic p of $\mathscr{F}_q$.

Theorem 7.81. *If $n = [\mathscr{F}_q : Z_p]$, then $q = p^n$.*

Proof. The integer n designates, of course, the number of elements in a basis of the field $\mathscr{F}_q$ over Z_p, and so every element of $\mathscr{F}_q$ is a unique linear combination of these n basis elements. The coefficients are in Z_p and, since there are p choices for each coefficient, there must be exactly p^n elements in $\mathscr{F}_q$. That is, $q = p^n$. ∎

A finite field with p^n elements is sometimes called a "Galois field" and designated $GF(p^n)$. It is a well-known fact that the nonzero elements of any field constitute a multiplicative group. Our next result shows that, in the finite case, this group has a very simple description—for it is cyclic.

Theorem 7.82. *The multiplicative group $\mathscr{F}_q^*$ of nonzero elements of $\mathscr{F}_q$, where $q = p^n$, is cyclic of order $q - 1$. Moreover, each element of the field is a solution of the equation $x^q - x = 0$.*

Proof. Since the field $\mathscr{F}_q$ has q elements, one of which must be the zero, there must be $q - 1$ nonzero elements in this field. Each of these elements will generate a cyclic subgroup of $\mathscr{F}_q^*$ and, by Lagrange's Theorem, must have an order which divides $q - 1$. Hence, if $k \in \mathscr{F}_q^*$, $k^{q-1} = 1$, and so k is a solution of $x^q - x = 0$. If t is the "exponent" of $\mathscr{F}_q^*$ (i.e., t is the largest order of any element in the field), it follows that each element of $\mathscr{F}_q^*$ is a solution of $x^t - 1 = 0$ [see Problem 31 of §4.12]. But this equation has at most t solutions in $\mathscr{F}_q$, whereas $x^t - 1 = 0$ has $q - 1$ distinct solutions in this field. Hence, $t \leq q - 1 \leq t$, so that $t = q - 1$, and this implies that $\mathscr{F}_q^*$ is cyclic of order $q - 1$ [Problem 3]. ∎

The multiplicity of finite fields is indicated by the following theorem.

Theorem 7.83. *For any prime number p and positive integer n, there exists a field $\mathscr{F}_q$ of degree n over Z_p, where $q = p^n$, the elements of $\mathscr{F}_q$ being the zeros of $x^q - x$ over Z_p.*

Proof. Let $\mathcal{K}$ be the splitting field of $f(x) = x^q - x$ over $\mathbf{Z}_p$, with r one of the zeros of $f(x)$ in $\mathcal{K}$. Then $x^q - x = (x - r)^k g(x)$, for some positive integer k, and where $g(x)$ is a polynomial in $\mathcal{K}[x]$ not divisible by $x - r$. Then $f'(x) = (x - r)^k g'(x) + k(x - r)^{k-1} g(x)$ is divisible by $(x - r)^{k-1}$, while $f'(x) = -1$ [Problem 4]. Hence, $k = 1$ and so r is a simple zero of $f(x)$. Since r was arbitrarily chosen, we have shown that all the zeros of $f(x)$ are distinct, and there are p^n of them in $\mathcal{K}$. It is quite elementary to prove [Problem 5] that the set of zeros of $f(x)$ in $\mathcal{K}$ constitute a subfield of $\mathcal{K}$ of p^n elements. This subfield must then coincide with $\mathcal{K}$ and be of degree n over $\mathbf{Z}_p$, thereby completing the proof. That this field is essentially unique is the statement in Problem 22 below. ∎

We have seen in Chapter 5 [Theorem 5.33], using a proof which was quite elementary, that any finite integral domain is a field. It is then somewhat natural to conjecture that possibly some other finite algebraic system might also be a field—if we relax one or more of the other usual "field" requirements. That this is, in fact, true is the statement of the famous theorem, due originally to Wedderburn, that all finite division rings are fields. The proof which we shall give is due to Witt, but we probably should warn the reader that all known proofs of this theorem are of a much higher order of difficulty than that of Theorem 5.33. Before giving the main proof (*which the student possibly should omit in a minimal course*), we need a brief digression to discuss "primitive roots of unity" and "cyclotomic polynomials", recalling, however, that both have been referred to earlier.

Definition. If $\mathcal{F}$ is any field, any zero of the polynomial $x^n - 1$ in $\mathcal{F}[x]$ is called an *n*th *root of unity*. If α is any *n*th root of unity, the *order* of α is the smallest positive integer m such that $\alpha^m = 1$, and it may be the case that $m \neq n$. If $m = n$, however, α is then called a *primitive* *n*th root of unity.

We know that any polynomial, and in particular $f(x) = x^n - 1$, has a splitting field; and a proof similar to that given in Theorem 7.83 above shows [Problem 6] that $f(x)$ has n distinct zeros $\alpha_1, \alpha_2, \ldots, \alpha_n$ in a splitting field $\mathcal{K}$ of $f(x)$ over $\mathcal{F}$, provided the characteristic p of $\mathcal{F}$ does not divide n. For the proof of the Wedderburn theorem, we are to be interested in the equation $x^n - 1$ as a polynomial in $\mathbf{Q}[x]$, and we are then able to assert that the field $\mathbf{C}$ of complex numbers splits this polynomial so that $x^n - 1 = (x - \alpha_1)(x - \alpha_2) \cdots (x - \alpha_n)$, where each α_i, $i = 1, 2, \ldots, n$, is a complex *n*th root of unity. These complex *n*th roots of unity are familiar to the student of college algebra, where De Moivre's theorem is available for their determination. The number $\alpha = \cos(2\pi/n) + i \sin(2\pi/n)$ is a primitive *n*th root of unity, and this implies that such a number generates the complete set of roots. We have seen in § 4.2 that this set is a multiplicative group which is then clearly cyclic [Problem 7], with any one of the primitive roots as a generator. Of course, for a given n, some of the complex nth roots of unity are primitive and some are not. For example, if we are considering the complex 4th roots of unity, we see that 1 and -1 are not primitive, whereas $\cos(\pi/2) + i \sin(\pi/2) = i$ and $\cos(\pi/2) - i \sin(\pi/2) = -i$ are primitive. Either of these latter two numbers would then generate the multiplicative group of complex 4th roots of unity.

Definition. If $\{\alpha_1, \alpha_2, \ldots, \alpha_m\}$ is the complete set of primitive complex nth roots of unity, then $\phi_n(x) = \prod_{i=1}^{m} (x - \alpha_i)$ is a polynomial called the *nth cyclotomic polynomial* in $\mathbf{C}[x]$.

As examples of cyclotomic polynomials, we may cite the following: $\phi_1(x) = x - 1$, $\phi_2(x) = x + 1$, $\phi_3(x) = x^2 + x + 1$, $\phi_4(x) = x^2 + 1$, $\phi_5(x) = x^4 + x^3 + x^2 + x + 1$, etc. In the preceding section, we gave brief consideration to a polynomial which we referred to as "cyclotomic"—but without further discussion of its properties except that it was irreducible. We note that all the coefficients of these polynomials *appear* to be integers, and the following lemma establishes this to be the case in general.

Lemma 1. *The nth cyclotomic polynomial $\phi_n(x)$ is a monic divisor in $\mathbf{Z}[x]$ of $x^n - 1$.*

Proof. In the symbolism of the above definition, each α_i is a primitive dth root of unity, for exactly one divisor d of n; and, if we collect the linear factors of $x^n - 1$ to form $\phi_n(x)$ and $\phi_d(x)$, for each *proper* divisor d of n, we can write $x^n - 1 = \phi_n(x) \prod_d \phi_d(x)$. It is then clear that $\phi_n(x)$ divides $x^n - 1$, and we use induction on n to prove that $\phi_n(x)$ is monic with integral coefficients. If $n = 1$, $\phi_1(x) = x - 1$, and the assertion is true. Our inductive assumption is that $\phi_t(x)$ is monic with integral coefficients for $t < n$, and so—in particular—if $t = d$ is any *proper* divisor of n. But then, $x^n - 1 = \phi_n(x)g(x)$, where $g(x)$ is a monic polynomial in $\mathbf{Z}[x]$, from which we conclude [Problem 13] that $\phi_n(x)$ is also monic with coefficients in $\mathbf{Z}$. The inductive proof is then complete. ∎

Lemma 2. *With $\phi_n(x)$ as in Lemma 1, $\phi_n(x)$ is a divisor in $\mathbf{Z}[x]$ of $(x^n - 1)/(x^d - 1)$, for any proper divisor d of n.*

Proof. We first note [Problem 14] that $x^d - 1 = \prod_{m \mid d} \phi_m(x)$, and since a divisor of d is also a divisor of n, we can express $x^n - 1$ with $x^d - 1$ as a factor. Moreover, inasmuch as $d < n$, the factor $x^d - 1$ does not have any factors in common with $\phi_n(x)$. It follows that $x^n - 1 = \phi_n(x) [(x^d - 1)g(x)]$, where $g(x) = \prod_m \phi_m(x)$ and this product is taken over all divisors m of n which do not divide d. Hence [Problem 15], we see that $\phi_n(x)$ divides $(x^n - 1)/(x^d - 1)$, and the coefficients of $\phi_n(x)$ are rational integers. ∎

Theorem 7.84 (Wedderburn). *Any finite division ring $\mathcal{A}$ is a field.*

Proof. Let $\mathcal{K}$ be the center of $\mathcal{A}$, so that all elements of $\mathcal{K}$ commute with every element of $\mathcal{A}$. The subring $\mathcal{K}$ is then a field, and, if there are q elements in $\mathcal{K}$, the whole ring $\mathcal{A}$ must contain q^n elements, for some positive integer n—since $\mathcal{A}$ is a vector space over $\mathcal{K}$ [Problem 18]. We shall show that $\mathcal{K} = \mathcal{A}$ by proving that $n = 1$.

For any element $a \in \mathcal{A}$, let N_a be the normalizer of a in $\mathcal{A}$: i.e., $N_a = \{x \in \mathcal{A} \mid ax = xa\}$. This normalizer contains q^r elements, for some divisor $r(a) = r$ of n, as may be seen by an application of Lagrange's Theorem to the nonzero elements of $\mathcal{A}$ and $\mathcal{K}$ [Problem 19]. However, by Theorem 4.91, the number of elements in $\mathcal{A}$ conjugate to a is the index of N_a in the multiplicative group of nonzero elements of $\mathcal{A}$. It follows that this number is $(q^n - 1)/(q^r - 1)$. But $a \in \mathcal{K}$ if and only if $r = r(a) = n$, and the "class equation" of Chapter 4 requires that the following equality be satisfied:

$$q^n - 1 = q - 1 + \sum_{r(a) \mid n,\, r(a) < n} (q^n - 1)/(q^{r(a)} - 1).$$

The summation in the above equality is over a complete set of representatives a, *not in the center*, of the conjugate classes of the multiplicative group of nonzero elements of $\mathcal{A}$. We now show that it must follow that $n = 1$.

By Lemmas 1 and 2, we know that $\phi_n(t)$ is an integer, for any $t \in \mathbf{Z}$, and this integer must divide $(t^n - 1)/(t^d - 1)$, with d as in the Lemmas. In particular, if we let $t = q$, a consideration of the class equation shows that $\phi_n(q)$ must divide $(q^n - 1)/(q^r - 1)$ and Lemma 1 tells us that $\phi_n(q)$ divides $q^n - 1$. Hence, $\phi_n(q)$ must divide $q - 1$. However, $\phi_n(q) = \Pi (q - \alpha_i)$, where this product is taken over all primitive nth roots of unity α_i, and [Problem 20] moreover, $|q - \alpha_i| > q - 1$, $\alpha_i \neq 1$. Hence, if $n > 1$, $|\phi_n(q)| = \Pi |q - \alpha_i| > q - 1 \geq 1$, so that $\phi_n(q)$ cannot divide $q - 1$, contrary to what we have just obtained. Thus $n = 1$, and since now $\mathcal{K} = \mathcal{A}$, we have shown that the ring $\mathcal{A}$ is identical with its center and so is a field. This completes the proof. ∎

PROBLEMS 7–8

*1. Why must the characteristic of a finite field be nonzero?

*2. If $\mathcal{F}$ is a subfield of either a finite field $\mathcal{K}$ or a finite extension field $\mathcal{K}$ of $\mathcal{F}$, why can one always consider $\mathcal{K}$ to be a field "over $\mathcal{F}$"?

*3. Explain the final remark in the proof of Theorem 7.82.

*4. In the proof of Theorem 7.83, why does $f'(x) = -1$?

*5. Prove that the zeros of $x^q - x$, in the field $\mathcal{K}$ of Theorem 7.83, make up a subfield of $\mathcal{K}$.

*6. Use the same argument as that given in the proof of Theorem 7.83 to show that $x^n - 1$, as a polynomial in $\mathcal{F}[x]$ for any field $\mathcal{F}$, has n distinct zeros in a splitting field.

*7. Prove that the complex nth roots of unity form a cyclic group.

8. Explain why any one of the primitive complex nth roots of unity is a generator of the group described in Problem 7.

9. Find the primitive complex 5th roots of unity.

10. Find the primitive complex 6th roots of unity.

**11. Verify that $\phi_4(x) = x^2 + 1$ is the 4th cyclotomic polynomial in $\mathbf{Z}[x]$.

12. Verify that $\phi_5(x) = x^4 + x^3 + x^2 + x + 1$ is the 5th cyclotomic polynomial in $\mathbf{Z}[x]$.

*13. Explain the final remark in the proof of Lemma 1.

*14. Explain the first equation in the proof of Lemma 2.

*15. Explain the final statement in the proof of Lemma 2.

16. Why must the center of a division ring be a field?

17. With reference to the proof of the Wedderburn theorem, explain why $\mathcal{A}$ is a vector space over $\mathcal{K}$.

*18. With reference to Problem 17 and the Wedderburn theorem, explain why there must be q^n elements in $\mathcal{A}$.

*19. In the notation of the proof of the Wedderburn theorem, explain why N_a contains q^r elements, where r is some positive integral divisor of n.

*20. In the proof of the Wedderburn theorem, explain why $|q - \alpha_i| > q - 1$, if α_i is any primitive nth root of unity, $n > 1$.

21. If a division ring is considered to be a vector space over its center, prove that its dimension cannot be 2 [see Problem 17].

**22. Prove that any two finite fields are isomorphic if they have the same number of elements.

23. If $b \in \mathrm{GF}(p^n)$, prove that the equation $x^p = b$ has a unique solution in this field.

24. If p is a prime integer, prove that $p^m - 1$ is an integral divisor of $p^n - 1$, for positive integers m and n, if and only if m divides n.

25. Use the result of Problem 24 to show that $\mathrm{GF}(p^n)$ contains $\mathrm{GF}(p^m)$ as a subfield, if m divides n.

26. Prove that any algebraic extension field $\mathrm{GF}(p^n)$ is separable over $\mathbf{Z}_p$.

27. Prove the equivalent of Lemma 1, if $x^n - 1$ is considered a polynomial in $\mathcal{F}[x]$, when $\mathcal{F}$ has characteristic p: i.e., show that $\phi_n(x)$ divides $x^n - 1$ and has coefficients in $\mathbf{Z}_p$, provided p does not divide n.

28. Prove that $x^2 + x + 1$ is irreducible over $\mathbf{Z}_2$, so that $\mathbf{Z}_2[x]/(x^2 + x + 1)$ is a 4-element field. Exhibit the addition and multiplication tables for this field.

29. Show that both x and $x + 1$ are generators of the 3-element multiplicative group of nonzero elements of the field in Problem 28.

30. Find representative elements of the field $\mathrm{GF}(3^2)$, noting that $x^2 + 1$ is irreducible over $\mathbf{Z}_3$.

7.9. A Glimpse of Galois Theory

We are now at the threshold of one of the most elegant theories in abstract algebra, but unfortunately it would take us too far beyond the goals of this book to pursue it in any more than a very cursory fashion. We are referring, of course, to the so-called "Galois theory," and suggest that the student who is interested in a thorough treatment consult one of the several fine treatises on this topic: for example, [2] and [7]. This theory is an excellent composite of the theory of groups with the theory of algebraic field extensions, and which has a very important application in the theory of equations. In this section, we shall attempt a very brief expository glimpse of the theory and include a descriptive explanation of the application to which we have just referred.

The Galois theory, when reduced to its bare essentials, is a study of some of the interrelationships of three mathematical objects: an irreducible polynomial $f(x) \in \mathcal{F}[x]$, for some field $\mathcal{F}$, and the splitting field $\mathcal{K}$ of $f(x)$; the set of automorphisms of $\mathcal{K}$ over $\mathcal{F}$; the set of permutations of the zeros of $f(x)$, induced by the automorphisms of $\mathcal{K}$ over $\mathcal{F}$. A general discussion of this theory is made complicated by the existence of irreducible but inseparable polynomials over modular fields. Such polynomials, of course, do not exist over nonmodular fields, so we shall simplify the remarks of this section by always assuming that the characteristic of the base field $\mathcal{F}$ is zero—and so every nonconstant irreducible polynomial in $\mathcal{F}[x]$ is then separable. Perhaps it would be worthwhile mentioning that *some* of the results to which we shall refer would not even be true, if this assumption were not made.

It will be a familiar fact to the student that it is possible for one zero of a polynomial $f(x) \in \mathcal{F}[x]$ to be in a certain extension field of $\mathcal{F}$, while some or all of the remaining zeros are not elements of this extension. For example, the field $\mathbf{Q}(\sqrt{2})$ contains the two zeros $\sqrt{2}$ and $-\sqrt{2}$ of $x^4 - x^2 - 2$ or $(x^2 - 2)(x^2 + 1)$, but certainly not the complex zeros i and $-i$. As another example, $\mathbf{Q}(\sqrt{2})$ contains the zeros $\sqrt{2}$ and $-\sqrt{2}$ of $x^4 - 5x^2 + 6$ but not the zeros $\sqrt{3}$ and $-\sqrt{3}$. We know, from Theorem 7.51, that every polynomial $f(x)$ of degree n over $\mathcal{F}$ has a splitting field $\mathcal{K}$ whose degree over $\mathcal{F}$ does not exceed $n!$. However, the degree of $\mathcal{K}$ may very well be less than this number. For example, if $f(x) = x^3 + x^2 - 2x - 2 = (x^2 - 2)(x + 1)$, it is evident that the splitting field of $f(x)$ is $\mathbf{Q}(\sqrt{2})$, which has degree 2 over $\mathbf{Q}$, while $3! = 6$. The "Theorem of the Primitive Element"—which we have recorded as the Corollary to Theorem 7.62—states that an arbitrary finite extension field over $\mathcal{F}$ is simple, and so is generated by a single element. In particular, the splitting field $\mathcal{K}$ of any irreducible polynomial $f(x) \in \mathcal{F}[x]$ is of this type, and so we can express $\mathcal{K} = \mathcal{F}(\alpha)$, for some "primitive" element α. A finite (algebraic) extension field of $\mathcal{F}$ is said to be *normal over* $\mathcal{F}$, if every polynomial in $\mathcal{F}[x]$, which has at least one zero in the extension field, has all of its zeros in this field. It may be stated as one of the important preliminary theorems of the Galois theory that *any splitting field $\mathcal{K}$ of $f(x)$ is normal over $\mathcal{F}$*.

There is always associated with any field its set of automorphisms, and in particular we are to be interested in the automorphisms of the above splitting field $\mathcal{K}$. The identity automorphism, by which each element of a field is mapped onto itself, is a trivial one which is present for all fields. And if $\mathcal{F} = \mathbf{R}$ and $\mathcal{K} = \mathbf{C}$, a nontrivial but very familiar $\mathbf{R}$-automorphism of $\mathbf{C}$ is that in which every complex number is mapped onto its conjugate: $a + bi \rightarrow a - bi$. It is an elementary matter to prove that the set of all automorphisms of a field forms a group, the group operation being, of course, the usual product of mappings. It is also easy to see that the subset of these automorphisms which leave fixed the elements of a given subfield of the given field also comprises a group—a subgroup of the group just mentioned. In particular, with the fields $\mathcal{F}$ and $\mathcal{K}$ as above, we may talk about the *group of automorphisms of $\mathcal{K}$ over $\mathcal{F}$*, or *$\mathcal{F}$-automorphisms*, a group which we shall designate by $\mathcal{G}(\mathcal{K}, \mathcal{F})$. The elements of $\mathcal{G}(\mathcal{K}, \mathcal{F})$ are those automorphisms of $\mathcal{K}$, which leave fixed the elements of $\mathcal{F}$—though conceivably also leave fixed other elements of $\mathcal{K}$ not in $\mathcal{F}$. However, it can be shown that the fact that $\mathcal{K}$ is normal over $\mathcal{F}$ forces $\mathcal{F}$ to be precisely the totality of elements of $\mathcal{K}$ left invariant by the automorphisms of $\mathcal{G}(\mathcal{K}, \mathcal{F})$, so that $\mathcal{F}$ *is the "fixed field" of this group*. The matter of a determination of the group $\mathcal{G}(\mathcal{K}, \mathcal{F})$ now arises, and we return to the polynomial $f(x)$, whose zeros in $\mathcal{K}$ may be designated $a_1, a_2, \ldots, a_n$. We have recalled earlier, however, that $\mathcal{K} = \mathcal{F}(\alpha)$, where α is a zero of an irreducible polynomial $g(x)$ of some degree m over $\mathcal{F}$ where, in general, $m \neq n$. A key point in the Galois theory is now the following: *The order of $\mathcal{G}(\mathcal{K}, \mathcal{F})$ is m; and if $\alpha = \alpha_1, \alpha_2, \ldots, \alpha_m$ are the zeros of $g(x)$, the m automorphisms of $\mathcal{G}(\mathcal{K}, \mathcal{F})$ are generated by the mappings $\alpha \rightarrow \alpha_i$, $i = 1, 2, \ldots, m$.* (We recall at this point that, since $\mathcal{K}$ is normal over $\mathcal{F}$, $\mathcal{K} = \mathcal{F}(\alpha_1) = \mathcal{F}(\alpha_2) = \cdots = \mathcal{F}(\alpha_m)$.)

As an illustration of an automorphism group $\mathcal{G}(\mathcal{K}, \mathcal{F})$, consider the field $\mathcal{K} = \mathbf{Q}(i, \sqrt{7})$, which can be shown to be the splitting field over $\mathbf{Q}$ of $x^4 - 3x^2 + 4$. A typical element of $\mathcal{K}$ can be expressed as $a + b\sqrt{7} + ci + d\sqrt{7}i$, with $a, b, c, d \in \mathbf{Q}$, and the following mappings describe the four automorphisms of $\mathcal{G}(\mathcal{K}, \mathcal{F})$:

$$S: \sqrt{7} \rightarrow -\sqrt{7} \qquad T: \sqrt{7} \rightarrow \sqrt{7} \qquad ST: \sqrt{7} \rightarrow -\sqrt{7} \qquad I: \sqrt{7} \rightarrow \sqrt{7}$$
$$\quad\ \ i \rightarrow i \qquad\qquad\quad\ i \rightarrow -i \qquad\qquad\quad i \rightarrow -i \qquad\qquad\ \ i \rightarrow i$$

It was remarked above that the original polynomial $f(x)$ and the new "primitive element" polynomial $g(x)$ are usually different. However, each automorphism of $\mathfrak{G}(\mathfrak{K}, \mathscr{F})$, as defined above in terms of the zeros of $g(x)$, also maps each zero of $f(x)$ onto a zero of $f(x)$ — and the result is a permutation of the zeros $a_1, a_2, \ldots, a_n$ of $f(x)$. The set of these induced permutations can be shown to form a group which is isomorphic to $\mathfrak{G}(\mathfrak{K}, \mathscr{F})$, and it is this group of permutations which is usually called the *Galois group of the equation* $f(x) = 0$. As we have just said, however, it is isomorphic to the group $\mathfrak{G}(\mathfrak{K}, \mathscr{F})$ of automorphisms.

It is generally regarded as the Fundamental Theorem of the Galois theory that *there is a one-to-one correspondence between the subfields* $\mathfrak{K}'$ *of* $\mathfrak{K}$, *which contain* $\mathscr{F}$, *and the subgroups* $\mathfrak{G}'$ *of* $\mathfrak{G}(\mathfrak{K}, \mathscr{F})$, *the fields* $\mathfrak{K}'$ *being the fixed fields of* $\mathfrak{G}'$; *moreover,* $\mathfrak{G}' = \mathfrak{G}(\mathfrak{K}, \mathfrak{K}')$ *while the order of* $\mathfrak{G}'$ *is* $[\mathfrak{K} : \mathfrak{K}']$. It is clear, of course, that the larger the order of $\mathfrak{G}'$, the smaller is the degree of the fixed field $\mathfrak{K}'$ associated with $\mathfrak{G}'$. The connection between the Galois theory and the theory of equations is dependent on the above Fundamental Theorem, and we shall attempt a brief summary of how this comes about. In the first place, a group $\mathfrak{G}$ is said to be *solvable* [see § 4.14] if there exists a finite chain of subgroups $\mathfrak{G}_i$, $i = 1, 2, \ldots, k$, for some integer k, such that $\mathfrak{G} = \mathfrak{G}_1 \supset \mathfrak{G}_2 \supset \mathfrak{G}_3 \supset \cdots \supset \mathfrak{G}_{k-1} \supset \mathfrak{G}_k = I$, where I is the identity subgroup of $\mathfrak{G}$, each $\mathfrak{G}_i$ is a normal subgroup of $\mathfrak{G}_{i-1}$, and such that the quotient group $\mathfrak{G}_{i-1}/\mathfrak{G}_i$ is cyclic ($i = 2, 3, \ldots, k$). In view of the above correspondence between subgroups of $\mathfrak{G}(\mathfrak{K}, \mathscr{F})$ and subfields of $\mathfrak{K}$ which contain $\mathscr{F}$, the solvability of $\mathfrak{G}(\mathfrak{K}, \mathscr{F})$ implies the presence of a chain of subfields $\mathfrak{K}_i$ of $\mathfrak{K}$, $i = 1, 2, \ldots, k$, such that $\mathscr{F} = \mathfrak{K}_1 \subset \mathfrak{K}_2 \subset \mathfrak{K}_3 \subset \cdots \subset \mathfrak{K}_k = \mathfrak{K}$ and where each $\mathfrak{K}_i$ is the fixed field of $\mathfrak{G}_i$. A further development of the theory—which we do not wish to detail here—then shows that each field $\mathfrak{K}_i$ can be obtained from the field $\mathfrak{K}_{i-1}$ by the adjunction of a finite number of "radicals," i.e., rth roots of elements in $\mathfrak{K}_{i-1}$ which we designate by $\sqrt[r]{a}$, for $a \in \mathfrak{K}_{i-1}$ and positive integers r. (It is at *this* point in the Galois theory that the cyclic property of the quotient group $\mathfrak{G}_{i-1}/\mathfrak{G}_i$ enters the picture.) Since $\mathfrak{K}$ can then be generated by the adjunction of a finite number of "radicals" to $\mathscr{F}$, and all the zeros of $f(x)$ lie in $\mathfrak{K}$, it is possible to solve the equation $f(x) = 0$ in $\mathfrak{K}$: in the terminology used, we say that $f(x) = 0$ is *solvable by radicals*. The important application of the Galois theory to the theory of equations is then that *an equation is solvable by radicals if and only if its Galois group is solvable*. The student is, of course, familiar with the "quadratic formula" for solving a quadratic equation over $\mathbf{Q}$ by radicals, and he may have some knowledge of the existence of other "radical" formulas for solving cubic and quartic equations—although these are much more complicated. The Galois groups of such equations are then solvable groups. However, it can be shown that the Galois group of a general quintic equation over $\mathbf{Q}$ is not solvable, and so the general quintic equation is not solvable by radicals—a result due to the mathematician Abel.

We close our discussion of Galois theory with a note of caution! From what we have said, the question of the solvability of a given irreducible equation is answered with an analysis of its Galois group, which in turn is equivalent to an analysis of the group of automorphisms of the splitting field of the equation over its field of coefficients. But this latter project is equivalent —in the notation used in this section—to a determination of the "primitive element" α, its minimum polynomial $g(x)$, and the zeros of $g(x)$ in the splitting field $\mathcal{K}$ of the original polynomial $f(x)$. When these three matters are taken care of, and the zeros of $f(x)$ in $\mathcal{K}$ are discovered, the determination of the permutation group which is the Galois group of $f(x) = 0$ is relatively simple. However, each of these preliminary projects—except in rather trivial or at least elementary cases—is far from simple. We again refer the student, interested in a fuller treatment of this topic, to the books mentioned at the beginning of this section.

References

[1] ALBERT, A. A.: *Modern Higher Algebra* (Chicago, University of Chicago Press, 1937).

[2] ARTIN, E.: *Galois Theory*, Second Edition (Notre Dame Mathematical Lectures, No. 2, 1946).

[3] BIRKHOFF, G. and MACLANE, S.: *A Survey of Modern Algebra*, Third Edition (New York, Macmillan, 1965).

[4] COURANT, R. and ROBBINS, H.: *What is Mathematics?* (New York, Oxford, (1941).

[5] HERSTEIN, I. N.: *Topics in Algebra* (Boston, Blaisdell, 1964).

[6] NIVEN, I.: *Irrational Numbers* (Carus Monograph No. 11, M.A.A., 1956).

[7] POSTNIKOV, M.: *Fundamentals of Galois Theory* (Groningen, Noordhoff, 1962).

[8] VAN DER WAERDEN, B. L.: *Modern Algebra*, Vol. 1 (New York, Ungar, 1949).

Selected Readings from The American Mathematical Monthly

CARLITZ, L.: *Classes of Pairs of Commuting Matrices over a Finite Field*, 70 (1963), 192–195.

DAYKIN, D. E.: *Generation of Irreducible Polynomials over a Finite Field*, 72 (1965), 646–648.

HARARY, F.: *A Parity Relation Partitions its Field Distinctly*, **68** (1961), 215–217.

HAUSNER, A.: *Algebraic Number Fields and the Diophantine Equation* $m^n = n^m$, **68** (1961), 856–861.

HODGES, J. H.: *The Matrix Equation* $AX = B$ *in a Finite Field*, **63** (1956), 243–244.

LIPMAN, J.: *Balanced Field Extensions*, **73** (1966), 373–374.

WARNER, S.: *Subfields in Finite Fields* (Problem), **72** (1965), 87–88.

WILANSKY, A.: *Isomorphic Groups* (Problem), **67** (1960), 925–926.

8 Lattices and Boolean Algebra

8.1. Introduction

A portion of the study of any algebraic system is devoted to certain, distinguished subsystems of elements, rather than to the elements themselves. For example, in our earlier study of groups, we became interested in normal subgroups, while the topic of ideals was of importance in our treatment of rings. In the case of groups, the culmination of our study from the point of view of invariant or normal subgroups was the Jordan-Hölder theorem. The notion of a "lattice" arises in an attempt to obtain an abstract system which includes such systems as the subgroups of a group, the normal subgroups of a group, and the ideals of a ring as special cases. Historically, lattices were first studied as Boolean algebras by George Boole (1815–1864). This early study was actually a study of the calculus of propositions, and it was not until much later that this logical system was recognized to be equivalent to a certain type of ring. The notion of a "partially ordered set" is central in the study of this chapter, and we make it precise with the following definition.

Definition. A *partially ordered set* or *poset* is a system consisting of a set S, the usual "equals" ($=$) relation, and a relation $\leq$ ("less than or equal to" or "contained in"), subject to the following conditions for a, b, $c \in S$:

P_1. $a \leq a$, for any $a \in S$ (reflexive property).
P_2.   If $a \leq b$ and $b \leq c$, then $a \leq c$ (transitive property).
P_3.   If $a \leq b$ and $b \leq a$, then $a = b$ (antisymmetric property).

Under these circumstances, the set S is also said to be "partially ordered" by the $\leq$ relation.

The postulates for a *partial order* relation should be compared with those of *order* or—more exactly—*simple order* as given in § 2.2, for the special case of "natural" order ($<$) of the natural numbers [see Problem 4]. If $a \leq b$ and $a \neq b$, it is customary to write $a < b$. Moreover, the notations $b \geq a$ and $b > a$ may be considered alternatives for $a \leq b$ and $a < b$, respectively. It is important to observe that, while the trichotomy law holds in a *simply* ordered set, it is not necessarily true that $a \leq b$ or $b \leq a$ for arbitrary a, b in a *partially* ordered set. If one of these relations holds for certain elements a and b, these elements are said to be *comparable*, and otherwise *uncomparable*. If every pair of elements of a partially ordered set are comparable, it is easily seen that the poset is then a simple or "linearly" ordered set, sometimes also called a *chain*. Probably the most familiar example of a poset which is a chain is the set of rational integers ordered by the usual $\leq$ relation. We shall look now at a few examples of partially ordered sets, but shall leave the verifications that these systems do satisfy the requirements of posets to the student [Problems 5, 6, 7].

Example 1. S is the collection of all subsets of a set, including $\emptyset$ and the whole set; the relation $\leq$ is set-theoretic inclusion.

Example 2. S is the set of all positive integers; $a \leq b$ means that $a \mid b$, for $a, b \in S$.

Example 3. S is the set $\mathbf{Q}$ of all rational numbers; the relation $\leq$ has its usual meaning for numbers.

Example 4. S is the set of all points, lines and planes of ordinary geometric 3-space; $a \leq b$ means that a lies on b.

Example 5. S is the set of all items for sale in a store; $a \leq b$ means that the price of a does not exceed the price of b.

Example 6. S is the set of all subgroups of a group; the relation $\leq$ is set-theoretic inclusion, as in Example 1.

If a_1 and a_2 are elements of a partially ordered set, such that $a_2 > a_1$ but there exists no element a such that $a_2 > a > a_1$ the element a_2 is said to *cover* a_1. If the set is *finite*, we may then connect any two *comparable* elements by a "descending" chain in which each element covers the adjacent element below it. Thus, if $a > b$, we can find elements $a_1, a_2, \ldots, a_n$ in the set such that $a = a_n > a_{n-1} > a_{n-2} > \cdots > a_2 > a_1 = b$, where each a_{i+1} covers a_i. As a result of this, it is possible to represent any finite, partially ordered set by means of a diagram. In such a diagram we represent the elements by points, and, if a_{i+1} is a cover for a_i, we place a_{i+1} above a_i and join them by a line segment. For any two elements a and b such that $a > b$, there is then a descending series of line segments from a to b. A few such diagrams—called *Hasse* diagrams—are shown in Figure 7. It is perhaps worthy of note in a Hasse diagram that

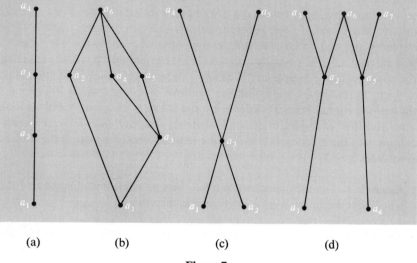

    (a)   (b)   (c)   (d)

Figure 7

we do not join all comparable elements with *single* line segments: this occurs for elements a, b only if either a covers b or b covers a. On the other hand, however, any two comparable elements are connected by a *sequence* of line segments—provided the poset is finite.

If two partially ordered sets can be represented by the same Hasse diagram, they may be said to be *isomorphic*. Of course, only finite posets have such diagrams, and so the following definition is generally more appropriate.

Definition. Two partially ordered sets S and S' are *isomorphic* or *order-isomorphic* if: (**1**) there is a one-to-one correspondence $s \leftrightarrow s'$ between the elements $s \in S$ and the elements $s' \in S'$; and (**2**) $s_1 \leq s_2$ if and only if $s_1' \leq s_2'$, for s_1, $s_2 \in S$ and s_1', $s_2' \in S'$.

If two partially ordered sets satisfy the requirements of an isomorphism, except that the ordering of corresponding elements in the two systems is reversed, the posets are said to be *inversely isomorphic*. The simplest example of this occurs when we use the identity mapping to map a poset onto itself, but with the partial order relation $\leq$ replaced by $\geq$ in the second system. It is immediate, of course, that if $\leq$ is a partial ordering so is $\geq$ [Problem 11], and this is the *Duality Principle* for posets: The converse of a partial ordering is also a partial ordering. This then leads us to the very important result that if any theorem is true for a poset, the dual of the theorem—obtained by reversing the partial ordering—is also true. If S is a finite poset, it is clear that the Hasse diagram of a poset inversely isomorphic to S may be obtained by simply inverting the diagram of S. It should also be realized, of course, that an inverse isomorphism can be made into an isomorphism by merely reversing *one* of the order relations.

We now approach the definition of a lattice by a consideration of *bounds*, a discussion which will be very reminiscent of that of § 2.5 in connection with the "completeness" property of real numbers. What was done in the earlier section may be seen, in fact, to be a special case of what we do here in more general terms.

An *upper bound* for a subset A of a partially ordered set S is an element u such that $u \geq a$, for every $a \in A$. This upper bound u is a *least upper bound* (l.u.b.) if $u \leq v$, for any upper bound v of A. A similar definition applies to *lower bounds*, and a *greatest lower bound* (g.l.b.), and it is clear that if a g.l.b. or l.u.b. exists, this element is unique [Problem 12]. However, it should be clear that even if S is finite, a subset A may have *neither* an upper nor a lower bound—a situation which cannot prevail, however, if S is any finite set of real numbers with their natural ordering. We now proceed to the definition of a lattice.

Definition. A *lattice* is a partially ordered set in which any two elements have a least upper bound and a greatest lower bound.

It is customary to denote the l.u.b. of a and b by $a \cup b$, and the g.l.b. of a and b by $a \cap b$. These are sometimes read "a cup b" and "a cap b," respectively. At other times the "union" and "intersection" terminology of set theory is used.

Let us now examine the five examples given above for partially ordered sets, and decide whether they are lattices. It is necessary, of course, to interpret the l.u.b. and g.l.b. in each case in the light of the meaning associated with the partial ordering. In Example 1—which we shall see later to be very basic in any study of lattices—it is clear that if A and B are arbitrary subsets of S, $A \cup B$ and $A \cap B$ are, respectively, the set-theoretic union and intersection of A and B. Since these always exist, the system in this example is a lattice. In Example 2, if a and b are any positive integers, the interpretation of $a \cup b$ will be the least common multiple and $a \cap b$ the greatest common divisor of a and b. Since these always exist, regardless of the choice of a and b, this system is also seen to be a lattice. In Example 3, it is clear the "cup" and "cap" will have the respective meanings of "greatest" and "least" of any two rational numbers. Again, these always exist, and this system is a simply-ordered lattice. In the case of Example 4, it is natural to interpret "cup" and "cap," respectively, as union and intersection in the geometric sense, but we see at once that two distinct points have no "cap." It is not difficult to remedy this defect, however, because if we include a certain "null" element 0 which *by definition* lies on every point of *S*, and also the whole of 3-space as an "all" element on which every element of *S* lies, we can see that this *slightly-altered* system is a lattice. As for Example 5, we first note that all items in the store which have the same price are being considered "equal" [Problem 13], and so distinct elements of the poset *S* have distinct prices. It is then clear that this example is quite like Example 3, with a similar inter-pretation given to "cup" and "cap." Hence, this poset *S* is also a lattice.

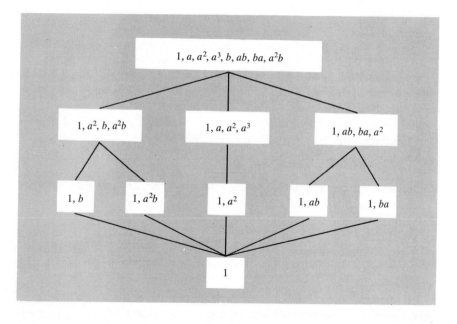

Figure 8

Finally, with respect to Example 6, we can interpret $A \cap B$, for any two subgroup elements of *S*, as the usual set-theoretic intersection—since we know this to be a group. The union $A \cup B$ will have to be interpreted as the subgroup in *S* that is generated by *A* and *B*: i.e., $A \cup B = [A, B]$, because the set-theoretic union of two subgroups is not necessarily a group. With this interpretation of g.l.b. and l.u.b., however, we see that the system in Example 7 is also a lattice. If we take a glance at the Hasse diagrams in

Figure 7, it is immediate that the first two are illustrations of lattices, while the last two are not [see Problem 14].

As an example of a lattice of subgroups consider the dihedral group $\{1, a, a^2, a^3, b, ab, ba, a^2b\}$ of order eight, where $a^4 = b^2 = 1$ and $a^3b = ba$. This group contains three subgroups of order four, and five subgroups of order two, as well as the identity subgroup. Each of the subgroups of order two is contained in one or more of the subgroups of order four, while the identity subgroup is contained in every one of the subgroups. The diagram of the lattice of subgroups of this dihedral group is shown in Figure 8.

PROBLEMS 8–1

*1. Give a complete definition of the greatest lower bound (g.l.b.) of a subset of a partially ordered set.

2. Show the conditions P_1 and P_3 of a partially ordered set can be replaced by the single condition: $a \leq b$ and $b \leq a$ if and only if $a = b$.

*3. Explain why $a \leq a \cup b \, (b \leq a \cup b)$ and $a \cap b \leq a \, (a \cap b \leq b)$, for elements a, b of a partially ordered set.

4. Verify that natural order in **N**, as defined in § 2.2, is a special case of partial order.

5. Verify that Examples 1 and 2 describe posets.

6. Verify that Examples 3 and 4 describe posest.

7. Verify that Examples 5 and 6 describe posets.

8. In (c) of Figure 7, explain why it would not be appropriate to draw a line segment from a_1 to a_4, even though $a_1 \leq a_4$.

9. In (b) of Figure 7, explain why it would not be appropriate to draw a line segment from a_1 to a_4, even though $a_1 \leq a_4$.

10. Decide, with reasons, whether the following are appropriate Hasse diagrams for posets: (a)   (b)

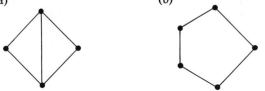

11. Explain why $\geq$ is a partial ordering of a set S whenever $\leq$ is a partial ordering of S.

*12. Explain why the least upper bound and the greatest lower bound of a subset of a partially ordered set are *unique* elements of the set.

13. Explain why, in the poset of Example 5, all articles of the same price must be considered "equal."

14. With reference to the Hasse diagrams of Figure 7, explain why (a) and (b) represent lattices while (c) and (d) do not.

**15. If a and b are elements of a partially ordered set such that $a \geq b$, prove that $a \cap b = b$.

16. Draw diagrams of two partially ordered sets, different from those in the text, which (a) are lattices; (b) are not lattices.

17. Draw diagrams for the following partially ordered sets:
  (a) the set of subsets of a set of four elements;
  (b) the set of subgroups of the cyclic group of order six [see Problem 26 of § 4.5];
  (c) the set of subgroups of S_3.

18. Let S be the set of all continuous functions on **R**. If we define $f \geq g$, for f and g in S, to mean that $f(x) \geq g(x)$, for each $x \in \mathbf{R}$, show that S is partially ordered by $\geq$.

19. Make suitable definitions of $f \cup g$ and $f \cap g$ so that the set S in Problem 18 is a lattice.

20. Draw the Hasse diagrams for all the possible partially ordered sets with 5 elements [cf. Problem 12 of § 8.3].

21. Prove that any two chains, as n-element posets, are either isomorphic or inversely isomorphic [see Problem 11 of § 8.3].

8.2. An Alternate Definition

It was a major part of the definition of a lattice, which we gave in the preceding section, that this system has a partial ordering. In this section, however, we shall see that order is not really essential, and that it is possible to give an equivalent definition of a lattice without any specific mention of any type of ordering. In this setting, a lattice can be considered more like the other members of the family of algebraic systems which we have discussed before, it being in fact a type of "universal algebra" with an accompanying set of "identical relations." [An "identical relation" is a relation which is satisfied by arbitrary elements of the system. For example, an identical relation in a commutative groupoid is $xy = yx$.] It is the purpose of the following theorem to derive these identical relations as simple consequences of our original definition.

Theorem 8.21. *If a, b, c are arbitrary elements of a lattice, the following equalities hold:*

  1. $a \cup b = b \cup a; a \cap b = b \cap a$ (commutative laws);
  2. $(a \cup b) \cup c = a \cup (b \cup c); (a \cap b) \cap c = a \cap (b \cap c)$ (associative laws);
  3. $a \cup a = a; a \cap a = a$ (idempotent laws);
  4. $(a \cup b) \cap a = a; (a \cap b) \cup a = a$ (absorption laws).

Proof. Since there are only syntactic differences between the l.u.b. of a and b and the l.u.b. of b and a, it is clear that $a \cup b = b \cup a$. A similar reflection shows that $a \cap b = b \cap a$, and **1** is verified. In order to establish **2**, we first note that $(a \cup b) \cup c \geq a \cup b$ and $(a \cup b) \cup c \geq c$, so that $(a \cup b) \cup c \geq a$, $(a \cup b) \cup c \geq b$, and $(a \cup b) \cup c \geq c$. Also if x is any element of the lattice such that $x \geq a$, $x \geq b$, $x \geq c$, then $x \geq (a \cup b)$ and so $x \geq (a \cup b) \cup c$. It follows that $(a \cup b) \cup c$ is the l.u.b. of a, b, c while a similar argument shows that a $\cup (b \cup c)$ is also the l.u.b. of a, b, c so that $(a \cup b) \cup c = a \cup (b \cup c)$. In a like way we can show that either $(a \cap b) \cap c$ or $a \cap (b \cap c)$ is the g.l.b. of a, b, c and so these two representations are equal, thus completing the verification of **2**. The definition of l.u.b. requires that $a \cup a = a$, while the definition of g.l.b. requires that $a \cap a = a$, stated in **3**. Finally, since $a \cup b \geq a$ [see Problem 3 of § 8.1], we have $(a \cup b) \cap a = a$; and since $a \geq a \cap b$, it follows that $(a \cap b) \cup a = a$. This establishes **4** and completes the proof of the theorem. ∎

We shall now show that these properties are not only characteristic of any lattice, but that they are sufficient to *define* this type of system. This result is embodied in the following theorem.

Theorem 8.22. *Let £ be a set in which are defined two binary operations ∪ and ∩, and which possess the properties listed in Theorem 8.21. It is then possible to define a partial ordering ≤ in £, such that £ is a lattice in which ∪ and ∩ are the l.u.b. and g.l.b., respectively.*

Proof. We must define a partial ordering $\leq$ in £, and then show that the resulting partially ordered system possesses properties P_1, P_2, and P_3 of § 8.1. The definition of the partial order relation can be made as follows: for elements a, $b \in$ £, $a \leq b$ if and only if $a \cup b = b$ [see Problem 4]. The desired properties of a lattice can now be established quite easily. By **3**, $a \cup a = a$, for any $a \in$ £, and so $a \leq a$, thereby obtaining P_1. If $a \leq b$ and $b \leq c$, for a, $b \in$ £, then $a \cup b = b$ and $b \cup c = c$. But then, making use of **2**, $a \cup c = a \cup (b \cup c) = (a \cup b) \cup c = b \cup c = c$. Hence, $a \leq c$, and P_2 is established. Finally, suppose $a \leq b$ and $b \leq a$, for a, $b \in$ £. Then $a \cup b = b$ and $b \cup a = a$, and so, by **1**, $a = b$, and we have obtained P_3. There remains only to show that $\cup$ and $\cap$ play the respective roles of least upper bound and greatest lower bound. Since $(a \cup b) \cap a = a$, by **4**, we have $a \leq a \cup b$; and a similar argument leads to $b \leq a \cup b$. Now let c be any element of £, such that $a \leq c$ and $b \leq c$. Then $a \cup c = c$ and $b \cup c = c$, and hence $(a \cup b) \cup c = a \cup (b \cup c) = a \cup c$. Thus $a \cup b \leq c$ and so $a \cup b$ is the l.u.b. of a and b. In like manner we can show that $a \cap b$ is the g.l.b. of a and b, thus completing the proof of the theorem. ∎

As a result of Theorem 8.22, we may then replace the postulates for a lattice, as given in § 8.1, by the four properties or "identical relations" listed in Theorem 8.21. We notice immediately that these properties are symmetric in the operations $\cup$ and $\cap$, so that any conclusion which we may derive in a lattice will lead us to an equally-valid conclusion if the roles of the operations $\cup$ and $\cap$ are interchanged. This is then the Principle of Duality as applied to a lattice, a principle which clearly parallels that given in § 8.1 for a poset: *Any statement which has been deduced from the axioms of a lattice remains valid in the lattice if the symbols $\cup$ and $\cap$ are interchanged.* For example, in Problem 4, we have asked the student to show that the condition $a \cup b = b$ implies that $a \cap b = a$. But now, by the Duality Principle for lattices, we may state without further argument that $a \cap b = b$ also implies that $a \cup b = a$; and this statement, with a "little commutativity" and the interchange of a and b gives us the result that $a \cap b = a$ implies $a \cup b = b$. Hence, $a \cup b = b$ and $a \cap b = a$ are equivalent conditions—and so *either one* may be used to define $a \leq b$. It should be clear—but we leave the verification to the student in Problem 6—that if a statement contains an inequality $a \leq b$, in the dual of the statement it is necessary to replace this by $b \leq a$.

Before leaving the postulates for this second description of a lattice, it should be pointed out that the eight listed in Theorem 8.21 are *not* independent—for it is possible to derive the idempotent laws from the other six [Problem 7]. However, it can be shown that *these remaining six laws* are independent, it being impossible to obtain any one of them from the remaining ones. Some problems in the following set are devoted to an investigation of this matter of independence [Problems 16–17].

PROBLEMS 8–2

*1. Give the proof, omitted in our verification of Theorem 8.22, that $a \cap b$ is the g.l.b. of a and b.

**2. Prove that if a and b are elements of a lattice such that $a \cup b = a \cap b$, then $a = b$.

3. Prove that if a, b, c are elements of a lattice such that $a \cup b \cup c = a \cap b \cap c$, then $a = b = c$.

*4. Prove, without use of the Duality Principle, that $a \cup b = b$ implies that $a \cap b = a$, for elements a, b in a lattice.

5. Use the result of Problem 4 to show that the equalities $a \cap b = a$ and $a \cup b = b$ are either both true or both false for lattice elements a, b.

6. Use the Duality Principle to show that in the dual of any lattice-theoretic result which involves $\leq$, this relation must be replaced by $\geq$.

*7. Show that the idempotent laws of a lattice follow from the others listed in Theorem 8.21.

8. Let $\circ$ designate a binary operation in a set, and suppose that this operation is commutative and associative while each element is idempotent (i.e., $x \circ x = x$, for any x in the set). Then if we define $a \leq b$ to mean that $a \circ b = b$, for elements a, b in the set, show that the set is partially ordered with $a \circ b$ the l.u.b. of a and b.

9. Note that each of the four lattice properties given in Theorem 8.21 has two parts, and check in each case that the second is the dual of the first.

10. Let $\mathfrak{L}$ be the set of all continuous functions on the interval $[0, 1]$. If we define $f \leq g$, for f, $g \in \mathfrak{L}$, provided $f(x) \leq g(x)$ for $x \in [0, 1]$, prove that $\mathfrak{L}$ becomes a partially ordered set.

11. Define union ∪ and intersection ∩ in the poset ℒ of Problem 10, in such a way that ℒ becomes a lattice.

12. Use the definition of a lattice given in this section to make what you consider to be an appropriate definition of a sublattice.

13. Prove that the set of binary relations in a set S forms a lattice identical with the usual lattice of subsets of $S \times S$.

14. Prove that the set of all equivalence relations in a set S forms a lattice with the usual set-theoretic definition of inclusion (≤).

15. Use your definition as given in Problem 12, and check whether the lattice in Problem 14 is a sublattice of the lattice in Problem 13.

16. What would you consider to be a decisive way of telling whether one of several characteristic laws of an algebraic system is independent of the others?

17. The following tables give the rules of composition for ∪ and ∩ for a 2-element algebraic system:

∪	a	b
a	a	a
b	b	b

∩	a	b
a	a	a
b	a	b

Verify that all the characteristic properties of a lattice, as described in Theorem 8.21, are satisfied by this system except for the commutative laws. What is the significance of this [see Problem 16]?

18. Imitate the type of example used in Problem 17 to prove that the absorption laws are independent of the other characteristic properties of a lattice.

19. The following tables give the rules of composition for a 5-element algebraic system with two operations (∪ and ∩):

∪	a	b	c	d	e
a	a	a	a	a	a
b	a	b	a	b	b
c	a	a	c	c	c
d	a	b	c	d	d
e	a	b	c	d	e

∩	a	b	c	d	e
a	a	b	c	d	e
b	b	b	e	d	e
c	c	e	c	d	e
d	d	d	d	d	e
e	e	e	e	e	e

Verify that all the characteristic properties of a lattice, as described in Theorem 8.21, are possessed by this system except for the associative law. What is the significance of this example? (Hint: check $b \cap (c \cap d)$ and $(b \cap c) \cap d$, and refer to Problem 16.)

20. Consider the eight vertices of a cube as designating the elements of a lattice, with the edges the "covering" lines, the cube being drawn so that two opposite vertices are the top and bottom elements of the 3-dimensional

resulting Hasse diagram. If the bottom element is labeled 1, and its three covering elements 2, 3, and 5, use the partial ordering of divisibility [see Example 2 of § 8.1] to complete the labeling of the diagram. Try to find an equivalent *plane* Hasse diagram!

**21. Construct the Hasse diagram for the lattice of subgroups of (a) the cyclic group of order 6; (b) $\math9_1 \times \math9_2$ where $\math9_1$ and $\math9_2$ are, respectively, the (multiplicative) cyclic groups of orders 3 and 4.

22. Construct the Hasse diagram for the lattice of the symmetric group (a) S_3; (b) S_4.

8.3. Sublattices and Isomorphism

It is usually the case that an algebraic system has subsystems of the same kind. Lattices are no exception to this, and it is customary to define a subset of a lattice $\mathcal{L}$ as a *sublattice* if it is closed with respect to the compositions $\cup$ and $\cap$ of $\mathcal{L}$. In other words, a sublattice of $\mathcal{L}$ is a subset which contains the l.u.b. and g.l.b. of every pair of elements of the subset. If a lattice is considered a "universal algebra" subject to the "identical relations" of Theorem 8.21, a sublattice is simply a subalgebra *within which* the *same* identical relations are satisfied. On the other hand, it is possible for a subset of a lattice $\mathcal{L}$ to be a lattice without being a sublattice of $\mathcal{L}$. In such a case, the compositions in the subset are not the same as those defined for the same elements when these are considered to be elements of $\mathcal{L}$. For example, Figure 9 may designate a portion of a lattice, with the "starred" elements belonging to a subset. Then, if a and b are considered elements of $\mathcal{L}$, $a \cup b = c \in \mathcal{L}$, whereas the corresponding l.u.b. in the subset is d. An example of this occurs when we consider the lattice $\mathcal{L}$ of subsets of a group $\math9$, along with the lattice $\mathcal{L}'$ of subgroups of $\math9$. Since every subgroup of $\math9$ is a subset of $\math9$, it is clear that $\mathcal{L}' \subset \mathcal{L}$. However, if $\mathcal{H}_1$ and $\mathcal{H}_2$ are arbitrary subgroups of $\math9$, the subset $\mathcal{H}_1 \cup \mathcal{H}_2$ is not in general a subgroup of $\math9$, and so is not a member of $\mathcal{L}'$. As we have already seen, it is necessary to define $\mathcal{H}_1 \cup \mathcal{H}_2$ to be the subgroup generated by $\mathcal{H}_1$ and $\mathcal{H}_2$, if $\mathcal{L}'$ is to be a lattice. While $\mathcal{L}'$ is a lattice, with this definition of $\cup$ and the same definition of $\cap$ as for $\mathcal{L}$, it is clear that $\mathcal{L}'$ is not a sublattice of $\mathcal{L}$.

In view of our alternate definition of a lattice as a universal algebra in which certain identical relations are satisfied, it is easy to extend the usual notions of homomorphism and isomorphism (and, of course, endomorphism and automorphism) to lattices. To wit, a mapping $a \to a'$ of a lattice $\mathcal{L}$ into a lattice $\mathcal{L}'$ is a *homomorphism* if

$$(a \cup b)' = a' \cup b' \text{ and } (a \cap b)' = a' \cap b',$$

where $a, b \in \mathcal{L}$ and $a', b' \in \mathcal{L}'$. If the mapping is bijective, the homomorphism is an *isomorphism*. In § 8.1, we defined an isomorphism between two posets

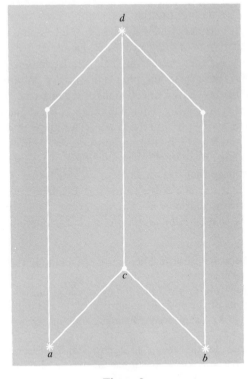

Figure 9

as a one-to-one mapping which preserves order both ways, and it happens that this isomorphic mapping—in the sense of partial ordering—is equivalent to the lattice isomorphism defined above. Moreover, it is usually easier to apply the poset definition in checking for a possible isomorphism between two lattices. Before proceeding with the proof of the equivalence theorem, however, it may be well to point out that, while an isomorphic imbedding of one lattice in another is also a poset isomorphism (as we shall see in the proof below), the converse of this statement does not hold in complete generality. For examples show that a poset isomorphism of two lattices is not necessarily a lattice isomorphism. The following theorem shows, however, that if the mapping is *surjective* or *onto*, the two types of isomorphism for lattices are equivalent.

Theorem 8.31. *Let $a \to a'$ be a bijective mapping of a lattice $\mathfrak{L}$ to a lattice $\mathfrak{L}'$. Then the mapping is an isomorphism if and only if $a \leq b$ in $\mathfrak{L}$ implies and is implied by $a' \leq b'$ in $\mathfrak{L}'$, i.e., if and only if both the mapping and its inverse are "order preserving."*

Proof. First, let us suppose that the mapping $a \to a'$ is an isomorphism, and that $a \leq b$, for elements $a, b \in \mathfrak{L}$. Then, $b = a \cup b$, and since the mapping is an isomorphism $b' = (a \cup b)' = a' \cup b'$. Hence $a' \leq b'$, so that the mapping of $\mathfrak{L}$ onto $\mathfrak{L}'$ is order preserving. In a similar manner, it can be shown [Problem 7] that the inverse mapping is also order preserving. Conversely, let us suppose that $a \to a'$ is a bijective mapping of $\mathfrak{L}$ to $\mathfrak{L}'$ which, along with its inverse, is order preserving. Then if $a \cup b = c$, for elements $a, b, c \in \mathfrak{L}$, we must show that $a' \cup b' = c'$. But if $a \cup b = c$, we know that $a \leq c$ and $b \leq c$, so that $a' \leq c'$ and $b' \leq c'$, by our assumption on the preservation of order under the mapping. Now let d' be any element of $\mathfrak{L}'$, such that $a' \leq d'$ and $b' \leq d'$, and suppose that d is an element of $\mathfrak{L}$ such that $d \to d'$. Then $a \leq d$ and $b \leq d$, so that $c = a \cup b \leq d$, and $c' \leq d'$. Hence c' is the l.u.b. of a' and b', which means that $c' = a' \cup b'$, as desired. In like manner [Problem 8], we can show that $(a \cap b)' = a' \cap b'$, and the theorem is established. ∎

PROBLEMS 8–3

1. Discover where the proof in Theorem 8.31 would fail if the mapping is not assumed to be bijective.

2. Let V be the "four group," i.e., the noncyclic group of order 4. Then draw Hasse diagrams of the poset of subgroups of V, and imbed in it the lattice of subgroups of V, using some distinguishing marks to identify the latter elements.

3. With reference to the group V in Problem 2, determine the number of possible (a) partially ordered subsets of the set V; (b) sublattices of the lattice of subgroups of V.

4. Give appropriate definitions of the concepts of endomorphism and automorphism as applied to a lattice.

**5. If b is any element of a lattice $\mathfrak{L}$, prove that the set of all elements $x \in \mathfrak{L}$, such that $x \leq b$, is a sublattice of $\mathfrak{L}$.

6. If a and b are elements of a lattice $\mathfrak{L}$, where $a \leq b$, show that the set of all elements $x \in \mathfrak{L}$, such that $a \leq x \leq b$, is a sublattice of $\mathfrak{L}$. We call such a sublattice an *interval* or *quotient* and denote it by b/a.

*7. Prove the point, omitted in the proof of Theorem 8.31, that the mapping $a' \to a$ is order preserving.

*8. Prove the point, omitted in the proof of Theorem 8.31, that $(a \cap b)' = a' \cap b'$, under the assumption that the mapping and its inverse are order preserving.

9. Prove that the set of invariant subgroups of a group $\mathfrak{G}$ comprises a sublattice of the lattice of subgroups of $\mathfrak{G}$, with l.u.b. and g.l.b. as in our discussion above.

10. If M is any operator set, prove that the set of M-subgroups of a group $\mathfrak{G}$ is a sublattice of the lattice of subgroups of $\mathfrak{G}$.

11. Prove that any two simply-ordered lattices with n elements are isomorphic. Explain why the notion of "inverse isomorphism," introduced in § 8.1, is not essential.

12. Prove that there are only five nonisomorphic 5-element lattices [cf. Problem 20 of § 8.1].

13. Construct Hasse diagrams for all possible lattices with either three or four elements.

14. Prove that the lattice of equivalence relations is not a sublattice of the lattice of binary relations in a set S [see Problems 13, 14 of § 8.2].

15. If a, b, c are elements of a lattice with $a \geq b$, prove that $a \cup c \geq b \cup c$ and $a \cap b \geq b \cap c$.

*16. By a *lattice polynomial* we mean an expression $f(a_1, a_2, \ldots, a_n)$ involving a finite number of elements $a_1, a_2, \ldots, a_n$ of a lattice, symbols of union and intersection, and possibly parentheses. Prove that lattices are "isotone functions of their variables": $a_i \geq b_i$, $i = 1, 2, \ldots, n$, implies that $f(a_1, a_2, \ldots, a_n) \geq f(b_1, b_2, \ldots, b_n)$. (Hint: Problem 15 is the special case of this result in which there is only one cup or cap. Hence use induction on the number of cups and/or caps in the lattice polynomial.)

**17. Use the result of Problem 16 to show, for elements a, b, c in any lattice, that $a \cap (b \cup c) \geq (a \cap b) \cup (a \cap c)$ and $a \cup (b \cap c) \leq (a \cup b) \cap (a \cup c)$. (Hint: $b \leq b \cup c$ and $c \leq b \cup c$).

18. If $a \geq b$, we know that $a \cap b = b$. Use this fact and the result of Problem 17 to prove the "one-sided modular law": $a \geq b$ implies $a \cap (b \cup c) \geq b \cup (a \cap c)$.

19. If a, b, c are three elements of a lattice with $a > c$, use the isotone property of Problem 16 to prove that $a \cup b \geq a \geq a \cap (b \cup c) \geq (a \cap b) \cup c \geq c \geq b \cap c$.

20. Under the conditions of Problem 19, prove that $a \cup b \geq c \cup b \geq b \geq b \cap a \geq b \cap c$.

21. Under the conditions of Problem 19, prove that $(b \cap a) \cup c \geq b \cap a$ and $c \cap b \geq a \cap (c \cup b)$.

22. A *free* lattice is one whose elements are subject only to the "identical relations" listed in Theorem 8.21. Use the results of Problems 19, 20, 21 to construct the Hasse diagram of the 9-element free lattice generated by a, b, c with $a > c$ and $a \neq b$. (Hint: the diagram contains the 5-element sublattice shown in Problem 10(b) of § 8.1.) What does this result imply concerning an arbitrary lattice polynomial $f(a, b, c)$?

8.4. Types of Lattices

It is usually possible to enlarge the set of postulates of an algebraic system, and thereby obtain a special system with properties not characteristic of the general system. In the case of groups, for example, we obtained the subclass of abelian groups by including the postulate of commutativity; and in Chapter 5 we gave some brief discussion of Noetherian rings, a subclass of rings with some properties not possessed by rings in general. In this section we shall consider some special kinds of lattices.

By the definition of l.u.b. and g.l.b., $a \cup b$ and $a \cap b$ are *unique* elements of a lattice containing a and b. In the proof of **2** of Theorem 8.21 this result was extended to take care of any three elements, and it can be shown by induction [Problem 1] that the l.u.b. and g.l.b. of *any finite* subset of elements of a lattice $\mathcal{L}$ is a unique element of $\mathcal{L}$. However, this result is not necessarily true for infinite subsets of elements, a fact which leads us to the next definition.

Definition. A lattice $\mathcal{L}$ is *complete* if any (finite or infinite) subset of $\mathcal{L}$ has a least upper bound and a greatest lower bound.

The lattice of subsets of a set is clearly complete: for, in this case, the l.u.b. of any subset of the lattice is the set-theoretic union of the elements of the subset and so is an element of the lattice; while the g.l.b. of any such subset is the set-theoretic intersection of the elements of the subset which, as a subset, is also an element of the lattice. It is not difficult to show that the lattice of subgroups of a group is also complete [Problem 2]. On the other hand, the lattice of rational numbers with the usual definition of $\leq$, is not complete: for example, the subset of rational numbers x such that $x^2 < 3$ has no rational l.u.b.

If there exists in a lattice $\mathcal{L}$ an element 1 such that $a \leq 1$, for every $a \in \mathcal{L}$, then 1 is known as the *all* or *identity* element of the lattice. If an element 0 exists in $\mathcal{L}$ such that $0 \leq a$, for every $a \in \mathcal{L}$, the element 0 is known as the *zero* element of the lattice. The elements 1 and 0 do not necessarily exist in a lattice, but it they exist they are unique [Problem 3].

If we consider $\cup$ to be the analogue of addition and $\cap$ to be the analogue of multiplication in a ring, the following definition will appear to be quite natural.

Definition. A lattice $\mathcal{L}$ is said to be *distributive* if $a \cap (b \cup c) = (a \cap b) \cup (a \cap c)$, for arbitrary elements $a, b, c \in \mathcal{L}$.

There are many examples of a distributive lattice, one of the most familiar being the lattice of subsets of a set, with the usual compositions of set-theoretic union and intersection [Problem 6]. However, while many lattices are distributive, there are also many important ones which are not. For example, the lattice of ideals of a ring is not a distributive lattice [Problem 13]. This leads us to the definition of another type of lattice, called "modular," which satisfies a somewhat less stringent condition than distributivity.

Definition. A lattice $\mathcal{L}$, such that $a \cap (b \cup c) = b \cup (a \cap c)$, for elements $a, b, c \in \mathcal{L}$ such that $a \geq b$, is said to be *modular*.

Since $a \geq b$ implies that $a \cap b = b$, the condition for modularity is precisely the distributive law for any triplet of elements a, b, c, where $a \geq b$. Hence any distributive lattice is modular, so that the class of distributive lattices is a subclass of the class of modular lattices. The great importance of modular lattices is due in part to the following result.

Theorem 8.41. *The lattice of invariant subgroups of a group $\mathfrak{G}$ is modular.*

Proof. We recall, for this lattice, that we identify $\leq$ with set inclusion, i.e., $\mathfrak{K}_1 \leq \mathfrak{K}_2$ means that $\mathfrak{K}_1 \subset \mathfrak{K}_2$, for elements (subgroups) $\mathfrak{K}_1$ and $\mathfrak{K}_2$ of the lattice. Moreover, $\mathfrak{K}_1 \cup \mathfrak{K}_2$ is the subgroup generated by $\mathfrak{K}_1$ and $\mathfrak{K}_2$, while $\mathfrak{K}_1 \cap \mathfrak{K}_2$ is the subgroup whose elements comprise the set-theoretic intersection of $\mathfrak{K}_1$ and $\mathfrak{K}_2$.

In any lattice we have the one-sided distributive law [cf. Problem 17, § 8.3] for arbitrary elements a, b, c of the lattice: $a \cap (b \cup c) \geq (a \cap b) \cup (a \cap c)$. For it is clear that $a \cap (b \cup c) \geq a \cap b$ and $a \cap (b \cup c) \geq a \cap c$, with the elements in an arbitrary lattice. In the present environment, this means that $\mathfrak{K}_1 \cap (\mathfrak{K}_2 \cup \mathfrak{K}_3) \geq (\mathfrak{K}_1 \cap \mathfrak{K}_2) \cup (\mathfrak{K}_1 \cap \mathfrak{K}_3)$, where $\mathfrak{K}_1, \mathfrak{K}_2, \mathfrak{K}_3$ are arbitrary (invariant) subgroups in the given lattice. If we now suppose that $\mathfrak{K}_1 \geq \mathfrak{K}_2$, as required in the definition of a modular lattice, the above property gives us immediately that $\mathfrak{K}_1 \cap (\mathfrak{K}_2 \cup \mathfrak{K}_3) \geq \mathfrak{K}_2 \cup (\mathfrak{K}_1 \cap \mathfrak{K}_3)$. It remains to show that $\mathfrak{K}_2 \cup (\mathfrak{K}_1 \cap \mathfrak{K}_3) \geq \mathfrak{K}_1 \cap (\mathfrak{K}_2 \cup \mathfrak{K}_3)$, and to this end let h be an arbitrary element of $\mathfrak{K}_1 \cap (\mathfrak{K}_2 \cup \mathfrak{K}_3)$. Since $\mathfrak{K}_2 \cup \mathfrak{K}_3 = [\mathfrak{K}_2, \mathfrak{K}_3]$, while $\mathfrak{K}_1, \mathfrak{K}_2$ and $\mathfrak{K}_3$ are invariant in the group $\mathfrak{G}$ of the theorem, it follows from Theorem 4.92 that $h = h_2 h_3 = h_1$, where $h_1 \in \mathfrak{K}_1, h_2 \in \mathfrak{K}_2$, $h_3 \in \mathfrak{K}_3$. Then $h_3 = h_2^{-1} h_1 \in \mathfrak{K}_1$, since $h_2 \in \mathfrak{K}_2 \subseteq \mathfrak{K}_1$, and so $h = h_2 h_3 \in \mathfrak{K}_2 \cup (\mathfrak{K}_1 \cap \mathfrak{K}_3)$. We have shown that $\mathfrak{K}_2 \cup (\mathfrak{K}_1 \cap \mathfrak{K}_3) \geq \mathfrak{K}_1 \cap (\mathfrak{K}_2 \cup \mathfrak{K}_3)$, and this result combined with the reversed inclusion obtained before implies that $\mathfrak{K}_1 \cap (\mathfrak{K}_2 \cup \mathfrak{K}_3) = \mathfrak{K}_2 \cup (\mathfrak{K}_1 \cap \mathfrak{K}_3)$. Hence the lattice of invariant subgroups is modular, as asserted. ∎

There are a number of definitions which are equivalent to the one we have given for a modular lattice. We shall state one of these, in the form of a theorem, and refer to others in the problems.

Theorem 8.42. *A lattice $\mathfrak{L}$ is modular if and only if $a \cap [(a \cap b) \cup c] = (a \cap b) \cup (a \cap c)$, for arbitrary elements $a, b, c \in \mathfrak{L}$.*

Proof. First let us suppose that $\mathfrak{L}$ is modular. Then, since $a \geq a \cap b$, the identity in the statement of the theorem follows directly from the usual definition of modular. Conversely, if this identity holds and we assume that $a \geq b$, then $a \cap b = b$ and the identity reduces to $a \cap (b \cup c) = b \cup (a \cap c)$; and this is seen to be our original requirement for a modular lattice. ∎

The importance of this result is that modular lattices are now seen to form a subclass of lattices which is on a par with any other type of "universal algebra." The modular lattices are characterized by one additional identical relation over those satisfied by a general lattice [Problem 9].

Our final special type of lattice is now described in the following definition.

Definition. A lattice $\mathfrak{L}$ with 0 and 1 is said to be *complemented* if there is associated with each element $a \in \mathfrak{L}$ an element $a' \in \mathfrak{L}$, such that $a \cup a' = 1$ and $a \cap a' = 0$. Either element a or a' is then said to be the *complement* of the other.

The lattice of subsets of a set S is complemented. For we identify the whole set S with 1 and the empty set with 0, and then define the complement of any subset of S as the collection of all elements of S which are not in the subset. It is clear that this definition satisfies the requirements of a complement.

Let $\mathfrak{L}$ be a complemented modular lattice, with $a \geq b$, for elements $a, b \in \mathfrak{L}$. Then there exists an element $b' \in \mathfrak{L}$ such that $b \cup b' = 1$ and $b \cap b' = 0$; and the modularity property gives $a = a \cap (b \cup b') = b \cup (a \cap b') = b \cup b_1$, where $b_1 = a \cap b'$. Since $b \cap b_1 = b \cap (a \cap b') = (b \cap b') \cap a = 0$, and $b \cup b_1 = a$, the element b_1 is what is known as a *relative complement* of b with respect to a. We have shown that if a and b are elements of a complemented modular lattice such that $a \geq b$, there exists a *relative complement* of b with respect to a, i.e., an element b_1 such that $b \cap b_1 = 0$ and $b \cup b_1 = a$.

PROBLEMS 8–4

*1. Give the inductive proof that any finite subset of elements of a lattice has a l.u.b.

**2. Prove that the lattice of subgroups of a group is complete.

*3. Why can there be at most one zero and one identity element in a lattice?

*4. If a lattice $\mathfrak{L}$ has an identity 1, prove that $a \cap 1 = a$ and $a \cup 1 = 1$, for an arbitrary element $a \in \mathfrak{L}$.

*5. If a lattice $\mathfrak{L}$ has an element 0, prove that $a \cap 0 = 0$ and $a \cup 0 = a$, for an arbitrary element $a \in \mathfrak{L}$.

6. Use a diagram to verify that $a \cap (b \cup c) = (a \cap b) \cup (a \cap c)$, where a, b, c are overlapping point sets on a plane.

7. If we define $a \leq b$ to mean that $a \mid b$, prove that the lattice of positive integers with this partial ordering is distributive. (In this case, $\cup$ is the g.c.d. and $\cap$ is the l.c.m.)

8. Write down the dual equivalent of the definition which we gave for a distributive lattice.

9. Why do we not consider the equality given in our first definition of a modular lattice an "identical relation"?

10. If x and y are complements in a modular lattice $\mathfrak{L}$ and $b \leq x \leq a$, for $a, b \in \mathfrak{L}$, prove that $a \cap (y \cup b)$ is a complement of x in the sublattice a/b (see Problem 6 of § 8.3).

11. Prove that the lattice of rational numbers, with the usual ordering, is not complete.

12. Prove that any simply-ordered lattice (i.e., a chain) is distributive.

13. Prove that the lattice of ideals in a ring is modular but not distributive.

14. Extend the proof of Theorem 8.41 to include the lattice of invariant M-subgroups of any group with operator set M.

15. Prove that the dual of the condition for modularity is valid in a modular lattice: i.e., if $a \le b$, then $a \cup (b \cap c) = b \cap (a \cup c)$.

**16. Prove that a modular lattice $\mathfrak{L}$ satisfies the following "weak cancellation law": $a \le b$, $a \cap c = b \cap c$, $a \cup c = b \cup c$, for arbitrary elements a, b, $c \in \mathfrak{L}$, imply that $a = b$.

17. Prove that a lattice which satisfies the "weak cancellation law" in Problem 16 is modular. (Hint: use the "one-sided modular law" of Problem 18, § 8.3; prove that $[a \cap (b \cup c)] \cap c = [b \cup (a \cap c)] \cap c$ and assume the dual statement.)

18. Prove that the 5-element lattice, whose Hasse diagram is shown in Problem 10(b) of § 8.1, is not modular.

19. Use the "one-sided modular law" of Problem 18, § 8.3, to prove that a lattice is modular if and only if it does not contain a sublattice isomorphic to the 5-element lattice referred to in Problem 18.

20. Prove that a lattice $\mathfrak{L}$ is distributive if and only if, for arbitrary elements a, b, $c \in \mathfrak{L}$, $(a \cap b) \cup (b \cap c) \cup (c \cap a) = (a \cup b) \cap (b \cup c) \cap (c \cup a)$.

21. Show that the lattice, whose Hasse diagram is shown below, is modular but not distributive.

22. Refer to Problem 6 of § 8.3 and prove that the quotient lattices $(a \cup b)/a$ and $b/(a \cap b)$ are isomorphic, for arbitrary elements a, b, in a modular lattice. (Hint: for $x \in b/(a \cap b)$, let $x \to x \cup a$ and for $y \in (a \cup b)/a$ let $y \to y \cap b$; then show that these mappings are inverses of each other.)

· **23.** Prove that a lattice $\mathfrak{L}$ is modular if the mappings suggested in the Hint to Problem 22 are inverses of each other, for arbitrary a, $b \in \mathfrak{L}$.

24. Prove that the lattice of subgroups of the alternating group A_4 on 4 symbols is not modular.

25. Find a nontrivial illustration of the result in Problem 22. (Hint: consider the lattice described in Problem 20 of § 8.2.)

26. Use Problem 21 and prove that a modular lattice is distributive if and only if it does not contain a sublattice isomorphic to the one whose Hasse diagram is shown in the Problem mentioned.

27. Use Problem 18 and prove that a lattice is modular if and only if it does not contain a sublattice isomorphic to the one whose Hasse diagram is shown in Problem 10(b) of § 8.1.

28. Prove that a lattice $\mathfrak{L}$ is distributive if and only if the "cancellation law" holds in it: $a \cup c = b \cup c$ and $a \cap c = b \cap c$ imply that $a = b$, for arbitrary elements a, b, $c \in \mathfrak{L}$.

8.5. A Brief Survey

In this section we shall indicate a few further results which can be obtained for certain lattices. No proofs are included here, but the student may find detailed discussions of most of these topics in the books listed in the References.

A lattice is said to satisfy the *descending chain condition* if it contains no infinite set of elements a_1, a_2, a_3, ... such that $a_1 > a_2 > a_3 > \cdots$, while the *ascending chain condition* has an analogous meaning. It is easy to see that if a lattice satisfies the descending chain condition and is also known to be complemented, there exist elements of the lattice which cover 0. These elements, sometimes called *atoms*, play an important part in the theory of complemented lattices.

If $\mathcal{L}$ is a modular lattice having 0 and 1, a finite chain of elements of $\mathcal{L}$ such that $0 = a_1 < a_2 < \cdots < a_{k-1} < a_k = 1$ is called a *normal series* of the lattice with k the *length* of the series. A *refinement* of the series is one which contains every a_i, $i = 1, 2, \ldots, k$. It is then possible to prove the analogue of Schreier's theorem for groups [see [4], p. 138]. *Any two normal series of a modular lattice have refinements of equal length.* If a normal series happens to have no further refinements, the series is said to be *principal* and we have the lattice equivalent of a portion of the Jordan-Hölder theorem of group theory: *If a modular lattice has principal series, all such series have the same length.* The proofs of these results are beyond the scope of this book. It is not difficult to see, however, that the existence of principal series in a sublattice follows from the existence of principal series in the lattice, and this leads us to one more form for the definition of a modular lattice: *A lattice is modular if and only if, in every sublattice with principal series, all these series have the same length.* It can be shown that the presence of *both* chain conditions for a modular lattice is sufficient to guarantee the existence of principal series in the lattice. For a lattice with principal series, the sublattice $a/0$ also has principal series, for any a in the lattice, and the length of this series is denoted by $l(a)$. It is then not difficult to obtain the *Fundamental Dimensionality Relation* for a modular lattice $\mathcal{L}$: for arbitrary $a, b \in \mathcal{L}$, $l(a \cup b) = l(a) + l(b) - l(a \cap b)$. The notion of " length " can be extended to a more general " positive real valuation " function on a lattice, and this in turn would lead to a study of " metric " lattices—modular lattices being then a special case. We shall not pursue this line further, however.

A study of modular lattices which satisfy the ascending chain conditions may be considered the lattice abstraction of a portion of the theory of ideals in a Noetherian ring. An element a of such a lattice $\mathcal{L}$ is said to be *reducible* if $a = a_1 \cap a_2$, for elements $a_1, a_2 \in \mathcal{L}$, where $a_1 > a$ and $a_2 > a$. It is then easy to see that any element of $\mathcal{L}$ can be represented as the intersection of a finite number of irreducible elements, where the meaning of "irreducible" is clear. If we define such a representation as *irredundant* when no one of its components may be omitted from the representation, it can be shown that the following theorem is true.

Theorem 8.51. *Let $\mathcal{L}$ be a modular lattice in which the ascending chain condition holds. Then, if an element $b \in \mathcal{L}$ is represented as the irredundant intersection of irreducible elements of $\mathcal{L}$, the number of these elements is uniquely determined by b.*

We shall not prove this theorem but we point out that it, as the analogue of the Remak-Krull-Schmidt theorem of group theory, once again demonstrates the closeness of the theory of groups with the theory of modular lattices. We caution, however, that the theory of lattices does not contain *all* of the theory of groups as a special case, due in part to the fact that the lattice of subgroups of a group is not modular. The final topic to be considered here is one which can be considered a very special type of lattice—a *Boolean algebra*.

8.6. Boolean Algebras

In recent years much interest has arisen in what are known as "Boolean algebras." The principal reason for this great interest is that many applications of this discipline have been found in connection with various systems of automation. We have already noted that the basic ideas of Boolean algebra were first introduced by George Boole, in an attempt to formalize a study of the calculus of propositions. For many years this type of algebra was considered to be essentially different from any of the more conventional algebraic systems, and it has been in only relatively modern times that the true position of Boolean algebra as an algebriac structure has been recognized. The proof that there is a connecting link between lattices and Boolean algebras has been obviated, however, in our present exposition by the following definition.

Definition. A *Boolean algebra* is a complemented and distributive lattice.

It may be well to repeat, of course, that Boolean algebras were not defined in this way by Boole, because the study of lattices is much more modern. A brief discussion of the Boolean algebra of propositions will be made later, however, so that the above definition may not seem so far removed from the ideas of Boole as it does at the outset.

It is easy to see that the set of all subsets of a set, with the usual compositions of intersection, union, and complementation is a Boolean algebra [Problem 1]. In fact, this example is so basic, that a Boolean algebra is sometimes defined as an abstraction of this algebra of sets. Some of the most important elementary propositions of Boolean algebra are described in the following theorem.

Theorem 8.61. *The complement a' of any element a of a Boolean algebra $\mathscr{B}$ is unique. The mapping $a \to a'$ of $\mathscr{B}$ to $\mathscr{B}$ is bijective, $(a')' = a$, and the following equalities are satisfied for arbitrary elements $a, b \in \mathscr{B} : (a \cup b)' = a' \cap b' ; (a \cap b)' = a' \cup b'$.*

Proof. Suppose a' and a_1 are both complements of an element $a \in \mathscr{B}$. Then $a \cup a' = a \cup a_1 = 1$, and $a \cap a' = a \cap a_1 = 0$. Moreover, $a_1 = a_1 \cap 1 = a_1 \cap (a \cup a') = (a_1 \cap a) \cup (a_1 \cap a') = 0 \cup (a_1 \cap a') = a_1 \cap a'$; and similarly $a' = a' \cap 1 = a' \cap (a \cup a_1) = (a' \cap a) \cup (a' \cap a_1) = 0 \cup (a' \cap a_1) = a' \cap a_1$. Since $a_1 \cap a' = a' \cap a_1$, it follows that $a' = a_1$, and so a has a *unique* complement, which we shall designate a'. In view of the definition of a complement, and the uniqueness just established, the complement of a' is a, i.e., $(a')' = a$. Furthermore, it follows from this that the mapping $a \to a'$ is bijective. Finally, suppose $a \geq b$, for elements $a, b \in \mathscr{B}$. Then since $a' \cap b \leq a' \cap a$, we have $a' = a' \cap 1 = a' \cap (b \cup b') = (a' \cap b) \cup (a' \cap b') = 0 \cup (a' \cap b') = a' \cap b'$. Hence $b' \geq a'$, and we have shown that the mapping $a \to a'$ inverts the partial ordering of the lattice. Now let $d = a \cup b$, so that $d \geq a$ and $d \geq b$, whence $a' \geq d'$ and $b' \geq d'$. If c' is any element of $\mathscr{B}$ such that $a' \geq c'$ and $b' \geq c'$, and c is the inverse image of c' under the mapping, it follows that $c \geq a$ and $c \geq b$. Hence $c \geq d$ and so $d' \geq c'$, i.e., d' is the g.l.b. of a' and b'. This means that $(a \cup b)' = a' \cap b'$, as desired in the theorem. The proof that $(a \cap b)' = a' \cup b'$ is similar [Problem 3]. ∎

The proof (in Theorem 8.61) that complements are unique in a Boolean algebra made use only of the distributive property of the lattice. Hence this result can be phrased as a property of any distributive lattice: *In a distributive lattice, complements are unique if they exist.* (If the student has proved the cancellation law for distributive lattices in Problem 28 of § 8.4, the uniqueness of complements follows immediately from this earlier result [Problem 8].) It probably should be stressed, however, that not all elements of a distributive lattice need have complements. For example, in Figures 10(a) and 10(b) we have shown the Hasse diagrams of two distributive lattices [Problems 9, 10], but in both cases the only elements with complements are 0 and 1. On the other hand, in Figures 10(c) and 10(d), we have·represented two lattices— reproduced for convenience from Problem 10(b) of § 8.1 and Problem 21 of § 8.4—in both of which the element a has two complements. We know, of course, that these two lattices are not distributive [Problems 11, 12].

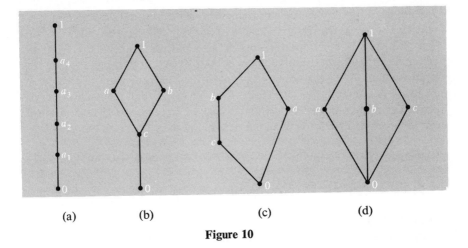

(a)   (b)   (c)   (d)

Figure 10

The relation between a Boolean algebra and other algebraic systems is made clear by our next theorem.

Theorem 8.62. *Any Boolean algebra is a ring if the ring operations of addition and multiplication are suitably defined.*

Proof. In order to make a Boolean algebra $\mathcal{B}$ into a ring, we first define the "product" ab of any two elements a, $b \in \mathcal{B}$ to be the same as $a \cap b$. The "sum" or "symmetric difference" of a and b is defined as follows: $a + b = (a \cap b') \cup (a' \cap b)$. It is a consequence of the distributive property of a Boolean algebra that $(b \cup a) \cap (b' \cup a') = [(b \cup a) \cap b'] \cup [(b \cup a) \cap a'] = [0 \cup (a \cap b')] \cup [(b \cap a') \cup 0] = (a \cap b') \cup (a' \cap b) = a + b$. In the case of the Boolean algebra of subsets of a set, the symmetric difference of two subsets is then seen to be the set of elements which belong to either but not both of the subsets. It is now possible to verify that $\mathcal{B}$ is a ring with these two operations of addition and multiplication. Our definition of $a + b$ implies that $a + b = b + a$, so that the system is commutative under addition. If we note that $(a + b)' = (a \cap b')' \cap (a' \cap b)' = (a' \cup b) \cap (a \cup b') = [(a' \cup b) \cap a] \cup [(a' \cup b) \cap b'] = (a \cap b) \cup (a' \cap b')$, it is easy to verify that addition is associative [Problem 4]. Since $a + 0 = (a \cap 1) \cup (a' \cap 0) = a$, the element 0 is the zero of the additive system of $\mathcal{B}$; and since $a + a = (a \cap a') \cup (a' \cap a) = 0$, each element a is its own additive inverse. Hence $\mathcal{B}$ is an additive abelian group. The operation of multiplication, which we identified with $\cap$, is associative, and it is elementary to check that $(a + b)c = ac + bc$. Since it is a postulate of any lattice that $\cap$ is commutative, it follows that $c(a + b) = ca + bc$, and this completes the proof that $\mathcal{B}$ is a ring with the given compositions. ∎

Since $a1 = a \cap 1 = a$, for any element a in the ring of Theorem 8.62, we see that 1 serves as the identity element of this ring. We have already remarked that this ring is commutative, and it also follows immediately from the definition of multiplication that $aa = a^2 = a$, so that each element of the ring is idempotent. We have seen earlier, however, that any ring of idempotent elements is commutative [Problem 14 of § 5.1] so that the really essential properties of the above ring are that *it has an identity* and that *its elements are idempotent*. This leads us to the next definition.

Definition. A ring is said to be *Boolean* if all of its elements are idempotent.

A partial converse to Theorem 8.62 is provided by the following theorem.

Theorem 8.63. *Any Boolean ring with an identity element is a Boolean algebra, after suitable definitions have been made for $\cup$ and $\cap$.*

Proof. We first give definitions for $\cup$ and $\cap$ as follows: $a \cup b = a + b - ab$ and $a \cap b = ab$, for arbitrary elements a, b in the ring. It is a matter for direct verification that the composition $\cup$ is associative, and it may be of interest to note that this is the "circle" composition that was introduced in Z in Problem 4 of § 3.1. We have recalled earlier that the property of commutativity is always a consequence of the idempotency of the elements of a system, and so our present system is commutative under multiplication. The other characteristic properties of a lattice, as given in our alternate definition in § 8.2, are immediate consequences of our definitions of $\cup$ and $\cap$ [Problem 6]. There remains to show that our lattice is distributive and complemented. Now $(a \cup b) \cap c = (a + b - ab)c = ac + bc - abc = ac + bc - abc^2 = ac + bc - acbc = (a \cap c) \cup (b \cap c)$, for arbitrary elements a, b, c in the ring, and so the distributive property is established for the lattice. Finally, if 1 and 0 are the respective identities of multiplication and addition for the ring, we have $a \cup 1 = a + 1 - a1 = 1$, and $a \cap 0 = a0 = 0$, for any ring element a. Hence, if we define $\leq$ as was done in Theorem 8.22, it follows that $a \leq 1$ and $0 \leq a$, so that 1 is the identity element and 0 is the zero element of the lattice. We now define $a' = 1 - a$, for any a in the ring, and so $a \cup a' = a + (1 - a) - a(1 - a) = 1$, while $a \cap a' = a(1 - a) = 0$. Hence the Boolean ring, with $\cup$ and $\cap$ defined as above is a Boolean algebra. ∎

PROBLEMS 8–6

*1. Prove that the set of all subsets of a set is a Boolean algebra with the usual operations of this system.

**2. With reference to the proof of Theorem 8.61, why does the fact that $(a')' = a$ imply that the mapping $a \to a'$ is bijective?

*3. Prove that $(a \cap b)' = a' \cup b'$, for arbitrary elements a, b of a Boolean algebra.

*4. Prove that the "symmetric difference" is an associative operation in a Boolean algebra.

*5. Prove that multiplication, as defined in Theorem 8.62, is distributive with respect to the operation of "symmetric difference" in a Boolean algebra.

*6. Prove that the properties listed in Theorem 8.21 are valid for the system described in Theorem 8.63, so that this system is a Boolean algebra.

7. Draw the Hasse diagram of a lattice with at least one element having more than one complement, and then check directly that it is not distributive.

8. Explain why the uniqueness of complements in a distributive lattice follows from the result of Problem 28 of § 8.4.

9. Prove directly that the "chain" lattice, pictured in Figure 10(a), is distributive.

10. Prove directly that the lattice, pictured in Figure 10(b), is distributive.

11. Prove directly that the lattice, pictured in Figure 10(c), is not distributive [cf. Problem 27 of § 8.4].

12. Prove directly that the lattice, pictured in Figure 10(d), is not distributive [cf. Problem 21 of § 8.4].

13. Draw the Hasse diagram of a nondistributive lattice—different from Figures 10(c) and 10(d)—and show that it has an element with more than one complement.

14. Prove that a free Boolean algebra with n generators has exactly 2^{2^n} elements. (Hint: see [7], p. 35.)

15. Show that the lattice depicted in Figure 10(c) provides us with a counter-example of the cancellation law for distributive lattices [see Problem 28 of § 8.4].

**16. In a Boolean algebra, prove that $a \le b$, $a \cap b' = 0$, and $a' \cup b = 1$ are equivalent conditions.

17. If $x \cup y = a$ and $x \cap y = b$, for elements x, y, a, b in a lattice, then x and y are said to be *relative complements with respect to the quotient* a/b. Prove that if x and y are complements in a modular lattice, and $b \le x \le a$, then the element $a \cap (b \cup y)$ is a relative complement of x with respect to a/b [cf. another type of "relative complement" in § 8.4].

18. A lattice is said to be *relatively complemented* if every quotient a/b in the lattice is complemented. Verify that the lattice of Figure 10(c) is complemented but not relatively complemented.

19. Refer to Problems 17 and 18 and prove that a modular complemented lattice is relatively complemented.

20. Review the proof that a ring $\mathcal{R}$ of idempotent elements is commutative with characteristic 2. Then explain why we could have defined $a \cup b = a + b + ab$ in the proof of Theorem 8.63.

21. Prove that if there exists a prime natural number p such that $pa = 0$ and $a^p = a$, for each a in a ring, the ring is commutative. (See pp. 144–146 of [5].)

8.7. The Boolean Algebra of Propositions

A Boolean algebra, as a complemented distributive lattice, is an algebraic system in which we have defined three operations $\cup$, $\cap$, and $'$, a partial ordering relation $\leq$, as well as two special elements 0 and 1. In addition, we assume the existence of an "equals" ($=$) relation, which has had the meaning of "identity" in the lattice. We have seen, of course, that these operations and relations are not all independent, for our first definition of a lattice started with a partially ordered set while the second started with a "universal algebra" without any ordering relation. In order to prove that a certain system is a Boolean algebra, it is not even necessary to verify all the properties of a complemented distributive lattice, for a much smaller list will suffice. This smaller list is, of course, much easier to check than the larger and more complete list. In fact, *it can be shown*—though we omit the proof and content ourselves with a series of problems at the end of this section [Problems 5–11]—that if a nonempty set has had defined in it the *identity* or *equals relation* ($=$) and *two operations* $\cap$ and $'$ which satisfy the five postulates below, the system is a Boolean algebra. These postulates are now stated, with x, y, z arbitrary elements of the set.

1. $x \cap y = y \cap x$.
2. $(x \cap y) \cap z = x \cap (y \cap z)$.
3. There exists an element 0 such that $x \cap x' = 0$.
4. If $x \cap y' = 0$ then $x \cap y = x$.
5. If $x \cap y = x$, then $x \cap y' = 0$.

If we wish to check the usual properties of a Boolean algebra, in the light of both definitions which we have given for a lattice, it will be necessary to define the identity element 1, the operation $\cup$, and the partial ordering $\leq$ as follows:

$$1 = 0'; \quad x \cup y = (x' \cap y')'; \quad x \leq y \text{ if } x \cap y = x.$$

It may be well to remind the reader that, as usual, the fact that the *binary* operation $\cap$ and the *unary* operation $'$ have been *defined in the set* implies that both $x \cap y$ and x' are unique elements—dependent only on the choice of x and y. If we start out with the set of all subsets of a given set, and define equality, intersection and complementation in the usual way, it is easy to see that the above postulates are satisfied—so that this basic system is in fact a Boolean algebra by the above criterion.

As an example of a Boolean algebra which may appear to be quite different from the algebra of sets, consider the set of all integral divisors of 110, i.e., the set {1, 2, 5, 10, 11, 22, 55, 110}. If x and y are any two elements of this set, let us define $x \cap y$ to be the g.c.d. of x and y, and x' to the quotient when 110 is divided by x. It can be shown that this set of integers, with the usual definition of equality and the definitions just given for $\cap$ and $'$ comprises a Boolean algebra. To establish this, one merely has to check the five postulates given above for this system. For instance, the third postulate asserts the existence of an element 0, such that for each integral divisor x of 110, the g.c.d. of x and the quotient $110/x$ is 0. In the system under observation, the natural number 1 plays the role of the zero of the Boolean algebra. Also, postulate **4** asserts that if x and y' have no common factor except 1, then x divides y. It can be readily checked that this requirement is indeed satisfied by all numbers of the given set. The other two postulates for a Boolean algebra can be similarly verified for our present system [Problem 1].

Probably the simplest system which satisfies the postulates of a Boolean algebra contains only the two elements 0 and 1, and we shall refer to this algebra as $\mathcal{B}(0, 1)$. The complete operation table for this system is given below in Table 2, in which due recognition should be given to the heading of each column.

Table 2

x	y	$x \cup y$	$x \cap y$	x'
1	1	1	1	0
1	0	1	0	0
0	1	1	0	1
0	0	0	0	1

Let us now consider the " Boolean algebra " or " calculus " of propositions. A proposition is a declarative statement or assertion, such as " A circle is round " or " A stone is soft." While the truth of some propositions may be in doubt, we shall consider only those propositions which can be labeled definitely true or definitely false. We shall say that a statement has the *truth value T* if it is true, and the *truth value F* if it is false.

If p and q are propositions, the *disjunction* of p and q is the proposition " p or q " and is denoted by $p \vee q$; this compound statement is true if *at least* one of p or q is true, and false if both these statements are false. For example, if p is the statement above concerning a circle and q is the statement about a stone, the proposition $p \vee q$ is " A circle is round or a stone is soft," and is a true statement. The *conjunction* of p and q is the proposition " p and q," and is denoted by $p \wedge q$; this compound statement is true if *both* p and q are true, and otherwise false. To continue the meanings tentatively assigned to p and q, it is clear that $p \wedge q$ is false since the statement, "A circle is round and a stone is soft" is false. The *negation* of a proposition p is "not p," and is denoted by $\sim p$; $\sim p$ is true when p is false, and $\sim p$ is false when p is true. For example, if p is the statement, "A circle is round," $\sim p$ is the statement "A circle is not round." In this case, p is true while $\sim p$ is false. In Table 3 below we have exhibited the truth values for the propositions $p \vee q, p \wedge q$, and $\sim p$, for all possible combinations of truth values for p and q. Such a table is known as a *truth table* for these simple compound propositions composed from p and q.

Table 3

p	q	$p \vee q$	$p \wedge q$	$\sim p$
T	T	T	T	F
T	F	T	F	F
F	T	T	F	T
F	F	F	F	T

A quick comparison of Table 3 with Table 2 reveals that these two tables are very much alike. In fact if we set up a correspondence in which p, q, T, F, $\vee$, $\wedge$, $\sim$ in the system of propositions correspond, respectively, to $x, y, 1, 0, \cup, \cap, '$ in $\mathcal{B}(0, 1)$, the two algebraic systems become indistinguishable and are then isomorphic. It should not be obscured, however, that in this correspondence we are letting *each* true proposition correspond to 1 and *each* false proposition correspond to 0. Hence we have essentially partitioned the set of all propositions into two disjoint subsets—those which are true and those which are false—and are considering the propositions in each subset respectively *equivalent* to each other.

It is possible and more natural, however, to consider a more general calculus of propositions in which "equivalence" is based on mutual implication rather than on truth value: that is, p and q are "equivalent" propositions if p implies q and q implies p or, symbolically, $p \leftrightarrow q$. It is not difficult to see [Problem 14] that this sort of equivalence is an "equivalence relation" as discussed in Chapter 1, and so again the set of all propositions is partitioned into disjoint subsets of equivalent elements. If we now define the operations $\vee$, $\wedge$, and $\sim$ in the "obvious" way in this collection of subsets [see Problem 15], we obtain the *Boolean algebra of propositions* or the "algebra of logic" —somewhat in the form in which it was first studied by George Boole. The elements of this algebra are the classes of equivalent propositions, each proposition being a composite of elementary propositions compounded with the three operations of the algebra. In general, the truth value of a compound proposition depends upon the truth values of the elementary propositions composing it. However, there are some propositions which are always true, regardless of the nature of their component propositions. These are called *tautologies*, and one of the simplest examples of a tautology is the proposition $p \lor (\sim p)$, because it is *true* for *any p*. On the other hand, a proposition such as $p \land (\sim p)$ is *false* for *any p*, and is a *contradictory statement* or an *absurdity*. In the Boolean algebra of propositions just discussed, the class of tautologies plays the role of the " all " element 1 while the class of absurdities is 0. For an interesting relationship between this general Boolean algebra of propositions and the rather primitive 2-element type discussed earlier, the student is invited to look at Problems 18–20.

It is possible to use the Boolean algebra properties of the calculus of propositions to discover the truth value of a complicated proposition—that is, to decide whether it is true or false. In view of the remarks immediately preceding, if p is the proposition and h is the homomorphism of the Boolean algebra of propositions onto $\mathcal{B}(0, 1)$, this reduces to a determination of whether $h(p) = 1$ or $h(p) = 0$. The following example—which may be found on pages 54–55 of [7]—illustrates the procedure.

Example. Of three counters, one is red, one is blue, and one is white, while one of the following statements is true and two are false: *A is red*; *B is not red*; *C is not blue*. Determine the color of each counter.

Solution. It will be convenient to use the lattice notation ′ for complementation instead of the usual symbol $\sim$ of logic. Then A_r and A'_r will designate, respectively, the propositions " A is red " and " A is not red," with an analogous notation for B and C, along with the other colors. We are given that one of the propositions is true and two are false, and this hypothesis may be seen to be equivalent to the *true* proposition p, where $p = (A_r \land B_r \land C_b) \lor (A'_r \land B'_r \land C_b) \lor (A'_r \land B_r \land C'_b)$. Since each counter is known to be either red, white, or blue, we also have that $A'_r = A_b \lor A_w$, $B'_r = B_b \lor B_w$, and $C'_b = C_r \lor C_w$. By using these equalities, it is possible to transform p into the form $(A_r \land B_r \land C_b) \lor [(A_b \lor A_w) \land (B_b \lor B_w) \land C_b] \lor [(A_b \lor A_w) \land B_r \land (C_r \lor C_w)]$, and this, in turn, can be expanded into a union of intersections, each of the latter containing either two or three components. A typical factor then has either the form $A_x \land B_y \land C_z$ or $A_x \land B_y$, $A_x \land C_y$, $B_x \land C_y$, wherein each of x, y, and z may be r, b or w. However, a contradiction will result if there are any repetitions of x, y, or z in the same factor (for example, $A_r \land B_r \land C_b$ is absurd), and if we replace all such factors by the " zero " 0 of the lattice, the original complex proposition reduces to $P = A_b \wedge B_r \wedge C_w$. Hence, $h(A_b \wedge B_r \wedge C_w)$ $= 1$; and this means that $A_b \wedge B_r \wedge C_w$ is true so that A is blue, B is red, and C is white.

It would take us far beyond the scope of this book to include a discussion of all the present-day applications of Boolean algebra to engineering, but we do make mere mention of one—the application to *switching circuits*. A relay is a set of switches, controlled by an electromagnet, which opens or closes certain contacts as it is energized. At any given instant, then, certain of the switches are closed and others are open, according as the relay is or is not energized. The elements of our associated mathematical system are $a, b, c, \ldots$, where each symbol designates a collection of switches which are *simultaneously* in either a closed or an open state. A short circuit —i.e., one which is always closed—is designated 1, while a permanently open circuit is designated 0. The notation a' (which is preferred here to the symbol $\sim a$) will designate a set of switches which are always in the state opposite to a. The "equivalence" relation which is introduced is in the sense of "electrical equivalence," so that an equivalence like $a \equiv b$ means that the switches identified with a are always in the same electrical state as those identified with b. In particular, $a \equiv 1$ indicates that a is a short circuit, while $a \equiv 0$ means that the switches composing a are open. At any instant, it is assumed that every a is either open or closed, and so either $a \equiv 1$ or $a \equiv 0$. We define the operations $\cup$ ("parallel") and $\cap$ ("series") in the usual sense of logic, recalling that the unary operation of comple- mentation has already been defined: $a \cap b \equiv 1 \leftrightarrow (a \equiv 1) \wedge (b \equiv 1)$, $a \cap b \equiv 0 \leftrightarrow (a \equiv 0) \vee (b \equiv 0)$; $a \cup b \equiv 1 \leftrightarrow (a \equiv 1) \vee (b \equiv 1)$, $a \cup b \equiv 0$ $\leftrightarrow (a \equiv 0) \wedge (b \equiv 0)$. Every switching circuit can then be represented as a polynomial in the circuit elements and the three symbols of operation, and it is hoped that the student will see emerging something which resembles a Boolean algebra. It can be shown that the classes of equivalent switching circuits do constitute the elements of such an algebra, and the operation table of this algebra is the same as that of $\mathcal{B}(0, 1)$. The two principal objectives in applying a Boolean analysis to switching circuits are to design a circuit with a given function and to simplify an existing circuit without altering its function. We do not wish to pursue this matter further here, but the interested student can consult one of the several references related to these matters which we have listed at the close of the chapter.

PROBLEMS 8–7

1. With reference to the discussion of this section, verify that the other two postulates for a Boolean algebra hold for the system of integral divisors of 110.

*2. Verify that the five posulates for a Boolean algebra which were not verified in this section are satisfied by the algebra of propositions.

3. Decide whether the following systems, with the designated operations, form Boolean algebras.
   (a) The set of integral divisors of 15, $x \cap y$ the l.c.m. of x and y, and x' identified with $15/x$.
   (b) The set of integral divisors of 24, $x \cap y$ the g.c.d. of x and y, and x' identified with $24/x$.
   (c) The set of natural numbers, $x \cap y$ the smaller of x and y, and $x' = 1$ for any x.
4. Let p and q be declaratory statements, as in the Boolean algebra of propositions discussed in this section. Define p' as usual, but give $p \wedge q$ the meaning of "p if and only if q" as described in the following table:

p	T	T	F	F
q	T	F	T	F
$p \wedge q$	T	F	F	T

Verify whether this algebra of propositions is a Boolean algebra.

Note: Use the five postulates for a Boolean algebra given in this section to obtain the properties given in Problems 5–11, for elements a, b, c of the algebra—arbitrary except as indicated.

**5. (a) $a \cap a = a$; (b) $a \leq a$.
 6. (a) $a \leq b$ if and only if $a \cap b' = 0$; (b) if $a \leq b$ and $b \leq a$, then $a = b$.
 7. (a) $a \cap b \leq a$; (b) if $a \leq b$ and $b \leq c$, then $a \leq c$.
 8. (a) $0 \leq a$; (b) $a \cap 0 = 0$.
 9. $(a')' = a$.   (Hint: let $(a')' = a''$, and show that $a'' \cap a' = a' \cap a'' = 0$, $a'' \leq a$ and $a \leq a''$.)
10. $a \cap b = (a' \cup b')'$.
11. $a \cup a = a$.
12. Verify that $\mathcal{B}(0, 1)$ satisfies the five postulates given in this section for a Boolean algebra.
13. Define the equivalence relation implied in this section for the 2-element Boolean algebra of propositions.
14. Prove that the "two way" implication ($\leftrightarrow$), discussed in this section, is an equivalence relation in the set of all propositions.
15. Elaborate on the "obvious" way to define the operations $\vee$, $\wedge$, and $\sim$ in the set of all propositions in order to obtain the algebra of logic.
16. Let us define the "conditional" $p \rightarrow q$, for propositions p and q, to mean $(\sim p) \vee q$. Show that this does not indicate a relation of premise and conclusion, but only that q is not false if p is true. What is implied by $p \rightarrow q$ if p is false?
**17. Use Problem 16 to decide which of the following conditionals are tautologies in the algebra of propositions: (a) $p \rightarrow \sim p$; (b) $(p \rightarrow \sim q) \rightarrow (\sim q \rightarrow p)$; (c) $(p \rightarrow q) \rightarrow (\sim q \rightarrow \sim p)$.

18. An *ideal* in a lattice is a subset which is closed under intersections, and the union of any element of the subset with any element of the lattice is in the subset. Show that the class of all true propositions is an ideal in the Boolean algebra of classes of propositions.

19. An ideal J in a lattice is *prime* [see Problem 18] provided $a \cup b \in J$ implies that either $a \in J$ or $b \in J$.

20. Use Problem 18 to discover a homomorphism of the Boolean algebra of classes of propositions onto the 2-element Boolean algebra.

21. Compare the meanings of "or" understood in the definitions of $p \vee q$ in the Boolean algebra of propositions and $a + b$ in Boolean rings.

22. If p and q are propositions, construct the truth table for $\sim p \wedge \sim q$.

23. Try to work the Example in this section if we know that one of the statements is false and two are true.

24. A student takes a true-false test consisting of five questions, the only one of which he knows the answer being number 2. He notes, however, that questions 1 and 5 must have opposite answers. Show that the student is able to determine all correct answers, provided he knows such a test always has more T than F answers, and that there are never three answers in a row which are the same.

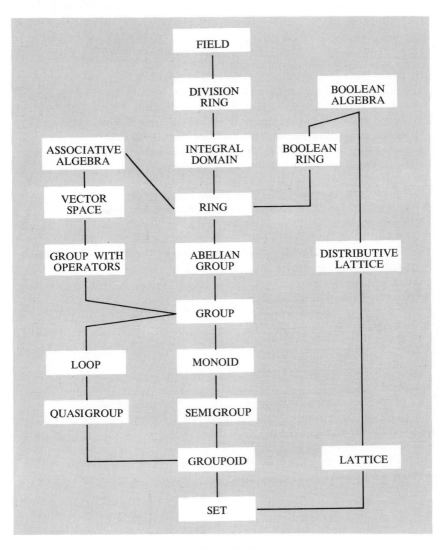

Some Algebraic Systems

References

[1] BIRKHOFF, G.: *Lattice Theory* (New York, A.M.S., Colloquium Publication, Vol. 25, 1948).

[2] COHN, P. M.: *Universal Algebra* (New York, Harper & Row, 1965).

[3] HOHN, F.: *Applied Boolean Algebra* (New York, Macmillan, 1960).

[4] JACOBSON, N.: *Lectures in Abstract Algebra*, Vol. 1, Chapter 7 (Princeton, N. J., Van Nostrand, 1951).

[5] KEMENY, J., MIRKIL, H., SNELL, J., THOMPSON, G.: *Finite Mathematical Structures* (Englewood Cliffs, N.J., Prentice-Hall, 1965).

[6] KUROSH, A. G.: *General Algebra* (New York, Chelsea, 1963).

[7] RUTHERFORD, D. E.: *Introduction to Lattice Theory* (New York, Hafner, 1965).

[8] WHITESITT, J.: *Boolean Algebra and Its Applications* (Addison-Wesley, Reading, Mass., 1961).

Selected Readings from The American Mathematical Monthly

FRINK, O.: *Ideals in Partially Ordered Sets*, **61** (1954), 223–234.

HOHN, F.: *Some Mathematical Aspects of Switching*, **62** (1955), 75–90.

MILLER, D. G.: *Postulates for Boolean Algebra*, **59** (1952), 93–96.

STUERMANN, W. E.: *Plotting Boolean Functions*, **67** (1960), 170–172.

WEISSMAN, J.: *Boolean Algebra, Map Coloring, and Interconnections*, **69** (1962), 608–613.

ZEMMER, J. L.: *A Boolean Geometry for the Integers*, **67** (1960), 56–57.

Appendix

Chapter 1

1. $S_1 \cup S_2 = \{A, E, I, L, N, R, T\}$, the elements in *either* S_1 or S_2; $S_1 \cap S_2 = \{A, E, L, R, T\}$, the elements in *both* S_1 and S_2.

8. To prove that $A = B$: let $x \in A$ and prove that $x \in B$; then let $y \in B$ and prove that $y \in A$.

2. Let $S_1 = \{a_1, a_2, \ldots, a_m\}$ and $S_2 = \{b_1, b_2, \ldots, b_n\}$, so that $S_1 \cup S_2 = \{a_1, a_2, \ldots, a_m, b_1, b_2, \ldots, b_n\}$. If we let $a_1 \to 1$, $a_2 \to 2$, $\ldots$, $a_m \to m$, $b_1 \to m + 1$, $b_2 \to m + 2$, $\ldots$, $b_n \to m + n$, we have established a one-to-one correspondence between the elements of $S_1 \cup S_2$ and $\{1, 2, \ldots, m + n\}$. Hence, the cardinal number of $S_1 \cup S_2$ is $m + n$, and $m + n$ is the sum of the cardinal numbers of S_1 and S_2.

9. If $A = B$, then $A - B = \phi$. Otherwise, the cardinality of $A - B$ may be any natural number—or even $\aleph_0$.

16. The set of integers which are perfect squares: $\{0, 1, 4, 9, \ldots\}$.

20. We define $A \times B \times C$, for sets A, B, C, to be the set of all triples (a, b, c) with $a \in A$, $b \in B$, $c \in C$. A *ternary relation* in a set S is then defined to be a subset of $S \times S \times S$.

PROBLEMS 1–4

13. (a) Suppose $s_1\alpha = s_2\alpha$, for s_1, $s_2 \in S$. Then $(s_1\alpha)\beta = (s_2\alpha)\beta$, $s_1(\alpha\beta) = s_2(\alpha\beta)$, $s_1 1_S = s_2 1_S$, and so $s_1 = s_2$. Hence α is injective, and a similar proof holds for β.

(b) Let t be an arbitrary element of T. Then $t = t(\beta\alpha) = (t\beta)\alpha$, so that $t\beta$ is an element of S which maps onto t under α. Inasmuch as t was arbitrary, this shows that α is surjective. A similar proof holds for β.

(c) Let t be an arbitrary element of T. Then $t = t(\beta\alpha) = (t\beta)\alpha$ and $t\beta = t\beta(\alpha\alpha^{-1}) = [t(\beta\alpha)]\alpha^{-1} = t\alpha^{-1}$. Hence $\beta = \alpha^{-1}$.

18. Two sets A and B are equivalent if and only if there is a one-to-one correspondence between the elements $a \in A$ and $b \in B$. But then the mapping $a \to b$ is a bijection from A to B (and $b \to a$ is a bijection from B to A).

Chapter 2

PROBLEMS 2–1

7. Since 1 is a nonsuccessor, $1^+ \neq 1$ and so $1 \in S$. Assume $k \in S$, i.e., $k^+ \neq k$. Then if $(k + 1)^+ = k + 1 = k^+$, it follows from the injective property of the mapping that $k + 1 = k^+ = k$. But this contradicts our inductive assumption, and so $(k + 1)^+ \neq k + 1$ whence $k + 1 \in S$. Hence, by the First Principle of Induction, $S = \mathbf{N}$, and so $n^+ \neq n$ for every $n \in \mathbf{N}$.

16. Let E_n designate the stated equality. Then, since $1^2 = (1)(1)(3)/3 = 1$, E_1 is true. If E_k is true, $1^2 + 3^2 + \cdots + (2k - 1)^2 = k(2k - 1)(2k + 1)/3$. But then, $1^2 + 3^2 + \cdots + (2k - 1)^2 + (2k + 1)^2 = k(2k - 1)(2k + 1)/3 + (2k + 1)^2 = [(2k + 1)/3][k(2k - 1) + 3(2k + 1)] = (k + 1)(2k + 1)(2k + 3)/3$. Hence, E_{k+1} is true, and E_n is true for all $n \in \mathbf{N}$ by the Induction Principle.

PROBLEMS 2–2

2. If $m^+ \not\leq n$, $m^+ > n$, i.e., $n < m^+$, so that $n = m + k$, for some $k \in \mathbf{N}$. If $k = 1$, $m^+ = n$; while if $k \neq 1$, $k = 1 + h$, for some $h \in \mathbf{N}$, so that $n = (m + 1) + h$, whence $m^+ < n$. In either case, we can assert that $m^+ \leq n$.

10. For example, the set $\{x \in \mathbf{Q} \mid 1 < x < 2\}$.

PROBLEMS 2–3

4. Let $x = \overline{(m, n)}$ and $0 = \overline{(r, r)}$. Then $0 + x = \overline{(r, r)} + \overline{(m, n)} = \overline{(r + m, r + n)} = \overline{(m, n)} = x$, by definition of equality. Similarly, $x + 0 = x$.

19. Let $0 \neq x = \overline{(m, n)} \in \mathbf{Z}$, so that $x^2 = \overline{(m, n)(m, n)} = \overline{(m^2 + n^2, 2mn)}$. Now $x^2 > 0$ if and only if $m^2 + n^2 + 2mn = (m + n)^2 > 4mn$, i.e., if and only if $m^2 - 2mn + n^2 = (m - n)^2 > 0$. Since the latter is known to be true $(m \neq n)$, it follows that $x^2 > 0$.

PROBLEMS 2–4

1. Since b is a positive integer, $b \geq 1$. It follows that $b|a| \geq |a|$, and so $a + b|a| \geq a + |a| \geq 0$.

17. If $a = b$, then $(a, b) = a = b = [a, b]$, by the definitions of g.c.d. and l.c.m. Conversely, suppose $(a, b) = [a, b]$. Since $(a, b) \mid a$ and $(a, b) \mid b$, then $(a, b)x = a$ and $(a, b)y = b$, for positive integers x, y. Similarly, our assumption implies that $a \mid (a, b)$ and $b \mid (a, b)$, so that $(a, b) = au$ and $(a, b) = bv$, for positive integers u, v. Hence, $aux = a$ and $bvy = b$, $ux = 1$ and $vy = 1$, whence $x = y = 1$ and so $a = b$.

PROBLEMS 2–5

14. If $x = \overline{(m, n)} \in \mathbf{Q}$, then $x + \overline{(0, a)} = \overline{(m, n)} + \overline{(0, a)} = \overline{(ma, na)} = \overline{(m, n)} = x$. Hence, $\overline{(0, a)}$ is the zero element of $\mathbf{Q}$.

17. Let $0 \neq b = \overline{(m, n)} \in \mathbf{Q}$. Then $\overline{(n, m)}\,\overline{(m, n)} = \overline{(mn, mn)} = 1$, by Problem 16, so that $b^{-1} = \overline{(n, m)}$. If $bx = a$, where $a = \overline{(r, s)} \in \mathbf{Q}$, then $x = b^{-1}(bx) = b^{-1}a = \overline{(n, m)}\,\overline{(r, s)} = \overline{(nr, ms)}$, and $ms \neq 0$.

Chapter 3

PROBLEMS 3–1

4. Since $a \circ b$ is an integer, for arbitrary $a, b \in \mathbf{Z}$, the *circle* composition is defined in $\mathbf{Z}$. This implies that $(a \circ b) \circ c = (a + b - ab) \circ c = (a + b - ab) + c - (a + b - ab)c = a + b + c - ab - ac - bc + abc$. Also $a \circ (b \circ c) = a + (b \circ c) - a(b \circ c) = a + b + c - bc - a(b + c - bc) = a + b + c - ab - ac - bc + abc$. Hence $(a \circ b) \circ c = a \circ (b \circ c)$, and $\mathbf{Z}$ is a semi-group under the *circle* composition.

16. The smallest generating set is $\{1\}$.

PROBLEMS 3–2

5. Let f and g be arbitrary mappings of a set S into itself. Then fg is also a mapping of S into itself, so that the composition of mappings defines the "product" fg in a satisfactory fashion. Moreover, by Problem 9 of § 1.4, this operation is associative. Finally, the mapping in which each element of S is mapped onto itself is the identity element of the system of mappings, and so it is a monoid.

12. Let $\mathcal{S} = \{a_1, a_2, \ldots, a_n\}$ be a finite monoid, and suppose that any solution of $ax = b$, for $a, b \in \mathcal{S}$, is unique if it exists. If a is an arbitrary element of $\mathcal{S}$, the elements $aa_1, aa_2, \ldots, aa_n$ are all distinct, by our assumption of uniqueness. Hence these elements comprise the complete set of elements of $\mathcal{S}$, so that if b is any element of $\mathcal{S}$, there exists an element $a_k \in \mathcal{S}$ such that $aa_k = b$. But this means that $x = a_k$ is a solution of $ax = b$, as asserted. A similar argument applies to the equation $ya = b$.

PROBLEMS 3–3

3. Let S and S' be isomorphic groupoids, with a' and b' arbitrary elements of S'. The definition of an isomorphism implies the existence of elements $a, b \in S$ such that $a \to a'$, $b \to b'$, $ab \to a'b'$, and $ba \to b'a'$. Since $ab = ba$, it follows that $a'b' = b'a'$, and so S' is commutative.

7. Let α designate the given mapping. Then, if $(a + bi)\alpha = a - bi$ and $(c + di)\alpha = c - di$, it follows that $[(a + bi) + (c + di)]\alpha = [(a + c) + (b + d)i]\alpha = (a + c) - (b + d)i = (a - bi) + (c - di) = (a + bi)\alpha + (c + di)\alpha$. Also, since $a - bi = c - di$ would imply that $(a - c) + (d - b)i = 0$, and hence $a = c$ and $b = d$, $a + bi = c + di$, the mapping α is one-to-one and hence an automorphism.

PROBLEMS 3–4

13. Let a, b be arbitrary elements of S_1. Then, the definition of the product of two mappings, along with the properties of a homomorphism, implies that $(ab)(f_1 f_2) = [(ab)f_1]f_2 = [(af_1)(bf_1)]f_2 = [(af_1)f_2][(bf_1)f_2] = [a(f_1 f_2)][b(f_1 f_2)]$. Hence, $f_1 f_2$ is a homomorphism of S_1 into S_3.

16. If α and β are arbitrary endomorphisms of S, the proof in Problem 16 shows $\alpha\beta$ is also an endomorphism of the semigroup S. Since the identity function on S, which maps each $s \in S$ onto s, is also an endomorphism, the system of endomorphisms has an identity element—which is the same as that of the monoid of functions. The associative property for endomorphisms has already been established—and is inherited in fact from this property [see Problem 9 of § 1.4] for functions and so the system of endomorphisms is a submonoid.

PROBLEMS 3–5

2. Let $a\alpha = A$, where α maps each $a \in S$ onto the class A of the regular partition with $a \in A$. Then, if $b\alpha = B$, for $b \in S$, and $ab \in C$, for a class C of the partition, $(ab)\alpha = C = AB = (a\alpha)(b\alpha)$, by definition of *regular*. Hence, α is a homomorphism.

11. (b) Suppose $a_1\psi = a_2\psi = 1$ and $b_1\psi = b_2\psi = -1$, for integers a_1, b_1. Then $a_1 + b_1$ is odd so that $(a_1 + b_1)\psi = -1$, and $a_2 + b_2$ is also odd so that $(a_2 + b_2)\psi = -1$. It follows that $a_1 + b_1$ and $a_2 + b_2$ are in the same equivalence class, and the partition is regular.

Chapter 4

PROBLEMS 4–1

11. Let $ab = ac$, for elements a, b, c in the semigroup. If we designate a' as a left inverse of a with respect to a left identity e', then $a'(ab) = a'(ac)$, $(a'a)b = (a'a)c$, $e'b = e'c$, whence $b = c$.

15. The results in Problems 13–14 assert that a left identity e of the semigroup is an identity, and that a left inverse a^{-1} is an inverse of a. But, by Problem 12, $ea = fa$ would imply $f = e$, and $a^{-1}a = ba$ would imply $b = a^{-1}$. Hence, the identity e and inverse elements a^{-1} are unique.

PROBLEMS 4–2

1.

.	1	−1
1	1	−1
−1	−1	1

19. To illustrate the type of verification needed for closure, we check the "product" $[1/t][1/(1-t)]$: when we substitute $1/(1-t)$ for t in the left factor, we obtain $1/[1/(1-t)] = (1-t)/1 = 1 - t \in \mathcal{G}$. Similarly for the other possible products. A little reflection on the nature of the "substitution" product should convince one that this product is associative. If not, a few checks—such as $[(1-t)(1/t)]((t-1)/t) = (1-t)[(1/t)(t-1)/t]$—might help. Since a "substitution" of t by t clearly leaves an element unchanged, t is a right identity; and four checks verify that t is also a left identity—and so *the* identity. Finally, each element may be seen to be its own inverse except for $1/(1-t)$ and $(t-1)/t$, these being inverses of each other. For example, $(1-t)(1-t) = 1 - (1-t) = t$; and $[1/(1-t)][(t-1)/t] = 1/[1 - (t-1)/t] = t/1 = t$. Hence $\mathcal{G}$ is a group.

PROBLEMS 4–3

6. (a) $\beta\gamma = \begin{pmatrix} 1 & 2 & 3 & 4 & 5 & 6 \\ 3 & 1 & 5 & 6 & 4 & 2 \end{pmatrix}$. Hence $\alpha(\beta\gamma) = \begin{pmatrix} 1 & 2 & 3 & 4 & 5 & 6 \\ 6 & 1 & 3 & 5 & 4 & 2 \end{pmatrix}$

$$= \begin{pmatrix} 1 & 2 & 4 & 5 & 6 \\ 6 & 1 & 5 & 4 & 2 \end{pmatrix}.$$

(c) $\alpha^2 = \begin{pmatrix} 1 & 3 & 4 \\ 3 & 4 & 1 \end{pmatrix}$. Hence $\alpha^2\beta = \begin{pmatrix} 1 & 2 & 3 & 4 & 5 & 6 \\ 1 & 6 & 4 & 3 & 5 & 2 \end{pmatrix}$

$$= \begin{pmatrix} 2 & 3 & 4 & 6 \\ 6 & 4 & 3 & 2 \end{pmatrix}.$$

8. $I \to (1)$, $H \to \begin{pmatrix} 1 & 2 & 3 & 4 \\ 3 & 4 & 1 & 2 \end{pmatrix}$, $V \to \begin{pmatrix} 1 & 2 & 3 & 4 \\ 2 & 1 & 4 & 1 \end{pmatrix}$, $D \to \begin{pmatrix} 1 & 4 \\ 4 & 1 \end{pmatrix}$,

$D' \to \begin{pmatrix} 2 & 3 \\ 3 & 2 \end{pmatrix}$, $R \to \begin{pmatrix} 1 & 2 & 3 & 4 \\ 2 & 4 & 1 & 3 \end{pmatrix}$, $R' \to \begin{pmatrix} 1 & 2 & 3 & 4 \\ 4 & 3 & 2 & 1 \end{pmatrix}$, $R'' \to \begin{pmatrix} 1 & 2 & 3 & 4 \\ 3 & 1 & 4 & 2 \end{pmatrix}$.

PROBLEMS 4–4

7. Since the sum of two continuous functions is a continuous function, the set of continuous functions is closed under addition. Now let f, g, h be any three continuous functions on **R**, and consider $f + (g + h)$ and $(f + g) + h$. If x is any real number, $x[f + (g + h)] = xf + x(g + h) = xf + (xg + xh)$, whereas $x[(f + g) + h] = x(f + g) + xh = (xf + xg) + xh$. Inasmuch as addition is associative in **R**, we have $xf + (xg + xh) = (xf + xg) + xh$, so that $f + (g + h)$ $(f + g) + h$, which establishes the associative law. The zero of the set is the function which has the value 0 for every real x, and we can designate this function 0. For it is clear that $x(f + 0) = x(0 + f) = xf$, for any function f of the set. Finally, we define $-f$, for any f of the set, so that $x(-f) = -(xf)$, and this function is easily seen to be continuous. That it has the characteristic property of an inverse follows from $x[f + (-f)] = xf + x(-f) = xf - xf = 0$, so that $f + (-f) = 0$. This shows that the set of continuous functions is a group under the given composition.

18. $\alpha^{-1} = \begin{pmatrix} 1 & 2 & 3 & 4 \\ 3 & 4 & 1 & 2 \end{pmatrix}$ and $\beta^{-1} = \begin{pmatrix} 1 & 3 & 5 \\ 3 & 5 & 1 \end{pmatrix}$, so that $(\alpha\beta)^{-1} = \beta^{-1}\alpha^{-1} =$

$$\begin{pmatrix} 1 & 3 & 5 \\ 3 & 5 & 1 \end{pmatrix}\begin{pmatrix} 1 & 2 & 3 & 4 \\ 3 & 4 & 1 & 2 \end{pmatrix} = \begin{pmatrix} 1 & 2 & 3 & 4 & 5 \\ 1 & 4 & 5 & 2 & 3 \end{pmatrix} = \begin{pmatrix} 2 & 3 & 4 & 5 \\ 4 & 5 & 2 & 3 \end{pmatrix}.$$

PROBLEMS 4–5

15. Let a and b be arbitrary elements of C_g. Then $gb = bg$, $(gb)b^{-1} = (bg)b^{-1}$, $g(bb^{-1}) = b(gb^{-1})$, and $b^{-1}g = gb^{-1}$, so that $b^{-1} \in N_g$. But then $g(ab^{-1}) = (ga)b^{-1} = (ag)b^{-1} = a(gb^{-1}) = a(b^{-1}g) = (ab^{-1})g$, from which we see that $ab^{-1} \in C_g$. It follows by Theorem 4.51 that C_g is a subgroup.

21. The symmetries of the rectangle are: $I =$ identity $= (1)$; $H =$ horizontal reflection $= \begin{pmatrix} 1 & 2 & 3 & 4 \\ 3 & 4 & 1 & 2 \end{pmatrix}$; $V =$ vertical reflection $= \begin{pmatrix} 1 & 2 & 3 & 4 \\ 2 & 1 & 4 & 3 \end{pmatrix}$;

$R =$ rotation through $180° = \begin{pmatrix} 1 & 2 & 3 & 4 \\ 4 & 3 & 2 & 1 \end{pmatrix}$.

But $I = (1)$, $H = \beta$, $V = \alpha$, and $R = \alpha\beta = \beta\alpha$, where $\alpha^2 = \beta^2 = (\alpha\beta)^2 = 1$. Hence $[\alpha, \beta]$ is the group of symmetries of the rectangle.

PROBLEMS 4–6

11. $\mathcal{G} = \{0, 1, 2, 3\}$. On finding the sums of the elements of $\mathcal{G}$ and $0, 1, 2, 3$, respectively, we obtain:

$$\pi_0 = \begin{pmatrix} 0 & 1 & 2 & 3 \\ 0 & 1 & 2 & 3 \end{pmatrix}, \ \pi_1 = \begin{pmatrix} 0 & 1 & 2 & 3 \\ 1 & 2 & 3 & 0 \end{pmatrix},$$

$$\pi_2 = \begin{pmatrix} 0 & 1 & 2 & 3 \\ 2 & 3 & 0 & 1 \end{pmatrix}, \ \pi_3 = \begin{pmatrix} 0 & 1 & 2 & 3 \\ 3 & 0 & 1 & 2 \end{pmatrix}$$

The only regular representation of $\mathcal{G}$ is then the group whose elements are $\{\pi_0, \pi_1, \pi_2, \pi_3\}$.

20. $\alpha^2 = (1) = \beta^2$, so that only first powers of α and β need occur in a product. We find easily that $\alpha\beta = (1423)$, $\beta\alpha = (1324)$, $\alpha\beta\alpha = (14)(23)$, $\beta\alpha\beta = (34)$,

$\alpha\beta\alpha\beta = (12)(34) = \beta\alpha\beta\alpha$. Since $\alpha\beta\alpha\beta\alpha = \beta\alpha\beta$ and $\beta\alpha\beta\alpha\beta = \alpha\beta\alpha$, we have obtained all elements of the group, and so $[\alpha, \beta] = \{1, \alpha, \beta, \alpha\beta, \beta\alpha, \alpha\beta\alpha, \beta\alpha\beta, \alpha\beta\alpha\beta = \beta\alpha\beta\alpha\}$.

PROBLEMS 4–7

8. (12), (13), (14), (23), (24), (34); (123), (132), (124), (142), (134), (143), (234,), (243).

12. Since every permutation is either even or odd, the set S of odd permutations along with the even permutations in A_n comprise all elements of S_n. If we multiply every element of S_n on the right by an arbitrary transposition π_t, the even permutations become odd and the odd permutations become even. Since S_n is a group, all these transformed permutations are distinct, and so the number of elements in S must be the same as the number in A_n. Hence the number in each is $n!/2$.

PROBLEMS 4–8

4. By the result of Problem 14 of § 4.5, any given subset of a finite group is a subgroup if the subset is closed under the group operation. We see that $(123)(123) = (132)$, $(132)(132) = (123)$, and $(123)(132) = (1)$, so that the given subset is closed, and therefore a subgroup. The coset decomposition of S_3, with respect to this subgroup is $S_3 = \{(1), (123), (132)\} \cup (12)\{(1), (123) 132\}$, or $S_3 = \{(1), (123), (132)\} \cup \{(12), (13), (23)\}$.

15. Let $\mathcal{K}$ be the additive subgroup of integers divisible by 6. Then the coset decomposition of $\mathbf{Z}$, relative to $\mathcal{K}$, can be expressed in the following form: $\mathbf{Z} = \mathcal{K} \cup (1 + \mathcal{K}) \cup (2 + \mathcal{K}) \cup (3 + \mathcal{K}) \cup (4 + \mathcal{K}) \cup (5 + \mathcal{K})$.

PROBLEMS 4–9

11. Since $\mathcal{K}$ is normal in $\mathcal{G}$, $a\mathcal{K} = \mathcal{K}a$ for any $a \in \mathcal{G}$. But every element of $\mathcal{K}$ is an element of $\mathcal{G}$, so that $h\mathcal{K} = \mathcal{K}h$ for any $h \in \mathcal{K}$. Hence $\mathcal{K}$ is normal in $\mathcal{K}$.

19. By Problem 16 of § 4.5, we know that the center C of a group is a subgroup. Let $c \in C$ and $g \in \mathcal{G}$, where C is the center of a group $\mathcal{G}$. Then, for arbitrary $x \in \mathcal{G}$, $x(g^{-1}cg) = xc(g^{-1}g) = xc = cx = cx(g^{-1}g) = x(cg^{-1}g) = x(g^{-1}cg)$. Hence $g^{-1}cg \in C$, and so C is normal.

PROBLEMS 4–10

2. In order to show that a subgroup $\mathcal{K}$ is *not* normal in a group $\mathcal{G}$, we need simply exhibit an element $a \in \mathcal{G}$ such that $a\mathcal{K} \neq \mathcal{K}a$. Now $(123) \in S_3$, but $(123)\{(1), (12)\} = \{(123), (23)\}$ whereas $\{(1), (12)\}(123) = \{(123), (13)\}$. Hence $[(12)]$ is not normal in S_3.

27. If $\mathcal{G} = [a]$ is the cyclic group, consider the homorphism $\alpha : a^r \rightarrow r$ of $\mathcal{G}$ onto $\mathbf{Z}$.
(a) If $o(\mathcal{G})$ is infinite, the correspondence $a^r \rightarrow r$ is one-to-one, and so the kernel of α is 1. By Theorem 4.103, $\mathcal{G} \cong \mathbf{Z}$.
(b) If $o(\mathcal{G}) = o(a) = n$, the kernel $\mathcal{K}$ of α is the set of elements a^r, where $r = nt$ for some nonnegative integer t. Then $\mathcal{G} = \mathbf{Z}/\mathcal{K} = \mathbf{Z}_n$, by Theorem 4.103.

PROBLEMS 4–11

7. Suppose $k_1 = h_1 g \in \mathfrak{K}$ and $k_2 = h_2 g \in \mathfrak{K}$, with $h_1 \neq h_2 \in \mathfrak{H}$. Then $g = h_1^{-1} k_1 = h_2^{-1} k_2$ and, since $h_1 \neq h_2$, this violates (2′) in the definition of a direct product. Hence there is only one element of $\mathfrak{K}$ in $\mathfrak{H}g$.

15. Let $\mathfrak{G}$ designate a group of order 6. If $\mathfrak{G}$ contains no element of order 6 (and so is not cyclic), the order of each element $x \neq 1$ must be 2 or 3—since $o([x])$ must divide 6. If $o([x]) = 2$, $[x] = C_2$; and if every element has order 2, $\mathfrak{G}$ must be a direct sum of cyclic groups isomorphic to C_2—by the conditions for a direct sum [see also Problem 6 of § 4.4]. But then $o(\mathfrak{G})$ must be some power of 2, contrary to assumption, and so there must exist in $\mathfrak{G}$ an element a of order 3. Thus $a, a^2, a^3 = 1$ are three distinct elements of $\mathfrak{G}$. If b is an additional element, it is easy to verify that the elements $1, a, a^2, b, ab, a^2b$ are all distinct, for a contradiction would result if we equated any two of them. (For instance, if we suppose $ab = a^2b$, then $a = a^2$, whereas $o(a) = 3$.) Hence, if there exists a noncyclic group of order 6, these are its six elements. Finally, if this system of six elements is to form a group, it must be closed. Hence either $b^2 = 1$, $b^2 = a$ or $b^2 = a^2$. It is easy to discard the latter two possibilities, so that $b^2 = 1$. Also, ba must be in the system, and since ba cannot be b or any power of a, either $ba = ab$ or $ba = a^2b$. However, if $ba = ab$, $\mathfrak{G}$ would be abelian, $(ab)^2 = 1$ and $\mathfrak{G}$ would be cyclic. Hence, if $\mathfrak{G}$ is noncyclic, $ba = a^2b$, i.e., $(ab)^2 = 1$. We have now obtained the complete multiplication table of a noncyclic group $\mathfrak{G}$ of order 6, and we observe that this is the only such group possible. That is, $\mathfrak{G} = [a, b]$, where $a^3 = b^2 = (ab)^2 = 1$.

PROBLEMS 4–12

23. Let $\mathfrak{G} = [a]$ be an infinite cyclic group. By Problem 26 of § 4.5, any subgroup of $\mathfrak{G}$ is cyclic. If $\mathfrak{H} = [a^r]$ and $\mathfrak{K} = [a^s]$ are any two nontrivial subgroups of $\mathfrak{G}$, then $1 \neq a^{rs} \in \mathfrak{H} \cap \mathfrak{K}$.

25. Let $n = p_1^{e_1} p_2^{e_2} \cdots p_r^{e_r}$ and $m = p_1^{f_1} p_2^{f_2} \cdots p_r^{f_r}$, where $0 \leq f_i \leq e_i, i = 1, 2, \ldots, r$. If $a_1, a_2, \ldots, a_r$ are the generators of the cyclic groups of orders $p_1^{e_1}, p_2^{e_2}, \ldots, p_r^{e_r}$, respectively, according to the decomposition asserted in the Basis Theorem, then the elements $a_1^{t_1}, a_2^{t_2}, \ldots, a_r^{t_r}$ (where $t_i = p_i^{e_i - f_i}, i = 1, 2, \ldots, r$) have orders $p_1^{f_1}, p_2^{f_2}, \ldots, p_r^{f_r}$, respectively. It is then clear (since $p_1, p_2, \ldots, p_r$ are distinct primes) that the element $a = a_1 a_2 \cdots a_r$ has order m and $[a]$ is a subgroup of order m.

PROBLEMS 4–13

17. Let $\mathscr{P}_1, \mathscr{P}_2, \ldots, \mathscr{P}_r$ be the Sylow p-subgroups of $\mathfrak{G}$, with orders powers of the primes $p_1, p_2, \ldots, p_r$, respectively. Since the primes are distinct, $\mathscr{P}_i \cap (\mathscr{P}_1 \cdots \mathscr{P}_{i-1} \mathscr{P}_{i+1} \cdots \mathscr{P}_r) = 1$, and so $\mathscr{P}_1 \mathscr{P}_2 \cdots \mathscr{P}_r = \mathscr{P}_1 \times \mathscr{P}_2 \times \cdots \times \mathscr{P}_r$. Since the order of this product is $o(\mathfrak{G})$, we must have $\mathfrak{G} = \mathscr{P}_1 \times \mathscr{P}_2 \times \cdots \times \mathscr{P}_r$.

28. (a) If there were a simple group of order $30 = 2 \cdot 3 \cdot 5$, its Sylow p-subgroups could not be unique or they would be normal. There would then be $1 + 5 = 6$ Sylow 5-subgroups containing 24 elements of order 5 and

$1 + 3^2 = 10$ Sylow 3-subgroups containing 20 elements of order 3. But this exceeds the number of elements in the group, so no simple group of order 30 can exist.

(b) Since $200 = 5^2 2^3$, a group of order 200 would contain n Sylow 5-subgroups of order 25, where $n = 1 + 5k$, $n \mid 200$ and k is some nonnegative integer. Since $(n, 5) = 1$, n would necessarily divide 8 and so $k = 0$. But then there would be a unique Sylow 5-subgroup, which would be normal. Hence, a group of order 200 can not be simple.

PROBLEMS 4–14

14. Let $\mathcal{G} = C_{30} = \{1, a, a^2, \ldots, a^{29}\}$, using multiplicative notation. The complete collection of subgroups of C_{30} are: $\mathcal{G} = C_{30}$, $C_{15} = \{1, a^2, a^4, \ldots, a^{28}\}$, $C_{10} = \{1, a^3, a^6, \ldots, a^{27}\}$, $C_6 = \{1, a^5, a^{10}, a^{15}, a^{20}, a^{25}\}$, $C_5 = \{1, a^6, a^{12}, a^{18}, a^{24}\}$, $C_3 = \{1, a^{10}, a^{20}\}$, $C_2 = \{1, a^{15}\}$, $C_1 = 1$. All subgroups of a cyclic group are normal, and we can then form the following composition series:

$$1 \lhd C_5 \lhd C_{15} \lhd \mathcal{G}; \qquad 1 \lhd C_3 \lhd C_6 \lhd \mathcal{G}.$$

The factor groups ("factors") of the series on the left are:

$$\mathcal{G}/C_{15} = \{C_{15}, aC_{15}\}, \; C_{15}/C_5 = \{C_5, a^2C_5, a^4C_5\},$$
$$C_5/1 = \{1, a^6, a^{12}, a^{18}, a^{24}\}.$$

The factor groups of the series on the right are:

$$\mathcal{G}/C_6 = \{C_6, aC_6, a^2C_6, a^3C_6, a^4C_6\}, \; C_6/C_3 = \{C_3, a^5C_3\}, C_3/1 = \{1, a^{10}, a^{20}\}$$

But $\mathcal{G}/C_{15} \cong C_6/C_3$, $C_{15}/C_5 \cong C_3/1$, and $C_5/1 \cong \mathcal{G}/C_6$ under the correspondences: $C_{15} \leftrightarrow C_3$, $aC_{15} \leftrightarrow a^5C_3$; $C_5 \leftrightarrow 1$, $a^2C_5 \leftrightarrow a^{10}$, $a^4C_5 \leftrightarrow a^{20}$; $1 \leftrightarrow C_6$, $a^6 \leftrightarrow aC_6$, $a^{12} \leftrightarrow a^2C_6$, $a^{18} \leftrightarrow a^3C_6$, $a^{24} \leftrightarrow a^4C_6$. A check of the multiplication tables of the associated factor groups verifies these isomorphisms.

18. If $a, b \in \mathcal{G}$, then $(a\mathcal{G}')(b\mathcal{G}') = ab\mathcal{G}' = ba(a^{-1}b^{-1}ab)\mathcal{G}' = ba\mathcal{G}' = (b\mathcal{G}')(a\mathcal{G}')$, since $a^{-1}b^{-1}ab \in \mathcal{G}'$. Hence, $\mathcal{G}/\mathcal{G}'$ is abelian. Moreover, if $\mathcal{G}/\mathcal{K}$ is abelian, the commutator $a^{-1}b^{-1}ab \in \mathcal{G}'$, for arbitrary $a, b \in \mathcal{G}$. Hence $\mathcal{G}' \subset \mathcal{K}$.

Chapter 5

PROBLEMS 5–1

13. Let $x = a + bi$ and $y = c + di$ be arbitrary Gaussian integers. Then $x - y = (a + bi) - (c + di) = a - c + (b - d)i$ and also $xy = (a + bi)(c + di) = ac - bd + (bc + ad)i$. Since both $x - y$ and xy are seen to be Gaussian integers, an application of Theorem 5.11 shows that the Gaussian integers form a subring of the ring of complex numbers.

19. Let $a, b \in C(\mathcal{R})$. Then, for arbitrary $x \in \mathcal{R}$, $(a - b)x = ax - bx = xa - xb = x(a - b)$, so that $a - b \in C(\mathcal{R})$. Also, $(ab)x = a(bx) = a(xb) = (ax)b = (xa)b =$

$x(ab)$, whence $ab \in C(\mathcal{R})$. It follows from Theorem 5.11 that $C(\mathcal{R})$ is a subring of $\mathcal{R}$.

PROBLEMS 5–2

2. Let $a, b \in \text{Ker } f$, so that $f(a) = f(b) = 0$. Then $f(a - b) = f(a) - f(b) = 0 - 0 = 0$, and $f(ab) = [f(a)][f(b)] = 0 \cdot 0 = 0$. It follows from Theorem 5.11 that Ker f is a subring of $\mathcal{A}$.

4. By the distributive laws for a ring, $(a + b)(c + d) = a(c + d) + b(c + d) = ac + ad + bc + bd$.

PROBLEMS 5–3

3. As usual let [3] designate the subgroup of $\mathbf{Z}$ consisting of all integral multiples of 3. To verify that $\mathbf{Z}_3$ is a field, we need only see that this system is closed under subtraction and multiplication, that there exists a zero and identity element, and that multiplicative inverses exist for nonzero elements: for all other field properties are inherited from $\mathbf{Z}$. Let $a + [3]$ and $b + [3] \in \mathbf{Z}_3$. Then $(a + [3]) - (b + [3]) = a - b + [3] \in \mathbf{Z}_3$ and $(a + [3])(b + [3]) = ab + [3] \in \mathbf{Z}_3$; the zero of $\mathbf{Z}_3$ is [3], and the identity element is $1 + [3]$; the elements $1 + [3]$ and $2 + [3]$ are idempotent and so each its own inverse—and these are the only two nonzero elements of $\mathbf{Z}_3$. Hence, $\mathbf{Z}_3$ is a field.

5. Let a be any element of the integral domain. Then $ae^2 = ae$ and $(ae - a)e = 0$. Since $e \neq 0$, and an integral domain contains no divisors of 0, we must have $ae - a = 0$, and so $ae = a$. Similarly $ea = a$, and e must be the identity element.

PROBLEMS 5–4

5. The one-to-one correspondence between the two systems is given by $1 \leftrightarrow \mathbf{1}$, $i \leftrightarrow \mathbf{i}, j \leftrightarrow \mathbf{j}, k \leftrightarrow \mathbf{k}$. Moreover, $ij = k \leftrightarrow \mathbf{k} = \mathbf{ij}$, $jk = i \leftrightarrow \mathbf{i} = \mathbf{jk}$, etc. Hence, the two groups are isomorphic.

12. Since u is a solution of the given equation, $u^3 = -4u^2 + 2u - 3$, and $u^4 = -4u^3 + 2u^2 - 3u = -4(-4u^2 + 2u - 3) + 2u^2 - 3u = 18u^2 - 11u + 12$. Hence $(2u^2 + 1)(3u^2 - 2u - 1) = 6u^4 - 4u^3 + u^2 - 2u - 1 = 108u^2 - 66u + 72 + 16u^2 - 8u + 12 + u^2 - 2u - 1 = 125u^2 - 76u + 83$. If u is transcendental, the product is $6u^4 - 4u^3 + u^2 - 2u - 1$.

PROBLEMS 5–5

11. There exists a' in the domain such that $a'a = 1$. Then, for any b in the domain, $\delta(b) = \delta[a'(ab)] \geq \delta(ab)$. But, in a Euclidean domain, $\delta(ab) \geq \delta(b)$, so that $\delta(ab) = \delta(b)$. In particular, if we let $b = 1$, we obtain $\delta(a1) = \delta(a) = \delta(1)$.

15. If $\mathcal{R}$ does not have an identity element, the subset of units in $\mathcal{R}$ must be empty. On the other hand, if a, b are units in $\mathcal{R}$, the inverses a^{-1} and b^{-1} exist and are units; and $(ab)(b^{-1}a^{-1}) = (b^{-1}a^{-1})(ab) = 1$ so that ab is also a unit. Since, in this case, $1 \in \mathcal{R}$ and 1 is a unit, the subset of units comprises a multiplicative subgroup. An example of a ring with an empty subgroup of units is provided by the ring of even integers.

PROBLEMS 5–6

9. If A is an ideal of $\mathbf{Z}$, either $A = (0)$ or A contains a smallest positive integer m. If $x \in A$, an application of the Division Algorithm leads us to $x = qm + r$, with $q, r \in \mathbf{Z}$ and $0 \leq r < m$. Since m is minimal, $r = 0$ and $x = qm$. Hence, $A = (m)$, as asserted.

13. (a)

$$x - 1 \mid \overline{x^2 - x - 6} \; x$$
$$\underline{x^2 - x}$$
$$-6$$

Hence, $x^2 - x - 6 = x(x - 1) + (-6)$, $6 = x(x - 1) + (x^2 - x - 6)$, and $1 = (x/6)(x - 1) + (1/6)(x^2 - x - 6)$.

PROBLEMS 5–7

7. (a) $-(2x + 1)$; (b) $-(4x^2 + 2)$; (c) $-(x^2 + 1)$.

19. Suppose $f(x) = r(x)s(x)$, where neither $r(x)$ nor $s(x)$ are units of $\mathbf{Q}(x)$. If d is the positive l.c.m. of the denominators of the coefficients of $r(x)$ and $s(x)$ taken together (we assume these rational coefficients are all in reduced fractional form), on multiplying by d we obtain $df(x) = \bar{r}(x) \cdot \bar{s}(x)$, with $\bar{r}(x)$, $\bar{s}(x) \in \mathbf{Z}[x]$. Since the combined set of coefficients on the right member of this equation is relatively prime, it follows that $d = 1$ so that $r(x), s(x) \in \mathbf{Z}[x]$. Hence, if $f(x)$ is irreducible in $\mathbf{Z}[x]$, it is also irreducible in $\mathbf{Q}[x]$.

PROBLEMS 5–8

1. Since $ab = ba$, we have $(a, b) \sim (a, b)$, so the relation is reflexive. If $(a, b) \sim (c, d)$, we have $ad = bc$ and also $cb = da$, whence $(c, d) \sim (a, b)$. Hence $\sim$ is symmetric. If $(a, b) \sim (c, d)$, and $(c, d) \sim (e, f)$, then $ad = bc$ and $cf = de$, so that $dafc = cbed$. Hence $af = be$, $(a, b) \sim (e, f)$ and the relation is transitive.

20. The ring $\mathbf{Z}_6$ has divisors of zero which, after $\mathbf{Z}_6$ has been imbedded in any system, would remain divisors of zero in the larger system. Hence the imbedding system could not be a field. Since $2 \cdot 3 = 6 \equiv 0 \pmod 6$, the class elements $\bar{2}$ and $\bar{3}$ are examples of divisors of zero in $\mathbf{Z}_6$.

PROBLEMS 5–9

16. (a) A is the ideal, consisting of all polynomials in $\mathbf{Z}[x]$ which are divisible by $x + 1$ (i.e., contain $x + 1$ as a factor). The elements of the quotient ring $\mathbf{Q}[x]/A$ are then cosets $a(x) + A$, where $a(x)$ is a polynomial not divisible by $x + 1$. Alternatively, we may regard the elements of the quotient ring as " residue " polynomials, whose terms involving $x + 1$ as a factor have been effectively eliminated.

35. The ideal $A + B$ consist of all integers expressible in the form $9a + 15b$, for integers a, b, and it is easy to see that $A + B = (3)$. The ideal $A \cap B$ consist of all integers which are simultaneously multiples of 9 and 15, and so $A \cap B = (45)$. By the theorem, $(3)/(15) \cong (9)/(45)$, while $(3)/(15) = \{\bar{0}, \bar{3}, \bar{6}, \bar{9}, \overline{12}\}$ and $(9)/(45) = \{\bar{0}, \bar{9}, \overline{18}, \overline{27}, \overline{36}\}$. It is clear that the isomorphic correspondence is that in the order listed.

6. (a) $\bar{4}$; (b) $\bar{2}$; (c) $\bar{3}$.

19. If $a + bi$ is an arbitrary complex number in familiar form, we examine the correspondence $a + bi \rightarrow \bar{a} + \bar{b} \cdot \bar{x}$ where, of course, $\bar{a} = a + (x^2 + 1)$, $\bar{b} = b + (x^2 + 1)$, $\bar{x} = x + (x^2 + 1)$. We note that $(\bar{x})^2 = x^2 + (x^2 + 1) = -1 + (x^2 + 1) = -1$, so that $\bar{x}$ "acts" like i. It is a simple matter to check that the above correspondence is one-to-one and that it preserves the operations of addition and multiplication.

1. Let A be the union of all ideals of the chain. Then, if $x, y \in A$, it follows that $x, y \in A_k$, for some finite k, $x - y \in A_k$ and A is a subgroup of the additive group of the ring. For any r in the ring, rx and xr are in A_k—and so in A— since A_k is a ring. Hence A is an ideal of the ring.

25. Let P be the given property, and let us assume that P is not valid in a certain ideal of the ring. By (iii) of Theorem 5.111, there must exist a maximal ideal A not possessing this property. However, since A is maximal without the property P, all proper divisors of A must possess P—and so also A by our assumption. Since this is a contradiction, the property P must be valid in all ideals of the ring.

2. $\sqrt{(12)}$ and $\sqrt{(72)}$ consist of those integers, some powers of which are divisible, respectively, by $12 = 2^2 \cdot 3$ and $72 = 2^3 \cdot 3^2$. It then follows that $\sqrt{(12)} = \sqrt{(72)} = (6)$.

15. The nonzero elements of the ideal (x^2, xy, y^2) in $\mathbf{Z}[x, y]$ are those polynomials, each term of which has degree at least 2. If $f(x, y)g(x, y)$ is in the ideal, whereas $f(x, y)$ is not, it then follows that the constant term of $g(x, y)$ is 0. Hence, $[g(x, y)]^2$ is in the ideal and so (x^2, xy, y^2) is primary.

Chapter 6

1. $(a_1, b_1) + (a_2, b_2) = (a_1 + a_2, b_1 + b_2) = (a_2 + a_1, b_2 + b_1) = (a_2, b_2) + (a_1, b_1)$.

$[(a_1, b_1) + (a_2, b_2)] + (a_3, b_3) = (a_1 + a_2, b_1 + b_2) + (a_3, b_3) = ((a_1 + a_2) + a_3, (b_1 + b_2) + b_3)) = (a_1 + (a_2 + a_3), b_1 + (b_2 + b_3)) = (a_1, b_1) + [(a_2, b_2) + (a_3, b_3)]$.

19. Let α and β be endomorphisms of the abelian group $\mathcal{G}$. Then, with the usual definition of the sum $\alpha + \beta$ for mappings, and for any $a, b \in \mathcal{G}$, we have $(a + b)(\alpha + \beta) = (a + b)\alpha + (a + b)\beta = a\alpha + b\alpha + a\beta + b\beta = a\alpha + a\beta + b\alpha$

$+ b\beta$ (this is where the abelian property of $\mathcal{G}$ is used) $= a(\alpha + \beta) + b(\alpha + \beta)$. This shows that $\alpha + \beta$ is an endomorphism of $\mathcal{G}$. The addition of endomorphisms is easily seen to be associative (as are all mappings) and commutative, while the endomorphism which maps every group element onto 0 is the zero endomorphism. For any endomorphism α of $\mathcal{G}$, we can define $-\alpha$ so that $a(-\alpha) = -(a\alpha)$, and so $\alpha + (-\alpha)$ is the zero endomorphism. Hence the endomorphisms of $\mathcal{G}$ form an abelian group. Since $(ab)(\alpha\beta) = [(ab)\alpha]\beta = [(a\alpha)(b\alpha)]\beta = [(a\alpha)\beta][(b\alpha)\beta] = [a(\alpha\beta)][b(\alpha\beta)]$, we see that $\alpha\beta$ is an endomorphism of $\mathcal{G}$. It is easy to check that $(\alpha + \beta)\gamma = \alpha\gamma + \beta\gamma$ and $\gamma(\alpha + \beta) = \gamma\alpha + \gamma\beta$, for arbitrary endomorphisms α, β, γ of $\mathcal{G}$, and this will complete the verification that the set of endomorphisms of $\mathcal{G}$ forms a ring.

PROBLEMS 6–2

4. (a) $\xi + 2\eta - 3\zeta = (1, -2, 3) + 2(-3, -2, 5) - 3(2, -5, 6) = (1, -2, 3) + (-6, -4, 10) + (-6, 15, -18) = (-11, 9, -5).$
   (b) $4(1, -2, 3) + 2x - 3(2, -5, 6) = 0 = (0, 0, 0)$. Hence, $2x = (6, -15, 18) + (-4, 8, -12) = (2, -7, 6)$, and so $x = (1, -7/2, 3)$.
19. For arbitrary $a \in \mathcal{R}$, $am = (a \cdot 1)m = a(1m)$ and also $am = (1 \cdot a)m = (1m)a$. Hence, $am = a(1m) = (1m)a$, so that the effect of m is to multiply each element of $\mathcal{R}$ by the element $1m$ in its center.

PROBLEMS 6–3

7. (a) Let $X_1 = (x_1, x_2, x_3, x_4)$ and $X_2 = (y_1, y_2, y_3, y_4)$, with the components integers. Then $X_1 + X_2 = (x_1 + y_1, x_2 + y_2, x_3 + y_3, x_4 + y_4)$, and we note that the components are integers. Also $cX_1 = (cx_1, cx_2, cx_3, cx_4)$, for any real number c, but cx_i is not necessarily an integer when x_i is an integer. Hence the system in (a) is not a subspace.
   (b) Let $X_1 = (x_1, x_2, x_3, x_4)$ and $X_2 = (y_1, y_2, y_3, y_4)$ where $x_2 = 2x_1$, $x_3 = x_1 + x_2$, $y_2 = 2y_1$, $y_3 = y_1 + y_2$. Then $X_1 + X_2 = (x_1 + y_1, x_2 + y_2, x_3 + y_3, x_4 + y_4)$ and $x_2 + y_2 = 2x_1 + 2y_1 = 2(x_1 + y_1)$, $x_3 + y_3 = (x_1 + x_2) + (y_1 + y_2) = (x_1 + y_1) + (x_2 + y_2)$, so that $X_1 + X_2$ is in the set. Also $cX_1 = (cx_1, cx_2, cx_3, cx_4)$, where $cx_2 = c(2x_1) = 2(cx_1)$ and $cx_3 = c(x_1 + x_2) = cx_1 + cx_2$, for any $c \in \mathbf{R}$. Hence cX_1 is in the set, and so by Theorem 6.32 the set comprises a subspace.
21. For any element $x + \mathcal{W}$ of $\mathcal{V}/\mathcal{W}$, and arbitrary $c \in \mathcal{F}$, we define: $c(x + \mathcal{W}) = cx + \mathcal{W}$. Then, to verify condition 2 of a vector space, with $y + \mathcal{W}$ an additional element of $\mathcal{V}/\mathcal{W}$: $c[(x + \mathcal{W}) + (y + \mathcal{W})] = c[(x + y) + \mathcal{W}] = cx + cy + \mathcal{W} = c(x + \mathcal{W}) + c(y + \mathcal{W}) = (cx + \mathcal{W}) + (cy + \mathcal{W})$; $(c_1 + c_2)(x + \mathcal{W}) = (c_1 + c_2)x + \mathcal{W} = c_1x + c_2x + \mathcal{W} = (c_1x + \mathcal{W}) + (c_2x + \mathcal{W}) = c_1(x + \mathcal{W}) + c_2(x + \mathcal{W})$; $(c_1c_2)(x + \mathcal{W}) = (c_1c_2)x + \mathcal{W} = c_1(c_2x) + \mathcal{W} = c_1[c_2x + \mathcal{W}] = c_1[c_2(x + \mathcal{W})]$; $1(x + \mathcal{W}) = 1x + \mathcal{W} = x + \mathcal{W}$. Since $\mathcal{V}/\mathcal{W}$ is known to be a quotient group, the verification that it is a vector space over $\mathcal{F}$ is complete.

PROBLEMS 6–4

7. The vectors (a_1, b_1), (a_2, b_2) are linearly dependent if and only if there exist nonzero scalars c_1, c_2 such that $c_1(a_1, b_1) + c_2(a_2, b_2) = (0, 0)$. But this vector

equation is equivalent to the two equations

$$c_1a_1 + c_2a_2 = 0,$$
$$c_1b_1 + c_2b_2 = 0,$$

and these equations have a nontrivial solution for c_1 and c_2 if and only if

$$\begin{vmatrix} a_1 & a_2 \\ b_1 & b_2 \end{vmatrix} = 0 = a_1b_2 - a_2b_1.$$

17. Let $\mathcal{V} = \mathcal{L}\{\alpha_1, \alpha_2, \ldots, \alpha_n\}$, where $\{\alpha_1, \alpha_2, \ldots, \alpha_n\}$ is a linearly independent subset [Corollary of Theorem 6.41] of the original set of generating vectors for $\mathcal{V}$. Then, for any $x \in \mathcal{V}$, $x = c_1\alpha_1 + c_2\alpha_2 + \cdots + c_n\alpha_n$, $c_1, c_2, \ldots, c_n \in \mathcal{F}$, where the linear independence of the $\{\alpha_i\}$ guarantees the uniqueness of the $\{c_i\}$. We are then able to define a function $f \in \hat{\mathcal{V}}$, such that $f(x) = c_1$. If $c_1 = 0$, for all $x \in \mathcal{V}$, $\mathcal{V} = \mathcal{L}\{\alpha_2, \alpha_3, \ldots, \alpha_n\}$, so that $\{\alpha_1, \alpha_2, \ldots, \alpha_n\}$ could not be a linearly independent set. Since this is a contradiction, $f(x) = c_1 \neq 0$, for at least one $x \in \mathcal{V}$.

PROBLEMS 6–5

3. (a) Since the equation $c_1 + c_2x + c_3x^2 = 0$ has at most two real solutions for x, for arbitrary scalars c_1, c_2, c_3, it follows that the equation cannot be identically 0. Hence 1, x, x^2 are linearly independent.

   (c) Since $(-1)1 + (1)\sin^2 x + (1)\cos^2 x = 0$, for every real x, it is clear that $\{1, \sin^2 x, \cos^2 x\}$ is a linearly dependent set. In this case, $c_1 = -1$, $c_2 = 1$, $c_3 = 1$.

17. The mapping $a + b\sqrt{2} \to a + b\sqrt{3}$, with $a, b \in \mathbf{Q}$, is clearly an isomorphism from $\mathbf{Q}[\sqrt{2}]$ to $\mathbf{Q}[\sqrt{3}]$ as vector spaces. However, if also $c + d\sqrt{2} \to c + d\sqrt{3}$ then

$$(a + b\sqrt{2})(c + d\sqrt{2}) = ac + 2bd + (bc + ad)\sqrt{2} \to ac + 2bd + (bc + ad)\sqrt{3}$$

$$\neq ac + 3bd + (bc + ad) = (a + b\sqrt{3})(c + d\sqrt{3}).$$

Hence, this mapping is not a ring isomorphism. Moreover, any other mapping $a + b\sqrt{2} \to a' + b'\sqrt{3}$ would lead to a similar conclusion, so the *rings* are not isomorphic.

PROBLEMS 6–6

3. There can be only 3 basis elements in the set, so consider the vectors $(-1, 2, 2)$, $(2, 2, -1)$, $(2, -1, 2)$. The equation

$$c_1(-1, 2, 2) + c_2(2, 2, -1) + c_3(2, -1, 2) = 0$$

is equivalent to the three equations

$$-c_1 + 2c_2 + 2c_3 = 0$$
$$2c_1 + 2c_2 - c_3 = 0$$
$$2c_1 - c_2 + 2c_3 = 0,$$

and these equations have a nontrivial solution if and only if

$$\begin{vmatrix} -1 & 2 & 2 \\ 2 & 2 & -1 \\ 2 & -1 & 2 \end{vmatrix} \neq 0.$$

Since this determinant is -27, we see that the vectors $(-1, 2, 2)$, $(2, 2, -1)$, $(2, -1, 2)$ comprise a basis.

It is clear from inspection that $(3, 0, -3) = (2, 2. -1) - (-1, 2, 2)$.

18. $\{\hat{\eta}_1, \hat{\eta}_2, \ldots, \hat{\eta}_n\}$ is a linearly independent set, for suppose $c_1\hat{\eta}_1 + c_2\hat{\eta}_2 + \cdots + c_n\hat{\eta}_n$ is the zero functional, i.e., $(c_1\hat{\eta}_1 + c_2\hat{\eta}_2 + \cdots + c_n\hat{\eta}_n)(\eta) = 0$, for all $\eta \in \mathcal{V}$. But then, if we let $\eta = \eta_i$, $0 = c_i\hat{\eta}_i(\eta_i) = c_i$, $i = 1, 2, \ldots, n$. To show that $\{\hat{\eta}_1, \hat{\eta}_2, \ldots, \hat{\eta}_n\}$ is a generating set for $\hat{\mathcal{V}}$, let $\hat{\eta} \in \hat{\mathcal{V}}$ be arbitrary, and suppose $\hat{\eta}(\eta_i) = c_i$, $i = 1, 2, \ldots, n$. Then, if $\eta = a_1\eta_1 + a_2\eta_2 + \cdots + a_n\eta_n \in \mathcal{V}$, $\hat{\eta}(\eta) = a_1c_1 + a_2c_2 + \cdots + a_nc_n$. On the other hand, $\hat{\eta}_i(\eta) = a_i$, and, on substituting in the preceding equation, $\hat{\eta}(\eta) = c_1\hat{\eta}_1(\eta) + c_2\hat{\eta}_2(\eta) + \cdots + c_n\hat{\eta}_n(\eta) = (c_1\hat{\eta}_1 + c_2\hat{\eta}_2 + \cdots + c_n\hat{\eta}_n)(\eta)$. Hence $\hat{\eta} = c_1\hat{\eta}_1 + c_2\hat{\eta}_2 + \cdots + c_n\hat{\eta}_n$, and the proof is complete.

PROBLEMS 6–7

1. By definition of T, $(c_1, c_2, c_3) + (d_1, d_2, d_3) = (c_1 + d_1, c_2 + d_2, c_3 + d_3)$ $\to (c_1 + d_1)\lambda + (c_2 + d_2)\mu + (c_3 + d_3)\nu = (c_1\lambda + c_2\mu + c_3\nu) + (d_1\lambda + d_2\mu + d_3\nu) = (c_1, c_2, c_3)T + (d_1, d_2, d_3)T$. Also $c(c_1, c_2, c_3) = (cc_1, cc_2, cc_3)$ $\to cc_1\lambda + cc_2\mu + cc_3\nu = c(c_1\lambda + c_2\mu + c_3\nu) = c[(c_1, c_2, c_3)T]$. Hence T is linear.

14. $[(1 - t)\xi + t\eta]T = [(1 - t)\xi]T + (t\eta)T = (1 - t)\xi^* + t\eta^*$, where $\xi^* = \xi T$ and $\eta^* = \eta T$. If $\xi^* \neq \eta^*$, then $(1 - t)\xi^* + t\eta^*$ will generate the straight line through the points ξ^* and η^*; if $\xi^* = \eta^*$, T maps all points of the given line onto the one point ξ^* or η^*.

PROBLEMS 6–8

9. By definition of T, $\varepsilon_1 T = [-(-1, 1) + (0, 1)]T = -(1, -2) + (0, 1) = (-1, 3) = -\varepsilon_1 + 3\varepsilon_2$, while $\varepsilon_2 T = 0\varepsilon_1 + 1\varepsilon_2$.

Hence the matrix of T is $\begin{bmatrix} -1 & 3 \\ 0 & 1 \end{bmatrix}$

13. $[y_1 \; y_2 \; y_3] = [-2 \; 3 \; 1] \begin{bmatrix} -1 & 0 & 3 \\ 1 & 1 & 1 \\ -2 & 0 & 1 \end{bmatrix} = [3 \; 3 \; -2]$,

so the desired image point is $(3, 3, -2)$.

(b) $[y_1 \; y_2 \; y_3] = [1 \; 1 \; 1] \begin{bmatrix} -1 & 0 & 3 \\ 1 & 1 & 1 \\ -2 & 0 & 1 \end{bmatrix} = [-2 \; 1 \; 5]$,

so the desired image point is $(-2, 1, 5)$.

PROBLEMS 6–9

14. By definition of a ring, the additive group of $\mathcal{R}$ is abelian. Moreover, for any $x \in \mathcal{R}$ (considered an abelian group) and arbitrary $r \in \mathcal{R}$, $rx \in \mathcal{R}$, so that the additive group of $\mathcal{R}$ is an $\mathcal{R}$-module. Since the ideals of $\mathcal{R}$ are closed under multiplication by elements of $\mathcal{R}$ (actually, either left or right multiplication), every ideal of $\mathcal{R}$ is a submodule.

15. Because it may be the case that some power of T is the identity or zero transformation. For example, if $T^2 = 1$, the transformation $1 + T + T^2$ would be indistinguishable from the transformation $2 + T$, with 1 and 2 properly interpreted as transformations.

PROBLEMS 6–10

2. This follows because $ra \in \mathcal{R}$, for elements a, b in any ring $\mathcal{R}$; and because $r(a + b) = ra + rb$ and $(a + b)r = ar + br$.

9. For any $x \in \mathcal{R}$, $(a\alpha\beta)x = (a\alpha \cdot x)\beta = (a\alpha)(x\beta) = (a \cdot x\beta)\alpha = [(ax)\beta]\alpha = (a\beta \cdot x)\alpha$ $= (a\beta\alpha)x$. It follows that $bx = 0$, where $b = a\alpha\beta - a\beta\alpha$. In like manner, we can show that $xb = 0$, so that $bx = xb = 0$, and b is an annihilator of $\mathcal{R}$.

Chapter 7

PROBLEMS 7–1

5. For arbitrary elements a, b in the intersection, both $a - b$ and ab are in each subfield and so also in the intersection. Hence, by Theorem 5.11, this intersection is a subring of the field. Moreover, since the inverse of any nonzero element of the intersection is also in the intersection, and the intersection is multiplicatively commutative, the assertion is established.

12. By Theorem 5.35, even a prime field must contain a subfield isomorphic to either $\mathbf{Q}$ or $\mathbf{Z}_p$. The definition of a prime field now requires that this subfield be the whole field.

PROBLEMS 7–2

1. Let A be the set of polynomials $q(x) \in \mathcal{F}[x]$ such that $q(k) = 0$. If $q_1(x)$ and $q_2(x) \in A$, then $q_1(k) = q_2(k) = q_1(k) - q_2(k) = 0$, so that $q_1(x) - q_2(x) \in A$. Hence, A is an additive abelian group. Moreover, since $aq(k) = 0$, for any $a \in \mathcal{F}$, whenever $q(k) = 0$, it follows that $aq(x) \in A$ if $q(x) \in A$. Hence, A is an ideal in $\mathcal{F}[x]$.

22. Let $u = \sqrt{2} - \sqrt{3}$. Then $u^2 = 2 + 3 - 2\sqrt{6} = 5 - 2\sqrt{6}$ and $2\sqrt{6} = 5 - u^2$. From this we obtain $24 = 25 - 10u^2 + u^4$ or $u^4 - 10u^2 + 1 = 0$. It may be easily checked by elementary methods that the polynomial $x^4 - 10x^2 + 1$ is irreducible over $\mathbf{Q}$, and so it is the minimum polynomial of u over $\mathbf{Q}$.

PROBLEMS 7–3

4. If k is algebraic over $\mathcal{F}$, $\phi(k) = 0$ for some polynomial $\phi(x) \in \mathcal{F}[x]$. But then, under the natural mapping, $0 \rightarrow 0$ and $\phi(x) \rightarrow \phi(k) = 0$, so that the mapping is not one-to-one.

16. A simple algebraic extension $\mathcal{F}(k)$ of degree n is a vector space over $\mathcal{F}$ with the n basis elements $1, k, k^2, \ldots, k^{n-1}$. Since a typical element of $\mathcal{F}(k)$ is expressible as $a_0 + a_1 k + \cdots + a_{n-1} k^{n-1}$, with $a_0, a_1, \ldots, a_{n-1} \in \mathcal{F}$, and there are only a finite number—say m—of choices for each of these coefficients, there are at most nm distinct elements in $\mathcal{F}(k)$.

PROBLEMS 7–4

8. Since k_i is algebraic over $\mathcal{F}$, k_i is a zero of an irreducible polynomial equation with coefficients in $\mathcal{F}$. However, $\mathcal{F} \subset \mathcal{F}_{i-1}$, and so these coefficients are also in $\mathcal{F}_{i-1}$; k_i is a zero of an irreducible factor of this polynomial with coefficients in $\mathcal{F}_{i-1}$.

17. Any element of $\mathbf{Q}(\sqrt{3})$ is expressible in the form $a + b\sqrt{3}$, with $a, b \in \mathbf{Q}$; and any element of $\mathbf{Q}(\sqrt{3}, \sqrt{2}) = [\mathbf{Q}(\sqrt{3})](\sqrt{2})$ is expressible in the form $u + v\sqrt{2}$, with $u, v \in \mathbf{Q}(\sqrt{3})$. Hence, any element of $\mathbf{Q}(\sqrt{3}, \sqrt{2})$ is expressible in the form $(a + b\sqrt{2}) + (c + d\sqrt{2})\sqrt{3} = a + b\sqrt{2} + c\sqrt{3} + d\sqrt{6}$, with $c, d \in \mathbf{Q}$. Since the degree of $\mathbf{Q}(\sqrt{2}, \sqrt{3})$ over $\mathbf{Q}$ is 4, as a result of Corollary 1 of Theorem 7.41, the set $\{1, \sqrt{2}, \sqrt{3}, \sqrt{6}\}$ is the desired basis.

PROBLEMS 7–5

4. Since $x^3 - 8 = (x - 2)(x^2 + 2x + 4)$, the zeros of $x^3 - 8$ in C are $2, -1 + \sqrt{3}i$ and $-1 - \sqrt{3}i$. It follows that $\sqrt{3}i$ (or $\sqrt{-3}$) generates the desired splitting field over $\mathbf{Q}$, and so its degree over $\mathbf{Q}$ is 2.

13. Let $b_0 + b_1 x + b_2 x^2 + \cdots + b_{n-1} x^{n-1} + (f(x))$ be an arbitrary element of $\mathcal{F}[x]/(f(x))$. The desired isomorphism is then that mapping in which this element is mapped onto $b_0' + b_1' x + b_2' x^2 + \cdots + b_{n-1}' x^{n-1} + (f^*(x))$.

PROBLEMS 7–6

2. (a) $x^2 - 5x + 6 = (x - 3)(x - 2)$; hence separable.
   (b) $x^2 - 2x + 1 = (x - 1)^2$; hence inseparable.
   (c) $x^3 - 3x^2 - x + 3 = (x - 1)(x + 1)(x - 3)$; hence separable.
   (d) $x^3 + 2x^2 - 11x - 12 = (x + 1)(x - 3)(x + 4)$; hence separable.

11. Any element of a finite extension of a field of characteristic 0 is algebraic, and so is a zero of an irreducible polynomial over this field. By Corollary 2, this polynomial is separable, and hence so is the extension field.

PROBLEMS 7–7

16. To illustrate, we consider the case where $q(-1) = 5$, $q(0) = 1$, and $q(1) = -1$. But then, $5 = 1 - b + c$, $1 = 0 + 0 + c$, and $1 = 1 - b + c$, and we see that these equations are inconsistent. A similar result happens in all cases except for that in which $q(-1) = 5$, $q(0) = 1$, and $q(-1) = -1$. In this case, we obtain the equations $5 = 1 - b + c$, $1 = 0 + 0 + c$, $-1 = 1 + b + c$, whence $b = -3$ and $c = 1$. Hence, the only possible polynomial is $x^2 - 3x + 1$.

20. Let $f(x)g(x) = h(x)$, where $f(x) = \sum_{i=0}^{m} a_i x^i$, $g(x) = \sum_{i=0}^{n} b_i x^i$, and $h(x) = \sum_{i=0}^{m+n} c_i x^i$. If $h(x)$ is not primitive, let us suppose that the g.c.d. of $c_0, c_1, \ldots, c_{m+n}$ is d, with d divisible by some prime p. Moreover, let a_r and b_s be the cofficients of smallest index, respectively, in $f(x)$ and $g(x)$ which are not divisible by p. (Inasmuch as $f(x)$ and $g(x)$ are primitive, these minimal-indexed elements must exist.) We now consider the coefficient c_{r+s} of x^{r+s}, which we may write as: $c_{r+s} = a_0 b_{r+s} + a_1 b_{r+s-1} + \cdots + a_{r-1} b_{s+1} + a_r b_s + a_{r+1} b_{s-1} + \cdots + a_{r+s} b_0$. But c_{r+s} and every term in the right member of this equation *except* $a_r b_s$ is divisible by p. Since this is a contradiction, our only alternative is to conclude that $h(x)$ is primitive, as asserted.

PROBLEMS 7–8

11. $x^4 - 1 = (x - 1)(x + 1)(x + i)(x - i)$, so that i and $-i$ are the two primitive 4th roots of unity. Hence $\phi_4(x) = (x - i)(x + i) = x^2 + 1$.

22. Let $\mathcal{H}$ and $\mathcal{K}$ be two fields with $q = p^n$ elements, for some prime p and integer $n > 0$. Since the prime field of both $\mathcal{H}$ and $\mathcal{K}$ is $\mathbf{Z}_p$, both can be considered extension fields of Z_p. Moreover, since each element of either field is a zero of the polynomial $x^q - x$ [Theorem 7.82], both $\mathcal{H}$ and $\mathcal{K}$ are splitting fields of this polynomial. It follows from Theorem 7.55 that $\mathcal{H}$ and $\mathcal{K}$ are isomorphic.

Chapter 8

PROBLEMS 8–1

8. Because this would imply the *nonexistence* of any x such that $a_1 \le x \le a_4$, whereas we know that $a_1 \le a_3 \le a_4$.

15. Since $a \ge b$ and $b \ge b$, it follows that b is a lower bound for a and b, whence $a \cap b \ge b$. But by Problem 3, $b \ge a \cap b$, so that $b = a \cap b$.

PROBLEMS 8–2

2. By definition of l.u.b., $a \cup b \ge a$ and $a \cup b \ge b$; and also $a \ge a \cap b$, $b \ge a \cap b$. Hence $a \cup b \ge a \ge a \cap b$ and $a \cup b \ge b \ge a \cap b$. If $a \cup b = a \cap b$, it then follows that $a = a \cup b = a \cap b = b$.

21. (a)

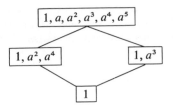

(b) Do not forget subgroups of $\mathcal{G}_1 \times \mathcal{G}_2$ which are subgroups of neither $\mathcal{G}_1$ nor $\mathcal{G}_2$: for example, the subgroup whose members are $\{1, a, a^2, b^2, ab^2, a^2b^2\}$, where $\mathcal{G}_1 = [a]$, $\mathcal{G}_2 = [b]$ and $a^3 = b^4 = 1$.

PROBLEMS 8–3

5. We must show that the set S of elements $x \in \mathcal{L}$, such that $x \geq b$, is closed under $\cup$ and $\cap$. Let x_1 and x_2 be elements of S, i.e., $x_1 \geq b$ and $x_2 \geq b$. Then $x_1 \cup x_2 \geq b$, by definition of l.u.b. and so $x_1 \cup x_2 \in S$. Also, b is a lower bound of x_1 and x_2, so that $x_1 \cap x_2 \geq b$, by definition of g.l.b. It follows that $x_1 \cap x_2 \in S$, and so S is a sublattice of $\mathcal{L}$.

17. Since $b \cup c \geq b$, Problem 16 implies that $a \cap (b \cup c) \geq a \cap b$; similarly, $a \cap (b \cup c) \geq a \cap c$. It then follows from the definition of a g.l.b. that $a \cap (b \cup c) \geq (a \cup b) \cup (a \cap c)$. The other inequality follows in like manner.

PROBLEMS 8–4

2. The l.u.b. of any set of subgroups of a group is a subgroup, by definition of $\cup$, and so is in the lattice. Also, the g.l.b. of the set is a subgroup and so is in the lattice. Hence the lattice is complete.

16. If a, b, c satisfy the given conditions, then $a = a \cup (a \cap c) = a \cup (b \cap c) = b \cap (a \cup c) = b \cap (b \cup c) = b$.

PROBLEMS 8–6

2. Suppose $a \to a'$ and $b \to a'$, for elements a, b of $\mathcal{B}$. Then, $(a')' = a$ and $(a')' = b$, and since complements are unique it follows that $a = b$. Hence the mapping is injective. But also, since $(a')' = a$, each element $a \in \mathcal{B}$ is the complement of an element $a' \in \mathcal{B}$, so that the mapping is surjective. Hence the mapping $a \to a'$ is bijective.

16. By the isotone property [Problem 16 of §8.3], if $a \leq b$ then $a \cap b' \leq b \cap b' = 0$ and so $a \cap b' = 0$. Conversely, if $a \cap b' = 0$, then $a \cup b = (a \cup b) \cap 1 = (a \cup b) \cap (b' \cup b) = (a \cap b') \cup b = 0 \cup b = 0$, whence $a \leq b$. Also, $a \cap b' = 0$ if and only if $a' \cup b = (a \cap b')' = 0' = 1$.

PROBLEMS 8–7

5. (a) $a \cap a' = 0$, by **3**. Hence, by **4**, $a \cap a = a$.
(b) $a \cap a = a$, by **5(a)**, above. Hence, $a \leq a$, by the definition of $\leq$.

17. (a) By Problem 16, $(p \to\, \sim p) =\, \sim p\, \vee\, \sim p =\, \sim p$, which asserts that p is not true. This is not a tautology, for its truth depends on the nature of p.

  (c) The assertion here, with the help of Problem 16, is $[\sim(\sim p \vee q] \vee [q \vee \sim p]$. Since any statement or its denial is true, this assertion is a tautology.

List of Special Symbols

The following is by no means a complete list of all symbols used in the book, but is rather a listing of certain symbols which have recurred frequently and have had the same meaning throughout most of the text.

N	natural numbers
Z	rational integers
$\mathbf{Z}_n$	rational integers mod n
Q	rational numbers
R	real numbers
C	complex numbers
$\mathcal{B}$	Boolean algebra
$\mathcal{E}$	integral domain
$\mathcal{F}$	field
$\mathcal{G}$	group
$\mathcal{L}$	lattice
$\mathcal{M}$	module
$\mathcal{Q}$	field of quotients
$\mathcal{R}$	ring
$\mathcal{S}$	general algebraic system, such as groupoid, semigroup or monoid
$\mathcal{V}$	vector space
$\hat{\mathcal{V}}$	dual of vector space $\mathcal{V}$
A_n	alternating group on n symbols
C_n	cyclic group of order n
M	operator set
S	set
S_n	symmetric group on n symbols
$M_n(\mathcal{A})$	system of $n \times n$ matrices with entries from $\mathcal{A}$
$\mathcal{R}[x]$	polynomial ring over $\mathcal{R}$

341

$\mathcal{F}(x)$	field of quotients of $\mathcal{F}[x]$
$[\mathcal{G} : \mathcal{H}]$	index of subgroup $\mathcal{H}$ in group $\mathcal{G}$
$[\mathcal{K} : \mathcal{F}]$	degree of field $\mathcal{K}$ over subfield $\mathcal{F}$
$o(a)$	order of element a in a group
$o(\mathcal{G})$	order of group $\mathcal{G}$
$\varnothing$	empty set
$a \mid b$	a divides b
$\oplus$	direct sum
$\times$	direct product
$\cong$	is isomorphic to
$\mathcal{R}$	relation
$a \sim b$	a is *equivalent* to b
$[a_1, a_2, \ldots, a_n]$	system generated by $a_1, a_2, \ldots, a_n$
Ker f	kernel of the homomorphism f
Im f	image of the homorphism f
PID	principal ideal domain
PIR	principal ideal ring
UFD	unique factorization domain
$\mathcal{H} \lhd \mathcal{G}$	$\mathcal{H}$ is a normal subgroup of $\mathcal{G}$

*Index**